THE BUTTERFLY BOOK

SPRING BUTTERFLIES

THE
BUTTERFLY BOOK

NEW AND THOROUGHLY REVISED EDITION

A Popular and Scientific Manual, Describing and Depicting all the Butterflies of the United States and Canada

BY

W. J. HOLLAND

PH.D., SC.D., LL.D., D.D., L.H.D.

Formerly Chancellor of the University of Pittsburgh, Director of the Carnegie Museum, Professor Extraordinario (honoris causa) De Biologia de la Universidad Nacional de México, Honorary Life Member of the International Entomological Congresses, Fellow of the American Philosophical Society, F. R. S. Edinb., F. E. S. and F. Z. S. London, Hon. Mem. R. Ac. Sc., Bologna, Membre Soc. Ent. France, Fellow Geol. Soc. of America, etc., etc.,

Officier de la Legion d'Honneur, France; Commendatore de la Corona d'Italia; Comendador de la Orden civil d'Alfonso XII, España; Commandeur de l'Ordre de la Couronne de Belgique, etc., etc.

ILLUSTRATED BY SEVENTY-SEVEN PLATES AND NUMEROUS FIGURES IN THE TEXT, GIVING OVER TWO THOUSAND REPRESENTATIONS OF NORTH AMERICAN BUTTERFLIES

DOUBLEDAY & COMPANY, INC.

GARDEN CITY, NEW YORK

PREFACE

PREFACE TO THE FIRST EDITION

A T some time or other in the life of every healthy young person there appears to be developed what has been styled "the collecting mania." Whether this tendency is due to the natural acquisitiveness of the human race, to an innate appreciation of the beautiful and the curious, or to the development of an instinct such as is possessed by the bower-bird, the magpie, and the crow, which have the curious habit of gathering together and storing away trifles which are bright and attractive to the eye, I leave to students of the mind to decide. The fact is patent that there is no village without its youthful enthusiast, whose collection of postage-stamps is dear to his heart, and no town in which there are not amateur geologists, archæologists, botanists, and zoölogists, who are eagerly bent upon the formation of collections of such objects as possess an attraction for them.

One of the commonest pursuits of boyhood is the formation of a collection of insects. The career of almost every naturalist of renown has been marked in its early stages by a propensity to collect these lower, yet most interesting and instructive, forms of animal life. Among the insects, because of their beauty, butterflies have always held a foremost place in the regard of the amateur collector. For the lack, however, of suitable instruction in the art of preserving specimens, and, above all, by reason of the almost entire lack of a convenient and well-illustrated manual, enabling the collector to identify, name, and properly classify the collections which he is making, much of the labor expended in this direction in the United States and Canada fails to accomplish more than the furnishing of temporary recreation. It is otherwise in Europe. Manuals, comprehensive in scope, and richly adorned with illustrations of the leading insect forms of Great Britain and the Continent, have been produced in great numbers in recent years in England, France, and Germany. The result is that the youthful collector enters the field in those countries in the possession of a vast advantage over his less fortunate American fellow. It is to meet this want on this side of the Atlantic that this volume has been written. Its aim is to guide the amateur collector in right paths and to prepare him by the intelligent accomplishment of his labors for the enjoyment of still wider and more difficult researches in this and allied fields of human knowledge. The work is confined to the fauna of the continent of North America north of the Rio Grande of Texas. It is essentially popular in its character. Those who seek a more technical treatment must resort to the writings of others.

If I shall succeed in this book in creating a more widespread interest in the world of insect life and thereby diverting attention in a measure from the persecuted birds, which I love, but which are in many species threatened with extinction by the too eager attentions which they are receiving from young naturalists, who are going forth in increased numbers with shot-gun in hand, I think I shall render a good service to the country.

I flatter myself that I have possessed peculiar facilities for the successful accomplishment of the undertaking I have proposed to myself, because of the possession of what is admitted to be undoubtedly the largest and most perfect collection of the butterflies of North America in existence, containing the types of W. H. Edwards, and many of those of other authors. I have also enjoyed access to all the other great collections of this country and Europe, and have had at my elbow the entire literature relating to the subject.

The successful development in recent months of the process of reproducing in colors photographic representations of objects has been to a certain degree the argument for the publication of this book at the present time. A few years ago the preparation of such a work as this at the low price at which it is sold would have been an utter impossibility. "The Butterflies of North America," by W. H. Edwards, published in three volumes, is sold at one hundred and fifty dollars, and, as I know, is sold even at this price below the cost of manufacture. "The Butterflies of New England," by Dr. S. H. Scudder, in three volumes, is sold at seventy-five dollars, and likewise represents at this price only a partial return to the learned author for the money, labor, and time expended upon it. The present volume, while not pretending to vie in any respect with the magnificence of the illustrations contained in these beautiful and costly works, nevertheless presents in recognizable form almost every species figured in them, and in addition a multitude of others, many of which have never before been delineated. So far as possible I have employed, in making the illustrations, the original types from which the author of the species drew his descriptions. This fact will no doubt add greatly to the value of the work, as it will not only serve as a popular guide, but have utility also for the scientific student.

I am under obligations to numerous friends and correspondents who have aided me, and take the present opportunity to extend to them all my hearty thanks for the generous manner in which they have assisted me in my pleasant task. I should fail, however, to follow the instincts of a grateful heart did I not render an especial acknowledgment to Mr. W. H. Edwards, of Coalburg, West Virginia, and Dr. Samuel H. Scudder, of Cambridge, Massachusetts. Justly esteemed as the two foremost lepidopterists of America, it is my honor to claim them as personal friends, whose kindness has much aided me in this labor of scientific love which I have undertaken. For the kind permission given me by Dr. Scudder to use various illustrations contained in the "Butterflies of New England" and other works, I am profoundly grateful.

I am under obligations to Messrs. Charles Scribner's Sons for permission to use the cuts numbered 46–49, 51–56, 59, 61, 62, and 74, which are taken from the work entitled "Taxidermy and Zoölogical Collecting," by W. T. Hornaday, and to the authorities of the United States National Museum and the heirs of the late Professor C. V. Riley for other illustrations.

Should this book find the favor which I have reason to think it deserves, I shall endeavor shortly to follow it by the preparation of a similar work upon the moths of the United States and Canada.

OFFICE OF THE CHANCELLOR, W. J. H.

WESTERN UNIVERSITY OF PENNSYLVANIA,

AUGUST 16, 1898.

PREFACE TO THE REVISED EDITION

"Unwearied personal observation and an impartial examination of the researches of others; the grateful admission and adoption of every real advance and illustration of science; but also a manly foresight and caution, which does not with eager levity adopt every novelty thrown out in haste and from the love of innovation; all these must go hand in hand, wherever scientific truth is to be successfully promoted." GESENIUS: Preface to Hebrew Grammar, Edit. 11, 1834, p. 7.

THE BUTTERFLY BOOK appeared in December, 1898. It was well received by the public and by working entomologists. Since then over sixty-five thousand copies have found their way into libraries, schools, and the hands of lovers of nature. The continued demand for the book suggests that it be for the greater part rewritten and enlarged, in order to make it more perfect. It originally contained figures of five hundred and thirteen species and varieties. About seven hundred valid species and several hundred named varieties occur in North America north of the Rio Grande of Texas. By adding the necessary plates and text I am able to give figures, not only of those, which were originally omitted, because found in remote parts of the continent, but also of a number described in recent years. In the very few cases, where figures are not given, the reader is informed where such illustrations, if they exist, may be found. The book thus becomes a complete illustrated manual, popular in form, but strictly scientific in content, of the butterflies of North America from the polar regions to the Gulf of Mexico.

For seventy years I have collected and studied butterflies. I have personally known or corresponded with all the leading lepidopterists during the past fifty years in both hemispheres on both sides of the equator. I have the entire literature at my command. The types, or typical specimens, of most of the species occurring in the United States and Canada are in my possession, or have been examined by me. I therefore believe that I am qualified for the task before me. I wish to make this book a farewell offering to the rising generation of entomologists in America, from the Gulf to Alaska.

In most cases I use generic names familiar because of their employment in Europe and America for over a century. Attempts to upset the long established nomenclature, through the validation as generic terms of the names used by Hübner in his *Tentamen*, have been properly discredited through one of the latest decisions of the International Commission on Zoölogical Nomenclature. A few

ix

Preface to the Revised Edition

changes given currency by recent compilers of "Check-lists," appear to be admissible, and I have accepted them; but many of them, founded upon misapprehension, I have disregarded. A number of so-called generic names called into being by my honored friend, the late Dr. S. H. Scudder, I have treated as subgeneric.

My heartiest thanks are hereby tendered to the host of scientific friends, who have generously aided me by the loan of material, by sending me photographs of types in their custody, and by answers to my numerous notes of inquiry. I am under special obligations to Captain N. D. Riley of the British Museum, Professor E. B. Poulton and Dr. Harry Eltringham of Oxford, England; and M. Réné Oberthür of Rennes, France. I owe a debt of gratitude to Dr. J. H. McDunnough and his associate, Mr. Arthur Gibson, of The Dominion Department of Agriculture, Ottawa, Canada, for the loan of specimens, and kind permission to reproduce some of the illustrations contained in the "Report of the Canadian Arctic Expedition." The unfailing kindness of the authorities in charge of the United States National Museum, The Field Museum of Natural History in Chicago, the Museum of the California Academy of Science in San Francisco, the Academy of Natural Sciences in Philadelphia, the American Museum of Natural History in New York, and the Museum of Comparative Zoölogy in Cambridge is gratefully acknowledged. In this connection I cannot forget the ready assistance rendered me by the late Dr. Harrison G. Dyar, and my steadfast friend, Dr. William Schaus; by Dr. Gerhard of the Field Museum; Dr. E. P. Van Duzee of San Francisco; Mr. R. C. Williams, Jr., and Mr. E. T. Cresson, Jr., of Philadelphia; Mr. F. E. Watson of New York; Mr. George P. Engelhardt of Brooklyn; and Dr. Thomas Barbour of Cambridge.

With characteristic generosity the late Dr. William Barnes of Decatur, Illinois, sent me to be figured on the plates of this book many paratypes and in some cases the holotypes of species named by him and his associates. In like manner my genial friend, Mr. J. D. Gunder of Pasadena, put in my hands types and paratypes of many species, which he has named. Mr. R. A. Leussler of Omaha was equally generous. To Mr. E. L. Bell of Flushing, L. I., and Mr. Frank M. Jones of Wilmington, Del., I render hearty thanks, as also to Professor A. W. Lindsey of Denison University, who gave me aid.

I should be false to the promptings of my heart did I not acknowledge the manifold and cheerful assistance, which at all times I have received from my immediate associates in the Entomological Laboratory of the Carnegie Museum, Messrs. Kahl, Krautwurm, and Klages. The first of these smilingly helped me to "search the literature," often a tedious task; the other two with deft fingers mounted the specimens shown on the plates, or patiently "lifted and carried."

Last, but not least, I must acknowledge my debt to my good friend and successor in the Directorship of the Carnegie Museum, Dr. Andrey Avinoff, an expert lepidopterist, who has been to me as a brother in the really huge undertaking, which this book represents.

THE CARNEGIE MUSEUM, PITTSBURGH   W. J. H.
        AUGUST 16, 1930.

TABLE OF CONTENTS

INTRODUCTION

The Eggs of Butterflies. Caterpillars: Structure, Form, Color, etc.; Moults;
Food of Caterpillars; Duration of Larval State; Transformation. *The Pupa,
or Chrysalis:* The Form of Chrysalids; Duration of Pupal Life; The Trans-
formation from the Chrysalis to the Imago. *Anatomy of Butterflies:* The
Head; The Thorax; The Abdomen; The Legs; The Wings; Internal Organs;
Polymorphism and Dimorphism; Albinism and Melanism; Monstrosities;
Mimicry. *The Distribution of Butterflies.*

Collecting Apparatus: Nets; Collecting-Jars; Field-Boxes; The Use of the
Net; Baits; Beating. *The Breeding of Specimens:* How to Get the Eggs of
Butterflies; Breeding-Cages; How to Find Caterpillars; Hibernating Cater-
pillars. *The Preservation of Specimens:* Papering Specimens; Mounting
Butterflies; Relaxing Specimens; The Preparation and Preservation of
Butterfly Eggs; The Preservation of Chrysalids; The Preservation of
Caterpillars. *The Preservation and Arrangement of Collections:* Boxes; Cab-
inets and Drawers; Labeling; Arrangement of Specimens; Insect Pests;
Greasy Specimens; Mould; Repairing Specimens; Packing and Forwarding
Specimens; Pins; The Forceps.

The Place of Butterflies in the Animal Kingdom; The Principles of Scientific
Arrangement; The Species; The Genus; The Family, etc.; Scientific Names;
Synonyms; Popular Names.

Early Writers; Later Writers; Periodicals.

THE BOOK

Table of Contents

DIGRESSION AND QUOTATIONS

INTRODUCTION

INTRODUCTION

CHAPTER I

THE LIFE-HISTORY AND ANATOMY OF BUTTERFLIES

"The study of butterflies,—creatures selected as the types of airiness and frivolity,—instead of being despised, will some day be valued as one of the most important branches of biological science."—BATES, *Naturalist on the Amazons.*

IN studying any subject, it is always well, if possible, to commence at the beginning; and in studying the life of animals, or of a group of animals, we should endeavor to obtain a clear idea at the outset of the manner in which they are developed. It is a familiar saying that "all life is from an egg." This statement is scientifically true in wide fields which come under the eye of the naturalist, and butterflies are no exception to the rule.

THE EGGS OF BUTTERFLIES

The eggs of butterflies consist of a membranous shell containing a fluid mass composed of the germ of the future caterpillar and the liquid food, which is neces-

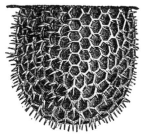

FIG. 1.—Egg of *Basilarchia archippus*, magnified 30 diameters (Riley).

FIG. 2.—Egg of *Basilarchia archippus*, natural size at the tip of leaf (Riley).

FIG. 3.—Egg of *Papilio turnus*, greatly magnified.

sary for its maintenance and development until it escapes from the shell. The forms of these eggs are various. Some are spherical, others hemispherical, conical, and cylindrical. Some are barrel-shaped; others have the shape of a cheese, and still others have the form of a turban. Many of them are angled, some depressed at the ends. Their surfaces are variously ornamented. Sometimes they are ribbed, the ribs running from the center outwardly and downwardly along the sides, like the meridian lines upon a globe. Between these ribs there is frequently found a

3

fine network of raised lines variously arranged. Sometimes the surface is covered with minute depressions, sometimes with a series of minute elevations variously disposed. As there is great variety in the form of the eggs, so also there is great variety in their color. Brown, blue, green, red, and yellow eggs occur. Greenish or

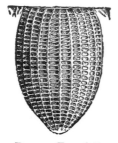

Fig. 4.—Egg of *Danais plexippus*, magnified 30 diameters (Riley).

Fig. 5.—Egg of *Danais plexippus*, natural size, on under side of leaf (Riley).

Fig. 6.—Egg of *Anthocharis genutia*, magnified 20 diameters.

Fig. 7.—Turban-shaped egg of *Lycæna pseudargiolus*, greatly magnified.

greenish-white are common tints. The eggs are often ornamented with dots and lines of darker color. Species which are related to one another show their affinity even in the form of their eggs. At the upper end of the eggs of insects there are one or more curious structures, known as micropyles (little doors), through which the

Fig. 8.—Egg of *Melitæa phaëtona*, greatly magnified.

Fig. 9.—Upper end of egg of *Pieris oleracea*, greatly magnified showing the micropyle.

Fig. 10.—Egg of *Polygonia comma*, laid in string-like clusters on the under side of leaf. (Magnified.)

Fig. 11.—Eggs of *Aglais antiopa*, laid in a mass on a twig.

spermatozoa of the male find ingress and they are fertilized. These can only be seen under a good microscope.

The eggs are laid upon the food-plant, upon which the caterpillar, after it is hatched, is destined to live, and the female reveals wonderful instinct in selecting plants, which are appropriate to the development of the larva. As a rule, the larvæ are restricted in the range of their food-plants to certain genera, or families of plants.

The eggs are deposited sometimes singly, sometimes in small clusters, sometimes in a mass. Fertile eggs, a few days after they have been deposited, frequently undergo a change in color, and it is often possible with a magnifying-glass to see through the thin shell the form of the minute caterpillar which is being developed within the egg. Unfruitful eggs generally shrivel and dry up after the lapse of a short time.

The period of time requisite for the development of the embryo in the egg varies. Many butterflies are single-brooded; others produce two or three generations during the summer in temperate climates, and even more generations in subtropical or tropical climates. In such cases an interval of only a few days, or weeks at the most, separates the time when the egg was deposited and the time when the larva is hatched. When the period of hatching, or emergence, has arrived, the little caterpillar cuts its way forth from the egg through an opening made either at the side or on the top. Many species have eggs which appear to be provided with a lid, a portion of the shell being separated from the remainder by a thin section, which, when the caterpillar has reached the full limit allowed by the egg, breaks under the pressure of the enlarging embryo within, one portion of the egg flying off, the remainder adhering to the leaf or twig upon which it has been deposited.

CATERPILLARS

Structure, Form, Color, etc.—The second stage, in which the insects we are studying exist, is known as the larval stage. The insect is known as a larva, or caterpillar. In general caterpillars have long, worm-like bodies. Frequently they are thickest about the middle, tapering before and behind, flattened on the under side. While the cylindrical shape is most common, there are some families in which the larvæ are short, oval, or slug-shaped, sometimes curiously modified by ridges and prominences. The body of the larvæ of lepidoptera consists normally of thirteen rings, or segments, the first constituting the head.

The head is always conspicuous, composed of horny or chitinous material, but varying exceedingly in form and size. It is very rarely small and retracted. It is generally large, hemispherical, conical, or bilobed. In some families it is ornamented by horn-like projections. On the lower side are the mouth-parts, consisting of the upper lip, the mandibles, the antennæ, or feelers, the under lip, the maxillæ, and two sets of palpi, known as the maxillary and the labial palpi.

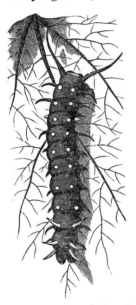

FIG. 12.—Caterpillar of *Papilio philenor* (Riley).

FIG. 13.—Head of caterpillar of *Papilio asterius*, front view, enlarged.

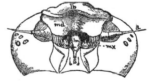

FIG. 14.—Head of caterpillar of *Danais plexippus*, lower side, magnified 10 diameters: *lb*, labrum, or upper lip; *md*, mandibles; *mx*, maxilla, with two palpi; *lm*, labium, or lower lip, with one pair of palpi; *s*, spinneret; *a*, antenna; *o*, ocelli. (After Burgess.)

In many genera the labium, or under lip, is provided with a short, horny projection known as the spinneret, through which the silk secreted by the caterpillar is passed. On either side, just above the mandibles, are located the eyes, or ocelli, which in the caterpillar are simple, round, shining prominences, generally only to be clearly distinguished by the aid of a magnifying-glass. These ocelli are frequently arranged in series on each side. The palpi are organs of touch connected with the maxillæ and the labium, or under lip, and are used in the process of feed-

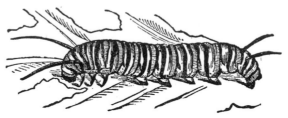

FIG. 15.—Head of caterpillar of *Danais plexippus*, side view, showing ocelli.

FIG. 16.—Caterpillar of *Danais plexippus*, Milkweed Butterfly (Riley).

FIG. 17.—Fore leg of caterpillar of *Aglais antiopa*, enlarged.

ing, and also when the caterpillar is crawling about from place to place. The larva appears to guide itself in great part by means of the palpi.

The body of the caterpillar is covered by a thin skin, which often lies in wrinkled folds, admitting of great freedom of motion. The body is composed, as we have seen, of rings, or segments, the first three of which, back of the head, correspond to the thorax of the perfect insect and the last nine to the abdomen of the butterfly. In each ring, with the exception of the second, the third, and the last, there is found on either side a small oval opening known as a spiracle, through which the creature breathes. As a rule, the spiracles of the first and eleventh rings are larger in size than the others.

Every caterpillar has on each of the first three segments a pair of legs, which are organs composed of three somewhat horny parts covered and bound together with skin, and armed at their extremities by a sharp claw (Fig. 17). These three pairs of feet in the caterpillar are always known as the fore legs, and correspond to the six which are found in the butterfly or the moth. In addition, in most cases, we find four pairs of prolegs on the under side of the segments from the sixth to the ninth, and another pair on the last segment, which latter pair are called the anal prolegs. These organs, which are necessary to the life of the caterpillar, do not reappear in the perfect insect, but are lost when the transformation from the caterpillar to the chrysalis takes place. There are various modifications of this scheme of foot-like appendages, only the larger and more highly developed forms of lepidoptera having as many pairs of prolegs as have been enumerated.

The bodies of caterpillars are variously ornamented: many of them are quite smooth; many are provided with horny projections, spines, and eminences. The coloration of caterpillars is as remarkable in the variety which it displays, as is the ornamentation by means of the prominences, of which we have just spoken. As caterpillars, for the most part, feed upon growing vegetation, multitudes of them are green in color, being thus adapted to their surroundings and securing a measure of protection. Many are brown, and exactly mimic the color of the twigs and branches upon which they rest, when not engaged in feeding. Not a few are very gaily colored, but in almost every case this gay coloring is found to bear some relation to the color of the objects upon which they rest.

Caterpillars vary in their social habits. Some species are gregarious, and are found in colonies. These frequently build for themselves defenses, weaving webs of silk among the branches, in which they are in part protected from their enemies

FIG. 18.—Anterior segments of caterpillar of Milkweed Butterfly, showing thoracic or true legs (Riley).

FIG. 19.—Proleg of caterpillar of *Aglais antiopa*, enlarged.

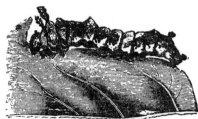

FIG. 20.—Caterpillar of *Basilarchia archippus* the Viceroy, natural size (Riley).

and also from the inclemencies of the weather. Most caterpillars are, however, solitary, and no community-life is maintained by the vast majority of species. Many species have the habit of drawing together the edges of a leaf, in which way they form a covering for themselves. The caterpillars of some butterflies are wood-boring, and construct tunnels in the pith, or in the soft layers of growing plants. In these cases, being protected and concealed from view, the caterpillars are generally white in their coloration, resembling in this respect the larvæ of wood-boring beetles. A most curious phenomenon has within comparatively recent years been discovered in connection with the larval stage of certain small butterflies belonging to the family *Lycœnidœ*. The caterpillars are carnivorous, or rather aphidivorous; they live upon aphids, or plant-lice, and scale-insects, and cover themselves with the white exudations or mealy secretions of the latter. This trait is characteristic of only one of our North American species, the Harvester (*Feniseca tarquinius*).

In addition to being protected from enemies by having colors which enable them to elude observation, as has been already stated, some caterpillars are provided with other means of defense. The caterpillars of the swallowtail butterflies are provided with a bifurcate or forked organ, generally yellow in color, which is protruded from an opening in the skin back of the head, and which emits a powerful odor (Fig. 22). This protrusive organ evidently exists only for purposes of defense, and the secretion of the odor is analogous to the secretion of evil odors by some of the vertebrate animals, as the skunk. The majority of caterpillars, when attacked by insect or other enemies, defend themselves by quickly hurling the anterior part of the body from side to side.

Moults.—Caterpillars in the process of growth and development from time to time shed their skins. This process is called *moulting*. Moulting takes place, as a

7

rule, at regular intervals, though there are exceptions to this rule. The young larva, having emerged from the egg, grows for a number of days, until the epidermis, or true skin, has become too small. It then ceases feeding, attaches itself firmly to some point, and remains quiet for a time. During this period certain changes are taking place, and then the skin splits along the middle line from the head to the extremity of the last segment, and the caterpillar crawls forth from the skin, which is left behind it, attached to the leaf or branch to which it was fastened. The skin of the head sometimes remains attached to the head of the caterpillar for a time after it has moulted, and then falls off to the ground. Ordinarily not more than five, and frequently only four, moults take place between hatching from the egg and the change into the chrysalis. In cases where caterpillars hibernate, or pass the winter in inaction, a long interval necessarily elapses between moults. Some arctic species are known in which the development from the egg to the perfect insect covers a period of two or three years, long periods of hibernation under the arctic snows taking place. The manner in which the caterpillar withdraws itself from its exuviæ, or old skin, is highly interesting. Every little spine or rough prominence is withdrawn from its covering, and the skin is left as a perfect cast of the creature which has emerged from it, even the hairs and spines attached to the skin being left behind and replaced by others.

FIG. 21.—Early stages of the goatweed butterfly: *a*, caterpillar; *b*, chrysalis; *c*, leaf drawn together at edges to form a nest, natural size (Riley).

The Food of the Caterpillar.—The vast majority of the caterpillars of butterflies subsist upon vegetable food, the only exception being the singular one already noted in which the larvæ feed upon scale-insects. Some of the *Hesperiidæ*, a group in which the relationship between butterflies and moths is shown, have larvæ which burrow in the roots and stems of vegetation.

FIG. 22.—Head of caterpillar of *Papilio troilus*, with scent-organs, or *osmateria*, protruded.

Duration of the Larval State.—The duration of the larval state varies greatly. In temperate climates the majority of species exist in the caterpillar state for from two to three months, and where hibernation takes place, for ten months. Many caterpillars, which hibernate, do so immediately after emerging from the egg and before having made the first moult. The great majority, however, hibernate after having passed one or more moults. With the approach of spring they renew their feeding upon the first reappearance of the foliage of their proper food-plant, or are transformed into chrysalids and presently emerge as perfect insects. A few species live gregariously during the period of hibernation, constructing for themselves a shelter of leaves woven together with strands of silk.

Transformation.—The larval, or caterpillar-stage, having been completed, and full development having been attained, the caterpillar is transformed into a pupa, or chrysalis. Of this, the third stage in the life of the insect, we now shall speak at length.

THE PUPA, OR CHRYSALIS

The caterpillars of many butterflies attach themselves by a button of silk to the under surface of a branch or stone, or other projecting surface, and are transformed into chrysalids, which are naked, and which hang perpendicularly from the surface to which they are attached. Other caterpillars attach themselves to surfaces by means of a button of silk, which holds the anal extremity of the chrysalis, and in addition by a girdle of silk, which passes around the middle of the chrysalis, holding it in place very much as a papoose is held on the back of an Indian squaw by a strap passed over the shoulders.

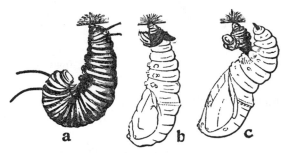

FIG. 23.—Caterpillar of *Danais plexippus*, undergoing change into chrysalis: *a*, Caterpillar just before rending of the skin; *b*, chrysalis just before the cremaster, or hook, at the end of the body is withdrawn; *c*, chrysalis holding itself in place by the folds of the shed skin caught between the edges of the abdominal segments, while with the cremaster, armed with microscopic hooks, it searches for the button of silk from which it is to hang (Riley). (Compare Fig. 24, showing final form of the chrysalis.)

The Form of Chrysalids.—The forms assumed by insects in this stage of their being vary greatly, though there is a general resemblance among the different families and subfamilies, so that it is easy for one who has studied the matter to tell approximately to what family the form belongs, even when it is not specifically known. Chrysalids are in most cases obscure in coloring, though a few are quite brilliant, and, as in the case of the common Milkweed Butterfly (*Danais plexippus*), ornamented with golden-hued spots. The chrysalids of the *Nymphalidæ*, one of the largest groups of butterflies are all suspended. The chrysalids of the *Papilionidæ* and the *Pieridæ* are held in place by girdles. The former are generally bifurcate, or cleft, at the upper end, and the latter pointed.

A study of the structure of all chrysalids shows that within them there is contained the immature butterfly. The segments of the body are ensheathed in the corresponding segments of the chrysalis, and soldered over these segments are ensheathing plates of chitinous matter, under which are the wings of the butterfly, as well as all the other organs necessary to its existence in the airy realm upon which it enters after emergence from the chrysalis. The practised eye

9

of the observer is soon able to distinguish the location of the various parts of the butterfly in the chrysalis, and when the time for escape draws near, it is in many cases possible to discern through the thin, yet tough and hard, outer walls of the chrysalis the spots and colors of the wings of the insect.

Duration of Pupal Life.—Many butterflies remain in the chrysalis stage only for a few weeks; others hibernate in this state, and in temperate climates a great

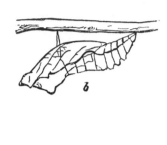

FIG. 24.—Chrysalis of *Danais plexippus*, final form (Riley).

FIG. 25.—Chrysalis of *Papilio philenor: a,* front view; *b,* side view, showing manner in which it is held in place by the girdle of silk (Riley).

many butterflies pass the winter as chrysalids. Where, as is sometimes the case, there are two or three generations or broods of a species during the year, the life of one brood is generally longer than that of the others, because this brood is compelled to overwinter, or hibernate. There are a number of butterflies known in

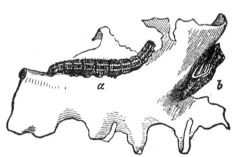

FIG. 26.—*Pieris protodice: a,* caterpillar; *b,* chrysalis (Riley).

FIG. 27.—Chrysalis of *Pieris oleracea* (Riley).

FIG. 28.—Butterfly (*Papilio asterius*) just out of chrysalis, before wings have spread.

temperate North America which have three broods: a spring brood, emerging from chrysalids which have overwintered; an early summer brood; and a fall brood. The chrysalids in the latter two cases generally represent only a couple of weeks at most in the life of the insect. In tropical and semi-tropical countries many species remain in the chrysalis form during the dry season, and emerge at the beginning of the rains, when vegetation is refreshed and new and tender growths occur in the forests.

The Transformation from the Chrysalis to the Imago.—The perfectly developed insect is known technically as the *imago*. When the time of maturity in the chrysalis state has been reached, the coverings part in such a way as to allow of the escape of the perfect insect, which, as it comes forth, generally carries with it some suggestion of its caterpillar state in the lengthened abdomen, which it with apparent difficulty trails after it until it secures a hold upon some object from which it may depend while a process of development (which lasts generally a few hours) takes place preparatory to flight. The imago, as it first emerges, is provided with small, flaccid wings, which, together with all the organs of sense such as the antennæ, require for their complete development the injection into them of the vital fluids which, upon first emergence, are largely contained in the cavities of the thorax and abdomen. Hanging pendant on a projecting twig, or clinging to the side of a rock, the insect remains fanning its wings, while by the strong process of circulation a rapid injection of the blood into the wings and other organs takes place, accompanied by their expansion to normal proportions, in which they gradually attain to more or less rigidity. Hardly anything in the range of insect life is more interesting than this rapid development of the butterfly after its first emergence from the chrysalis. The body is robbed of its liquid contents in a large degree; the abdomen is shortened up; the chitinous rings which compose its external skeleton become set and hardened; the wings are expanded, and then the moment arrives when, on airy pinions, the creature that has lived a worm-like life for weeks and months, or which has been apparently sleeping the sleep of death in its cerements, soars aloft in the air, the companion of the sunlight and the breezes.

ANATOMY OF BUTTERFLIES

The body of the butterfly consists of three parts—the head, the thorax, and the abdomen.

The Head.—The head is globular, its breadth generally exceeding its length. The top is called the *vertex*; the anterior portion, corresponding in location to the human face, is called the *front*. Upon the sides of the head are situated the large *compound eyes*, between which are the *antennæ*, or "feelers," as they are sometimes called. Above the mouth is a smooth horny plate, the *clypeus*. The *labrum*, or upper lip, is quite small. On both sides of the mouth are rudimentary *mandibles*, which are microscopic objects. The true suctorial apparatus is formed by the *maxillæ*, which are produced in the form of semi-cylindrical tubes, which, being brought together and interlocking, form a complete tube, which is known as the *proboscis*, and which, when not in use, is curled up spirally, looking like a watch-spring. At the upper end of the proboscis, in the head, is a bulb-like enlargement, in the walls of which are inserted muscles which have their origin on the inner wall of the head. When these muscles contract, the bulb-like cavity is enlarged, a vacuum is produced, and the fluids in the cup of the flower flow up the proboscis and into the bulb. The bulb is also surrounded by muscles, which, when contracting, compress it. The external opening of the tube has a flap, or valve, which, when the bulb is compressed, closes and causes the fluid in it to flow backward into the gullet and the stomach. The arrangement is mechanically not unlike that in a bulb-syringe used by physicians. The process of feeding in the case of the butterfly is a process of pumping honeyed water out of the flowers into the

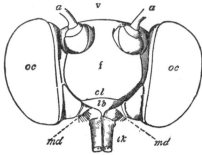

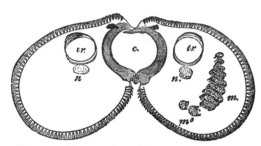

FIG. 29.—Head of Milkweed Butterfly, stripped of scales and greatly magnified (after Burgess): *v*, vertex; *f*, front; *cl*, clypeus; *lb*, labrum, or upper lip; *md*, mandibles; *a*, antennæ; *oc*, eyes; *tk*, spiral tongue, or proboscis.

FIG. 30.—Cross-section of the sucking-tube of the Milkweed Butterfly, to show the way in which the halves unite to form a central canal (*c*): *tr*, tracheæ, or air-tubes; *n*, nerves; *m*, *m³*, muscles of one side. (Magnified 125 diameters.) (Burgess.)

stomach. The length of the proboscis varies; at its base and on either side are placed what are known as the maxillary palpi, which are very small. The lower

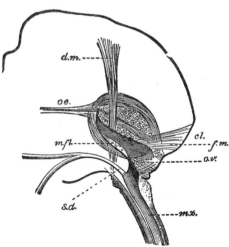

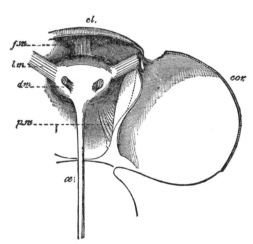

FIG. 31.—Longitudinal section of the head of the Milkweed Butterfly: *cl*, clypeus; *mx*, left maxilla, the right being removed; *mfl*, floor of mouth; *æ*, œsophagus, or gullet; *ov*, mouth-valve; *sd*, salivary duct; *dm* and *fm*, dorsal and frontal muscles, which open the sac. (Magnified 20 diameters.) (Burgess.)

FIG. 32.—Interior view of head of Milkweed Butterfly: *cl*, clypeus; *cor*, cornea of the eye; *æ*, œsophagus, or gullet; *fm*, frontal muscle; *dm*, dorsal muscles; *lm*, lateral muscles; *pm*, muscles moving the palpus (Burgess).

lip, or *labium*, which is also almost obsolete in the butterflies, has on either side two organs known as the *labial palpi*, which consist of three joints. In the butterflies the labial palpi are generally well developed, though in some genera they are quite small. The antennæ of butterflies are always provided at the extremity with a club-shaped enlargement, and because of this clubbed form of the antennæ the entire group are known as the *Rhopalocera*, the word being compounded from the Greek word ῥώπαλον (*rhopalon*), which means a *club*, and the word κέρας (*keras*) which means a *horn*.

It will be observed from what has been said that the head in these creatures is to a large extent the seat of the organs of sense and alimentation. What the function of the antennæ may be is somewhat doubtful, the opinion of scientific men being divided. The latest researches would indicate that these organs, which have been regarded as the organs of smell and sometimes as the organs of hearing, have probably a compound function, possibly enabling the creature to hear, certainly to smell, but also, perhaps, being the seat of impressions which are not strictly like any which we receive through our senses.

Thorax.—The thorax is more or less oval in form, being somewhat flattened upon its upper surface. It is composed of three parts, or segments, closely united,

FIG. 33. — Labial palpus of *Colias*, magnified 10 diameters.

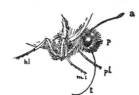

FIG. 34. — *Colias philodice: a*, antenna; *p*, extremity of palpus; *pl*, prothoracic leg; *ml*, mesothoracic leg; *hl*, metathoracic or hind leg; *t*, proboscis.

FIG. 35. — Leg of butterfly: *c*, coxa; *tr*, trochanter; *f*, femur; *t*, tibia; *tar*, tarsus.

which can only be distinguished from one another by a careful dissection. The anterior segment is known as the prothorax, the middle segment as the mesothorax, and the after segment as the metathorax. The legs are attached in pairs to these three subdivisions of the thorax, the anterior pair being therefore sometimes spoken of as the prothoracic legs, the second pair as the mesothoracic legs, and the latter pair as the metathoracic legs (Fig. 34). To either side of the mesothorax are attached the anterior pair of wings, over which, at their insertion into the body, are the *tegulæ*, or lappets; on either side of the metathorax are the posterior pair of wings. It will be seen from what has been said that the thorax bears the organs of locomotion. The under side of the thorax is frequently spoken of by writers, in describing butterflies, as the *pectus*, or breast.

The Abdomen.—The abdomen is formed normally of nine segments, and in most butterflies is shorter than the hind wings. On the last segment there are various appendages, which are mainly sexual in their nature.

The Legs.—Butterflies have six legs, arranged in three pairs, as we have already seen. Each leg consists of five parts, the first of which, nearest the body, is called the *coxa*, with which articulates a ring-like piece known as the *trochanter*.

To this is attached the *femur*, and united with the femur, forming an angle with it, is the *tibia*. To the tibia is attached the *tarsus*, or foot, the last segment of which bears the claws, which are often very minute and blunt in the butterflies, though in moths they are sometimes strongly hooked. The tibiæ are often armed with spines. In some groups of butterflies the anterior pair of legs is aborted, or dwarfed, either in one or both sexes, a fact which is useful in determining the location of species in their systematic order.

The Wings.—The wings of butterflies consist of a framework of horny tubes which are in reality double, the inner tube being filled with air, the outer tube with

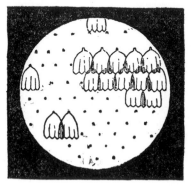

FIG. 36.—Magnified representation of arrangement of the scales on the wing of a butterfly.

FIG. 37.—Androconia from wings of male butterflies: *a, Euptychia euryta; b, Argynnis aphrodite; c, Pieris oleracea.*

blood, which circulates most freely during the time that the insect is undergoing the process of development after emergence from the chrysalis, as has been already described. After emergence the circulation of the blood in the outer portion of the tubes is largely, if not altogether, suspended. These horny tubes support a broad membrane, which is clothed in most species upon both sides with flattened scales, which are attached to the membrane in such a way that they overlap one another like the shingles on a roof. These scales are very beautiful objects when examined under a microscope, and there is considerable diversity in their form as well as in their colors. The males of many species have peculiarly shaped scales arranged in tufts and folds, which are called androconia, and are useful in microscopically determining species (Fig. 37). The portion of the wings, which is nearest to the thorax at the point where they are attached to the body, is called the *base*; the middle third of the wing is known as the *median* or *discal area*, the outer third as the *limbal area*. The anterior margin of the wings is called the *costal margin*; the outer edge is known as the *external margin*, the inner edge as the *inner margin*. The shape of the wings varies very much. The tip of the front wing is called the apex, and this may be rounded, acute, falcate (somewhat sickle-shaped), or square. The angle formed by the outer margin of the front wing with the inner margin is commonly known as the *outer angle*. The corresponding angle on the hind wing is known as the *anal angle*, and the point which corresponds to the tip or apex of the front wing is known as the *external angle* (Fig. 38). A knowledge of these terms is necessary in order to understand the technical descriptions which are given by authors.

If a wing is examined with the naked eye, or even with a lens, a clear conception of the structure of the veins can rarely be formed. Therefore it is generally necessary to remove from the wings the scales which cover them, or else bleach them. The scales may be removed mechanically by rubbing them off. They may be made transparent by the use of chemical agents. In the case of specimens which are so valuable as to forbid a resort to these methods, a clear knowledge of the structure of the veins may be formed by simply moistening them with pure benzine or chloroform, which enables the structure of the veins to be seen for a few moments. The evaporation of these fluids is rapid, and they produce no ill effect upon the color and texture of the wings. In the case of common species, or in the case of such as are abundantly represented in the possession of the collector, and the practical destruction of one or two of which is a matter of no moment, it is easy to use the first method. The wing should be placed between two sheets of fine writing-paper which have been moistened by the breath at the points where the wing is laid, and then by lightly rubbing the finger-nail or a piece of ivory, bone, or other hard substance over the upper piece of paper, a good many of the scales may be removed. This process may be repeated until almost all of them have been taken off. This method is efficient in the case of many of the small species when they are still fresh; in the case of the larger species the scales may be removed by means of a camel's-hair pencil such as is used by painters. The chemical method of bleaching wings is simple and inexpensive. For this purpose the wing should be dipped in alcohol and then placed in a vessel containing a bleaching solution of some sort. The best agent is a solution of chloride of lime. After the color has been removed from the wing by the action of the chloride it should be washed in a weak solution of hydrochloric acid. It may then be cleansed in pure water and mounted upon a piece of glass, as microscopic slides are mounted and thus preserved. When thus bleached the wing is capable of being minutely studied, and all points of its anatomy are brought clearly into view.

The veins in both the fore and hind wings of butterflies may be divided into simple and compound veins. In the fore wing the simple veins are the costal, the radial, and the submedian; in the hind wing, the costal, the subcostal, the upper and lower radial, the submedian, and the internal are simple. The costal vein in the hind wing is, however, generally provided near the base with a short ascending branch which is known as the precostal vein. In addition to these simple veins there are in the fore wing two branching veins, one immediately following the costal, known as the subcostal, and the other preceding the submedian, known as the median vein. The branches of these compound veins are known as nervules. The median vein always has three nervules. The nervules of the subcostal veins branch upwardly and outwardly toward the costal margin and the apex of the fore wing. There are always from four to five subcostal nervules. In the hind wing the subcostal is simple. The median vein in the hind wing has three nervules as in

15

the fore wing. Between the subcostal and the median veins, toward the base in both wings, is inclosed the cell, which may be wholly or partially open at its outer extremity, or closed. The veinlets which close the cell at its outward extremity are known as the discocellular veins, of which there are normally three. From the point of union of these discocellular veins go forth the radial veins known respectively as the upper and lower radials, though the upper radial in many genera is emitted from the lower margin of the subcostal.

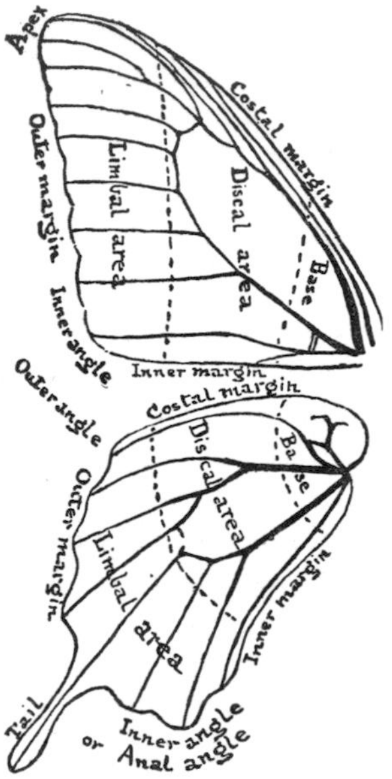

An understanding of these terms is, however, more readily derived from a study of the figure in which the names of these parts are indicated (Fig. 40).

Butterflies generally hold their wings erect when they are at rest, with their two upper surfaces in proximity, the under surfaces alone displaying their colors to the eye. Only in a few genera of the larger butterflies, and these tropical species, with which this book does not deal, is there an exception to this rule, save in the case of the *Hesperiidæ*, or "skippers," in which very frequently, while the anterior wings are folded together, the posterior wings lie in a horizontal position.

FIG. 38.—Outline of wing, giving names of parts.

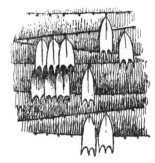

FIG. 39.—Arrangement of scales on wing of butterfly.

Internal Organs.—Thus far we have considered only the external organs of the butterfly. The internal organs have been made the subject of close study and research by many writers, and a volume might be prepared upon this subject. It will, however, suffice for us to call the attention of the student to the principal facts.

The muscular system finds its principal development in the thorax, which bears the organs of locomotion. The digestive system consists of the proboscis, which has already been described, the gullet, or œsophagus, and the stomach, over which is a large, bladder-like vessel called the food-reservoir, a sort of crop preceding the true stomach, which is a cylindrical tube; the intestine is a slender tube, varying in shape in different genera, divided into the small intestine, the colon, and the rectum. Butterflies breathe through spiracles, little oval openings on the sides of the segments of the body, branching from which inwardly are the tracheæ, or bronchial tubes. The heart, which is located in the same relative position as the spine in vertebrate animals, is a tubular structure. The nervous system lies on the lower or ventral side of the body, its position being exactly the reverse of that which is found in the higher animals. It consists of nervous cords and ganglia, or nerve-knots, in the different segments. Those in the head are more largely developed than elsewhere, forming a rudimentary brain, the larger portion of which consists of two enormous optic nerves. The student who is desirous of informing himself more thoroughly and accurately as to the internal anatomy of these insects may consult with profit some of the treatises which are mentioned in the list of works dealing with the subject which is given elsewhere in this book.

Polymorphism and Dimorphism.—Species of butterflies often show great differences in the different broods which appear. The brood which emerges in the springtime from the chrysalis, which has passed the winter under the snows, may differ very strikingly from the insect which appears in the second or summer brood; and the insects of the third or fall brood may differ again from either the spring or the summer brood. The careful student notes these differences. Such species are called polymorphic, that is, appearing under different forms. Some species reveal a singular difference between the sexes, and there may be two forms of the same sex in the same species. This is most common in the case of the female butterfly, and where there are two forms of the female or the male such a species is said to have dimorphic females or males. This phenomenon is revealed in the case of the well-known Turnus Butterfly; in the colder regions of the continent the females are yellow banded with black, like the males, but in more southern portions of the continent black females are quite common, and these dark females were once thought, before the truth was known, to constitute a separate species.

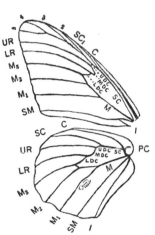

FIG. 40.—Wing of *Danais plexippus*, showing the names of the veins and nervules: *C, C,* costal veins; *SC,* subcostal vein; *SC₁,* etc., subcostal nervules; *UR,* upper radial; *LR,* lower radial; *M,* median veins; *M₁, M₂, M₃,* median nervules; *SM,* submedian veins; *I,* internal veins; *PC,* precostal nervule; *UDC, MDC, LDC,* upper, middle, and lower discocellulars.

Albinism and Melanism.—Albinos, white or light-colored forms, are quite common among butterflies, principally among the females. On the other hand, melanism, or a tendency to the production of dark or even black forms, reveals itself. Melanism is rather more common in the case of the male sex than in the female sex. The collector and student will always endeavor, if possible, to preserve these curious *aberrations*, as they are called. We do not yet entirely understand what are the causes which are at work to produce these changes in the color, and all such aberrant specimens have interest for the scientific man. However, to name them and give them standing as subspecific forms is more or less objectionable, except in cases, where they constantly occur.

Monstrosities.—Curious malformations and monstrosities sometimes occur among insects, as in other animals, and such malformed specimens should likewise be preserved when found. One form of malformation which is not altogether uncommon consists in an apparent confusion of sexes in specimens, the wings of a male insect being attached to the body of a female, or half of an insect being male and half female.

Mimicry.—One of the most singular and interesting facts in the animal kingdom is what has been styled mimicry. Certain colors and forms are possessed by animals, which adapt them to their surroundings in such wise that they are in

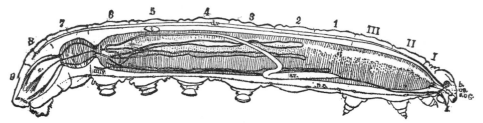

FIG. 41.—Longitudinal section through the larva of *Danais plexippus*, ♂, to show the internal anatomy (the Roman numerals indicate the thoracic, the Arabic the abdominal segments): *b*, brain; *sog*, subœsophageal ganglion; *nc*, nervous cord; *œ*, œsophagus; *st*, stomach; *i*, intestine; *c*, colon; *sv*, spinning-vessel of one side; *s*, spinneret; *mv*, Malpighian vessel, of which only the portions lying on the stomach are shown, and not the multitudinous convolutions on the intestine; *t*, testis; *dv*, dorsal vessel; the salivary glands are not shown. (Magnified 3 diameters). (Burgess).

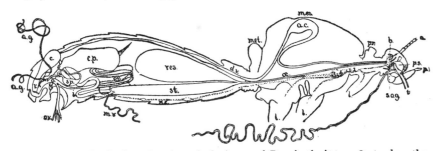

FIG. 42.—Longitudinal section through the imago of *Danais plexippus*, ♀, to show the internal anatomy: *t*, tongue; *p*, palpus; *a*, antenna; *pr*, prothorax; *mes*, mesothorax; *met*, metathorax; *ps*, pharyngeal sac; *b*, brain; *sog*, subœsophageal ganglion; 1–2, blended first and second ganglia of the larva; 3–4, blended third and fourth ganglia of the larva; *l, l, l*, the three legs; *ac*, aortal chamber; *dv*, dorsal vessel; *œ*, œsophagus; *res*, reservoir for air or food; *st*, stomach; *mv*, Malpighian vessels; *i*, intestine; *c*, colon; *r*, rectum; *cp*, copulatory pouch; *o*, oviduct; *ag*, accessory glands; *sp*, spermatheca; *ov*, ovaries (not fully developed); *nc*, nervous cord. (Magnified 3 diameters). (Burgess.)

a greater or less degree secured from observation and attack. Or they possess forms and colors which cause them to approximate in appearance other creatures, which for some reason are feared or disliked by animals which might prey upon them. In consequence of this resemblance they enjoy partial or entire immunity. Some butterflies, for instance, resemble dried leaves, and as they are seated upon the twigs of trees they wholly elude the eye. This illustrates the first form of mimicry. Other butterflies so closely approximate in form and color species, which birds and other insects will not attack because of the disagreeable juices which their bodies contain, that they are shunned by their natural enemies, in spite of the fact that they belong to groups of insects which are ordinarily greedily devoured by insectivorous animals. A good illustration of this fact is found in the case of the

Viceroy, which belongs to a group which is not specially protected, but is often the prey of insect-eating creatures. This butterfly has assumed almost the exact color and markings of the Milkweed Butterfly, *Danais plexippus*, which is distasteful to birds, and hence enjoys peculiar freedom from the attacks of enemies. Because this adaptation of one form to another evidently serves the purpose of defense this phenomenon has been called "protective mimicry." The reader who is curious to know more about the subject will do well to consult the writings of Mr. Alfred Russel Wallace and Mr. Darwin, who have written at length upon mimicry among butterflies. There is here a field of most interesting inquiry for the student.

The Distribution of Butterflies.—Butterflies are found everywhere that plants suited to the nourishment of the caterpillars are found. There are some species which are arctic and are found in the brief summer of the cold North and upon the lofty summits of high mountains which have an arctic climate. Most of them are, however, children of the sun, and chiefly abound in the temperate and tropical regions of the earth. While the number of species which are found in the tropics vastly exceeds the number of species found in the temperate zone, it is apparently true that the number of specimens of certain species is far more numerous in temperate regions than in the tropics. Very rarely in tropical countries are great assemblages of butterflies to be seen, such as may be found in the summer months in the United States, swarming around damp places, or hovering over the fields of blooming clover or weeds. In the whole vast region extending from the Rio Grande of Texas to the arctic circle it is doubtful whether more than seven hundred true species of butterflies are found. On the continent of Europe there are only about four hundred and fifty species. The number of species of butterflies and the number of species of birds in the United States are very nearly the same. If we include in both groups named subspecies and varieties, the number is greatly increased.

IMMORTALITY

A butterfly basked on a baby's grave,
  Where a lily had chanced to grow:
"Why art thou here with thy gaudy dye,
When she of the blue and sparkling eye
  Must sleep in the churchyard low?"

Then it lightly soared thro' the sunny air,
  And spoke from its shining track:
"I was a worm till I won my wings,
And she, whom thou mourn'st, like a seraph sings;
  Would'st thou call the blest one back?"
                                        SIGOURNEY.

CHAPTER II

"What hand would crush the silken-wingèd fly,
  The youngest of inconstant April's minions,
Because it cannot climb the purest sky,
  Where the swan sings, amid the sun's dominions?
Not thine."

                                        SHELLEY.

"Do not mash your specimens!"—THE PROFESSOR.

COLLECTING APPARATUS

Nets.—In the capture of insects of all orders, and especially of butterflies and moths, one of the most important instruments is the net. Some German naturalists make use of what are known as shears (*Scheren*), which are like gigantic scissors, having at the end two large oval rings, upon which wire gauze or fine netting is stretched. With this implement, which looks like an old-fashioned candle-snuffer of colossal size, specimens may be caught without much injury. Shears are, however, not greatly in vogue. The favorite instrument is the net. Nets may be made in various ways and of various materials. There are a multitude of devices which have been invented for enabling the net to be folded up, so as to occupy but little space when not in use. The simplest form of the net, which can be made almost anywhere, is constructed as follows: A rod—preferably of bamboo, or some other light, stiff material—is used as the handle, not more than five feet in length. Attached to this at its upper end, a loop or ring made of metal, or some moderately stiff yet flexible material, should be tied securely. Upon this there should be sewed a bag of fine netting, preferably tarletan. The bag should be quite long, not less than eighteen inches deep; the ring should be not less than a foot in diameter. Such a net can be made at a cost of but a few cents, and will be, in most cases, as efficient as any of the more expensive nets which are more carefully constructed. A good, cheap ring for a net may be made by using the brass ferrule of a fishing-rod. The ferrule should be at least three quarters of an inch in diameter. Into this insert the ends of a metal ring made by bending brass, aluminum, or iron wire into the proper form. When the ends have been inserted into the ferrule, melted solder may be poured into it, and the ends of the wire forming the ring will be thus firmly secured in the ferrule. The ferrule can then be inserted into its mate placed at the end of a bamboo rod. I have commonly obtained for this purpose the last joint or butt of a fishing-rod as the handle of a net. Such a handle can often be purchased for a small sum from a dealer in fishing-rods. It can be made very cheaply. Any kind of a stick, if not too heavy, will do. It is sometimes convenient to have it in your power to lengthen the handle of your net so as to reach objects which are at some elevation above the head, and for this purpose I employ handles which may be lengthened by jointed extensions. In collecting in tropical countries, among tall shrubbery and undergrowth, such nets often prove service-

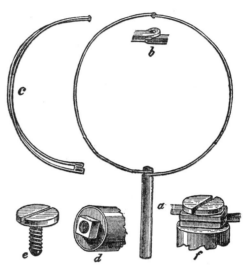

able. One of the most successful collectors I ever had in my employment made his net by simply bending a piece of bamboo into the form of the frame of an Indian snowshoe, to which he attached a handle about a foot and a half in length, and to this he affixed a bag of netting. He was, however, a Japanese, and had singular dexterity in the capture of specimens with this simple apparatus. When tarletan cannot be had, ordinary mosquito-netting will do as the material for the bag. It is, however, too coarse in the mesh for very delicate and minute species. Very fine netting for the manufacture of the bags is made in Switzerland, and can be obtained from reputable dealers. But green "tarletan," which may be bought at almost any dry-goods store, is cheap and excellent.

FIG. 43.—Plan for folding net-ring: *c*, halves of ring detached; *b*, upper joint of the halves; *a*, ring set; *d*, cap of ferrule; *f*, cap of ferrule, showing screw in place; *e*, screw (Riley).

In order to protect and preserve the net, it is well to bind it with a strip of muslin, about two inches wide, attached to the entire circumference of the ring.

FIG. 44.—*a*, net; *b*, ferrule to receive handle; *c*, wire hoop to be fastened in the upper end of the ferrule (Riley).

For my part, I prefer gray or green as the color for a net. White should be avoided, as experience shows that a white net will often alarm an insect, when a net of darker material will not cause it to fly before the collector is ready to bring the net down over the spot where it is settled.

Collecting-Jars.—In killing insects various methods have been used. The most approved method is to employ a jar charged with cyanide of potash. For large moths and butterflies cyanide of potash serves very well. Carbonate of ammonia has been used, but bleaches green insects. It is well to sometimes put a drop or two of chloroform into the collecting-jar. The chloroform stuns the insect, and its struggles quickly cease. The main objection to chloroform is the fact that it induces rigidity of the thoracic muscles, which later interferes with handsome setting.

In preparing a poisoning-jar use one which has a ground-glass stopper, the mouth of which is about three inches in diameter. This will be large enough for most specimens. I have found it well to have such jars partly covered with leather after the fashion of a drinking flask. An opening in the leather is left on either

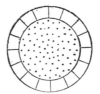

FIG. 45.—*a*, ring of metal tied with wire at *a*; *b*, ferrule; *c*, plug put in before pouring in solder (Riley).

FIG. 46.—Cyanide-jar prepared for use: *P*, perforated cardboard; *Cy*, lumps of cyanide of potash.

FIG. 47.—Piece of paper punctured and slit for pasting over the cyanide in the collecting-jar.

side, permitting an inspection of the contents. The leather protects from breakage. At the bottom of such a jar a few lumps of cyanide of potash, about the size of a filbert, should be placed. Over these place a little cotton, or sawdust, to prevent the lumps from rattling about loosely at the bottom. Over the cotton paste a piece of strong white paper, perforated with holes. In securing the white paper over the cyanide, the writer has resorted to a simple method which is explained in the annexed diagram. A piece of paper is placed under the jar, and a circle the size of the inside of the jar is traced upon it. Then a disk is cut out about an inch greater in diameter than the original circle (Fig. 47). The paper is punctured over the surface included within the inner line, and then, with a scissors, little gashes are made from the outer circumference inwardly so as to permit folding up the edges of the disk. A little gum tragacanth is then applied to these upturned edges; it is inserted into the jar and pasted securely over the cyanide by the upturned flaps. A jar thus charged will last for a long time, if kept properly closed when not in use. Cyanide of potash has a tendency to melt down in the presence of moisture, and in very humid climates or damp places, if the jar is not kept well stoppered, the cyanide will quickly become semi-fluid, the paper will become moist, and specimens placed in the jar will be injured or completely ruined. It is well, however, to bear in mind the fact that the fumes of hydrocyanic acid (prussic acid), which are active in producing the death of the insect, will not be given off in sufficient volume unless there is a small amount of moisture present in the jar; and in a very dry climate the writer has sometimes found it necessary to put a drop of water into the jar. Jelly glasses with tin tops are even better than jars and may be prepared in the same way.

Field-Boxes.—In collecting butterflies it is often possible to kill, or half-kill, the specimens contained in the net by a smart pinch administered to the insect by the thumb and the first finger, the pressure being applied from without the net (Fig. 48). This mode of procedure, however, unless the operator is careful, is apt to damage the specimens. The writer prefers to hold the insect firmly between the thumb and the first finger, and apply a drop or two of chloroform from a vial which should be carried in the upper left-hand vest-pocket. The application of the chloroform causes the insect to cease its struggles immediately, and it may then be placed in the poisoning-jar, or it may be pinned into the field-box. The field-box, which should be worn at the side, securely held in its place by a strap going over the shoulder and by another strap around the waist, may be provided with poisoning apparatus. The box should be of tin, and should have securely fastened in one corner some lumps of cyanide, tied in gauze. The box should

Fig. 48.—Method of disabling a butterfly by pinching it when in the net.

be very tight, so that when it is closed the fumes of the cyanide may be retained. The bottom should be covered with cork, upon which the specimens, as they are withdrawn from the poisoning-jar, should be pinned. It is well to bear strictly in mind that it is a mistake to continue to put one specimen after another into the poisoning-jar until it is half filled or quite filled with specimens. In walking about the field, if there are several insects in the jar at a time, they are likely to become rubbed and their beauty partially destroyed by being tossed about as the collector moves from place to place. A large insect, placed in a jar in which there are one or two smaller insects, will in its death-struggles injure the latter. So, as fast as the insects are partially asphyxiated, or deprived of the power of motion, they should be removed from the poisoning-jar to the poisoning-box, where they are pinned in place and prevented from rubbing one against the other. Some collectors prefer simply to stun the insects, and then pin them into the field-box, where they are left in whole or in part to recover their vitality, to be subsequently put to death upon the return of the collector from the field. This mode of procedure, while undoubtedly yielding beautiful specimens, appears to the writer to be cruel, and he does not therefore approve of it.

The Use of the Net.—In the use of the net the old saying is true that "practice makes perfect." The bag of the net should be sufficiently long to allow of its being completely closed when hanging from the ring on either side. It is possible to sweep into the net an insect which is fluttering through the air, and then by a turn of the hand to close the bag and to capture the specimen. When the insect has alighted upon the ground it is best to clap the net over it and then to raise the net with one hand. Very many species have the habit of flying upward. This is particularly true of the skippers, a group of very vigorous and swift-flying butterflies. The writer prefers, if possible, to clap the net over the specimens and then to allow them to rise, and, by inserting the wide-mouthed collecting-jar below, to capture them without touching them at all with the fingers. So far as possible the fingers should not be allowed to come in contact with specimens, whether in or out of the net, though some persons acquire an extremely delicate yet firm touch, which enables them to handle the wings of frail species without removing any of the scales. Nothing is more unsightly in a collection than specimens that have been caught and rubbed by the fingers.

Baits.—Moths are frequently taken by the method of collecting known as "sugaring." But it may also be employed for butterflies. For this purpose a mixture of beer and cheap brown sugar may be used. If the beer be stale drippings, so much the better. In fact, it is well, if the collector intends to remain in one locality for some time, to make a mixture of beer and sugar some hours or a day in advance of its application. In semi-tropical countries a mixture of beer and sugar is hardly as good as a mixture of molasses and water into which a few tablespoonfuls of Jamaica rum have been put. A mixture thus prepared seems to attract more effectually than the first prescription. Having provided a pail with a quart or two of the mixture, the collector resorts to the point where he proposes to carry on his work. With an ordinary whitewash brush the mixture is applied to the trunks of trees, stumps, fence-rails, and other objects. It is well to apply the mixture to a series of trees and posts located on the side of a bit of woodland, or along a path through forests, if comparatively open and not too dense. The writer has rarely had success in sugaring in the depths of forests. His greatest success has always been on paths and at the edge of woods. Many beetles and other insects come to the tempting sweets, and separate jars for capturing these should be carried in the pocket. The collector never should attempt to kill beetles in the same jar into which he is putting butterflies. The hard, horny bodies and spiny legs of beetles will make sad havoc with the delicate wings of butterflies.

In these arid days of "prohibition" many good people, who are law-abiding, but ardent collectors of moths and butterflies, have written to me asking what substitute to use for beer. "Near beer" is pretty good. I use it sometimes, when I can get it. Following in the footsteps of the late William Jennings Bryan, who was not an entomologist, I have tried grape-juice, but it does not work well, until you have had it exposed to the air for a couple of days in a crock, with a couple of pieces of good yeast mixed with it, and a lot of molasses added to the mixture. Cider and molasses makes fairly good bait, if the mixture has been left long enough in the open to start fermentation.

Other baits besides these may be employed. Some writers recommend boiling dried apples and mashing them into a pulp, adding a little rum to the mixture, and applying this to the bark of trees. In tropical countries bananas, especially rotten bananas, seem to have a charm for insects. The cane-trash at sugar-mills is very attractive. If possible, it is well to obtain a quantity of this trash and scatter it along forest paths. Some insects have very peculiar appetites and are attracted by things loathsome. The ordure of carnivorous animals seem to have a special charm for some of the most magnificently colored and the rarest of tropical butterflies. A friend of mine in Africa, who collected for me for a number of years, used to keep civet-cats, the ordure of which was collected and placed at appropriate points in the forest paths; and he was richly rewarded by obtaining many insects which were not obtained in any other way. Putrid fish have a charm for other species, and dead snakes, when rankly high, will attract still others. It may be observed that after the trees have been treated for a succession of days or nights with the sweetening mixture spoken of above, they become very productive. When collecting in Japan I made it a rule to return in the morning to the spots that I had sugared for moths the evening before, and I was always amply repaid by finding multitudes of butterflies and even a good many day-flying moths seated upon the mossy bark, feasting upon the remnants of the banquet I had provided the evening before. There is no sport—I do not except that of the angler—which is more fascinating than the sport derived by an enthusiastic entomologist from the practice of "sugaring." It is well, however, to know always where your path leads, and not to lay it out in the dusk, as the writer once did, when staying at a well-known summer resort in Virginia. The path which he had chosen as the scene of operations was unfortunately laid, all unknown to himself, just in the rear of the poultry-house of a man who sold chickens to the hotel; and when he saw the dark lantern mysteriously moving about, he concluded that some one with designs upon his hens was hidden in the woods, and opened fire with a seven-shooter, thus coming very near to abruptly terminating the career of an ardent entomologist.

Beating.—There are many species which are apparently not attracted by baits, such as we have spoken of in the preceding paragraph. The collector, passing through the grove, searches diligently with his eye and captures what he can see, but does not fail also with the end of his net-handle to tap the trunks of trees and to shake the bushes, and as the insects fly out, to note the point where they settle, and then make them his prey. It is well in this work, as in all collecting, to proceed somewhat leisurely, and to keep perfectly cool. The caricature sometimes found in newspapers of the ardent lepidopterist running like a "quarter-back" across a ten-acre lot in quest of some flying insect does not represent the truly skilful collector, whose movements are more or less stealthy and cautious.

THE BREEDING OF SPECIMENS

By breeding it is possible to obtain specimens in the most perfect condition. Bred specimens which have not had an opportunity to fly are always preferred on account of their freshness of color and perfection of form. A great many species, which apparently are exceedingly rare, may often be obtained in considerable numbers by the process of breeding, the caterpillar being more readily found than the perfect insect. Although the process of breeding involves a good deal of labor and care, it affords a most delightful field for observation, and the returns are frequently of the very greatest value.

How to Get the Eggs of Butterflies.—The process of breeding may begin with the egg. The skilful eye of the student will detect the eggs of butterflies upon the leaves upon which they have been deposited. The twig may be cut and placed in a vase, in water, and kept fresh until the minute caterpillar emerges, and then from time to time it may be transferred to fresh leaves of the same species of plant, and it will continue to make its moults until at last it is transformed into a chrysalis, and in due season the butterfly emerges. Eggs may frequently be obtained in considerable numbers by confining the female under gauze, with the appropriate food-plant. A knowledge of the food-plant may often be obtained by watching the female and observing upon what plants she deposits her eggs. The exceedingly beautiful researches of Mr. W. H. Edwards were largely promoted by his skill in inducing females to oviposit upon their food-plants. He did this generally by confining the female with the food-plant in a barrel or nail-keg, the bottom of which had been knocked out, and over the top of which he tied mosquito-netting. The plant was placed under the keg. The insects thus confined may be fed with a mixture of honey and water placed upon the leaves.

In collecting caterpillars it is well to have on hand a number of small boxes in which to place them, and also a botany-box in which to bring from the field a supply of their appropriate food.

The process of breeding may begin with the caterpillar. The collector, having discovered the caterpillar feeding upon the branch of a certain plant, provides the creature with a constant supply of the fresh foliage of the same plant, until it finally pupates.

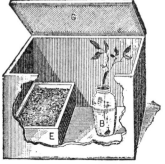

FIG. 49.—Cheap form of breeding-cage: *G*, lid covered with mosquito-netting; *E*, pan of earth; *B*, bottle for food-plant.

Breeding-Cages.—Various devices for breeding caterpillars and rearing moths and butterflies are known. One of the most important of these devices is the breeding-cage, which is sometimes called a vivarium. The simplest form of the vivarium is often the best. In breeding some species the best method is simply to pot a plant of the species upon which the larva is known to feed, and to place the potted plant in a box over which some mosquito-netting is tied. The writer frequently employs for this purpose cylinders of glass over the top of which perforated cardboard is placed. This method, however, can be resorted to only with the more minute forms and with plants that do not attain great height. Another form of vivarium is represented in the following woodcut (Fig. 50). The writer has successfully employed, for breeding insects upon a large scale, ordinary store boxes provided with a lid made by fastening together four pieces of wood, making a frame large enough to cover the top of the box, and covering it with gauze. The food-plant is kept

26

fresh in bottles or jars which are set into the boxes. Be careful, however, after you have put the branches upon which the caterpillars are feeding into the jars, to stuff something into the neck of the jar so as to prevent the caterpillar from accidentally getting into the water and drowning himself—a mishap which otherwise might occur. When breeding is undertaken on a still larger scale, it may be well to set apart for this purpose a room, preferably in an outbuilding, all the openings leading from which should be carefully closed so as to prevent the escape of the caterpillars.

How to Find Caterpillars.—Many species of caterpillars are not hard to discover; they are more or less conspicuous objects, and strike the eye. Some species conceal themselves by weaving together the leaves of the plant on which they feed, or by bending a single leaf into a curved receptacle in which they lie hidden. Others conceal themselves during the daytime about the roots of trees or under bark or stones, only emerging in the night-time to feed upon the foliage. The collector will carefully search for these. The presence of caterpillars is generally indicated by the ravages which they have committed upon the foliage. By carefully scanning a branch the collector will observe that the leaves have been more or less devoured. Generally underneath the tree will be found the frass, or ejectamenta, of the caterpillar. The presence of the ejectamenta and the evidence of the ravages committed by the larvæ upon the foliage will give the collector a clue to the whereabouts

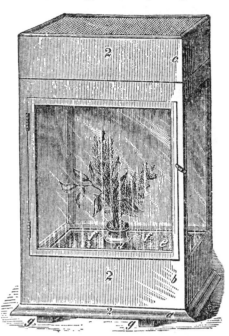

FIG. 50.—Breeding-cage: *2a*, base, battened at *g* to prevent warping; *2b*, removable body of cage, inclosing zinc pan, *f, f,* containing jar for plant, *d,* and filled with five inches of soil, *e*; *2c*, removable top, covered with wire gauze. The doors and sides are of glass (Riley).

of the caterpillar. The writer has found it generally advantageous to search for caterpillars that feed upon trees along the wide, sandy margins of brooks and rivers. The frass is easily discovered upon the sand, and by casting the eye upward into the foliage it is often easy to detect the insect. The pavements in towns and cities which are bordered by trees may also very well be scanned for evidence of the presence of caterpillars. A favorite collecting-ground of the writer is one of the large cemeteries of the city in which he lives, in which there are numerous trees and a great quantity of shrubbery. Wood-boring species, as a rule, are more difficult to obtain and rear than those that feed upon the foliage.

Hibernating Caterpillars.—While some difficulty attends the preservation of chrysalids in the case of those species which pupate in the fall and pass the winter in the chrysalis state under the ground, far more difficulty attends the preservation of species which hibernate in the caterpillar state. As a rule, it is found best to expose the boxes containing these species in an ice-house or other cold place, keeping them there until there is available an abundant supply of the tender shoots of the plant upon which they are in the habit of feeding. They may then be brought forth from cold storage and placed in proximity to the food-plant, upon which they will proceed to feed.

THE PRESERVATION OF SPECIMENS

Papering Specimens.—When time and opportunities do not suffice for the proper preparation of butterflies for display in the permanent collection, the

FIG. 51.—Butterfly in envelope.

collector may, in the case of the larger species, conveniently place them in envelopes, with their wings folded (Fig. 51), and they may then be stored in a box until such time as he is able to relax the specimens and properly mount them. Thousands of insects are thus annually collected. The small drug envelopes, or the larger pay-roll envelopes, which may be bought in boxes by the thousand of any stationer for a comparatively small sum, are preferable because of their convenience. Many collectors, however, paper their specimens in envelopes, which they make of oblong bits of paper adapted to the size of the insect. The process of making the envelope and of papering the insect is accurately depicted in the accompanying cut (Fig. 52). The writer finds it good in the case of small butterflies to place them in boxes between layers of cheap plush or velvet. A small box, a few inches long, may be provided, and at its bottom a layer of velvet is placed; upon this a number of small butterflies are laid. Over them is placed a layer of velvet, with its soft pile facing the same side of the velvet at the bottom. On top of this another piece of velvet is laid, with its pile upward,

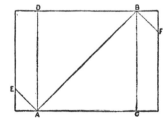

FIG. 52.—Method of folding paper for envelopes: first fold on line *AB*; then on *AD* and *CB*; then on *BF* and *EA*.

and other specimens are again deposited, and over this another piece of velvet is laid, and so on. If the box is not filled full at once, it is well to have enough pieces of velvet cut to fill it, or else place cotton on top, so as to keep the layers of velvet from moving or shaking about. A yard or two of plush or velvet will suffice for the packing of a thousand specimens of small butterflies.

Mounting Butterflies.—When the collector has time enough at his disposal he should at once mount his specimens as they are intended to be displayed in the collection. We shall now proceed to explain the manner in which this is most advantageously accomplished. The insect should first of all be pinned. The pin should be thrust perpendicularly through the thorax, midway between the wings, and at a considerable elevation upon the pin. It should then be placed upon the setting-board or setting-block. Setting-boards or setting-blocks are pieces of wood having a groove on the upper surface of sufficient depth to accommodate the body of the insect and to permit the wings to be brought to the level of the upper surface of the board (Fig. 53). They should also be provided either with a cleft or a hole, which will permit the pin to be thrust down below the body of the insect for a considerable distance. As a rule, the wings of all specimens should be mounted at a uniform elevation of about seven eighths of an inch above the point of the pin. This is known as the "continental method" of mounting, and is infinitely

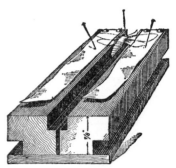

FIG. 53.—Setting-board designed by the author. The wings of the insect are held in place by strips of tracing-muslin, such as is used by engineers. The grooves at the side serve to hold the board in place in the drying-box. (See Fig. 59.)

FIG. 54.—Setting-block: A, holes to enable the pin to reach to the cork; C, cork, filling groove on the bottom of the block; B, slit to hold thread.

FIG. 55.—Setting-block with butterfly expanded upon it.

FIG. 56.—Setting-needle.

preferable to the old-fashioned "English method," in which the insect was pinned low down upon the pin, so that its wings touched the surface of the box.

Setting-blocks are most advantageously employed in setting small species, especially the *Hesperiidæ*, the wings of which are refractory. When the insect has been pinned upon the setting-board or setting-block, the next step is to set the wings in the position which they are to maintain when the specimen is thoroughly dry. This is accomplished by means of what are known as "setting-needles" (Fig. 56). Setting-needles may be easily made by simply sticking ordinary needles into wooden matches from which the tips have been removed. In drawing the wings into position, care should be taken to plant the setting-needle behind the strong nervure on the costal margin of the wing; otherwise the wings are liable to be torn and disfigured. The rule in setting lepidoptera is to draw the anterior wing forward in such a manner that the posterior margin of this wing is at right angles to the axis of the body, the axis of the body being a line drawn through the head to the extremity of the abdomen. The hind wing should then be moved forward, its anterior margin lying under the opposing margin of the front wing. When the wings have thus been adjusted into the position which they are to occupy, slips of tracing-muslin or of paper should be drawn down over them and securely pinned, the setting-needles being removed.

29

In pinning down the strips which are to hold the wings in place, be careful to pin around the wing, but never, if possible, through it. When the wings have been adjusted in the position in which they are to remain, the antennæ, or feelers, should be attended to and drawn forward on the same plane as the wings and secured in place. This may ordinarily be done by setting pins in such a position as to hold them where they are to stay. Then the body, if it has a tendency to sag down at the end of the abdomen, should be raised. This may also be accomplished by means of pins thrust beneath on either side. The illustration (Fig. 58) shows more clearly what is intended. When the insect has been set, the board should be put aside in a place where it will not be molested or attacked by pests, and the

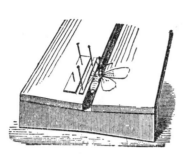

FIG. 57.—Setting-board with moth expanded upon it (Riley).

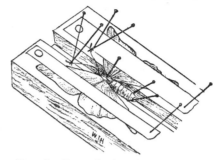

FIG. 58.—Butterfly pinned on board, showing method of holding up body and pinning down antennæ.

specimens upon it allowed to dry. A box with shelves in it is often used for this purpose. This box should have a door at the front covered with wire gauze, and the back should also be open, covered with gauze, so as to allow a free circulation of air. A few balls of naphthaline placed in it will tend to keep away mites and other pests. The time during which the specimen should remain on the board until it is dried varies with its size and the condition of the atmosphere. Most butterflies and moths in dry weather will be sufficiently dried to permit of their removal from the setting-boards in a week; but large, stout-bodied moths may require as much as two weeks, or even more time, before they are dry enough to be taken off the boards. The process of drying may be hastened by placing the boards in an oven, but the temperature of the oven must be quite low. If too much heat is applied, great injury is sure to result. Only a careful and expert operator should resort to the use of the oven, a temperature above 120° F. being sure to work mischief.

Relaxing Specimens.—When butterflies or moths have been put up in papers or mounted on pins without having their wings expanded and set it becomes necessary, before setting them, to relax them. This may be accomplished in several ways. If the specimens have been pinned it is best to place them on pieces of sheet-cork on a tray of sand which has been thoroughly moistened and treated with a good dose of carbolic acid. Over all a bell-glass is put. A tight tin box will serve the same purpose, but a broad sheet of bibulous paper should always be put over the box, under the lid, before closing it, and in such a way as to leave the edges of the paper projecting around the edges of the lid. This is done to absorb the moisture which might settle by condensation upon the lid and drop upon the specimens. In a bell-glass the moisture generally trickles down the sides. Earthenware crocks

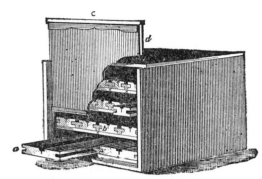

with closely fitting lids are even better than tin boxes, but they must have paper put over them, before closing, in the same way as is done when tin boxes are used. When specimens have been reserved in papers or envelopes these should be opened a little and laid upon damp, carbolized sand under a bell-glass or in a closed receptacle of some kind. Papered specimens may also be placed in their envelopes between clean towels, which have been moistened in water to which a little carbolic acid has been added. The

FIG. 59.—Drying-box: *a*, setting-board partly pulled out; *b*, T-shaped strip working in groove on setting-board; *c*, front door, sliding down by tongue, *d*, working in a groove at side in front.

towels should be wrung out quite dry before using them. The method of placing between towels should never be used in the case of very small and delicate species and those which are blue or green in color. Great care must be exercised not to allow the insects to become soaked or unduly wet. This ruins them. They

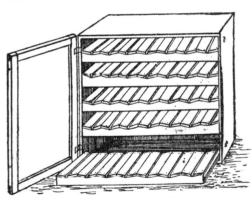

FIG. 60.—Drying-box (Riley).

should, however, be damp enough to allow the wings and other organs to be freely moved. When the insects have been relaxed they may be pinned and expanded on setting-boards like freshly caught specimens. It is well in setting the wings of relaxed specimens, after having thrust the pin through the body, to take a small forceps and, seizing the wings just where they join the body, gently move them so as to open them and make their movement easy before pinning them upon the setting-board. The skilful manipulator in this way quickly ascertains whether they have been sufficiently relaxed to admit of their being readily set. If discovered to be too stiff and liable to break they must be still further relaxed. Dried specimens which have been relaxed and then mounted generally require only a short time to dry again, and need rarely be kept more than twenty-four hours upon the setting-boards.

The process of setting insects upon setting-blocks is exactly the same as when

31

setting-boards are used, with the simple difference that, instead of pinning strips of paper or tracing-muslin over the wings, the wings are held in place by threads or very narrow tapes, which are wound around the block. When the wings are not covered with a very deep and velvety covering of scales the threads or tapes may be used alone; but when the wings are thus clothed it becomes necessary to put bits of paper or cardboard over the wings before wrapping with the threads. Unless this is done the marks of the threads will be left upon the wings. Some little skill, which is easily acquired by practice, is necessary in order to employ setting-blocks to advantage, but in the case of small species and species which have refractory wings they are much to be preferred to the boards.

The Preparation and Preservation of Eggs.—The eggs of butterflies may be preserved by simply putting them into tubes containing alcohol, or they may be placed in vials containing dilute glycerine or a solution of common salt. The vials should be kept tightly corked and should be marked by a label written with a lead-pencil and placed within the bottle, upon which the name of the species and the date of collection should be noted, or a reference made to the collector's note-book. Unless the eggs of insects are preserved in fluid they are apt in many cases to dry up and become distorted, because, on account of their small size, it is impossible to void them of their contents. The larvæ escaping from eggs often void the shell very neatly, leaving, however, a large orifice. Such remnants of shells may be preserved, as they often are useful in showing some of the details of marking; but great vigilance in securing them should be exercised, for almost all the larvæ of butterflies have the curious habit of whetting their appetites for future repasts by turning around and either wholly or partially devouring the shell of the egg which they have quitted. Eggs are most neatly mounted in the form of microscopic slides in glycerine jelly contained in cells of appropriate depth and diameter. It is best, if possible, to mount several specimens upon the same slide, showing the side of the egg as well as the end. A cabinet filled with the eggs of butterflies thus mounted is valuable and curious.

The Preservation of Chrysalids.—Chrysalids may be deprived of their vitality by simply immersing them in alcohol, or they may be killed by means of chloroform, and they may then be fastened upon pins like the imago, and arranged appropriately in the collection with the species. Some chrysalids, however, lose their color when killed in this way, and it is occasionally well to void them of their contents by making an opening and carefully removing the parts that are contained within, replacing with some material which will prevent the chrysalis from shrinking and shriveling. This method of preserving need, however, be resorted to only in exceptional cases. When a butterfly has escaped from its chrysalis it frequently leaves the entire shell behind, with the parts somewhat sundered, yet, nevertheless, furnishing a clear idea of the structure of the chrysalis. If no other specimen of the chrysalis can be obtained than these voided shells they should be preserved.

The Preservation of Caterpillars.—The caterpillars of butterflies when they first emerge from the egg, and before they make the first moult, are, for the most part, extremely small, and are best preserved as microscopic objects in cells filled with glycerine. After each successive moult the larva increases rapidly in size. These various stages in the development of the caterpillar should all be noted and preserved, and it is customary to put up these collections in vials filled with alcohol or a solution of formaline (which latter, by the by, is preferable to alcohol), or to inflate them. The method of inflation secures the best specimens.

FIG. 61.—Apparatus for inflating larvæ: *B*, foot-bellows; *K*, rubber tube; *C*, flask; *D*, anhydrous sulphuric acid; *E*, overflow-flask; *F*, rubber tube from flask; *G*, standard with cock to regulate flow of air; *H*, glass tube with larva upon it; *I*, copper drying-plate; *J*, spirit-lamp.

In inflating larvæ the first step is carefully to remove the contents of the larval skin. This may be done by making an incision with a stout pin or a needle at the anal extremity, and then, between the folds of a soft towel or cloth, pressing out the contents of the abdominal cavity. The pressure should be first applied near the point where the pellicle has been punctured, and should then be carried forward until the region of the head is reached. Care must be exercised to apply only enough pressure to expel the contents of the skin without disturbing the tissues which lie nearest to the epidermis, in which the pigments are located, and not to remove the hairs which are attached to the body. Pressure sufficient to bruise the skin should never be applied. A little practice soon imparts the required dexterity. The contents of the larval skin having been removed, the next step is to inflate and dry the empty skin. A compact statement of the method of performing this operation is contained in Hornaday's "Taxidermy and Zoölogical Collecting," from the pen of the writer, and I herewith reproduce it:

"The simplest method of inflating the skins of larvæ after the contents have been withdrawn is to insert a straw or grass stem of appropriate thickness into the opening through which the contents have been removed, and then by the breath to inflate the specimen, while holding over the chimney of an Argand lamp, the flame of which must be regulated so as not to scorch or singe it. Care must be taken in the act of inflating not to unduly distend the larval skin, thus producing a distortion, and also to dry it thoroughly. Unless the latter precaution is observed a subsequent shrinking and disfigurement will take place. The process of inflating in the manner just described is somewhat laborious, and while some of the finest specimens which the writer

FIG. 62.—Tip of inflating-tube, with armature for holding larval skin.

has ever seen were prepared in this primitive manner, various expedients for lessening the labor involved have been devised, some of which are to be highly commended.

"A comparatively inexpensive arrangement for inflating larvæ is a modification of that described in the 'Entomologische Nachrichten' (1879, vol. v, p. 7), devised by Mr. Fritz A. Wachtel (Fig. 61). It consists of a foot-bellows such as is used by chemists in the laboratory, or, better still, of a small cylinder such as is used for holding gas in operating the oxyhydrogen lamp of a sciopticon. In the latter case the compressed air should not have a pressure exceeding twenty pounds to the square inch, and the cock regulating the flow from the cylinder should be capable of very fine adjustment. By means of a rubber tube the air is conveyed from the cylinder to a couple of flasks, one of which contains concentrated sulphuric acid, and the other is intended for the reception of any overflow of the hydrated sulphuric acid which may occur. The object of passing the air through sulphuric acid is to rob it, so far as possible, of its moisture. It is then conveyed into a flask, which is heated upon a sand-bath, and thence by a piece of flexible tubing to a tip mounted on a joint allowing vertical and horizontal motion and secured by a standard to the working-table. The flow of air through the tip is regulated by a cock. Upon the tip is fastened a small

FIG. 63.—Drying-oven: A, lamp; B, pin to hold door open; C, door open; D, glass cover.

rubber tube, into the free extremity of which is inserted a fine-pointed glass tube. This is provided with an armature consisting of two steel springs fastened upon opposite sides, and their ends bent at right angles in such a way as to hold the larval skin firmly to the extremity of the tube. The skin having been adjusted upon the fine point of the tube, the bellows is put into operation, and the skin is inflated. A drying apparatus is provided in several ways. A copper plate mounted upon four legs, and heated by an alcohol-lamp placed below, has been advocated by some. A better arrangement, used by the writer, consists of a small oven heated by the flame of an alcohol-lamp or by jets of natural gas, and provided with circular openings of various sizes, into which the larval skin is introduced (Fig. 63).

"A less commendable method of preserving larvæ is to place them in alcohol. The larvæ should be tied up in sacks of light gauze netting, and a label of tough paper, with the date and locality of capture, and the name, if known, written with a lead-pencil, should be attached to each such little sack. Do not use ink on labels to be immersed, but a hard lead-pencil. Alcoholic specimens are liable to become shriveled and discolored, and are not nearly as valuable as well-inflated and dried skins.

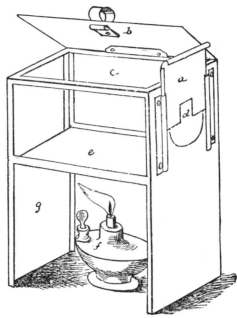

"When the skins have been inflated they may be mounted readily by being placed upon wires wrapped with green silk, or upon annealed aluminum wire. The wires are bent and twisted together for a short distance and then made to diverge. The diverging ends are pressed together, a little shellac is placed upon their tips, and they are then inserted into the opening at the anal extremity of the larval skin. Upon the release of pressure they spread apart, and after the shellac has dried the skin is firmly held by them. They

FIG. 64.—Drying-oven: *a*, sliding door; *b*, lid; *c*, body of oven with glass sides; *d*, opening for inserting inflating-tube; *e*, copper bottom; *f*, spirit-lamp; *g*, base (Riley).

may then be attached to pins by simply twisting the free end of the wire about the pin, or they may be placed upon artificial imitations of the leaves and twigs of their appropriate food-plants."

THE PRESERVATION AND ARRANGEMENT OF COLLECTIONS

The secret of preserving collections of lepidoptera in beautiful condition is to exclude light, moisture, and insect pests. Light ultimately bleaches many species, moisture leads to mold and mildew, and insect pests devour the specimens. The main thing is therefore to have the receptacles in which the specimens are placed dark and as nearly as possible hermetically sealed and kept in a dry place. In order to accomplish this, various devices have been resorted to.

Boxes.—Boxes for the preservation of specimens are made with a tongue on the edges of the bottom fitting into a groove upon the lid, or they may be made with inside pieces fastened around the inner edge of the bottom and projecting so as to catch the lid. The accompanying outlines show the method of joining different forms of boxes (Figs. 65 67). The bottom of the box should be lined with some substance which will enable the specimens to be pinned into it securely.

35

For this purpose sheet-cork about a quarter of an inch thick is to be preferred to all other substances. Ground cork pressed into layers and covered with white paper is manufactured for the purpose of lining boxes. Turf compressed into sheets about half an inch thick and covered with paper is used by many European collectors. Sheets of aloe-pith or of the wood of the yucca, half an inch thick, are used, and the pith of corn-stalks (Indian corn or maize) may also be employed, laid into the box and glued neatly to the bottom. The corn-pith should be cut into

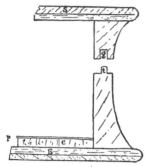

FIG. 65.—Detail drawing of front of box, made to resemble a book: s, s, sides, made of two pieces of wood glued together across the grain; t, tongue; g, groove; c, cork; p, paper covering the cork.

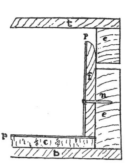

FIG. 66.—Detail drawing of front of box: t, top; b, bottom; e, side; f, strip, nailed around inside as at n; c, cork; p, paper lining.

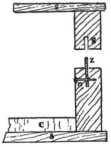

FIG. 67.—Detail drawing of box, in which the tongue, z, is made of strips of zinc let into a groove and fastened as at n; g, groove to catch tongue; s, s, top and bottom; c, cork.

pieces about half an inch square and joined together neatly, covering it with thin white paper after the surface has been made quite even and true. Cork is, however, the best material, for, though more expensive than the other things named, it has greater power to hold the pins, and unless these are securely fixed and held in place great damage is sure to result. A loose specimen in a box will work incalculable damage. Boxes should be made of light, thoroughly seasoned wood, and should be very tight. They are sometimes made so that specimens may be pinned both upon the top and the bottom, but this is not to be commended. The depth of the box should be sufficient to admit of the use of the longest insect-pin in use, and a depth between top and bottom of two and a quarter inches is therefore sufficient. Boxes are sometimes made with backs in imitation of books, and a collection arranged in such boxes presents an attractive external appearance. A very good box is made for the United States Department of Agriculture and for the Carnegie Museum in Pittsburgh (Fig. 68). This box is thirteen inches long, nine inches wide, and three inches thick (external measurement). The depth between the bottom and the lid on the inside is two and one eighth inches. The ends and sides are dovetailed; the top and bottom are each made of two pieces of light stuff, about one eighth of an inch thick, glued together in such a way that the grain of the two pieces crosses at right angles, and all cracking and warping are thus prevented. The lids are secured to the bottoms by brass hooks fitting into eyelets.

Such boxes provided with cork do not cost more than fifty-five cents apiece when bought in quantities. Boxes may be made of stout pasteboard about one eighth or three sixteenths of an inch thick, with a rabbet-tongue on the inside. Such boxes are much used in France and England, and when well and substantially made are most excellent. They may be obtained for about thirty-five cents apiece lined with compressed cork.

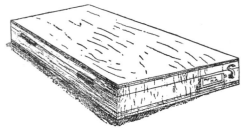

FIG. 68.—Insect-box for preservation of collections.

Cabinets and Drawers.—Large collections which are intended to be frequently consulted are best preserved in cabinets fitted with glass-covered drawers. A great deal of variety exists in the plans which are adopted for the display of specimens in cabinets. Much depends upon the taste and the financial ability of the collector. Large sums of money may be expended upon cabinets, but the main thing is to secure the specimens from dust, mould, and insect pests. The point to be observed most carefully is so to arrange the drawers that they are, like the boxes, practically air-tight. The writer employs as the standard size for the drawers in his own collection and in the Carnegie Museum a drawer which is twenty-two inches long, sixteen inches wide, and two inches deep (inside measurement). The outside dimensions are: length, twenty-three inches exclusive of face; breadth, seventeen inches; height, two and three eighths inches. The covers are glazed with double-strength glass. They are held upon the bottoms by a rabbet placed inside of the drawer and nearly reaching the

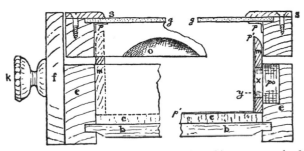

FIG. 69.—Detail drawing of drawer for cabinet: *e, e,* ends; *b,* bottom; *c,* cork; *p, p,* paper strips in corners of lid to exclude dust; *g, g,* glass of cover, held in place by top strips, *s, s; m, m,* side pieces serving as rabbets on inside; *po,* pocket in ends and sides, sawn out of the wood; *x,* opening through the rabbet into this pocket; *g,* holes through the paper lining, *p¹,* allowing fumes of naphthaline to enter interior of drawer; *f,* front; *k,* knob; *o,* lunette cut in edge of the top piece to enable the lid to be raised by inserting the fingers.

lower surface of the glass on the cover when closed. The drawers are lined upon the bottom with cork five sixteenths of an inch thick, and are papered on the bottom and sides with good linen paper, which does not easily become discolored. Each drawer is faced with cherry and has a knob. These drawers are arranged in cabinets built in sections for convenience in handling. The two lower sections each contain thirty drawers, the upper section nine. The drawers are arranged in three perpendicular series and are made interchangeable, so that any drawer will fit into any place in any one of the cabinets. This is very necessary, as it admits of the easy rearrangement of collections. On the sides of each drawer a pocket is cut on the inner surface, which communicates through an opening in the rabbet with the interior. The paper lining the inside is perforated over this opening with a number of small holes. The pocket is kept filled with naphthaline crystals, the fumes of which pass into the interior and tend to keep away pests. The figure given on page 37 gives the details of construction (Fig. 69). Such drawers can be made at a cost of about $3.50 apiece, and the cost of a cabinet finished and supplied with them is about $325, made of cherry, finished in imitation of mahogany.

Some persons prefer to have the bottoms as well as the tops of the drawers in their cabinets made of glass. In such cases the specimens are pinned upon narrow strips of wood covered with cork, securely fastened across the inside of the drawers. This arrangement enables the under side of specimens to be examined and compared with as much freedom as the upper side, and without removing them from the drawers; but the strips are liable at times to become loosened, and when this happens great havoc is wrought among the specimens, if the drawer is moved carelessly. Besides, there is more danger of breakage.

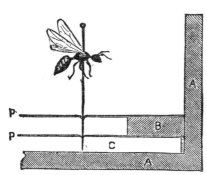

FIG. 70.—A, A, side and bottom of box; B, frame fitting into box; C, space which must be left between frame and bottom of box; P, P, paper stretched on frame.

Another way of providing a cheap and very sightly lining for the bottom of an insect-box is illustrated in Fig. 70. A frame of wood like a slate-frame is provided, and on both sides paper is stretched. To stretch the paper it ought to be soaked in water before pasting to the frame; then when it dries it is as tight and smooth as a drum-head.

The beginner who has not a long purse will do well to preserve his collections in boxes such as have been described. They can be obtained quite cheaply and are most excellent. Cabinets are more or less of a luxury for the amateur, and are only a necessity in the case of great collections, which are constantly being consulted. The boxes may be arranged upon shelves. Some of the largest and best collections in the world were originally preserved in boxes.

Riker Mounts.—A method of preserving and displaying butterflies, which was invented by Mr. Clarence B. Riker of Maplewood, New Jersey, bears his name. It is not well adapted to use in large scientific collections, which are constantly receiving additions, which necessitate more or less frequent rearrangement of specimens, but it has the advantage, if properly employed, of guarding securely against injury, as well as being light and portable. It may be recommended in the case of small collections, which are to be sent out by museums for use in schools. In preparing "Riker mounts" the first step is to procure, or make, a series of strong but light boxes of appropriate size, which should be shallow, not more than one inch deep, inside measurement, except in cases where large thick-bodied moths are to be shown, when a little deeper boxes are required. The sides of the boxes should be made of bass-wood or pine, not more than three eighths of an inch in thickness. The upper edges of the sides must be chamfered inside, so as to let in and securely hold the glass, which forms the top of each box. The bottoms of the boxes may be made of strong paste-board (binders-board), or thin three-ply veneer, glued and bradded to the four sides, which make the "frame" of the box. The glass tops should fit exactly into the frame, or "sash," when the sides and bottom have been put together. When the boxes are ready, the next step is to fill the inside of the boxes with thin layers of cotton batting, not packing too tightly. The uppermost layer should fit very neatly into the box. When this has been done, the butterflies or moths, with the pins removed from their bodies, if they have been previously pinned, should be arranged where they are to stay, with a place for their labels below each specimen. When putting the insects in place it is best by pressure to make a shallow groove in the soft underlying material to accommodate the body of each insect. Any blunt-edged tool will "do the trick." When the bodies of all the insects have been adjusted to their little cotton cradles, in which they are to stay, and the labels have been put into their proper places, take the glass top of the box, which has been cleaned from all dust on the inner side, and gently and carefully lay it in place. It will hold the insects and their labels, where they are to remain. It is well just before laying on the glass

to put in with a pipette at the lower corners a few drops of carbon bisulphide or chloroform, to kill any minute pests, which may have unnoticed lodged in the cotton or on the specimens. The whole "contraption" should then be bound together neatly with binders muslin, strong paper, or buckram. I prefer buckram. Figure 71 shows the end of such a box. The Carnegie Museum sends out to the

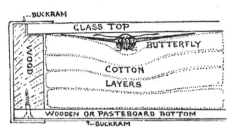

FIG. 71.—Plan of Riker Mount.

common schools of Pittsburgh and Allegheny County many such boxes every year as loans and they are passed from one pupil to another and help to teach the children by ocular inspection what they ought to know about insect life. Not only butterflies, but all other insects, may be put up in such portable cases.

Double-glass Mounts.—Another way of mounting lepidoptera, enabling both the upper and lower sides of the wings to be shown in a small portable case, is only adapted to single specimens. Both the bottom and the top of the container are made of glass. Above the glass bottom, supported upon a neat closely fitting frame running around the inner borders of the box are placed two pieces of glass, leaving a space at the middle sufficiently wide to accommodate the body of the butterfly. When the insect, with its wings properly expanded, has been dropped into place, with its body in the opening between the two supporting glasses, two other pieces of glass of the same size as the supports, are laid down so as to cover the outer parts of the wings, and secured in place by a frame corresponding in color, size, and thickness with the lower support. Then over all a covering glass is placed and the whole affair is neatly bound around with book-muslin, buckram, or leather. The Dentons of Wellesley, Massachusetts, have used this form of mount to display some of the more gorgeous tropical species, and they are often seen for sale in the windows of shop-keepers, but while safe containers and showing both sides of the specimen, such method of mounting consumes far too much time and is far too expensive for employment by any but amateurs with bulky pocket-books. They are principally sold as ornaments to people who purchase "curios."

Labeling.—Each specimen should have on the pin below the specimen a small label giving the date of capture, if known, and the locality. Below this should be a label of larger size, giving its scientific name, if ascertained, and the sex. Labels should be neat and uniform in size. A good size for labels for large species is about one inch long and five eighths of an inch wide. The labels should be written in a fine but legible hand. Smaller labels may be used for smaller species. A crow-quill pen and India ink are to be preferred in writing labels.

Arrangement of Specimens.—Specimens are best arranged in rows. The males should be pinned in first in the series, after them the females. Varieties should follow the species. After these should be placed any aberrations or monstrosities which the collector may possess. The name of the genus should precede all the species contained in the collection, and after each species the specific name should be placed. Fig. 72 shows the manner of arrangement.

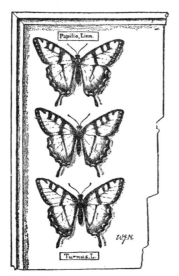

FIG. 72.—Manner of arranging specimens in cabinet.

Insect Pests.—In order to preserve collections, great care must be taken to exclude the various forms of insect pests, which are likely, unless destroyed and kept from attacking the specimens, to ruin them utterly in comparatively a short time. The pests which are most to be feared are beetles belonging to the genera *Dermestes* and *Anthrenus*. In addition to these beetles, which commit their ravages in the larval stage, moths and mites prey upon collections. Moths are very infrequently, however, found in collections of insects, and in a long experience the writer has known only one or two instances in which any damage was inflicted upon specimens by the larvæ of moths. Mites are much more to be dreaded.

In order to prevent the ravages of insects, all specimens, before putting them away into the boxes or drawers of the cabinet in which they are to be preserved, should be placed in a tight box in which chloroform, or, better, carbon bisulphide, in a small pan is put, and they should be left here for at least twenty-four hours, until it is certain that all life is extinct. Then they should be transferred to the tight boxes or drawers in which they are to be kept. The presence of insect pests in a collection is generally first indicated by fine dust under the specimen, this dust being the excrement of the larva which is committing depredations upon the specimen. In case the presence of the larva is detected, a liberal dose of chloroform should at once be administered to the box or tray in which the specimen is contained. The specimen itself ought to be removed, and may be dipped into benzine. Naphthaline crystals or camphor is generally employed to keep out insect pests from boxes. They are very useful to deter the entrance of pests, but when they have once been introduced into a collection neither naphthaline nor camphor will kill them. Naphthaline is prepared in the form of cones attached to a pin, and these cones may be placed in one corner of the box. However, a good substitute for the cones may very easily be made by taking the ordinary mothballs which are sold everywhere. By heating a pin red-hot in the flame of an alcohol-lamp it may be thrust into the moth-ball; as it enters it melts the naphthaline, which immediately afterward cools and holds the pin securely fixed in the moth-ball. In attaching these pins to moth-balls, hold the pin securely in a forceps while heating it in the flame of the lamp, and thrust the red-hot pin into the center of the ball. Naphthaline crystals and camphor may be secured in the corner of the box by tying up a quantity of them in a small piece of netting and pinning the little bag thus made in the corner of the tray. But this is not as neat in appearance as are the pinned "moth-balls." By following these directions insect pests may

FIG. 73.—Naphthaline cone.

be kept out of collections. It is proper to observe that while carbon bisulphide is more useful even than chloroform in killing pests, and is also cheaper, it should be used with great care, because when mixed with atmospheric air it is highly explosive, and its use should never take place where there are lamps burning or where there is fire. Besides, its odor is extremely unpleasant, unless it has been washed in mercury.

Greasy Specimens.—Specimens occasionally become greasy. When this happens they may be cleansed by pinning them down on a piece of cork secured to the bottom of a closed vessel, and gently filling it with benzine, refined gasoline, or ether. After leaving them long enough to remove all the grease they may be taken out of the bath and allowed to dry in a place where there is no dust. This operation should not take place near a lighted lamp or a fire.

Mould.—When specimens have become mouldy or mildewed it is best to burn them up, if they can be spared. If not, after they have been thoroughly dried, remove the mould with a sable or camel's-hair pencil which has been rubbed in carbolic acid (crystals liquefied by heat). Mildew in a cabinet is hard to eradicate, and heat, even to burning, is about the only cure, except the mild use of carbolic acid in the way suggested, or a strong vapor of formaldehyde, which kills, but does not remove mildew.

Repairing Specimens.—Torn and ragged specimens are to be preferred to none at all. "The half of a loaf is better than no bread." Until the torn specimen can be replaced by a better, it is always well to retain it in a collection. But it is sometimes possible to repair torn specimens in such a way as to make them more presentable. If an antenna, for instance, has been broken off, it may be replaced neatly, so that only a microscopic examination will disclose the fact that it was once away from the place where it belonged. If a wing has been slit, the rent may be mended so neatly that only a very careful observer can detect the fact. If a piece has been torn out of a wing, it may be replaced by the corresponding portion of the wing of another specimen of the same sex of the same species in such a way as almost to defy detection. The prime requisites for this work are patience, a steady hand, a good eye, a great deal of "gumption," a few setting-needles, a jeweler's forceps, and a little shellac dissolved in alcohol. The shellac used in replacing a missing antenna should be of a thickish consistency; in repairing wings it should be well thinned down with alcohol. In handling broken antennæ it is best to use a fine sable pencil, which may be moistened very lightly by applying it to the tip of the tongue. With this it is possible to pick up a loose antenna and place it wherever it is desired. Apply the shellac to the torn edges of a broken wing with great delicacy of touch and in very small quantity. Avoid putting on the adhesive material in "gobs and slathers." Repairing is a fine art, which is only learned after some patient experimentation, and is only to be practised when absolutely necessary. The habit of some dealers of patching up broken specimens with parts taken from other species is highly to be reprobated. Such specimens are more or less caricatures of the real thing, and no truly scientific man will admit such scarecrows into his collection, except under dire compulsion.

Packing and Forwarding Specimens.—It often becomes necessary to forward specimens from one place to another. If it is intended to ship specimens which have been mounted upon pins they should be securely pinned in a box lined with cork. A great many expanded specimens may be pinned in a box by resorting to the method known as "shingling," which is illustrated in Fig. 74. By causing the wings of specimens to overlap, as is shown in the figure, a great many can be accommodated in a small space. When the specimens have been packed the box should be securely closed, its edges shut with paper, after some drops of chloroform have been poured into the box, and then this box should be placed in an outer box containing excelsior, hay, cotton, or loose shavings in sufficient abundance to prevent the jarring of the inner box and consequent breakage. Where specimens are forwarded in envelopes, having been collected in the field, and are not pinned, the precaution of surrounding them with packing such as has been described is not necessary, but the box in which they are shipped should always be strong enough to resist breakage. Things forwarded by mail or by express always receive rough treatment, and the writer has lost many fine specimens which have been forwarded to him, because the shipper was careless in packing, or the boxes were not strong.

Pins.—In the preceding pages frequent reference has been made to insect-pins. These are pins which are made longer and thinner than is the case with ordinary pins, and are therefore adaptable to the special use to which they are put.

42

There are a number of makers whose pins have come into vogue. What are known as Karlsbader and Kläger pins, made in Germany, were formerly widely used. They are made of ordinary pin-metal in various sizes. The Karlsbader pins have very fine points, but, owing to the fineness of the points and the softness of the metal, they are very apt to buckle, or turn at the points. The Kläger pins are not exposed to the same objection, as the points are not quite so fine. The best pins, however, which are now made are of steel, lacquered, possessing very great

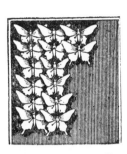

FIG. 75.—Butterfly-forceps, half-size.

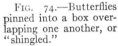

FIG. 74.—Butterflies pinned into a box overlapping one another, or "shingled."

FIG. 76.—Insect-forceps.

strength and considerable flexibility. The writer has never known them to buckle at the tip, even when forced through the hardest insect tissues. While these pins are a trifle more expensive than the white pins, they are greatly to be preferred, because, even if one does now and then rust, they do not decompose as the white pins often do. The latter in contact with the fats and other substances in the bodies of insects, often decompose. A bulging mass of green crystals (verdigris) is formed where the pin passes through the insect, discoloring the specimen, and the pin is rotted, breaking off on being touched. Then there is trouble.

The Forceps.—An almost indispensable instrument is the forceps. There are many forms; but it is not necessary to speak of all of them. Small fine-pointed forceps, such as are used by jewelers, with either straight or curved tips are most useful in handling small and delicate specimens. In pinning insects into boxes or trays the form of forceps shown in Fig. 75 is good when handling large specimens with broad wings. The tip of the forceps can be thrust under the insect to grasp the pin, and then it can be lifted from the cork bottom of the tray without danger of breakage. The small forceps represented in Fig. 76 is useful in pinning down small specimens. When handling pinned specimens it is best to take hold of the pin below the body of the insect and force it into the cork by gentle and steady pressure. If an insect is taken up above the body by the fingers, or with a forceps, the fingers or the forceps may slip, and the specimen may be badly broken. Great care should be used in handling pinned specimens.

CHAPTER III

"Winged flowers, or flying gems."

MOORE.

AT the base of all truly scientific knowledge lies the principle of order. There have been some who have gone so far as to say that science is merely the orderly arrangement of facts. While such a definition is defective, it is nevertheless true that no real knowledge of any branch of science is attained until its relationship to other branches of human knowledge is learned, and until a classification of the facts of which it treats has been made. When a science treats of things, it is necessary that these things should become the subject of investigation, until at last their relation to one another, and the whole class of things to which they belong, has been discovered. Men who devote themselves to the discovery of the relation of things and to their orderly classification are known as systematists.

The great leader in this work was the immortal Linnæus, the "Father of Natural History," as he has been called. Upon the foundation laid by him in his work entitled "Systema Naturæ," or "The System of Nature," all who have followed after him have labored, and the result has been the rise of the great modern sciences of botany and zoölogy, which treat respectively of the vegetable and animal kingdoms.

The Place of Butterflies in the Animal Kingdom.—The animal kingdom, for purposes of classification, has been subdivided into various groups known as subkingdoms. One of these subkingdoms contains those animals which, being without vertebræ, or an internal skeleton, have an external skeleton, composed of a series of horny rings, attached to which are various organs. This subkingdom is known by naturalists under the name of the *Arthropoda*. The word *Arthropoda* is derived from the Greek language, and is compounded of two words, ἄρθρον (*arthron*), meaning a *joint*, and πούς (*pous*), meaning a *foot*. The *Arthropoda* seem at first sight to be made up of jointed rings and feet; hence the name.

The subkingdom of the *Arthropoda* is again subdivided into six classes. These are the following:

Class I. The *Crustacea* (Shrimps, Crabs, Water-fleas, etc.).

Class II. The *Podostomata* (King-crabs, Trilobites [fossil], etc.).

Class III. The *Malacopoda* (*Peripatus*, a curious genus of worm-like creatures, found in the tropics, and allied to the Myriapods in some important respects).

Class IV. The *Myriapoda* (Centipedes, etc.).

Class V. The *Arachnida* (Spiders, Mites, etc.).

Class VI. The *Insecta* (Insects).

44

That branch of zoölogy which treats of insects is known as entomology.

The *Insecta* have been variously subdivided by different scientific writers, but the following subdivision has much in it to commend it, and will suffice as an outline for the guidance of the student.

CLASS VI. INSECTS (INSECTS PROPER)

HETEROMETABOLA

For the most part undergoing only a partial metamorphosis in the development from the egg to the imago.

ORDERS

1. *Thysanura.*
   Suborders:
      Collembola (Podura, Springtails).
      Symphyla (Scolopendrella).
      Cinura (Bristletails, etc.).
2. *Ephemerida* (May-flies).
3. *Plecoptera* (Stone-flies).
4. *Mallophaga* (Bird-lice).
5. *Isoptera* (Termites, etc.).
6. *Psocoptera* (Book-lice).
7. *Platyptera* (Hellgramites, etc.).
8. *Neuroptera* (Ant-lions, etc.).
9. *Mecoptera* (Scorpion-flies).
10. *Trichoptera* (Caddis-flies).
11. *Odonata* (Dragon-flies).
12. *Thysanoptera* (Thrips).
13. *Parasitica* (Lice).
14. *Homoptera* (Cicada, Leaf-hoppers, etc.).
15. *Heteroptera* (Ranatra, Belostoma, Squash-bugs, etc.).
16. *Dermaptera* (Earwigs).
17. *Orthoptera* (Grass-hoppers, Mantis, Cockroaches, etc.).
18. *Coleoptera* (Beetles).

METABOLA

Undergoing for the most part a complete metamorphosis from egg, through larva and pupa, to imago.

ORDERS

19. *Aphaniptera* (Fleas).
20. *Diptera.*
    Suborders:
       Orthorhapha (Hessian Flies, Buffalo-gnats, Mosquitos, Crane-flies, Horse-flies).
       Cyclorhapha (Syrphus, Bot-flies, Tsetse, House-flies, etc.).
21. *Lepidoptera.*
    Suborders:
       Rhopalocera (Butterflies).
       Heterocera (Moths).
22. *Hymenoptera.*
    Suborders:
       Terebrantia (Saw-flies, Gall-wasps, Ichneumon-flies, etc.).
       Aculeata (Ants, Cuckoo-flies, Digger-wasps, True Wasps, Bees).

The Classification of Butterflies

It will be seen by glancing at the foregoing table that the butterflies and moths are included as suborders in the twenty-first group of the list, to which is applied the name *Lepidoptera*. This word, like most other scientific words, is derived from the Greek, and is compounded of the noun λεπίς (*lepis*), which signifies a *scale*, and the noun πτερόν (*pteron*), which signifies a *wing*. The butterflies and moths together constitute the order of scale-winged insects. The appropriateness of this name will no doubt be at once recognized by every reader, who, having perhaps unintentionally rubbed off some of the minute scales which clothe the wings of a butterfly, has taken the trouble to examine them under a microscope, or who has attentively read what has been said upon this subject in the first chapter of this book. By referring again to the classification which has been given, it will be noted that the last four orders in the list agree in that the creatures included within them undergo for the most part what is known as a complete metamorphosis; that is to say, they pass through four successive stages of development, existing first as eggs, then as worm-like larvæ, or caterpillars, then as pupæ, and finally as perfect, fully developed insects, gifted for the most part with the power of flight, and capable of reproducing their kind. All of this has been to some extent already elucidated in the first chapter of the present volume, but it may be well to remind the reader of these facts at this point.

A question which is frequently asked by those who are not familiar with the subject relates to the manner in which it is possible to distinguish between moths and butterflies. A partial answer can be made in the light of the habits of the two classes of lepidoptera. Butterflies are diurnal in their habits, flying between sunrise and dusk, and very rarely taking the wing at night. This habit is so universal that these insects are frequently called by entomologists "the diurnal lepidoptera," or are simply spoken of as "diurnals." It is, however, true that many species of moths are also diurnal in their habits, though the great majority of them are nocturnal, or crepuscular, that is, flying at the dusk of the evening, or in the twilight of the early morning. Upon the basis of mere habit, then, we are able only to obtain a partial clue to the distinction between the two suborders. A more definite distinction is based upon structure, and specifically upon the structure of the antennæ. Butterflies have long, thread-like antennæ, provided with a swelling at the extremity, giving them a somewhat club-shaped appearance (Fig. 77). This form of antennæ is very unusual among the moths, and only occurs in a few rare genera, found in tropical countries, which seem to represent connecting-links between the butterflies and the moths. All the true moths which are found within the limits of the United States and Canada have antennæ which are not club-shaped, but are of various other forms. Some moths have thread-like antennæ tapering to a fine point; others have feather-shaped antennæ; still others have antennæ which are prismatic in form, and provided with a little hook, or spur, at the end; and there are many modifications and variations of these forms. The club-shaped form of the antennæ of butterflies has led naturalists to call them *Rhopalocera*, as has been already explained in speaking of this subject on page 13. Moths are called *Heterocera*. The word *Heterocera* is compounded of the Greek

46

word ἕτερον (*heteron*), meaning *other*, and the Greek word κέρας (*keras*), meaning a *horn*. They are lepidoptera which have antennæ which are *other than club-shaped*. Besides the distinctions which exist in the matter of the form of the antennæ, there are distinctions in the veins of the wings, and in the manner of carrying them when at rest or in flight, which are quite characteristic of the two groups; but all of these things the attentive student will quickly learn for himself by observation.

FIG. 77.—Antennæ of butterflies.   FIG. 78.—Antennæ of moths.

Scientific Arrangement.—Having thus cast a passing glance at the differences which exist between moths and butterflies, we take up the question of the subdivision of the butterflies into natural groups. Various systems of arranging butterflies have been suggested from time to time by learned writers, and for a knowledge of these systems the student may consult works which treat of them at length. It is sufficient to observe that in modern science, for purposes of convenience, as well as from regard for essential truth, all individuals are looked upon as belonging to a *species*. A species includes all those individuals, which have a common ancestry, and are so related in form and structure as to be manifestly separable from all other similarly constituted assemblages of individuals. For instance, all the large cats having a tawny skin, and in the male a shaggy mane, constitute a species, which we call the lion; the eagles in the eastern United States, which in the adult plumage of the male have a snow-white head and neck and a white tail, constitute a species, which we know as the "white-headed" or "bald-headed" eagle. Species may then be grouped together, and those which are manifestly closely related to one another are regarded as forming a natural assemblage of species, to which we give the name of a *genus*. For example, all the cats, such as the house-cat, the lion, the tiger, the puma, and the jaguar, are grouped together by naturalists, and form a genus, to which is given the Latin name *Felis*, meaning *cat*. The name of the genus always comes before that of the species. Thus the tiger is spoken of scientifically as *Felis tigris*. The genera which are closely related to one another may again be assembled as *subfamilies;* and the subfamilies may be united to form *families*. For instance, all the various genera of cats form a family, which is known as the *Felidæ*, or the Cat Family. A group of families constitutes a *suborder* or an *order*. The cats belong to the *Carnivora*, or order of flesh-eating animals.

In zoölogy family names are formed with the termination *-idæ*, and subfamily names with the termination *-inæ*.

The Classification of Butterflies

Everything just said in regard to the classification of the higher animals applies likewise to butterflies. Let us take as an illustration the common Milkweed Butterfly. Linnæus for a fanciful reason gave this insect the specific name *Plexippus* by which it is distinguished from all other butterflies. It belongs to the genus *Danais*. The genus *Danais* is one of the genera which make up the subfamily of the *Danainæ*. The *Danainæ* belong to the great family of the *Nymphalidæ*. The *Nymphalidæ* are a part of the suborder of the *Rhopalocera*, or true butterflies, one of the two great subdivisions of the order *Lepidoptera*, belonging to the great class *Insecta*, the highest class in the subkingdom of the *Arthropoda*. The matter may be represented in a tabular form, in the reverse order from that which has been given:

Subkingdom, *Arthropoda*.
    Class, *Insecta*.
        Order, *Lepidoptera*.
            Suborder, *Rhopalocera*.
                Family, *Nymphalidæ*.
                    Subfamily, *Danainæ*.
                        Genus, *Danais*.
                            Species, *plexippus* (Milkweed Butterfly).

Subspecies.—A still further subdivision is in some cases recognized as necessary. A species which has a wide range over an extensive territory may vary in different parts of the territory within which it is found. The butterflies of certain common European species are found also in Japan and Corea, but, as a rule, they are much larger in the latter countries than they are in Europe, and in some cases somewhat differently marked. Naturalists therefore distinguish the Asiatic from the European form by giving the former what is known as a subspecific name. Similar differences occur among butterflies on the continent of North America. The great yellow and black-barred swallowtail butterfly known as *Papilio turnus* occurs from Florida to Winnipeg. But the specimens from the far north are always much smaller than those from other regions, and have a dwarfed appearance. This dwarfed form constitutes what is known as a local race, or subspecies. The members of a species which occur upon an island frequently differ in marked respects from specimens which occur upon the adjacent mainland. By isolation and the process of through-breeding the creature has come to acquire characteristics, which separate it in a marked degree from the closely allied continental form, and yet not sufficiently to justify us in treating it as a distinct species. It represents what is known as an insular race, and we therefore give it a name. Naturalists also distinguish between seasonal, dimorphic, melanic, and albino forms or varieties. Names descriptive or designatory of these forms are frequently applied to them. All of this will become plainer in the course of the study of the succeeding pages, and in the effort to classify specimens, which the student will make.

Sex.—The designation of the sex is important in the case of all well-ordered collections of zoölogical specimens. As a measure of convenience, the male is usually indicated by the sign of Mars, ♂, while the female is indicated by the sign of Venus, ♀. The inscription, "*Argynnis Diana,* ♂," therefore means that the specimen is a male of *Argynnis Diana*, and the inscription, "*Argynnis Diana,* ♀," means that the specimen is a female of the same species. These signs are invariably employed by naturalists to mark the sexes.

The Division of Butterflies into Families.—Without attempting to go deeply into questions of classification at the present point, it will be well for us to note the subdivisions which have been made into larger groups, known as *families*, and to show how these may be distinguished from one another. There are seven families represented in the territory covered by this book. They are the following:

1. The NYMPHALIDÆ, or "Brush-footed Butterflies."
2. The LIBYTHEIDÆ, or "Snout-butterflies."
3. The RIODINIDÆ, or "Metal-marks."
4. The LYCÆNIDÆ, "Hair-streaks," "Coppers," and "Blues."
5. The PIERIDÆ, or "Whites," and "Sulphurs."
6. The PAPILIONIDÆ, the "Swallow-tails" and allies.
7. The HESPERIIDÆ, or the "Skippers."

The NYMPHALIDÆ, the "Brush-footed Butterflies."

The butterflies of this family may be distinguished as a great class from all other butterflies by the fact that *in both sexes the first, or prothoracic, pair of legs is greatly dwarfed, useless for walking, and therefore carried folded up against the breast.* From this peculiarity they have also been called the "Four-footed Butterflies." This is the largest of all the families of the butterflies, and has been subdivided into many subfamilies. Some of the genera are composed of small species, but most of the genera are made up of medium-sized or large species. The family is geologically very ancient, and most of the fossil butterflies which have been discovered belong to it. The caterpillars are in most of the subfamilies provided with horny or fleshy projections. The chrysalids always hang suspended by the tail.

The LIBYTHEIDÆ, the "Snout-butterflies."

This is a very small family, closely related to the preceding, in which it has been incorporated by many authors. Its most striking characteristic at first glance is the great prolongation of the labial palpi, whence the name "Snout-butterflies." The family is geologically very ancient and fossil specimens have been found in the early Tertiary.

The RIODINIDÆ, the "Metal-marks."

This family is distinguished from others by the fact that *the males have four ambulatory or walking feet, while the females have six such feet. The antennæ are relatively longer than in the Lycænidæ.* The butterflies belonging to this great group are mostly confined to the tropics of the New World, and only a few genera and species are included in the region covered by this volume. They are usually quite small, but are colored in a bright and odd manner, being spotted and checkered. Many are extremely brilliant in their colors. *The caterpillars are small and contracted. Some are said to have chrysalids which are suspended; others have chrysalids girdled and attached at the anal extremity, like the Lycænidæ. The butterflies in many*

49

genera have the habit of alighting on the underside of leaves, with their wings expanded, like some moths.

The Lycænidæ, the "Gossamer-winged Butterflies."

This great family comprises the butterflies which are familiarly known as the "Hair-streaks," the "Blues," and the "Coppers." *The males have four and the females six walking feet. The caterpillars are small, short, and slug-shaped. The chrysalids are provided with a girdle, are attached at the end of the abdomen, and lie closely appressed to the surface upon which they have undergone transformation.* Blue is a very common color in this family, which includes some of the gayest of the small forms which are found in the butterfly-world. *In alighting they always carry their wings folded together and upright.*

The Pieridæ, the "Whites," and "Sulphurs."

This is a very large family, ranging from the subarctic regions of both the northern and southern hemispheres, and extensively developed in the tropics, where there are many mimicking species. They have *six walking feet in both sexes. The caterpillars do not have osmateria, as is the case in the Papilionidæ. The wings of the imago are not tailed, but generally rounded, or in exceptional genera produced at the apex of the fore wings or angulated on the outer margin of the hind wings. Except in mimetic forms the dominant color of the wings is some shade of white or yellow, with dark borderings and markings, which often follow the neuration. The eggs are elongated pyramidal. The chrysalids are girdled, attached at the end of the abdomen, compressed laterally, the wing-sheaths often greatly expanded, and the upper end of the chrysalis often strongly produced, not bifurcate.*

The Papilionidæ, the "Swallow-tails" and allies.

These butterflies *have six walking feet in both sexes. The caterpillars are elongate, and provided with osmateria, or protrusive organs secreting a powerful and disagreeable odor. The chrysalids are elongate, attached at the anal extremity, and held in place by a girdle of silk, but not closely appressed to the surface upon which they have undergone transformation, more or less expanded laterally, and generally bifurcate at the upper end. The eggs are globular.* To this family belong some of the largest and showiest genera, mainly Indo-australian in habitat.

The Hesperiidæ, or the "Skippers."

They are generally *small in size, with stout bodies, very quick and powerful in flight. They have six walking feet in both sexes. The tibiæ of the hind feet, with few exceptions, have spurs. The caterpillars are cylindrical, smooth, tapering forward and backward from the middle, and generally having large globular heads. For the most part they undergo transformation into chrysalids which have a girdle and an anal hook, or cremaster, in a loose cocoon, composed of a few threads of silk,* and thus approximate the moths in their habits. The genus *Megathymus* has the curious habit of burrowing in its larval stage in the underground stems of yuccas.

To one or the other of these seven families all the butterflies, numbering over six hundred and fifty species, and many subspecies, which are found from the Rio Grande of Texas to the arctic circle, can be referred.

Scientific Names.—From what has been said it is plain to the reader that the student of this delightful branch of science is certain to be called upon to use some rather long and, at first sight, uncouth words in the pursuit of the subject. But experience, that best of teachers, will soon enable him to master any little difficulties which may arise from this source, and he will come finally to recognize how useful these terms are in designating distinctions which exist, but which are often wholly overlooked by the uneducated and unobservant. It is not, however, necessary that the student should at the outset attempt to tax his memory with all of the long scientific names which he encounters in this and similar books. The late Dr. Horn of Philadelphia, who was justly regarded during the latter years of his life as the most eminent student of the *Coleoptera*, or beetles, of North America, once said to the writer that he made it a religious duty not to try to remember all the long scientific names belonging to the thousands of species in his collection, but was content to have them attached to the pins holding the specimens in his cabinets, where he could easily refer to them. The student who is engaged in collecting and studying butterflies will very soon come, almost without effort, to know their names, but it is not a sin to forget them.

In writing about butterflies it is quite customary to abbreviate the generic name by giving merely its initial. Thus in writing about the Milkweed Butterfly, *Danais plexippus*, the naturalist will designate it as "*D. plexippus.*" To the specific name he will also attach the name of the man who gave this specific name to the insect. As Linnæus was the first to name this insect, it is proper to add his name, when writing of it, or to add an abbreviation of his name, as follows: "*D. plexippus* Linnæus," or "Linn." In speaking about butterflies it is quite common to omit the generic name altogether and to use only the specific name. Thus after returning in the evening from a collecting-trip, I might say, "I was quite successful to-day. I took twenty *Aphrodites*, four *Myrinas*, and two specimens of *Atlantis.*" In this case there could be no misunderstanding of my meaning. I took specimens of three species of the genus *Argynnis*—*A. aphrodite*, *A. myrina*, and *A. atlantis;* but it is quite enough to designate them by the specific names, without reference to their generic classification.

If, as is often the case, a butterfly was originally placed in another genus than that to which it is now assigned, it is usage to place the name of the author of the species in parentheses (). Thus *Danais plexippus* (L.) means that the butterfly was originally put into another genus, in this case the genus *Papilio*. Linnæus called all butterflies *Papilio*. He had only one genus, but used subdivisions, which in part correspond to modern genera.

Synonyms.—It is a law among scientific men that the name first given to an animal or plant shall be its name and shall have priority over all other names. Now, it has happened not infrequently that an author, not knowing that a species has been described already, has redescribed it under another name. Such a name applied a second time to a species already described is called a *synonym*, and may be published after the true name. Sometimes species have had a dozen or more different names applied to them by different writers, but all such names rank as synonyms according to the law of priority. The law of priority also applies to the names of genera, subfamilies, families, and other classificational terms. Exceptions to the strict law of priority may be made where a name by usage has become so familiar and so firmly established that to replace it would only breed confusion. But this is perhaps not the place to discuss this subject at length.

Popular Names.—Common English names for butterflies are much in vogue in England and Scotland, and there is no reason why English names should not be given to butterflies, as well as to birds and to plants. In the following pages this has been done to a great extent. I have used the names coined by Dr. S. H. Scudder and by others, so far as possible, and have in other cases been forced myself to coin names which seemed to be appropriate, in the hope that they may come ultimately to be widely used. The trouble is that ordinary people do not take pains to observe and note the distinctions which exist among the lower animals. The vocabulary of the common farmer, or even of the ordinary professional man, is bare of terms to point out correctly the different things which come under the eye. All insects are "bugs" to the vulgar, and even the airy butterfly, creature of grace and light, is put into the same category with roaches and fleas. Apropos of the tendency to classify as "bugs" all things which creep and are small, it may be worth while to recall the story, which Frank Buckland tells in his "Log-book of a Fisherman and Naturalist," of an adventure which he had, when a schoolboy, at the booking-office of the London, Chatham, and Dover Railway Company in Dover. He had been for a short trip to Paris, and had bought a monkey and a tortoise. Upon his return from sunny France, as he was getting his ticket up to London, Jocko stuck his head out of the bag in which his owner was carrying him. The ticket-agent looked down and said, "You will pay half-fare for him." "How is that?" exclaimed young Buckland. "Well, we charge half-fare for dogs." "But this is not a dog," replied the indignant lad; "this is a monkey." "Makes no difference," was the answer; "you must pay half-fare for him." Reluctantly the silver was laid upon the counter. Then, thrusting his hands into the pocket of his greatcoat, Buckland drew forth the tortoise, and, laying it down, asked, "How much do you charge for this?" The ancient receiver of fares furbished his spectacles, adjusted them to his nose, took a long look, and replied, "We don't charge nothin' for them; them's insects." It is to be hoped that the reader of this book will in the end have a clearer view of facts as to the classification of animals than was possessed by the ticket-agent at Dover.

"And Adam gave names to all cattle, and to the fowl of the air, and to every beast of the field." *Genesis*, II, 20.

But Adam overlooked the insects. The "sons of Adam" have given names to more than two hundred thousand species of insects since Linnæus took up the unfinished task of Adam.

CHAPTER IV

BOOKS ABOUT NORTH AMERICAN BUTTERFLIES

Early Writers.—The earliest descriptions of North American butterflies are found in writings which are now almost unknown, except to the close student of science. Linnæus described and named a number of the commoner North American species, and some of them were figured by Charles Clerck, his pupil, whose work entitled "Icones" was published at Stockholm in the year 1764. Clerck's work is exceedingly rare, and the writer believes that there is only one other copy, besides that in his possession, in North America. Johann Christian Fabricius, a pupil of Linnæus, who was for some time a professor in Kiel, and attached to the court of the King of Denmark, published between the year 1775 and the year 1798 a number of works upon the general subject of entomology, in which he gave descriptions, very brief and unsatisfactory, of a number of North American species. His descriptions were written, as were those of Linnæus, in the Latin language. About the same time that Fabricius was publishing his works, Peter Cramer, a Dutchman, was engaged in giving to the world the four large quartos in which he endeavored to figure and describe the butterflies and moths of Asia, Africa, and America. Cramer's work was entitled "Papillons Exotiques," and contained recognizable illustrations of quite a number of the North American forms. The book, however, is rare and expensive to-day, but few copies of it being accessible to American students.

Jacob Hübner, who was born at Augsburg in the year 1761, undertook the publication, at the close of the Eighteenth century, of an elaborate work upon the European butterflies and moths, parallel with which he undertook a publication upon the butterflies and moths of foreign lands. The title of this work is "Sammlung Exotischer Schmetterlinge." To this work was added, as an appendix, partly by Hübner and partly by his successor and co-laborer, Karl Geyer, another, entitled "Zuträge zur Sammlung Exotischer Schmetterlinge." The two works together are illustrated by six hundred and sixty-four colored plates. This great publication contains some scattered figures of North American species. There is almost no text. It is a picture-book, but none the worse for that. A good copy sells for from three hundred and fifty to four hundred dollars, or even more. A facsimile edition edited by Kirby has been issued by Wytsmann of Brussels. Like the original, it is expensive and now hard to get.

The first work which was largely devoted to an account of the lepidoptera of North America was published in England by Sir James Edward Smith, who was a botanist, and who gave to the world in two volumes some of the plates which had been drawn by John Abbot, an Englishman who lived for a number of years in Georgia. The work appeared in two folio volumes, bearing the date 1797. It is entitled "The Natural History of the Rarer Lepidopterous Insects of Georgia." It contains one hundred and four plates, in which the insects are represented in their various stages upon their appropriate food-plants. Smith and Abbot's work contains original descriptions of only about half a dozen of the North American butterflies, and figures a number of species which had been already described by earlier authors. It is mainly devoted to the moths. This work is now rare and commands a very high price.

The next important work upon the subject was published by **Dr. J. A. Bois-duval** of Paris, a celebrated entomologist, who was assisted by Major John E. Leconte. The work appeared in the year 1833, and is entitled "Histoire Générale et Monographie des Lépidoptères et des Chenilles de l'Amérique Septentrionale." It contains seventy-eight colored plates, each representing butterflies of North America, in many cases giving figures of the larva and the chrysalis as well as of the perfect insect. The plates were based very largely upon drawings made by John Abbot, and represent ninety-three species, while in the text there are only eighty-five species mentioned, some of which are not figured. What has been said of all the preceding works is also true of this: it is very rarely offered for sale, can only be found upon occasion, and commands a high price.

In the year 1841 Dr. Thaddeus William Harris published "A Report on the Insects of Massachusetts which are Injurious to Vegetation." This work, which was originally brought out in pursuance of an order of the legislature of Massachusetts, by the Commissioners of the Zoölogical and Botanical Survey of the State, was republished in 1842, and was followed by a third edition in 1852. The last edition, revised and improved by Charles L. Flint, Secretary of the Massachusetts State Board of Agriculture, appeared in 1862. This work contains a number of figures and descriptions of the butterflies of New England, and, while now somewhat obsolete, still contains a great deal of valuable information, and is well worth being rescued by the student from the shelves of the second-hand book-stalls in which it is now and then to be found. For the New England student of entomology it remains to a greater or less extent a classic.

In 1860 the Smithsonian Institution published a "Catalogue of the Described Lepidoptera of North America," a compilation prepared by the Rev. John G. Morris. This work, though very far from complete, contains in a compact form much valuable information, largely extracted from the writings of previous authors. It is not illustrated.

With the book prepared by Dr. Morris the first period in the development of a literature relating to our subject may be said to close, and the reader will observe that until the end of the sixth decade of the Nineteenth Century very little had been attempted in the way of systematically naming, describing, and illustrating the riches of the insect fauna of this continent. Almost all the work, with the exception of that done by Harris, Leconte, and Morris, had been done by European authors.

Later Writers.—At the close of the Civil War this country witnessed a great intellectual awakening, and every department of science began to find its zealous students. In the annals of entomology the year 1868 is memorable because of the issue of the first part of the great work by William H. Edwards, entitled "The Butterflies of North America." This work, brought to completion in 1897 with the publication of the third volume, stands a lasting monument to the scientific attainments and the inextinguishable industry of its learned author. The three volumes are most superbly illustrated, and contain a wealth of original drawings, representing all the stages in the life-history of numerous species, which has never been surpassed. Unfortunately, while including a large number of the species known to inhabit North America, the book is nevertheless not what its title would seem to imply, and is far from complete, hundreds of species not being represented in any way, either in the text, or in the illustrations. In spite of this fact it remains to the American student a classic.

A work even more elaborate in its design and execution, contained in three volumes, is "The Butterflies of New England," by Dr. Samuel Hubbard Scudder, published in the year 1886. No more exhaustive monograph on any scientific subject has ever been published than this, and it must remain a lasting memorial of the colossal industry and vast learning of the author, one of the most eminent scientific men whom America has produced. But it is restricted to a minor part of our fauna.

While the two great works which have been mentioned have illustrated to the highest degree not only the learning of their authors, but the advances which have been made in the art of illustration within somewhat recent years, they do not stand alone as representing the activity of students in this field. A number of smaller, but useful, works appeared from time to time. Among these must be mentioned "The Butterflies of the Eastern United States," by Professor G. H. French. This book, which contains four hundred and two pages and ninety-three figures in the text, was published in Philadelphia in 1886. It is an admirable little work, with the help of which the student may learn much in relation to the subject; but it greatly lacks in illustration, without which all such publications are not attractive or thoroughly useful to the student. In the same year appeared "The Butterflies of New England," by C. J. Maynard, a quarto containing seventy-two pages of text and eight colored plates, the latter not very good. In 1878 Herman Strecker of Reading, Pennsylvania, published a book entitled "Butterflies and Moths of North America," which is further entitled "A Complete Synonymical Catalogue." It gives only the synonymy of some four hundred and seventy species of butterflies, and was not continued by the author, as was apparently his intention. It makes no mention of the moths, except upon the title-page. For the scientific student it has some value. The same author published in parts a work illustrated by fifteen colored plates, entitled "Lepidoptera—Rhopaloceres and Heteroceres—Indigenous and Exotic," which came out from 1872 to 1879, and contains recognizable figures of many North American species. It is now out of print and difficult to obtain.

Books About North American Butterflies

In 1891 there appeared in Boston, from the pen of C. J. Maynard, a work entitled "A Manual of North American Butterflies." This is illustrated by ten indifferently executed plates and a number of cuts in the text. The work is unfortunately characterized by serious defects, which make its use unsatisfactory in the correct determination of species and their classification.

In 1893 Dr. Scudder published two books, both of them useful, though brief, one of them entitled "The Life of a Butterfly," the other, "A Brief Guide to the Commoner Butterflies of the Northern United States and Canada." Both of these books were published in New York by Messrs. Henry Holt & Co., and contain valuable information in relation to the subject, being to a certain extent an advance upon another work published in 1881 by the same author and firm, entitled "Butterflies."

In December, 1898, "The Butterfly Book" appeared. The first printing was sold in advance of the appearance of the volume. Over sixty-five thousand copies have been printed. It remains the only book, which in comprehensive manner deals with the diurnal lepidoptera of the continent north of Mexico. The present edition aims at completeness, so far as this territory is concerned.

One of the most colossal undertakings of its kind was the publication of "The Biologia Centrali-Americana." The late Frederick Ducane Godman, a very wealthy and equally learned English gentleman, conceived the idea of bringing out an encyclopedic work upon the archeology, botany, and zoölogy of Central America and Mexico. He invoked the aid of the ablest specialists in Europe and America. He spared no expense. The volumes began to appear in parts in 1879. The work was finally completed in 1915. It comprises, exclusive of the volumes devoted to archeology, fifty-seven folio volumes superbly printed and lavishly illustrated. Volumes 36–38 contain the Rhopalocera, or Butterflies, two volumes of text (1269 pp.) and one containing one hundred and twelve colored plates, depicting many hundreds of species of butterflies. In the preparation of this part of the work Mr. Godman was joined by his brother-in-law, the late Osbert Salvin. They are a monument to the munificence of Mr. Godman, and the erudition and industry of the joint authors. The work is almost indispensable to the critical student of the butterflies of the southwestern states of the United States, inasmuch as many species found in Mexico cross our southern border. It is, however, a now rare and costly work, a complete set costing several thousands of dollars.

In 1904 Professor John Henry Comstock and his amiable wife, Mrs. Anna Botsford Comstock, sent forth through the press of D. Appleton & Company, New York, a book entitled: "How to Know the Butterflies, A Manual of the Butterflies of the Eastern United States," pp. i-xii, pp. 1–311, with colored plates I—XLV. This book, which is beautifully printed and illustrated, only gives descriptions and illustrations of one hundred and twenty-three of the commoner species and their varieties, which are mainly found east of the Mississippi River and principally in the state of New York. It is a beautiful work and of value to beginners living in the northeastern part of our great country.

In 1905 the late W. G. Wright of San Bernardino, California, brought out a book, entitled "The Butterflies of the West Coast." It contains two hundred and fifty-seven pages, the two last being an "Appendix" devoted to three species of day-flying moths. It contains thirty-two colored plates, representing four hundred and eighty-three species or varieties of butterflies, besides the three moths already mentioned. The author, who was a most enthusiastic and diligent collector, unfortunately did not possess the technical knowledge necessary to give authority to his work, and many of his identifications of species are quite erroneous. Where he named and figured new species, which are really such, his descriptions and figures have value. The work must be consulted by systematists, but, often is very misleading.

In 1906 Dr. Adalbert Seitz of Darmstadt, Germany, began the issue in parts of a huge work, entitled "Die Gross-Schmetterlinge der Erde," or in English "The Macro-lepidoptera of the World." He invoked in this almost stupendous undertaking the aid of numerous specialists on both sides of the Atlantic. The work, which is in folio, appears in parts, each part containing a number of pages of text and corresponding colored plates. When finally completed it will comprise a formidable array of great volumes. The sections of the work, which deal with the butterflies of the Palearctic Region (Europe, North Africa, and Temperate Asia), Tropical and Subtropical Africa, and the two Americas, have been completed. The American Section, two volumes of text and one of plates, contains one thousand one hundred and forty-one pages and one hundred and ninety-four colored plates, giving recognizable figures of many of the species found in the United States, as well as Central and South America. This work is useful for reference, and, while the acquisition of the entire great work is necessarily limited to persons of large means, it nevertheless should be found in all the larger libraries and especially in those of the principal museums of America. It, however, is not free from errors, and some of the butterflies of the United States are omitted.

In 1911 the late Dr. William Barnes of Decatur, Illinois, well known as an assiduous collector of lepidoptera, began the publication of a series of papers under the title "Contributions to the Natural History of the Lepidoptera of North America." Four volumes, royal octavo, of this work have appeared and parts 1–3 of Vol. V, have been issued, the last part bearing the date April 12, 1924. Dr. Barnes had the collaboration in this work of Drs. J. H. McDunnough, August Busck, A. W. Lindsey, and Mr. Foster H. Benjamin. Numerous descriptions of new species and varieties of butterflies and remarks upon their classification and synonymy are contained in this valuable series of papers, which, however, is devoted principally to the Heterocera, or moths.

A valuable contribution to our knowledge of the *Hesperioidea* of Northern America is the paper published by Professor A. W. Lindsey in the "University of Iowa Studies," Vol. IX, No. 4. It has been frequently consulted by the writer, as have also been the series of papers by Skinner and Williams which appeared in the Transactions of the American Entomological Society, Vols. XLVIII, *et seq.*, dealing with this superfamily. Dr. Lindsey's entire collection and all of his microscopic slides are now the property of the Carnegie Museum.

In the year 1915 the firm of Doubleday, Page, and Co., induced the writer to prepare for them a small pocket-manual dealing with the commoner butterflies found in the more densely inhabited parts of the United States. This booklet I called "The Butterfly Guide." It contains colored figures of two hundred and fifty species and varieties, among them a few showy forms, which I had not figured in "The Butterfly Book" and which only rarely occur on our southern borders. The book is one of a series of pocket manuals on natural history published by the same firm, and its successor, Doubleday, Doran, and Company.

A contribution to our knowledge of the butterflies of arctic America is contained in Vol. III of the "Report of the Canadian Arctic Expedition, 1913–18." It is from the pen of Mr. Arthur Gibson, and appeared in January, 1922, as Part I (i) of the volume, pp. li–58i, illustrated by one text-figure and Plates I–V, of which the two last are colored. Several new species of butterflies are described and figured.

In 1927 Dr. John Adams Comstock of Los Angeles published "The Butterflies of California," containing three hundred and thirty-four pages, numerous figures in the text, and sixty-three colored plates, illustrating almost all of the species and varieties known to occur in California. In scientific accuracy it is superior to the work of Wright, but unfortunately gives currency to a number of names which are untenable, the author having in part followed the "Check-list" of Barnes and Benjamin, which is replete with errors.

MANUALS OF GENERAL ENTOMOLOGY

There have been a number of books published upon insects, in which the authors have given a general account of the different orders, and in which, of course, they have devoted a number of pages to the lepidoptera.

One of the earliest of these compendiums is Professor A. S. Packard's "Guide to the Study of Insects and A Treatise on Those Injurious and Beneficial to Crops for the Use of Colleges, Farm Schools, and Agriculturists," published by Henry Holt and Company, New York. Numerous editions of this work appeared from 1869 until recent years. The seventh edition, 1883, before me as I write, contains six hundred and sixty-eight text-figures and fourteen uncolored plates. The lepidoptera are discussed on pp. 229–357. Only nine butterflies are figured in the cuts.

In 1888 Dr. John Henry Comstock brought out a work entitled: "An Introduction to Entomology," containing pp. i–iv + 1–234. It was published at Ithaca, New York, by the author. This was followed in 1895 by the same author in a greatly enlarged and more profusely illustrated form, entitled: "A Manual for the Study of Insects," by John Henry Comstock and Anna Botsford Comstock, Ithaca, N. Y., Comstock Publishing Co. The order Lepidoptera was discussed in Chapter XVIII, pp. 191–412. The butterflies are discussed on pp. 364–412. In addition to the colored plate, which serves as a frontispiece and delineates four of our commoner butterflies, there are thirty species figured in the text. The latest work by the same authors, covering the same subject, appeared in 1924 under the title, "An Introduction to Entomology."

In 1905 Professor Vernon Kellogg brought out a volume entitled "American Insects," pp. i–ii + 1–674. There are eight hundred and twelve figures in the text and thirteen colored plates. The lepidoptera are discussed on pp. 429–458 and plates IX to XI are devoted to them. Only a comparatively few butterflies are figured.

A very useful and convenient pocket-manual for the study of general entomology is that prepared by Dr. F. E. Lutz of the American Museum of Natural History, published by Messrs. G. P. Putnam Sons. The butterflies are treated on pp. 115–146, and nine plates, five of which are colored, show forty-one of the commoner species occurring in the vicinity of New York City.

CATALOGS

Reference has already been made to the "Synonymical Catalogue of the Butterflies of North America," published by Herman Strecker of Reading. (See page 55). It is now obsolete.

W. H. Edwards in connection with the publication of "The Butterflies of North America" published in each of the three succeeding volumes lists of the species known to him, and in the "Transactions of the American Entomological Society," Vol. XI, 1884, pp. 62–337, published a "Revised Catalog of the Diurnal Lepidoptera of America North of Mexico," which still must be consulted by the critical student, but lacks all reference to many species now known to be found in the United States.

In 1898 Dr. Henry Skinner of the Academy of Natural Sciences in Philadelphia published his "Synonymic Catalog of the North American Rhopalocera," pp. i–xvi + 1–100 + i xvi. Dr. Skinner's catalog is useful, because it gives a more abundant citation of authorities than is given by Edwards.

In 1902 the United States National Museum published as Bulletin No. 53, "A List of the North American Lepidoptera and Key to the Literature of This Order of Insects," by Dr. Harrison G. Dyar, pp. i–xix + 1–723. The butterflies are treated in the first sixty-two pages of this list. Dr. Dyar was assisted in his work by the late Professor C. H. Fernald, the late Rev. George D. Hulst, and Dr. August Busck, the latter cataloging certain groups of microscopic moths.

CHECK-LISTS

Check-lists are papers, which from time to time appear, listing the species under the genera, to which the writer believes them to belong. They may be used in arranging collections. Most of those, which have appeared, are now obsolete and are no longer worthy of mention.

In 1917 there appeared the "Check-List of the Lepidoptera of Boreal America," by Drs. William Barnes and James McDunnough, which was published at Decatur, Ill. This is the best list of species which is at present available, although a number of species have been described since it was published, and changes must accordingly be made.

The student in possession of the present revised edition of The Butterfly Book will find that it may serve at once as a manual and also as a check-list.

PERIODICAL LITERATURE

The reader must not suppose that the only literature relating to the subject, which we are considering, is to be found in the volumes and papers just mentioned. The original descriptions and the life-histories of a large number of the species of butterflies of North America originally appeared in the pages of scientific periodicals and in the journals and proceedings of different learned societies. Among the more important publications, which are rich in information in regard to our theme, may be mentioned those relating to entomology issued by the United States National Museum, the United States Department of Agriculture, and the Departments of Agriculture of the various American Commonwealths. Among the latter Riley's "Missouri Reports" hold high rank. Many valuable papers are contained in "The Transactions of The American Entomological Society," "Psyche," "The Bulletin of The American Association of Economic Entomologists," the "Bulletin of The Brooklyn Entomological Society," "Papilio," "Entomologica Americana," the "Journal of The New York Entomological Society," the "publications" of The Entomological Society of Washington, of The Academy of Natural Sciences of Philadelphia, and The Boston Society of Natural History, the "Annals of The Entomological Society of America," "The Canadian Entomologist," "The Entomological News," the "Bulletin of The Southern California Academy of Sciences," the various publications of "The California Academy of Sciences, San Francisco," "The Pan-Pacific Entomologist," and "The Annals of the Carnegie Museum."

The critical student in reality must have access to several thousands of volumes in order to make sure of his determinations. All of the literature alluded to in the foregoing brief sketch has lain at the hands of the writer and hundreds of other volumes, which it would take a book to merely catalog.

The present volume is an attempt to gather together, boil down, and in compact form present the results of the study of some hundreds of writers, and give the cream of a life-time of study to the reader, accompanied by recognizable figures of typical specimens of all the butterflies of the United States, Canada, Newfoundland, Greenland, and Alaska. The owner of this book saves himself the purchase of a library, the cost of which would run into many thousands of dollars, and spares himself the work of travelling from Boston to San Francisco, and from Montreal to Pasadena to consult collections in museums or private hands. The author has tried to do this for him, and has even crossed the ocean many times to ensure acquaintance with what is lodged in the museums and libraries of Europe, bearing upon "our butterflies."

THE BUTTERFLIES
OF
NORTH AMERICA NORTH OF MEXICO

"Lo, the bright train their radiant wings unfold!
With silver fringed, and freckled o'er with gold:
On the gay bosom of some fragrant flower
They, idly fluttering, live their little hour;
Their life all pleasure, and their task all play,
All spring their age, and sunshine all their day."
MRS. BARBAULD

HUGO'S "FLOWER TO BUTTERFLY"

"Sweet, live with me, and let my love
    Be an enduring tether;
  Oh, wanton not from spot to spot,
    But let us dwell together.

"You've come each morn to sip the sweets
    With which you found me dripping,
  Yet never knew it was not dew,
    But tears, that you were sipping.

"You gambol over honey meads
    Where siren bees are humming;
  But mine the fate to watch and wait
    For my beloved's coming.

"The sunshine that delights you now
    Shall fade to darkness gloomy;
  You should not fear if, biding here,
    You nestled closer to me.

"So rest you, love, and be my love,
    That my enraptured blooming
  May fill your sight with tender light,
    Your wings with sweet perfuming.

"Or, if you will not bide with me
    Upon this quiet heather,
  Oh, give me wing, thou beauteous thing,
    That we may soar together."
EUGENE FIELD

ORDER LEPIDOPTERA
SUBORDER RHOPALOCERA (BUTTERFLIES)

FAMILY I

NYMPHALIDÆ (THE BRUSH-FOOTED BUTTERFLIES)

Nymphalidæ Swainson, Phil. Mag. (2) I, 1827, p. 127.

THIS family is composed of butterflies of medium and large size, though a few of the genera are made up of species which are quite small. They may be distinguished from all other butterflies by the fact that the first pair of legs in both sexes is atrophied or greatly reduced in size, so that they cannot be used in walking, but are carried folded up upon the breast. The fore feet are without tarsal claws, and hence the name "Brush-footed Butterflies" has been applied to them. As the anterior pair of legs is apparently useless, they have been called "The Four-footed Butterflies," which is a misnomer. The atrophy, or loss of function, of the first pair of legs, shows them to hold an advanced position in the evolutionary scale, and we accordingly, in common with many other students of biological phenomena, place them at the head of the list in the Rhopalocera.

Egg.—The eggs of the *Nymphalidæ*, for the most part, are dome-shaped or globular, and are marked with raised longitudinal lines extending from the summit toward the base over the entire surface or over the upper portion of the egg. Between these elevations are often found finer and less elevated cross-lines. In a few genera the surface of the eggs is covered with reticulations arranged in geometrical patterns (see Fig. 1).

Caterpillar.—The caterpillars of the *Nymphalidæ*, as they emerge from the egg, have heads the diameter of which is larger than that of the body, and they are covered with a number of wart-like elevations from which hairs arise. The body of the immature larva generally tapers from before backward (see Pl. III, figs. 7 and 11). The mature larva is cylindrical in form, sometimes, as in the *Satyrinæ*, thicker in the middle. Often one or more of the segments are greatly swollen in whole or in part. The larvæ are generally ornamented with fleshy projections or branching spines.

Chrysalids.—The chrysalids are for the most part angular, and often have strongly marked projections. As a rule, they hang with the head downward, having the cremaster, or anal hook, attached to a button of silk woven on the under

63

Nymphalidæ (the Brush-footed Butterflies)

surface of a branch, a stone, or some other projecting surface. A few boreal species construct loose coverings of threads of silk at the roots of grasses, and here undergo their transformations. The chrysalids are frequently ornamented with golden or silvery spots.

This is the largest of all the families of butterflies, and it is also the most widely distributed. It is represented by species which have their abode in the cold regions of the far North and upon the lofty summits of mountains, where summer reigns for but a few weeks during the year; and it is enormously developed in equatorial lands, including here some of the most gloriously colored species in the butterfly-world. But although these insects appear to have attained their most superb development in the tropics, they are more numerous in the temperate regions than other butterflies, and a certain fearlessness, and fondness for the haunts of men, which seems to characterize some of them, has brought them more under the eyes of observers. The literature of poetry and prose, which takes account of the life of the butterfly, has mainly dealt with forms belonging to this great assemblage of species.

In the classification of the Brush-footed Butterflies various subdivisions have been suggested by learned authors, but the species found in the United States and the countries lying northward upon the continent may all be included in the following groups, or subfamilies:

1. The *Danainæ*, the "Milkweed Butterflies."
2. The *Ithomiinæ*, the "Glassy-wings."
3. The *Heliconiinæ*, the Heliconians.
4. The *Nymphalinæ*, the Nymphs.
5. The *Satyrinæ*, the Satyrs.

The insects belonging to these different subfamilies may be distinguished by the help of the following analytical table, which is based upon that of Professor Comstock, given in his "Manual for the Study of Insects" (p. 396), which in turn is based upon that of Dr. Scudder, in "The Butterflies of New England" (Vol. I, p. 115).

KEY TO THE SUBFAMILIES OF THE NYMPHALIDÆ OF THE UNITED STATES AND CANADA

Front pair of legs atrophied in imago.

I. With the veins of the fore wings not greatly swollen at the base.

    A. Antennæ naked.
        (*a*) Fore wings less than twice as long as broad—*Danainæ*.
        (*b*) Fore wings twice as long as broad and often translucent, the abdomen extending far beyond the inner margin of the hind wings—*Ithomiinæ*.

    B. Antennæ clothed with scales, at least above.
        (*a*) Fore wings at least twice as long as broad—*Heliconiinæ*.
        (*b*) Fore wings less than twice as long as broad; cell of hind wing open, or feebly closed in a few genera; veins of fore wings not swollen at base—*Nymphalinæ*.

II. With some of the veins of the fore wings greatly swollen at the base—*Satyrinæ*.

It may be here parenthetically stated that the arrangement of families, subfamilies, and genera in this volume closely follows that of earlier printings with slight modifications. In the main the order is that given by Kirby in his "Catalogue of the Diurnal Lepidoptera," generally followed by English authors. It is based upon the view, to which allusion has been made, that the *Nymphalidæ* from the evolutionary standpoint hold an advanced position.

German authors, recently followed by some Americans, place the *Papilionidæ* at the head of their systems. All writers appear to be in agreement in locating the *Hesperiidæ* as the terminal group in their classificational schemes. The order of arrangement, so far as families are concerned, is not of vital importance; but it is of major importance that genera should be placed in the families to which they belong.

We proceed to present the various genera and species of *Nymphalidæ*, which occur within our territorial limits. The reader will do well to accompany the study of the descriptions, which are generally brief, by a careful examination of the figures in the plates. In this way a very clear idea of the different species in most instances can be obtained, but with the study of the book should always go, if possible, the study of the living things themselves. Knowledge of nature founded upon books is at best second-hand. To the fields and the woods, then, net in hand! Splendid as may be the sight of a great collection of butterflies from all parts of the world, their wings

"Gleaming with purple and gold,"

no vision is so exquisite and so inspiring as that which greets the true aurelian as in shady dell or upon sun-lit upland, with the blue sky above him and the flowers all around him, he pursues his pleasant, self-imposed tasks, drinking in health at every step.

Speaking of "health" I recall that I once met the veteran entomologist, Henry Ulke, briskly walking along Pennsylvania Avenue in Washington. He was ninety-two years old, as I happened to know. He was a well known painter, whose portraits of the great men, who dominated during the period of the Civil War, are treasured at the Capital. He was also a most enthusiastic coleopterist, whose great collection not long before I had purchased for the Carnegie Museum.

"Heinrich," I said to him, "how is it that you have discovered the fountain of eternal youth?" Laughing, he replied: "My dear Doctor, you know that I have spent much of my life collecting *beetles*. That took me out of doors. If you want to live long, go after *beetles*." He might have added *butterflies*.

65

SUBFAMILY DANAINÆ (THE MILKWEED BUTTERFLIES)

DANAINÆ Bates, Journ. Ent., II, 1864, p. 176; Kirby, Syn, Catal. Diurn, Lep., 1871, p. 1

Synonym: *Euplœinæ* Scudder, Butt. New England, I, 1889, p. 114.

> "Lazily flying
> Over the flower-decked prairies, West;
> Basking in sunshine till daylight is dying,
> And resting all night on Asclepias' breast;
> Joyously dancing,
> Merrily prancing,
> Chasing his lady-love high in the air,
> Fluttering gaily,
> Frolicking daily,
> Free from anxiety, sorrow, and care!"
>
> C. V. RILEY.

Butterfly.—Large to medium-sized butterflies; head large; antennæ inserted on the summit, stout, not covered with scales, the club long and not broad; palpi stout; thorax somewhat compressed, with the top arched. Abdomen moderately stout, the males having conspicuous clasps on either side of the eighth segment. Fore wings greatly produced at the apex and more or less excavated about the middle of the outer border; hind wings rounded and generally much smaller than the fore wings; outer margin regular, without tails, the inner margin channeled, so as to enfold the abdomen. Fore legs greatly atrophied in the male, less so in the female; these atrophied legs are not provided with claws, but on the other legs the claws are well developed.

Egg.—Ovate conical, broadly flattened at base and slightly truncate at top, with many longitudinal ribs and transverse cross-ridges (see Fig. 4).

Caterpillar.—On emerging from the chrysalis the head is not larger than the body; the body has a few scattered hairs on each segment. On reaching maturity the head is small, the body large, cylindrical, without hair, and conspicuously banded with dark stripes upon a lighter ground, and on some of the segments there are generally erect fleshy processes of considerable length (see Fig. 16). The caterpillars feed upon different species of milkweed (*Asclepias*).

Chrysalis.—Relatively short and thick, rounded, with very few projections, tapering very rapidly over the posterior part of the abdomen; suspended by a long cremaster from a button of silk (see Fig. 24); frequently ornamented with golden or silvery spots.

This subfamily reaches its largest development in the tropical regions of Asia. Only one genus is represented in our fauna, the genus *Danais*.

Genus DANAIS Latreille*

Synonyms: *Danaida* Latreille; *Danaus* Latreille; *Anosia* Scudder.

Butterfly.—Large-sized butterflies; fore wings long, greatly produced at the apex, having a triangular outline, the outer margin approximately as long as the inner margin; costal border regularly bowed; outer border slightly excavated, the outer angle rounded; hind wings well rounded, the costal border projecting just at the base, the inner margin likewise projecting at the base and depressed, so as to form a channel clasping the abdomen. On the edge of the first median nervule of the male, about its middle, there is a scent-pouch covered with scales.

Egg.—Ovate-conical, ribbed perpendicularly with many raised cross-lines between the ridges; pale green in color.

Caterpillar.—Cylindrical, fleshy, transversely wrinkled, having on the second thoracic and eighth abdominal segment pairs of very long and slender fleshy filaments, which are generally black; body ornamented by dark bands upon a greenish-yellow ground-color.

Fig. 79.—Neuration of the genus *Danais*.

Chrysalis.—Stout, cylindrical, rapidly tapering on the abdomen; suspended from a button of silk by a long cremaster; pale green, ornamented with golden spots.

There are two species of the genus found in our fauna, one, *D. plexippus*† (Linnæus) which is distributed over the entire continent as far north as southern Canada, and the other, *D. berenice* (Cramer) which is confined to the extreme southwestern portions of the United States, being found in Texas and Arizona.

---

*As all well informed students know, Linnæus did not use the word *Danaus* as a generic term and it is incorrect to employ it as such, attributing it to him. Latreille in 1805 proposed the generic name *Danaida* (daughter of Danaus), and, as Aurivillius has clearly shown, this long abandoned name has "priority." In 1809 Latreille substituted *Danaus* for it; and later in 1819 amended the name to *Danais*. In those days there was no "International Commission on Zoölogical Nomenclature" to lay down rules to be followed by naturalists. Latreille thought that he had a right to improve the names he had used, if he saw fit to do so. For about a century nobody questioned his procedure, and in almost all books upon butterflies for nearly a hundred years the name *Danais* has been used to designate the Milkweed Butterflies. In this book I shall follow the precedent set by the great majority of past and present writers.

†Captain N. D. Riley (Trans. Ent. Soc. London, Vol. LXXVI, pt. 2, 1929, p. 451) has clearly shown that Linnæus had a specimen of our Monarch Butterfly before him in his collection, when he wrote his description of *Papilio plexippus;* that the oriental species, which some writers claim ought to bear the name *plexippus*, was at that time in all probability unknown to Linnæus, and that therefore the specific name *plexippus*, by which most writers have designated the insect, is its *true scientific appellation*. The oriental insect is *Danais genutia* (Cramer).

(1) **Danais plexippus** (Linnæus). Pl. VII, fig. 1, ♂ (The Monarch).

Butterfly.—The upper surface of the wings is bright reddish, with the borders and veins broadly black, with two rows of white spots on the outer borders and two rows of pale spots of moderately large size across the apex of the fore wings. The males have the wings less broadly bordered with black than the females, and on the first median nervule of the hind wings there is a black scent-pouch.

Egg.—Ovate-conical; well represented by Fig. 4 of this book.

FIG. 80.—Swarm of Milkweed Butterflies resting on a tree. Photographed at night by Professor C. F. Nachtrieb. (From "Insect Life," vol. v, p. 206, by special permission of the United States Department of Agriculture.)

Caterpillar.—Bright yellow, or greenish-yellow, banded with shining black, and furnished with black fleshy thread-like appendages before and behind. It likewise is well delineated in Fig. 16, as well as on Pl. III, fig. 5.

Chrysalis.—About an inch in length, pale green, spotted with gold (see Fig. 24, and Pl. IV, figs. 1–3).

The butterfly is believed to be polygoneutic, that is to say, many broods are produced annually; and it is believed by writers that with the advent of cold weather these butterflies migrate to the South; the chrysalids and caterpillars which may be undeveloped at the time of the frosts are destroyed; and that, when these insects reappear, as they do every summer, they represent a wave of migration coming northward from the warmer regions of the Gulf States. It is not believed that any of them hibernate in any stage of their existence. This insect sometimes appears in great swarms on the eastern and southern coasts of New England and New Jersey in late autumn. The swarms pressing southward are arrested by the ocean. The writer has seen trees on the New England coast in the middle of September, and later in New Jersey, when the foliage had already fallen, so completely covered with clinging masses of these butterflies as to present the appearance of trees in full autumnal foliage. (Fig. 80).

This butterfly is a great migrant, and within quite recent years with Yankee instinct has crossed the Pacific, probably on merchant vessels, the chrysalids being possibly concealed in bales of hay, and has found lodgment in Australia, where it has greatly multiplied in the warmer parts of the Island Continent, and has thence spread northward and westward, until in its migrations it has reached Java and Sumatra, and long ago took possession of the Philippines. Moving eastward on the lines of travel, it has established a more or less precarious foothold for itself in southern England, as many as two or three dozen of these butterflies having been taken in a single year in the United Kingdom. It is well established in the Cape Verde Islands; and soon we may expect to hear of it as having taken possession of the continent of Africa, in which the family of plants upon which the caterpillars feed is well represented.

(2) **Danais berenice** (Cramer). Pl. VII, fig. 2, ♂ (The Queen).

This butterfly is smaller than the Monarch, and the ground-color of the wings is a livid brown. The markings are somewhat similar to those in *D. plexippus*, but the black borders of the hind wings are relatively wider, and the light spots on the apex of the fore wings are whiter and differently located, as may be learned from the figures given on Pl. VII.

There is a variety of this species, which has been called **D. strigosa** by H. W. Bates (Pl. VII ,fig. 3, ♂), which differs only in that on the upper surface of the hind wings the veins as far as the black outer margin are narrowly edged with grayish-white, giving them a streaked appearance. This insect is found in Texas, Arizona, and southern New Mexico.

All of the *Danainæ* are "protected" insects, being by nature provided with secretions which are distasteful to insectivorous animals. These acrid secretions are probably due to the character of the plants upon which the caterpillars feed, which are more or less rank, and some of them even poisonous. Enjoying on this account immunity from attack, they all in the process of time have been mimicked by species in other genera, which are not thus immune. This protective resemblance is well illustrated on Pl. VII. The three upper figures represent, as we have seen, species of the genus *Danais*; the two lower figures two species of the genus *Basilarchia*. Fig. 4 is the male of *B. archippus*, a very common species in the northern United States, which mimicks the Monarch. Fig. 5 represents the same sex of *B. obsoleta*, a species which is found in Arizona, and there flies in company with the Queen, and its variety, *D. strigosa*, which latter it more nearly resembles.

Genus LYCOREA Doubleday

The genus is mainly confined to tropical America, where it is represented by over a dozen species and varieties. The butterflies are rather large in size with elongated wings, recalling in outline those of certain species of *Heliconius* and the *Ithomiinæ*. In color the wings are some shade of brownish yellow or orange, heavily bordered with black, with small light spots near the margins, and the disks of the wings traversed by dark bands, which are parallel to the costal margins. The larval history and transformations of these insects show that they belong to the *Danainæ*. Only one species thus far has been credited to our fauna, and is reported from Texas and the Keys of Florida. It is a variety of *L. cleobæa* Godart, to which Doubleday and Hewitson gave the subspecific name *atergatis*.

(1) **Lycorea cleobæa,** subsp. **atergatis** Doub. & Hew., Pl. LV, fig. 1, ♂.

The figure given is sufficient to permit of identification.

SUBFAMILY ITHOMIINÆ (THE GLASSY-WINGS)

"There be Insects with little hornes proaking out before their eyes, but weak and tender they be, and good for nothing; as the Butterflies."—PLINY, PHILEMON HOLLAND's Translation.

Butterfly.—This subfamily is composed for the most part of species of moderate size, though a few are quite large. The fore wings are invariably greatly lengthened and generally are at least twice as long as broad. The hind wings are relatively small, rounded, and without tails. The wings in many of the genera are transparent. The extremity of the abdomen in both sexes extends far beyond the margin of the hind wings, but in the female not so much as in the male. The antennæ are not clothed with scales, and are very long and slender, with the club also long and slender, gradually thickening to the tip, which is often drooping. The fore legs are greatly atrophied in the males, the tibia and tarsi in this sex being reduced to a minute knob-like appendage, but being more strongly developed in the females.

The life-history of none of the species reputed to be found in our fauna has been carefully worked out. The larvæ are smooth, covered in most genera with longitudinal rows of conical prominences.

The chrysalids are said to show a likeness to those of the *Danainæ*, being short, thick, and marked with golden spots. Some authors are inclined to view this subfamily as merely constituting a section of the *Danainæ*. The insects are, however, so widely unlike the true *Danainæ* that it seems well to keep them separate in our system of classification. In appearance they approach the Heliconians more nearly than the Danaids. Ithomiid butterflies swarm in the tropics of the New World, and several hundreds of species are known to inhabit the hot lands of Central and South America. But one genus is found in the Old World, *Hamadryas*, confined to the Australian region. They are protected like the Danaids and the Heliconians. In flight they somewhat resemble dragon-flies of the genus *Agrion*, their narrow wings, greatly elongated bodies, and slow, flitting motion recalling these insects, which are known by schoolboys as "darning-needles."

Three genera are said to be represented in the extreme southwestern portion of the United States. I myself have never received specimens of any of them, which indisputably came from localities within our limits.

Genus MECHANITIS Fabricius

Butterfly.—Butterflies of moderate size, with the fore wings greatly produced, the inner margin bowed out just beyond the base, and deeply excavated between this projection and the inner angle. The lower discocellular vein in the hind wings is apparently continuous with the median vein, and the lower radial vein being parallel with the median nervules, the median vein has in consequence the appearance of being four-branched. The submedian vein of the fore wings is forked at the base. The costal margin of the hind wings is clothed with tufted erect hairs in the male sex. The fore legs of the male are greatly atrophied, the tarsi and the tibia being fused and reduced to a small knob-like appendage. The fore legs of the female are also greatly reduced, but the tarsi and tibia are still recognizable as slender, thread-like organs.

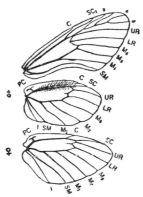

The caterpillars are smooth, cylindrical, ornamented with rows of short fleshy projections.

The chrysalids are short and stout, suspended, and marked with golden spots.

There are numerous species belonging to this genus native to tropical America.

Fig. 81.—Neuration of the genus *Mechanitis*. The letters refer to the names of the veins. (After Schatz.)

(1) **Mechanitis lycidice** Bates var. **californica** Reakirt, Pl. VIII, fig. 2, ♂. (The Californian Long-wing).

Reakirt described this form in the "Proceedings of the Ent. Soc. of Philadelphia," Vol. V, p. 223, giving "Los Angeles, California," as its habitat. The figure on our plate is that of one of Reakirt's specimens, which was in the Mead Collection, when I acquired it. It is a subspecies of *M. lycidice* Bates, but not the variety *isthmia* Bates, with which some recent writers have confounded it. It differs from *isthmia* in having the subapical spots of the fore wing yellow, not white, as in *isthmia*, and having the hind wings traversed by a continuous broad band of dark brown running through the middle of the wing, whereas in *isthmia* this band is represented by only two or three small dark spots beyond the cell near the outer margin.

It is extremely doubtful whether this insect occurs in California, though it may turn up in northern Mexico.

Genus ITHOMIA Hubner

Synonym: *Dynothea* Reakirt.

The genus *Ithomia* includes a very large number of species in the American tropics.

Butterfly.—Of medium size, related to *Mechanitis*, but with shorter wings, and much longer body. In the hind wings of the males near the anterior border there is a suboval corneous space, enclosed between the costal and subcostal veins above the cell, which bears a tufted arrangement of androconia, or scent-scales.

Early Stages.—Very little has been written about these, and nothing about those of the species here being considered.

Genus Dircenna

(1) **Ithomia anaphissa** (Herr.-Schæff.). Pl. VIII, fig. 3, ♂.

In the first edition of this book this insect was named *"Ceratinia lycaste Fabricius."* The figure is that of a specimen so labelled by Reakirt. At the time I hastily accepted Reakirt's determination as correct, but long since discovered

my mistake. The insect, which Reakirt called *lycaste* Fabr., and attributed to California, is undoubtedly *Ithomia anaphissa* H.–S., a Central American insect.

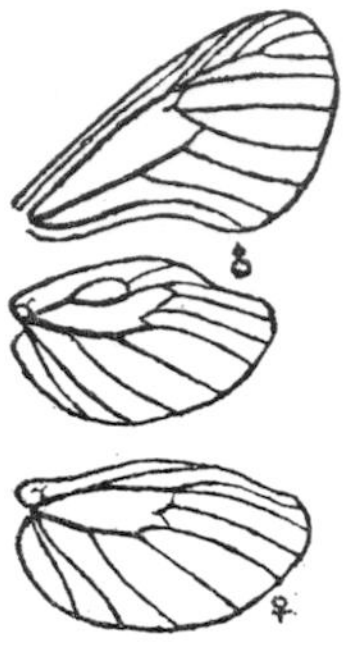

There has been some discussion as to the identity of the insect named *lycaste* by Fabricius. His brief Latin description might apply to a number of species. The type seems to be lost. Fortunately the Library of Oxford University is in possession of the long series of water-color drawings of the types of the species named by Fabricius, known as "Jones' Icones." I am indebted to Professor E. B. Poulton of Oxford for enlisting on my behalf the kind services of that incomparable artist and lepidopterist, Dr. H. Eltringham, who has supplied me with a facsimile in color of the drawing of *Papilio lycaste* Fabricius. This is reproduced in this volume (Pl. LXXII, fig. 2). It confirms the fact that

FIG. 82. Neuration of genus *Ithomia*.

Reakirt was in error, as I was also in following him. The insect named *lycaste* by Fabricius has been classified for years as belonging to the genus *Ithomia*. The figure on our plate has the body too short for that genus, but this may be due to an error of the draftsman. In its markings it approaches, but differs from the insect named *panamensis* Bates. In some respects it resembles *I. megalopolis* Felder. Can it represent the mimicking form *Phyciodes quintilla* Hew.?

It is quite clear to me that the species *lycaste*, whatever it may be, does not belong to our fauna.

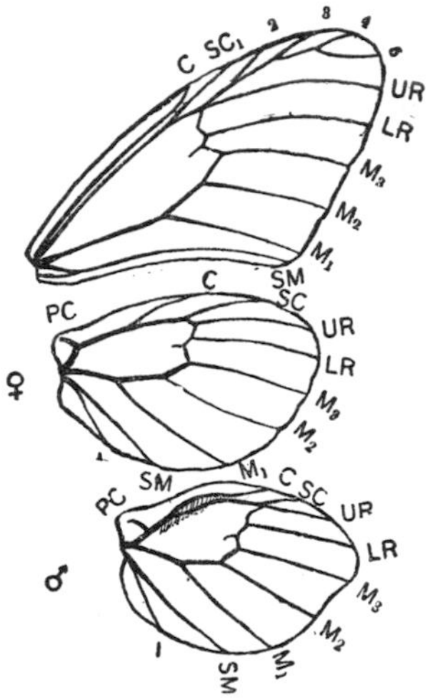

Genus DIRCENNA Doubleday

FIG. 84.—Fore leg of *Dircenna klugi*, magnified.

Butterfly.—Medium-sized butterflies, for the most part with quite transparent wings. The most characteristic features of this genus, separating it from its near allies, are the thread-like front feet of the females, furnished with four-jointed tarsi (Fig. 84), the very hairy palpi, and the wide cell of the hind wing, abruptly terminating about the middle of the wing. Furthermore, in the male sex the hind wing is strongly bowed out about the middle of the costal margin, and the costal vein tends to coalesce with the subcostal about the middle.

FIG. 83.—Neuration of the genus *Dircenna*. (After Schatz.)

Early Stages.—Very little is as yet known about the early stages of these insects, and what has been said of the characteristics of the caterpillars and chrysa-lids of the subfamily of the *Ithomiinæ* must suffice us here.

This genus numbers a large array of species which are found in the hottest parts of the tropics of the New World. They fairly swarm in wooded paths amid the jungle of the Amazonian region, and no collection, however small, is ever re-ceived from those parts without containing specimens belonging to the group.

(1) **Dircenna klugi** (Geyer), Pl. VIII, fig. 1, ♂ (Klug's Dircenna).

Butterfly.—Fore wings transparent gray, broken by clear, transparent, color-less spots at the apex, on the outer borders, and on the middle of the wing. The inner margin of the fore wing is black. The hind wings are transparent yellowish, with a narrow black outer border marked with small whitish spots. The body is black, with the thorax spotted with white. Expanse: 2.75 inches.

The specimen figured in the plate is from Mexico. Whether the insect has ever been taken within the limits of the United States is uncertain. It is another of the species attributed to our fauna by Reakirt, but which since his day has not been caught by any of the numerous butterfly-hunters who have searched the region in which he said it occurs.

SUPERSTITIONS

"If a butterfly alights upon your head, it foretells good news from a distance. This super-stition obtains in Pennsylvania and Maryland.

"The first butterfly seen in the summer brings good luck to him who catches it. This notion prevails in New York.

"In western Pennsylvania it is believed that if the chrysalids of butterflies be found sus-pended mostly on the under sides of rails, limbs, etc., as it were to protect them from rain, there will soon be much rain, or, as it is termed, a 'rainy spell'; but, on the contrary, if they are found on twigs and slender branches, that the weather will be dry and clear."—FRANK COWAN, *Curious History of Insects*, p. 229.

SUBFAMILY HELICONIINÆ (THE HELICONIANS)

"Men, like butterflies,
Show not their mealy wings but to the summer."
SHAKESPEARE, *Troilus and Cressida*, act iii, sc. iii.

MEDIUM or large-sized butterflies, with the fore wings twice as long as broad; hind wings relatively small and rounded upon the outer margin; without tails. Palpi produced. Antennæ, which are nearly as long as the body, provided at the tip with a gradually tapering club, thicker and stouter than in the *Ithomiinæ*, and clothed with scales on the upper surface. Fore legs very feebly developed in both sexes. Eggs cylindrical, twice as high as wide, tapering rather abruptly toward the

FIG. 85.—Neuration of the genus *Heliconius*.

apex, which is truncated; ribbed longitudinally, with strongly developed crossridges, giving the egg a somewhat pitted appearance. Caterpillar, when emerging from the egg, with head somewhat larger than the body; each segment clothed with hairs, which upon the first moult are replaced by branching spines. The caterpillar, when it reaches maturity, provided with six branching spines on each segment. Chrysalis very peculiar in shape, strongly angulated, and covered with curious projections, which cause it to somewhat resemble a shriveled leaf.

These butterflies are extremely numerous in the tropics of the New World, and are there represented by a number of genera, which are rich in species. Most of them are very gaily colored, the prevalent tints being black banded with yellow or crimson, sometimes marked with a brilliant blue luster. They are evidently very strongly protected. Belt, in his "Naturalist in Nicaragua," tells us that birds and other animals observed by him invariably refused to eat these butterflies, although they swarm in the forests; and he vainly endeavored to induce a monkey, which was very fond of insects, to eat them, the creature revealing by his grimaces that they were extremely distasteful to him. Mr. Wallace believes their immunity from attack is owing to a "strong, pungent, semi-aromatic, or medicinal odor, which seems to pervade all the juices of their system."

Genus HELICONIUS Latreille

The description of the subfamily applies to the genus sufficiently well to obviate the necessity of a more particular description, as there is but a single species in our fauna.

74

(1) **Heliconius charithonius** (Linnæus). Pl. VIII, fig. 5, ♂ (The Yellow-barred Heliconian; The Zebra).

The figure of the butterfly given upon the plate obviates the necessity for a full description.

The caterpillar feeds upon the passion-flower. The chrysalis, which is dark brown, has the power, when disturbed, of emitting a creaking sound, as it wriggles about, a property which is reported to be characteristic of all the insects in the genus. This butterfly is found in the hotter portions of the Gulf States, and is rather abundant in Florida, in the region of the Indian River and on the head-waters of the St. Johns. It ranges southward all over the lowlands of Mexico, Central America, and the Antilles.

"'Where the Sam Hill,' he blazed, 'do all these footy little devils come from, anyhow? Where am I to put a beast of a bug when the next one that's exactly like it is entirely different the next time you look at it? There's too much beginning and no end at all to this game!'

. . . .

"There was, for instance, the common Dione vanillæ, that splendid Gulf Fritillary, which haunts all the highways of the South. She's a long-wing, but she's not a Heliconian; she's a silver-spot, but she's not an Argynnis. She bears a striking family likeness to her fine relations, but she has certain structural peculiarities which differentiate her. Whose word should he take for this, and why? Wherein lay those differences? He began, patiently, with her cylinder-shaped yellow-brown, orange-spotted caterpillar, on the purple passion-flowers in our garden; he watched it change into a dark-brown chrysalis marked with a few pale spots; he saw emerge from this the red-robed lady herself, with her long fulvous fore wings, and her shorter hind wings smocked with black velvet, and her under-frock flushed with pinkish orange and spangled with silver. And yet, in spite of her long marvelous tongue—he was beginning to find out that no tool he had ever seen, and but few that God Himself makes, is so wonderful as a butterfly's tongue— she hadn't been able to tell him that about herself which he most wished to find out. *That* called for a deeper knowledge than he as yet possessed.

"But he knew that other men knew. And he had to know. He meant to know. For the work gripped him as it does those marked and foreordained for its service."
MARIE CONWAY OEMLER in *Slippy Magee, The Butterfly Man*, pp. 72–73.

75

SUBFAMILY NYMPHALINÆ (THE NYMPHS)

"Entomology extends the limits of being in new directions, so that I walk in nature with a sense of greater space and freedom. It suggests, besides, that the universe is not rough-hewn, but perfect in its details. Nature will bear the closest inspection; she invites us to lay our eye level with the smallest leaf and take an insect view of its plane."—THOREAU.

"My butterfly-net and pocket magnifying-glass are rare companions for a walk in the country."— WILLIAM HAMILTON GIBSON, *Sharp Eyes*, p. 117.

Butterflies.—Mainly of moderate or large size, though some of the genera contain quite small species. The antennæ are always more or less heavily clothed with scales, and are usually as long as the abdomen, and in a few cases even longer. The club is always well developed; it is usually long, but in some genera short and stout. The palpi are short and stout, densely clothed with scales and hairs. The thorax is relatively stout, in some genera exceedingly so. The fore wings are relatively broad, the length being to the breadth in most cases in the ratio of 5 to 3, or 3 to 2, though in a few mimetic forms these wings are greatly produced, and narrow, patterned after the outline of the Heliconians and Ithomiids, which they mimick. The fore wings are in most genera produced at the apex, and more or less strongly excavated on the outer margin below the apex. The discoidal cell is usually less than half the length of the wing from base to tip. It is occasionally open, but is more generally closed at its outer extremity by discocellular veins diminishing in thickness from the upper to the lower outer angle of the cell. The costal nervure usually terminates midway between the end of the cell and the tip. The two inner subcostal nervules usually arise before the end of the cell; the outer subcostal nervules invariably arise beyond the end of the cell.

The hind wings are rounded or angulated, with the outer border scalloped or tailed; the inner border always affords a channel for the reception of the abdomen. The costal nervule invariably terminates at the external angle of this wing. The discoidal cell is almost always open, or faintly closed by a slender veinlet, which it is not easy to detect; the anal vein is never lacking. In the neotropical genus *Clothilda* the cell is distinctly closed, this being "the exception, which proves the rule."

The fore legs are greatly reduced in the male, less so in the female.

Egg.—Either somewhat globular, or barrel-shaped, with the sides marked with net-like elevations, or vertically ribbed (see Figs. 1, 8, 10).

Caterpillar.—When first emerging from the egg generally furnished with long hairs rising singly from wart-like elevations, which are arranged either in longitudinal rows or in geometric patterns (Fig. 86). As the caterpillars pass their

76

successive moults the hairs are transformed into branching spines or tubercles (see Pl. III, figs. 28–38).

Chrysalis.—Invariably suspended from a button of silk, and frequently furnished, especially on the dorsal or upper surface, with a number of prominences; the head is usually bifurcate, or cleft (see Pl. IV, figs. 21, 39, etc.).

This is the largest of all the sub-families of the butterflies, and is widely distributed, including many of the most beautifully colored and most vigorous species which are known.

Some recent writers have placed the genera *Colænis* and *Dione* under the *Heliconiinæ*, a most unnatural arrangement. One or two authors have even gone so

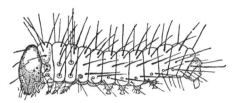

FIG. 86.—Caterpillar of *Aglais antiopa*, just hatched. (Greatly magnified.) (After Scudder.)

far as to set up a new subfamily under the name *Euidinæ*, into which they put the *Heliconiinæ*, the genus *Eueides*, and the genera *Colænis* and *Dione*. The genus *Eueides* is nearly related to the American *Acræidæ* (*Actinote*) having relatively short and stoutly clubbed antennæ, with the cell of the hind wing closed. *Colænis* and *Dione* are true Nymphalids, with the cell of the hind wing open. They mimic the Heliconians in the outline of their wings, but the resemblance is superficial, and not structural.

Genus COLÆNIS Doubleday

Butterfly.—Butterflies of moderately large size; fore wings greatly produced and relatively narrow; hind wings evenly rounded and relatively small, bright reddish-brown, with darker markings. The species are mimicks, and in the elongation of their wings reveal the influence of the Heliconians, protected species, which abound in the regions in which the genus attains its greatest development. Median vein in the upper wing characterized by the presence at the base of a minute, thorn-like, external projection; second subcostal nervule emitted beyond the cell; cell of the hind wing open.

FIG. 87.—Neuration of the genus *Colænis*, slightly less than natural size.

The life-history of the three species found within our fauna has not as yet been carefully worked out. Aside from a knowledge of the fact that the caterpillars closely resemble in many respects the caterpillars of the two succeeding genera, being provided with branching spines on their bodies, we do not know as yet enough to give any complete account of the early stages of these insects.

(1) **Colænis julia** (Fabricius). Pl. VIII, fig. 6, ♂ (Julia).

Upper side dark reddish-orange; borders black; a black band extends from the costa at the end of the cell to the outer margin on the line of the third median nervule; the costal area on the hind wings silver-gray; wings on the under side pale rusty-red, mottled with a few darker spots, principally on the costa, at the end of the cell, and at the apex of the primaries. There are a few crimson marks at the base of the hind wings, and two light-colored lunules near the inner angle of the hind wings. Expanse of wing: 3.50 in.

This butterfly, which mimicks the genus *Heliconius* in the outline of the wings, is very common in the tropics of America, and only appears as an occasional visitant in the extreme south.

(2) **Colænis delila** (Fabricius). Pl. VIII, fig. 4, ♂ (Delila).

Delila very closely resembles *Julia*, and principally differs in being paler in color and without the black band extending from the costa to the outer margin of the primaries. This species has nearly the same form and the same size as the preceding, and, like it, is occasionally found in southern Texas. It is very common in Central America and the West Indies. One of the earliest memories of my childhood relates to a collection of Jamaican butterflies in which were a number of specimens of this butterfly.

(3) **Colænis cillene** (Cramer). Pl. LXXI, fig. 1, ♂; fig. 2, ♀ (Cillene).

This species, which is closely allied to *C. delila* and is the prevalent form in Cuba, occurs quite commonly on Key Largo, southern Florida, whence I have recently obtained some excellent specimens collected by Mr. J. R. Haskin.

Genus DIONE Hübner

Synonym: *Agraulis* Boisduval & Leconte.

Butterfly.—Head large; antennæ moderately long, with the club flattened; tip of the abdomen not extending beyond the inner margin of the hind wings; cell of the hind wings open; primaries elongated, nearly twice as long as broad, with the exterior margin excavated; secondaries at the outer margin denticulate. The prevalent color of the upper side of the wings is fulvous, adorned with black spots and lines, the under side of the wings paler brown, in some of the species laved with pink and brilliantly adorned with large silvery spots, as in the genus *Argynnis*.

Egg.—Conoidal, truncated on top, with fourteen ribs running from the apex to the base, between which are rows of elevated striæ, causing the surface to appear to be covered with quadrangular pits.

Larva.—Cylindrical in its mature stage, tapering a little from the middle toward the head, which is somewhat smaller than the body. The head and each segment of the body adorned with branching spines.

Chrysalis.—On the dorsal surface of the abdomen having a number of small projections. At the point where the abdominal and thoracic segments unite on the dorsal side there is a deep depression, succeeded on the middle of the thorax by a rounded elevation composed of the wing-cases. At the vertex of the chrysalis there is a conical projection; on the ventral side it is bowed outwardly.

This genus is confined to the New World, and contains five species. It is closely related to the genus *Colænis* on the one hand and to the genus *Argynnis* on the other. It is distinguished from *Colænis* by the more robust structure of the palpi, which closely approximate in form the palpi of the genus *Argynnis*. It is distinguished from the species of the genus *Argynnis* by the form of the wings. The larva feeds upon different species of *Passiflora*.

(1) **Dione vanillæ** (Linnæus). Pl. VIII, fig. 7, ♂ (The Gulf Fritillary).

Butterfly.—Upper side bright fulvous; the veins on the fore wings black, more so near the tip; four black spots on the outer border, and three discal spots of the same color; three irregular black spots toward the end of the cell, pupilled with white; hind wings with a black border inclosing rounded spots of the ground-color; between the base and the outer margin three or four black spots; under side of the fore wings light orange, the markings of the upper side showing through upon the under side; apex of the front wing brown, inclosing light silvery spots; secondaries brown, with numerous elongated bright silver spots and patches. The female does not differ from the male, except that she is darker and the markings are heavier. Expanse: 2.50–3.25 in.

FIG. 88.—Neuration of the genus *Dione*.

Caterpillar.—Cylindrical, with the head somewhat smaller than the body; pale yellowish-brown in color, marked with longitudinal dark-brown bands, of which the two upon the side are deeper in color than the one upon the back, which latter band is sometimes almost entirely effaced; the base is slaty-black. There are orange spots about the spiracles. There are six rows of black branching spines upon the body, and two similar spines upon the head, these latter somewhat recurved. The feet and legs are black. The caterpillar feeds upon the various species of passionflower which are found in the Southern States.

Chrysalis.—Dark brown, marked with a few small pale spots.

This species ranges from the latitude of southern Virginia southward to Arizona and California. It is abundant also in the Antilles and Mexico.

Genus EUPTOIETA Doubleday

Butterfly.—Of medium size; wings yellowish-brown, marked with black; under side devoid of silvery spots, such as are found in the genera *Dione* and *Argynnis*. Palpi with second joint strongly developed, increasing in thickness from behind forward, and thickly covered with long hair, its third joint very small and pointed. Antennæ terminated by a conspicuous pear-shaped club. The cell of the fore wing closed by a very feeble lower discocellular vein, which unites with the median vein at the origin of the second median nervule; cell of the hind wing open, though occasionally there are traces of a feebly developed lower discocellular vein on this wing. The outer margin of the fore wing slightly excavated below the apex, the outer margin of the hind wing somewhat strongly produced at the end of the third median nervule.

Egg.—Short, subconical, with from thirty to forty vertical ribs, pale green in color.

Caterpillar.—Cylindrical, with short branching spines arranged in longitudinal rows upon the body, the spines on the first segment being bent forward over the head. Head somewhat smaller in the mature stage than the body.

Chrysalis.—Suspended, marked upon its dorsal side with a number of small angular eminences, with the head and ventral side evenly rounded.

The larva of these insects feeds upon various species of passion-flower. It is also said to feed upon violets. The butterflies frequent open fields, and are sometimes exceedingly abundant in worn-out lands in the Southern States.

There are two species of this genus, both of which are found in the United States, and range southwardly over the greater portion of Central and South America.

Fig. 89.—Neuration of the genus *Euptoieta.*

(1) **Euptoieta claudia** (Cramer). Pl. VIII, fig. 9, ♂ (The Variegated Fritillary).

Butterfly.—Upper side of both wings dull ferruginous, darker toward the base, crossed by an irregular black median line, which is darker, broader, and more zigzag on the fore wing than on the hind wing; this line followed outwardly on both wings by a pair of more or less wavy limbal lines, inclosing between them a series of round blackish spots. Outer margin black, with the fringes pale fulvous, checkered with black at the end of each nervule. At the end of the cell in the fore wing are two black lines inclosing paler fulvous spots, and both wings near the base have some curved black lines. On the under side fore wings marked somewhat as on the upper side, but paler in color, with a large apical patch of brownish-gray broken by a transverse band of darker brown. Hind wings dark brown, with the markings of the upper side obscurely repeated, mottled with gray, and crossed by a broad central band of pale buff.

The species varies very much, according to locality, both in size and in the depth of the markings. Expanse: 1.75–2.75 inches.

Egg.—Conoidal, relatively taller than the eggs of the genus *Argynnis*, which closely resemble it. There is a depression at the apex, surrounded by a serrated rim, formed by the ends of the vertical ribs, of which there are about twenty, some longer and some shorter, about half of them reaching from the apex to the base. Between these vertical ribs there are a multitude of smaller cross-ridges.

Caterpillar.—Cylindrical, reddish-yellow in color, marked with two brown lateral bands and a series of white spots upon the back. There are six rows of short branching spines upon the body, which are black in color; the two uppermost of these spines on the first segment much elongated and directed forward. Head smaller than the body in the mature caterpillar, black. On the under side the caterpillar is pale or whitish; legs blackish-brown. It feeds upon the passion-flower.

Chrysalis.—Pearly-white, marked with black spots and longitudinal streaks.

This species has been taken as far north as Long Island and Connecticut, though it is a very rare visitant in New England; it is quite common in Virginia and thence southward, and occurs not infrequently in Illinois, Indiana, Iowa, and Nebraska, ranging westward and southward over the entire continent to the Isthmus of Panama, and thence extending over the South American continent, wherever favorable conditions occur.

(2) **Euptoieta hegesia** (Cramer). Pl. VIII, fig. 8, ♂ (The Mexican Fritillary).

The upper side is marked very much as in the preceding species, but all the lines are finer and somewhat more regular, and the basal and discal areas of the hind wings are without dark spots in most specimens. The under side is less mottled and more uniformly dark rusty-brown than in *E. claudia*. Expanse: 2 in.

The life-history of this species has not as yet been thoroughly worked out, but there is every reason to believe that the insect in its early stages very closely approaches the Variegated Fritillary. It is a southern form, and is taken in Arizona and southern California. It is common in Central and South America.

LUTHER'S SADDEST EXPERIENCE

"Luther, he was persecuted,
Excommunicated, hooted,
Disappointed, egged, and booted;
Yelled at by minutest boys,
Waked up by nocturnal noise,
Scratched and torn by fiendish cats,
Highwayed by voracious rats.

"Oft upon his locks so hoary
Water fell from upper story;
Oft a turnip or potato
Struck upon his back or pate, Oh!
And wherever he betook him,
A papal bull was sure to hook him.

"But the saddest of all
I am forced to relate:

Of a diet of worms
He was forced to partake—
Of a *diet of worms*
For the Protestants' sake;
Munching crawling caterpillars,
Beetles mixed with moths and millers;
Instead of butter, on his bread,
A sauce of butterflies was spread.
Was not this a horrid feast
For a Christian and a priest?

"Now, if you do not credit me,
Consult D'Aubigné's history.
You'll find what I have told you
Most fearfully and sternly true."
Yale Literary Magazine, 1852

Genus ARGYNNIS Fabricius
(The Fritillaries; the Silver-spots)

Synonym: *Dryas* Tutt, Barnes & Benjamin.*

"July is the gala-time of butterflies. Most of them have just left the chrysalis, and their wings are perfect and very fresh in color. All the sunny places are bright with them, yellow and red and white and brown, and great gorgeous fellows in rich velvet-like dresses of blue-black, orange, green, and maroon. Some of them have their wings scalloped, some fringed, and some plain; and they are ornamented with brilliant borders and fawn-colored spots and rows of silver crescents. . . . They circle about the flowers, fly across from field to field, and rise swiftly in the air; little ones and big ones, common ones and rare ones, but all bright and airy and joyous—a midsummer carnival of butterflies."—FRANK H. SWEET.

Butterfly.—Of medium or large size, generally with the upper surface of the wings reddish-fulvous, with well-defined black markings consisting of waved transverse lines, and rounded discal and sagittate black markings near the outer borders. On the under side of the wings the design of the fore wings is generally somewhat indistinctly repeated, and the hind wings are marked more or less profusely with large silvery spots. In a few cases there is wide dissimilarity in color between the male and the female sex; generally the male sex is marked by the brighter red of the upper surface, and the female by the broader black markings, the paler ground-color, and the sometimes almost white lunules, which are arranged outwardly at the base of the sagittate spots along the border.

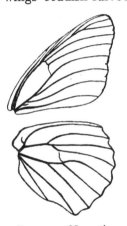

FIG. 90.—Neuration of the genus *Argynnis*.

Eyes naked; palpi strongly developed, heavily clothed with hair rising above the front, the last joint very small and pointed. Antennæ moderately long, with a well-defined, flattened club. Abdomen shorter than the hind wings; wings more or less denticulate. Subcostal vein provided with five nervules, of which the two innermost are invariably given forth before the end of the cell; the third subcostal nervule always nearer the fourth than the second. Cell of the fore wing closed by a fine lower discocellular vein, which invariably joins the median vein beyond the origin of the second nervule. The hind wing has a well-defined precostal nervule; the cell in this wing is closed by a very thin, scarcely perceptible lower discocellular vein, which joins the median exactly at the origin of the second median nervule. Fore feet of the males slender, long, and finely clothed with hair; fore feet of the females of the same size as those of the males, but thin, covered with scales, and only on the inner side of the tibiæ clothed with moderately long hair.

---

*Hübner never used the name *Dryas* in a generic sense. It was employed by him as a "Stirps-name," *i.e.* as a family-name. *Dryas* Tutt is a pure synonym of *Argynnis*.

Egg.—Conoidal, truncated, and inwardly depressed at the apex, rounded at the base, and ornamented on the sides by parallel raised ridges, not all of which reach the apex. Between these ridges there are a number of small raised cross-ridges.

Caterpillar.—Cylindrical, covered with spines, the first segment always bearing a pair of spines somewhat longer than the others. All of the species of North America, so far as their habits are known, feed upon violets at night. During the daytime the caterpillars lie concealed.

Chrysalis.—Angular, adorned with more or less prominent projections. Head bifid.

The genus *Argynnis* is one of the largest genera of the Brush-footed Butterflies. It is well represented in Europe and in the temperate regions of Asia, some magnificent species being found in the Himalayas and in China and Japan. It even extends to Australia, and several species have been discovered on the slopes of the volcanic peaks, Kilima-Njaro and Ruwenzori in Africa. But it has found its greatest development upon the continent of North America, exclusive of Florida and the warmer parts of the Gulf States. The species composing this genus are among our most beautiful butterflies. Owing to the fact that there is a great tendency in many of the forms closely to approximate one another, the accurate distinction of many of the species has troubled naturalists, and it is quite probable that some of the so-called species will ultimately be discovered to be subspecies, or local races. The species found in the eastern part of the United States have been carefully studied and their life-history has been worked out so thoroughly that little difficulty is found in accurately determining them. The greatest perplexity occurs in connection with those species which are found in the region of the Rocky Mountains. While silvery spots are characteristic of the under side of most of the fritillaries, in some species the light spots are not silvered; in others the silvering is evanescent, occurring in the case of some individuals, and being absent in the case of others.

Species founded upon the presence or absence of the silvering of the spots on the under side of the wings, are in some cases of doubtful validity. In the opinion of the writer, the absence of silvering may be due to physiological conditions, which do not act with invariable uniformity. This view, however, can only be established by extensive experiments in breeding, which so far have not been made.

The specific nomenclature of the species found in the western parts of the American continent is greatly confused. Attempts to set things straight made in recent years appear to have not been quite successful. In the following pages an effort has been made to disentangle the confusion, but the writer well knows that some of his contemporaries will not agree with him, and that he may encounter some criticism.

The *Idalia*-group
Subgenus SPEYERIA Scudder

(1) **Argynnis idalia** (Drury). Pl. X, fig. 3, ♀; Pl. V, fig. 4, *chrysalis*. (The Regal Fritillary.)

Butterfly.—Upper side of fore wings of male bright fulvous, marked very much as in other species of the genus. Upper side of hind wings black, glossed with blue, having a marginal row of fulvous and a submarginal row of cream-colored spots. On the under side the fore wings are fulvous, with a marginal row of silver crescents, and some silvery spots on and near the costa. Hind wings dark olive-brown, marked with three rows of large irregular spots of a dull greenish-silvery color. The female is at once distinguished from the male by having the marginal row of spots on the hind wings cream-colored, like the submarginal row, and by the presence of a similar row of light spots on the fore wings. Expanse: 2.75–4.00in.

Egg.—In form like those of other species of *Argynnis*.

Caterpillar.—Moults five times before attaining to maturity. When fully developed it is 1.75 inches long, black, banded and striped with ochreous and orange-red, and adorned with six rows of fleshy spines surmounted by several black bristles. The spines composing the two dorsal rows are white, tipped with black; those on the sides black, tinted with orange at the point where they join the body. The caterpillar feeds on violets, and is nocturnal in its habits.

Chrysalis.—Brown, mottled with yellow and tinted on the wing-cases with pinkish; about an inch long, and in outline not departing from the other species of the genus.

This exceedingly beautiful insect ranges from Maine to Nebraska. It is found in northern New Jersey, the mountainous parts of New York and Pennsylvania, and is reported from Arkansas and Nebraska. It is rather local, and frequents open spots on the borders of woodlands. At times it is apparently common, and then for a succession of seasons is scarce. It flies from the end of June to the beginning of September.

The *Diana*-group
Subgenus SEMNOPSYCHE Scudder

(2) **Argynnis diana** (Cramer). Pl. IX, fig. 1, ♂; fig. 2, ♀ (The Diana Fritillary).

Butterfly.—The figures given upon our plate suffice to identify this well marked species, and it is not necessary, therefore, to give a lengthy description. Expanse: 3.25–4.00 in.

Egg.—Pale greenish-white, and conformed in outline to type.

Caterpillar.—Velvety-black, adorned with six rows of fleshy spines armed with bristles. The spines are orange-red at the base. The head is dull brown.

Chrysalis.—Dusky-brown, with lighter-colored short projections on the dorsal side.

This splendid butterfly, which is the most magnificent species of the genus, is confined to the southern portion of the Appalachian region, occurring in the two Virginias and Carolinas, northern Georgia, Tennessee, and Kentucky, and being occasionally found in the southern portion of Ohio and Indiana, and in Missouri and Arkansas.

The *Nokomis*-group

(3) **Argynnis nokomis** Edwards. Pl. X, fig. 1, ♂; fig. 2, ♀ (The Nokomis Fritillary).

Synonym: *apacheana* Skinner.

Butterfly.—The male on the upper side is bright fulvous, with the characteristic markings of the genus. On the under side the wings are pale cinnamon-buff, with the fore wings laved with bright pink at the base and on the inner margin. The spots of the upper side reappear on the under side as spots of silver bordered narrowly with black. The female has the ground-color of the upper side yellowish, shading outwardly into fulvous. All the black markings of the male sex reappear in this sex, but are much broader, and tend to fuse and run into one another, so as to leave the yellow ground-color merely as small subquadrate or circular spots, and wholly to obliterate them at the base of the wings. On the under side this sex is marked like the male, but with all the markings broader, and the inner margin of the hind wing greenish in fresh specimens. Expanse: 3.40–3.60 inches.

This species, the male of which resembles the male of *A. leto*, and the female in some respects the same sex of *A. diana*, has been taken in Arizona, southern Utah and California. We have no knowledge of its life-history.

(4) **Argynnis nitocris** Edwards. Pl. XIII, fig. 4, ♂, type, *under side*. (The Nitocris Fritillary).

Butterfly.—The male is bright reddish-fulvous, marked like *A. nokomis*. Under side of fore wings cinnamon-red, ochre-yellow at the tip. Hind wings deep rusty-red, with a broad yellowish-red submarginal belt. The silver spots are as in *A. nokomis*. Female on the upper side blackish-brown, darker than *A. nokomis*. The extradiscal spots in the transverse rows are pale yellow, and the submarginal spots whitish. Under side of fore wings bright red, with the tip yellow; hind wings on this side dark brown, with a submarginal yellow belt. Expanse: 3.25–3.75 inches.

This species, like the preceding, is from Arizona, and nothing is known of its egg, caterpillar, or chrysalis. It is closely related to the following species.

(5) **Argynnis cœrulescens** Holland. Pl. LV, fig. 3, ♂; fig. 2, ♀, fig. 4, ♀ *under side*, types (The Mexican Fritillary).

Butterfly.—This lovely insect, like those of the *Nokomis*-group, to which it belongs, is near *A. nitocris* in its markings, but may be easily distinguished by the much deeper and more solidly dark color of the inner two thirds of the wings of the male on the upper side; and by the much bluer color of the light spots on the wings of the female. Expanse: ♂ 2.75–3; ♀ 3–3.2 in.

85

The insect was originally described from the high table-lands of Chihuahua, Mexico, but occurs at corresponding altitudes (7500 ft.) in Arizona (Huachuca Mts.)

(6) **Argynnis leto** Edwards. Pl. IX, fig. 5, ♂; fig. 6, ♀ (The Leto Fritillary).

Butterfly.—Male on the upper side marked much as *A. nokomis*, but the ground-color duller red, and the basal area much darker. Under side of the fore wings pale fulvous, upon which the markings of the upper side reappear; but there are no marginal silver crescents. Both wings on the under side shaded with brown toward the base; hind wings traversed by a submarginal band of light straw-yellow. Female marked as the male, but the ground-color is pale straw-yellow, and all the darker markings are deep blackish-brown, those at the base of both wings being broad and running into one another, so that the inner half of the wings appears to be broadly brownish-black. On the under side this sex is marked as the male, but with the dark portions blacker and the lighter portions pale yellow. Expanse: 2.50–3.25 inches.

The life-history of this insect remains to be worked out. It is one of our most beautiful species, and ranges from southern California to British Columbia, thence eastward to North Dakota, Wyoming, and Colorado.

An insignificant variety, in which the marginal spots on the upper side of the wings of the male tend to disappear, was named **letis** by Wright.

The variety **charlottii** Barnes (Pl. LVI, fig. 1, ♂, type) has the ground-color lighter (inclining to whitish); the basal area in the male darker on the upper side, and the silvery markings on the under side not quite as large as in typical *leto*. It was first described from Glenwood Springs, Colorado.

The *Cybele*-group

(7) **Argynnis cybele** (Fabricius). Pl. IX, fig. 3, ♂; fig. 4, ♀; Pl. XIII, fig. 1, ♀, *under side*; Pl. V, figs. 1–3, *chrysalis* (The Great Spangled Fritillary).

Butterfly.—The male is much like the male of *A. leto*, but the dark markings of the upper surface are heavier, and the under sides of the hind wings are more heavily silvered. The yellowish-buff submarginal band on the under side of the hind wings is never obliterated by being invaded by the darker ferruginous of the marginal and discal tracts of the wing. The female has the ground-color of the wings paler than the male, and both wings from the base to the angled median band on the upper side are dark chocolate-brown. All the markings of the upper side in this sex are heavier than in the male. On the under side the female is like the male. Expanse: 3.00–4.00 inches.

Egg.—Short, conoidal, ribbed like those of other species, and honey-yellow.

Caterpillar.—The larva in the mature state is black. The head is blackish, shaded with chestnut behind. The body is ornamented with six rows of shining black branching spines, generally marked with orange-red at their base. The caterpillar, which is nocturnal, feeds on violets, hibernating immediately after being hatched from the egg, and feeding to maturity in the following spring.

Chrysalis.—Dark brown, mottled with reddish-brown or slaty-gray.

This species, which ranges over the Atlantic States, except Florida and southern Georgia, and the valley of the Mississippi, exclusive of the hotter parts of the Gulf States, seems to be single-brooded in the north and double-brooded in Virginia, the Carolinas, and regions westward in the same latitude.

There is considerable variation in this species through its wide range. In the northern areas, which it reaches, there is a distinct tendency towards melanism, while in the western areas there is a marked tendency toward a generally lighter coloration of the wings, with a reduction of the size of the silvery spots on the lower side.

(7a) **Argynnis cybele** subsp. **krautwurmi** subsp. nov. Pl. LVI, fig. 2, ♀, type (Krautwurm's Fritillary).

♀. *Upper side.* Ground-color not bright fulvous, as in typical *A. cybele*, but pale buff; basal and median areas of both wings dark fuscous; fore wing near the apex more or less clouded with fuscous, the subapical spots tending to fuse with each other, the marginal light spots, especially toward the costa, becoming whitish. Hind wing with the outer margin more or less fuscous; the broad light band between the marginal and inner area light buff, punctuated about the middle by a row of five small black dots, located at the outer extremities of the second row of silvery spots of the under side, which are faintly indicated upon the upper side. *Under side.* Fore wing clouded near the apex with dark fuscous, upon which the apical and subapical small silvery spots stand out conspicuously. The inner third of the wing is not as bright pinkish red as in typical *cybele*, but obscure grayish buff. Hind wing with the basal and mesial areas dark umber, only slightly invading on the inner side the broad light submarginal band. The second row of silvery spots on this side lack the dark terminal markings, which are revealed on the upper side; the spots composing the outer row of silvery markings are relatively large and distinct, varying in form from triangular to suboval; between the outer row of silvery spots and the extreme outer margin the hind wings are broadly of the same color as the basal half of the hind wing. The thorax and abdomen on the upper side are dark conformed in color to the adjacent wings; on the lower side they are paler. Legs pale brownish. Expanse: 2.87–3.15 inches.

Described from four female specimens, type and paratypes, from Les Cheneaux, Upper Peninsula of Michigan. I take pleasure in naming this rather striking form in honor of my associate, Mr. Bernard Krautwurm, who collected the specimens a number of years ago.

(8) **Argynnis carpenteri** Edwards. Pl. LV. fig. 5, ♂; fig. 6, ♀, types (Carpenter's Fritillary).

The above name was originally given to a pair of butterflies taken on Taos Peak, New Mexico. The form has since been taken at other localities in New Mexico, where it appears to be constant both in form and markings. It replaces at considerable elevations, in the region where it occurs, its close ally, *A. cybele*, of the Atlantic and Mid-western States. Expanse: ♂, 2.25 in.; ♀, 2.75 in.

(9) **Argynnis columbia** Henry Edwards. Pl. XIV, fig. 3, ♂, type (The Columbian Silver-spot).

Butterfly.—The male has the upper side of the fore wings pale reddish-fulvous. In the median band of both wings the spots do not flow together, but are separate and moderately heavy. The under side of the fore wings is pale fulvous, buff at the tip; spots silvered. The hind wings on the under side are light rusty-red, but little mottled with buff on the disk; the submarginal band is narrow, buff, and sometimes almost wholly obscured by the darker ground-color. The spots, which are small, are well silvered. The female is much lighter than the male, and, as usual, the dark lines are heavier than in that sex. The spots of the median band are bent and partly lanceolate, and the light spots of the outer border are whitish. Expanse, 2.25–2.50 inches.

Caterpillar, etc.—The early stages have not as yet been worked out.

The types came from the Caribou mining region in British Columbia, and are in my possession. *A. columbia* may be regarded as a somewhat diminutive race of *A. cybele*, occurring in the extreme northwestern range of the latter, and modified by environment. As species go in this genus it may be regarded as distinct, but revealing its ancestry.

(10) **Argynnis aphrodite** (Fabricius). Pl. XIV, fig. 11, ♀, *under side;* Pl. V, fig. 5, *chrysalis* (The Aphrodite Fritillary).

Butterfly.—Closely resembles *cybele*, but generally smaller; the yellow submarginal band on the lower side of hind wings narrower than in *cybele*, and often wholly wanting, the hind wings being broadly brown, particularly in the female sex. The under side of the fore wings at the base and on the inner margin is also brighter red.

The caterpillar, chrysalis, and egg of this species closely resemble those of *cybele*. The caterpillar has, however, a velvety-black spot at the base of each spine; the chrysalis has the tubercles on the back shorter than in *cybele*, and the basal segments are particolored, and not uniformly colored, as in *cybele*.

The insect is common in the northeastern parts of the United States, and is particularly abundant on the mountains of New York, Pennsylvania, and West Virginia.

(11) **Argynnis alcestis** Edwards. Pl. X, fig. 6, ♂, *under side*, type (The Ruddy Silver-spot).

Butterfly.—Very much like *aphrodite*, from which it may be most easily distinguished by the fact that the hind wings on the under side are uniformly reddish cinnamon-brown, without any band of buff on the outer margin. Expanse: 2.50–3.00 inches. The insect flies from late June to the end of August.

Egg.—Greenish, conoidal, with about eighteen vertical ribs.

Caterpillar.—Head black, yellowish behind. The body velvety-black, ornamented with black spines which are yellowish at their basal ends. The caterpillar feeds on violets.

Chrysalis.—Reddish-brown or gray, irregularly mottled and striped with black, the abdominal segments slaty-gray, marked with black on the edges where the short angular projections are located.

This butterfly is mainly found in the Western States, extending from north-western Ohio to Montana. It largely replaces *aphrodite* in these regions. I have once or twice taken it in western Pennsylvania.

(12) **Argynnis cypris** Edwards. Pl. XII, fig. 3, ♂; fig. 4, ♀, types (The New Mexican Silver-spot).

Butterfly.—This species may be distinguished from its not distant ally, *A. aphrodite*, by its relatively longer and narrower fore wings, the narrower black lines, and the brighter fulvous color of the upper side; the absence of the pinkish shade of the fore wings at their bases, and the deep cinnamon on the inner two-thirds of the hind wings on the under side. Expanse: 2.75–3.15 in.

Caterpillar, etc.—Although W. H. Edwards had chrysalids of this species, from which butterflies emerged, he published nothing about the larval stages. The species ranges through Colorado, Utah, and New Mexico.

(13) **Argynnis hesperis** Edwards. Pl. XII, fig. 1, ♂; fig. 2, ♀, types (The Hesperis Fritillary).

Butterfly.—The male on the upper side of the wings is fulvous, shaded with dark fuscous for a short distance from the base. The black spots of the median band are rather broad, and seem to coalesce through dark markings along the nervules. The under side of the fore wings is pale ferruginous, tinged with a little buff at the tips, which, together with the outer margin, are somewhat heavily clouded with dark ferruginous. The under side of the hind wings is dark ferrugin-ous, with a narrow buff submarginal band, which in some specimens is almost lost. The female is paler than the male in the ground-color of the upper side, the black markings are heavier, the marginal lines fuse, as do also the sagittate mar-ginal markings, leaving the marginal spots between them, which are quite light in color, deeply bordered on all sides by black. The under side is like that of the male, but darker and richer in color. In neither sex are the light spots marked with silver; they are opaque, yellowish-white. Expanse: 2.25–2.40 inches.

Caterpillar, etc.—The life-history remains to be learned.

Habitat.—Not uncommon among the mountains of Colorado and westward.

(14) **Argynnis nausicaä** Edwards. Pl. XI, fig. 9, ♂, type (The Arizona Silver-spot).

Synonym: *arizonensis* Elwes.

Butterfly.—The species is related to the foregoing, but is rather smaller in size. The upper side of the wings is dusky reddish-brown, with the characteristic markings of the genus. On the under side the fore wings are pink, laved with buff at the tip. The hind wings on this side are deep cinnamon-brown, mottled with buff on the inner two-thirds; a narrow but clearly defined submarginal band of bright yellowish-buff surrounds them. The silvery spots are clearly marked. The female has the black markings broader and more conspicuous than the male. Expanse: 2.25–2.50 inches.

Quite common in the mountain-valleys of Arizona, at from six to seven thousand feet above sea-level, in July and August. Early stages undescribed, but probably similar to those of allied species.

(15) **Argynnis atlantis** Edwards. Pl. X, fig. 9, ♂, paratype; Pl. V. fig. 6, *chrysalis* (The Mountain Silver-spot).

Synonym: *nikias* Ehrman.

Butterfly.—Resembling *aphrodite*, but smaller, with narrower wings; base of the wings on the upper side deeper brown; on the under side of wings much darker than in *aphrodite*, with narrow pale yellowish submarginal band, which is sharply defined and always present. Expanse: 2.5 in.

Egg.—Conoidal, with twelve to fourteen ribs, honey-yellow. The caterpillars are hatched in the fall, and hibernate without feeding until the following spring.

Caterpillar.—Head dark blackish-brown. Body velvety-purple above, a little paler on the under side. The usual spines occur on the body, and are black, grayish at the base. The larva feeds on violets.

Chrysalis.—The chrysalis is light brown, speckled, except on the abdominal segments, with black.

The species ranges from the Maritime Provinces southward along the Appalachian mountains into West Virginia, and westward and northward as far as Alaska. Specimens from the far north are as a rule smaller and darker than those from the south.

(16) **Argynnis halcyone** Edwards. Pl. XIII, fig. 5, ♂; fig. 6, ♀, *under side*, types (The Halcyone Silver-spot).

Butterfly.—♂. The primaries are produced and relatively narrow, fulvous on the upper side, with the black markings distinct, the mesial band of the secondaries confluent. The fore wings on the under side are pale fulvous, reddish at the base, pale buff at the end of the cell and on the costal margin before the apex; the subapical and marginal series of spots are not much silvered. The hind wings have the inner two-thirds deep reddish-brown, slightly mottled with buff. The marginal band is buff, and all the spots are well silvered.

♀.—The female, which is considerably larger than the male, is marked much as in that sex; but all the black markings are heavier, and on the under side of the primaries the base and inner margin are laved with red. The marginal band on the hind wings is not as distinct in this sex as in the male, in many specimens being somewhat obscured by olive-brown. Expanse, ♂, 2.50 inches; ♀, 2.90–3.10 inches.

Early Stages.—Not known.

This species is found in southern Colorado and the adjacent parts of Utah and Arizona.

(17) **Argynnis semiramis** Edwards. Pl. XIII, fig. 2, ♂, *under side;* fig. 3, ♀, types (The Semiramis Silver-spot).

Butterfly, ♂.—The wings are bright fulvous on the upper side, with the black markings slight on the fore wings and even slighter on the hind wings. The under side of the fore wings is cinnamon-red at the base and on the inner half of the wing; beyond this buff. The apical patch and the outer margin are brown. The upper marginal spots and two spots on the subapical patch are well silvered. The hind wings are rusty-brown from the base to the second row of spots, mottled with lighter brown. The marginal belt is clear brownish-buff. All the spots are well silvered.

♀.—The female on the upper side is colored like the male, with the dark markings somewhat heavier. On the under side the fore wings are laved over almost their entire surface with red, the upper angle of the cell alone being buff. The hind wings in many specimens are fawn-colored throughout, except that the marginal band is paler. In a few specimens the ground is darker and the band more distinct. All the spots are well silvered. Expanse: ♂, 2.60 inches; ♀, 2.75–3.00 inches.

Early Stages.—The life-history of this butterfly has not been ascertained.

The species appears to be very common at San Bernardino, California, and at one time was widely distributed from that locality by the late W. G. Wright as *A. coronis* Edw., from which it is quite distinct.

The *Lais*-group

(18) **Argynnis lais** Edwards. Pl. XIV, fig. 12, ♂; fig. 13, ♀, types (The Northwestern Silver-spot).

Butterfly.—The male is bright reddish-fulvous on the upper side, slightly obscured by fuscous at the base. The discal band of spots common to both wings is broken and irregular, and the spots on the hind wings are quite small. The fore wings on the under side are buff at the tips and pale red at the base and on the inner margin, lighter at the inner angle. The under side of the hind wings as far as the outer margin of the discal row of silvery spots is dark brown, mottling a yellowish ground. The submarginal band of the hind wings is pale yellow and moderately broad. The female is marked much as the male, but the discal band of spots on the upper side of the fore wings is confluent and broader, the fringes whitish, and the spots included between the sagittate marginal spots and the marginal lines paler than in the male sex. Expanse: 2.00–2.20 inches.

Caterpillar, etc.—The early stages are unknown.

Habitat.—This species is found in the territories of Alberta and Assiniboia, and in British Columbia among the foothills and the lower slopes of the mountain-ranges.

(19) **Argynnis electa** Edwards. Pl. X, fig. 8, ♂, type (The Electa Silver-spot).

Butterfly.—The male is dull reddish-fulvous on the upper side. The black markings are narrow. The base of both wings is slightly obscured. On the under side the fore wings are pale cinnamon-red, with the tip dark cinnamon-red. The hind wings are broadly dark cinnamon-red, mottled on the disk with a little buff. The submarginal band is buff, quite narrow, and often invaded by the ground-color of the inner area. The silvery spots are usually very well marked and distinct, though in a few instances the silvery color is somewhat obscured. The female has the black markings a little heavier than in the male; otherwise there is but little difference between the sexes. Expanse: 2.00–2.25 inches.

Caterpillar, etc.—Early stages unknown.

This species has by some writers been confused with *A. atlantis*, from which it is at once separated by its smaller size, relatively broader wings, lighter color, and narrower markings. Through the regrettable failure to correctly identify the type of this species, because W. H. Edwards had inadvertently left a couple of specimens of *A. cornelia* mixed up with his long set of *A. electa*, when he described the former species, Dr. McDunnough was led to sink *A. cornelia* as a synonym of *A. electa*. The two species are entirely distinct.

(20) **Argynnis cornelia** Edwards. Pl. XI, fig. 8, ♂, type (Miss Owen's Fritillary).

Butterfly, ♂.—The upper side of both wings is dark brown from the base to the mesial band of spots, with the exception of the outer end of the cell. The space beyond the band is reddish-fulvous; the dark markings are not very heavy; the two marginal lines are fine, and confluent at the ends of the nervules. The under side of the fore wings is reddish-brown from the base to the outer margin on the inner half of the wing; the outer spaces toward the apex are yellowish; the sub-apical patch is reddish-brown, inclosing a small silvery spot; the outer margin is reddish-brown, adorned with five small silvery spots toward the apex. The hind wings on the under side are almost solid reddish-brown to the clear yellow sub-marginal belt, only slightly mottled on the discal area with buff. The spots are small and well silvered.

♀.—The female on the upper side is duller red, with the dark markings heavier; the marginal spots on the fore wings are pale yellowish, and the marginal lines are confluent on the upper half of these wings. The wings on the under side in this sex are as in the male, but the ground-color on the inner half of the wings is darker, and the spots are more brilliantly silvered. Expanse: 2.30–2.50 inches.

Early Stages.—Unknown.

This pretty species is found with *A. electa* and *A. hesperis* in Colorado. It was originally described from specimens taken at Manitou and Ouray, and named by Edwards in honor of a deceased daughter of Professor Owen of the University of Wisconsin.

The *Zerene*-group

(21) **Argynnis chitone** Edwards. Pl. XIV, fig. 16, ♀, type (The Chitone Fritillary).

Butterfly, ♂.—The wings on the upper side are dull fulvous, greatly obscured by brown at the base of the wings. The dark spots and markings are not heavy. The fore wings on the under side are yellowish-fulvous at the base and on the inner half of the wing; the apical patch and the nervules on the apical area are heavy ferruginous; the marginal spots are buff, with no silver. The hind wings on the under side are light ferruginous, mottled with buff; the belt is broad, clear buff; the outer margin is brown. All the spots are small and imperfectly silvered.

♀.—The female is nearly the same shade as the male, with the marginal spots on the under side always silvered, the remainder without silver, or only now and then with a few silvery scales. Expanse: 2.25–2.50 inches.

Early Stages.—Not ascertained.

This species occurs in southern Utah and Arizona.

(22) **Argynnis bremneri** Edwards. Pl. X, fig. 7, ♂, type (Bremner's Silver-spot).

Butterfly.—The male on the upper side is bright fulvous. The black markings, especially those about the middle of the wing, are heavy. Both wings at the base are clouded with fuscous, the under side of the primaries red toward the base, buff on the apical area; the subapical and the upper marginal spots well silvered; the hind wings with the inner two-thirds more or less deeply ferruginous, a little mottled with buff, very rarely encroached upon by the dark color of the inner area, except occasionally near the anal angle. Expanse: ♂, 2.40 inches; ♀, 2.70 inches.

Early Stages.—The early stages have not as yet been described.

Habitat.—This species is found in Oregon, Washington, Montana, and in the southern portions of British Columbia and Vancouver's Island.

(23) **Argynnis hippolyta** Edwards. Pl. XII, fig. 10, ♂, type (The Hippolyta Fritillary).

Butterfly.—The male is fulvous upon the upper side, all the dark markings being heavy and black, and the basal areas of the wings clouded with fuscous, this dark clouding on the hind wings reaching down and nearly covering the inner angle. The fore wings on the under side are buff, laved with pale red at the base, marked with ferruginous on the outer margin and about the subapical spots. The submarginal and subapical spots are silvered, especially the latter. The hind wings are deep ferruginous, mottled with buff. The submarginal band is buff, narrow, and dusted with more or less ferruginous. All the spots are well silvered. The female has the basal area of the fore wings bright pinkish-fulvous, and the belt of the secondaries almost lost in the deep ground-color.

The name **A. cottlei** has been given by Comstock to a specimen of this species in which the light spots on the under side are not silvered.

Habitat.—Washington and British Columbia.

(24) **Argynnis behrensi** Edwards. Pl. XIV, fig. 10, ♂, *under side*, type (Behrens' Fritillary).

Butterfly.—The male on the upper side is dull fulvous, clouded with fuscous at the base, the black markings much narrower and lighter than in the preceding species. The primaries on the under side are pale fulvous, clouded with dark brown at the apex. The subapical spots and the upper spots of the marginal series on this wing are well silvered. The hind wings on the under side are deep reddish-brown, with the marginal band only faintly indicated. All the spots are distinctly well silvered. The female does not differ materially from the male, except in the

93

larger size and the somewhat paler ground-color of the upper side of the wings. On the under side the wings are exactly as in the male, with the marginal band even less distinct than in that sex.

Early Stages.—Not yet ascertained.

Habitat.—The type specimens upon which the foregoing description is founded came from Mendocino in California.

(25) **Argynnis oweni** Edwards. Pl. XII, fig. 5, ♂; fig. 6, ♂, *under side, types* (Owen's Silver-spot).

Butterfly, ♂.—The wings on the upper side are dull reddish-fulvous, not much obscured with brown on the base, the black markings moderately heavy, the two marginal lines tending to flow together. The fore wings on the under side are yellowish-buff from the base to the outer row of spots, or in some specimens with the buff lightly laved with reddish; the nerves reddish-brown. The subapical patch is dark brown, with a small silvered spot; the five submarginal spots are small and obscurely silvered. The hind wings are dark brown on the discal area and outer margin, with a rather narrow grayish-buff submarginal band, strongly invaded by projections of the dark brown of the discal area. The spots of the outer discal row are generally well silvered; the inner spots less so in most cases.

♀.—The female has the wings more or less mottled with yellowish outside of the mesial band. The black markings are very heavy in this sex. On the under side the spots are well silvered.

The dark markings on the upper side of the wings of the male are much heavier than in *A. behrensi.* On the under side of the wings in both sexes it may be distinguished from *behrensi* by the fact that the ground-color toward the base is mottled with yellow, and not solid brown as in *behrensi.* Expanse: 2.25–2.40 inches.

Early Stages.—Unknown.

Habitat.—This species abounds on Mount Shasta in California at an elevation of seven to eight thousand feet above sea-level.

(26) **Argynnis zerene** Boisduval (1852). Pl. XIV, fig. 9, ♂, *under side.* **Argynnis hydaspe,** Boisd., ♀, type (1869). Pl. LXXI, fig. 4 (The Zerene Fritillary).

Synonym: *hydaspe* Boisd.

Butterfly.—The male on the upper side is reddish-fulvous, with rather heavy black markings, the mesial band of spots being confluent. The under side of the fore wings is reddish, inclining to pink, with the apex laved with buff. The hind wings have the ground-color purplish-gray, mottled on the inner two-thirds with ferruginous. The spots are not silvered, but are a delicate gray color. The female is colored like the male, but the red at the base of the fore wings in this sex is deeper and the yellow at the apex of the primaries contrasts much more strongly. The spots on the under side in the female sex are frequently well silvered, though in many specimens they are colored exactly as in the male sex. Expanse of wing: ♂, 2.17 inches; ♀, 2.50 inches.

It is quite impossible to distinguish typical specimens of *A. zerene* Boisd. from typical specimens of *A. hydaspe* named by the same author seventeen years later. I figure one of Boisduval's types of *A. hydaspe*, which was sent by the author to W. H. Edwards, and is now in my possession. Comparing it with the figure of *A. zerene* Boisd. (Oberthür, Pl. XCV, fig. 9) the identity of the two insects is disclosed.

A slight variety of this insect has been named and figured as *A. conchyliatus* by Comstock (See "Butt. Calif.", p. 84, Pl. 26, figs. 1–2); and another as *A. viridicornis* by the same author, (*l. c.*, p. 85, Pl. 25, figs. 3–5). In the former the ground-color of the under side of the wings is darker, and the light spots smaller; in the latter the reverse is true.

Early Stages.—Unknown.

(27) **Argynnis monticola** Behr. Pl. XIII, fig. 7, ♂, *under side*, fig. 8, ♂; Pl. XIV, fig. 17, ♀. (Behr's Fritillary).

Closely allied to the preceding species, but in both sexes the upper surface of the wings is lighter fulvous and the dark markings in consequence are more strongly accentuated. The under sides are not as much shaded with fuscous as in *A. zerene*. Most specimens incline prevalently to purplish on the under side of the wings and specimens in which this is most pronounced were set apart as var. *purpurascens* by Henry Edwards. This tendency is very marked in specimens taken about Soda Springs in the region of Mt. Shasta.

Early Stages.—Unknown.

(28) **Argynnis rhodope** Edwards. Pl. XI, fig. 6, ♀, *under side*, type (The Rhodope Fritillary).

This is probably a more northern race of *A. monticola* in which the ground-color of the under side of the wings is very dark maroon. Thus far it has only been reported from Washington and British Columbia.

(29) **Argynnis sakuntala** Skinner. Pl. LVI, fig. 4, ♀, paratype, *under side* (The Sakuntala Silver-spot).

This is another form closely allied to *A. zerene* and *A. rhodope*. It may be only a local race. It was originally described from Kaslo, British Columbia. The specific name *sakuntala* is dangerously near to *Argynnis sakontala* Kollar, which designates a race of *A. childreni* from the Himalayas. It would appear to be desirable to change the specific name, and in that case it would be most appropriate to name the form *A. skinneri* in honor of the first describer.

(30) **Argynnis rupestris** Behr. Pl. XII, fig. 8, ♂; fig. 9, ♂, *under side* (The Cliff-dwelling Fritillary).

Butterfly, ♂.—Upper side of fore wings deep reddish fulvous, with the black markings very heavy. Fore wings on the under side buff, shaded with red at the base and on the inner margin. The spots are buff, without any silver. Hind wings buff, mottled with cinnamon-red, sometimes dark, sometimes lighter. The marginal belt is narrow, buff, encroached upon by the darker color of the median area at the ends of the oval spots. None of the spots is silvered, except very lightly in exceptional cases.

95

Genus Argynnis

♀.—The female much like the male on the upper side, with the dark markings much heavier, ground-color somewhat paler, and the marginal row of spots quite light. The wings on the under side are more brightly tinted than in the male, and the marginal spots are more or less silvered. Expanse: ♂, 2.00 inches; ♀, 2.20 inches.

Early Stages.—Nothing is as yet known about the egg and larva.

Habitat.—Quite abundant at a considerable elevation upon Mount Shasta, Mount Bradley, and in the Weber Mountains in Utah.

(31) **Argynnis inornata** Edwards. Pl. XIII, fig. 10, ♀, *under side*, type (The Plain Fritillary).

Butterfly, ♂.—Resembles *A. rupestris* in its markings, but is somewhat paler, the black margins are heavy and the black markings on the disk comparatively light; the base of the wings is obscured with fuscous. On the under side fore wings cinnamon-brown, with the apical area buff. Hind wings reddish-brown, with the marginal band clear buff. All the spots are buff, and completely devoid of silvery scales.

♀.—Paler than the male on the upper side. Fore wings on the under side orange-fulvous; hind wings pale greenish-brown, mottled with buff. In some specimens a few silver scales are found on the submarginal spots. Expanse: ♂, 2.50 inches; ♀, 2.70 inches.

Early Stages.—Unknown.

Habitat.—California and Nevada.

The *Coronis*-group

(32) **Argynnis coronis** Edwards (Behr MS.). Pl. XI, fig. 10, ♂; fig. 11, ♀; var. **laura** Edwards, Pl. XII, fig. 11, ♂; fig. 12, ♀. (The Coronis Fritillary).

Synonyms: *juba* Boisduval; *liliana* Barnes & McDunnough (not Henry Edwards).

Butterfly.—♂. Wings on the upper side yellowish fulvous, with but little brown obscuring the base; dark markings not heavy, but sharply defined. On the under side the fore wings are buff, with the basal area orange-fulvous; subapical and submarginal spots more or less imperfectly silvered; hind wings brown, mottled with reddish; discal area buff; belt pale yellowish buff; spots on this wing well silvered.

♀. Paler than the male, with the markings on the upper side heavier; on the under side much as in the male. Expanse: ♂, 2.10–2.5 in.; ♀, 2.5–3.00 in.

(32a) Var. *laura* Edwards. This is a smaller and darker form, found in Nevada and elsewhere, which contrasts in tint and its smaller size with the larger typical form, originally described from lower and less arid localities in California.

Early Stages.—Little is as yet known of these.

Habitat.—Central California and eastward, at moderate elevations.

(33) **Argynnis platina** Skinner. Pl. XVIII, fig. 7, ♂, paratype (Skinner's Fritillary).

Butterfly, ♂.—The original description of this species, contained in the "Canadian Entomologist," vol. xxix, p. 154, is as follows:

"♂.—Expands two and a half inches. Upper side: Rather light tawny or even light buff. Black markings dense and wide, with outer halves of wings looking rather clear or open, with rows of round spots not very large; marginal border light; bases of wings not much obscured. Under side: Superiors have the two subapical silver spots and silver spots on margin well defined; color of inner half of wing rosy. The silver spots on the inferiors are large and well defined, and placed on a very light greenish-gray ground. The intermediate buff band is well defined, comparatively wide, and very light in color. ♀ —The ground-color in the inferiors below is reddish-brown in the female."

Early Stages.—Unknown.

Habitat.—Utah and Idaho. It is possibly a varietal form of *A. coronis*, specimens, agreeing very nearly with the type figured on the plate, being contained in the Edwards collection under the name of *A. coronis.*

(34) **Argynnis snyderi** Skinner. Pl. XVIII, fig. 6, ♂, paratype (Snyder's Fritillary).

Butterfly, ♂.—The wings on the upper side are light tawny, but little obscured by fuscous at the base. The black markings are moderately heavy and very sharply defined against the lighter ground-color. The outer margin is distinctly but not heavily marked. On the under side of the fore wings there are two subapical and five marginal silver spots. The ground-color of the under side of the hind wings is grayish-green, with a narrow pale-buff marginal belt. The spots are large and well silvered.

♀.—The female is much like the male, but on the hind wings the ground-color from the base to the outer belt is brownish. Expanse: ♂, 3.00 inches; ♀ 3.30 inches.

Early Stages.—Unknown.

Habitat.—Utah.

(35) **Argynnis gunderi** Comstock. Pl. LIX, fig. 25, ♂, *under side* (Gunder's Fritillary).

This is apparently an aberrant form of *A. snyderi*, in which the under side of the hind wings is very pale yellowish, and the marginal markings tend to disappear.

(36) **Argynnis californica** Skinner. Pl. LVI, fig. 5, ♂, paratype, *under side* (The Californian Fritillary).

The insect may be only a variety of *A. coronis* Edwards.

(37) **Argynnis utahensis** Skinner. Pl. LVI, fig. 3, ♂, paratype, *under side* (The Utah Fritillary).

The figure on our plate reveals that the differences between *A. californica* Skinner and *A. utahensis* Skinner are almost microscopic. The insects are puzzlingly near to each other, and in a long series the two forms seem to melt into each other. I am inclined to regard them as being at best local races of *A. coronis* Edwards.

(38) **Argynnis macaria** Edwards. Pl. XIII, fig. 9, ♂, type (The Macaria Silver-spot).

Butterfly, ♂.—The upper side of the wings is yellowish-fulvous, the black markings very light. The fore wings on the under side are orange-red, at the apex yellowish-buff. The subapical upper marginal spots are lightly silvered. The hind wings are yellowish-buff on the outer third, mottled with brown on the basal and median areas. The marginal belt is clear buff. The spots are large and well silvered.

♀.—The female is paler than the male. On the upper side of the hind wings the second row of silver spots is indicated by spots much paler than the ground. The black markings are lighter than in the male. Expanse: ♂, 2.00 inches; ♀, 2.20 inches.

Early Stages.—Unknown.

Habitat.—California, but still quite rare in collections.

Calippe-group

(39) **Argynnis callippe** Boisduval. Pl. XI, fig. 1, ♂; fig. 2, ♀; fig. 3, ♀ *under side* (The Callippe Silver-spot).

Butterfly.—This species may easily be recognized by the general obscuration of the basal area of the wings, the light-buff quadrate spots on the discal area of the fore wings, and the clear oval spots of the same color on the hind wings, as well as by the light triangular marginal spots, all standing out distinctly on the darker ground. The wings on the under side are quite pale buff, with the spots large and well silvered. Expanse: 2.30–3.00 inches.

Early Stages.—Unknown.

Habitat.—Abundant in California.

(40) **Argynnis liliana** Henry Edwards. Pl. XIII, fig. 11, ♂, type (The Liliana Silver-spot).

Synonym: *coronis* Barnes & McDunnough (not W. H. Edwards).

Butterfly, ♂.—The wings on the upper side are reddish-fulvous. The black markings and the spots are slight. The fore wings on the under side are yellowish-buff; the base and the hind margin to below the cell, brown, with buff on the median interspaces. The outer end of the cell is yellowish-buff. The subapical patch is brown, adorned by two or three well-silvered spots. The five upper marginal spots are well silvered. The hind wings are brown, but little mottled with buff. The spots are well silvered. The marginal belt is narrow, ochreous-brown.

♀.—The female is much paler than the male, and the marginal spots on both wings are much lighter. On the under side the wings are as in the male sex, with the basal area and the nervules of the fore wings red. Expanse: ♂, 2.20 inches; ♀, 2.35 inches.

Egg.—W. H. Edwards gives the following description: "Conoidal, truncated, depressed at summit, marked vertically by twenty-two or twenty-three ribs, which are as in other species of the genus; the outline of this egg is much as in *eurynome*, the base being broad, the top narrow, and the height not much more than the breadth; color yellow."

Caterpillar.—The same author has given us a description of the caterpillar immediately after hatching; but, as the young larvæ were lost after being sent to Maine to be kept over winter, we do not yet know the full life-history.

Habitat.—Northern California and Utah, so far as is known at present.

Nevadensis-group

(41) **Argynnis nevadensis** Edwards. Pl. X, fig. 4, ♂, *under side*, type (The Nevada Fritillary).

Butterfly, ♂.—The ground-color is pale fulvous, but little obscured with fuscous at the base. The outer margins are heavily bordered with black. The dark markings of the discal area are not heavy. The fore wings on the under side are pale buff, the spots well silvered; the hind wings are greenish; the belt is narrow and clear, and the spots are large and well silvered.

♀.—The female is much like the male, but larger and paler. The outer margin of the fore wings in this sex is more heavily marked with black, and the marginal spots are light buff in color. Expanse: ♂, 2.50–3.00 inches; ♀, 3.00–3.50 inches.

Dr. McDunnough has described two varietal forms of this species, to which he has given the names *calgariana* and *semivirida*.

Early Stages.—These remain to be discovered.

Habitat.—Rocky Mountains of Utah, Nevada, Montana, and British America.

(42) **Argynnis meadi** Edwards. Pl. XIV, fig. 1, ♂; fig. 2, ♂, *under side*, types (Mead's Silver-spot).

Butterfly.—This species is very closely allied to the preceding, of which it may be an extreme variation, characterized by the darker color of the fore wings on the upper side, the nervules being heavily bordered with blackish, and the deeper, more solid green of the under side of the wings. All the specimens I have seen are considerably smaller in size than *A. nevadensis*.

Early Stages.—Wholly unknown.

Habitat.—From Utah northward to the province of Alberta in British America.

(43) **Argynnis edwardsi** Reakirt. Pl. XI, fig. 4, ♂; fig. 5, ♀ (Edwards' Fritillary).

Butterfly.—This beautiful insect is closely related to the Nevada Fritillary, from which it may be distinguished by the brighter color of the upper side, the heavier black borders, especially in the female sex, and the olive-brown color of the under side of the hind wings. The olivaceous of these wings greatly encroaches upon the marginal belt. Expanse: 3.00–3.25 inches.

Early Stages.—These have been carefully and minutely described by Edwards in the "Canadian Entomologist," vol. xx, p. 3. They are not unlike those of *A. atlantis* in many respects.

Habitat.—Not uncommon in Colorado and Montana.

Adiaste-group

(44) **Argynnis adiaste** Behr. Pl. XIV, fig. 4, ♀ (The Adiaste Fritillary). Synonym: *adiante* Boisduval.

Butterfly, ♂.—The wings on the upper side are bright fulvous; the black markings are slight. The fore wings on the under side are pale buff, much lighter at the apex, laved with orange-red at the base. The hind wings are pale buff, clouded with fawn color on the basal and discal areas. All the spots which are generally silvered in other species are in this species wholly devoid of silvery scales.

♀.—The female is like the male, but the black markings on the upper side are heavier, and the basal area and inner half of the primaries are laved with brighter and deeper red. Expanse: ♂, 2.30–2.40 inches; ♀, 2.30–2.60 inches.

Early Stages.—Unknown.

Habitat.—Southern California; somewhat local in its habits.

(45) **Argynnis atossa** Edwards. Pl. XIII, fig. 12, ♂, type (The Atossa Fritillary).

Butterfly, ♂.—The upper side is bright yellowish-fulvous, with the wings at the base slightly dusted with brown. The margins of both wings are bordered by a single line, there being no trace of the outer line usually found in other species of the genus. The dark markings of the outer margin are almost entirely absent, and those of the discal and basal areas very greatly reduced. On the under side both wings are very pale, the spots entirely without silver, in some specimens even their location being but faintly indicated. The fore wings at the base and on the inner margin are laved with bright red.

♀.—The female resembles the male, except that the red on the under side of the fore wings is in many specimens very bright and fiery. Expanse: ♂, 2.50 inches; ♀, 2.75–3.00 inches.

Early Stages.—Entirely unknown.

Habitat.—This butterfly, which is still rare in collections, has been taken in southern California. It may be an extreme variation of *A. adiaste* Behr.

Eurynome-group

(46) **Argynnis montivaga** Behr. Pl. X, fig. 5, ♂, *under side* (The Mountain Rambler).

Butterfly.—This species in both sexes very closely approximates *A. eurynome.* The main points of distinction consist in the somewhat darker red of the upper side of the wings, the slightly heavier dark markings, and the absence on the under side, especially of the hind wings, of the olive-green shade which is characteristic of typical specimens of *A. eurynome*. The mottling of the basal and median areas on this side is reddish-brown. The spots are more or less silvered on the under side. Expanse: ♂, 1.75 inch; ♀, 1.90 inch.

Early Stages.—Unknown.

Habitat.—The Sierras of California and the mountains of Nevada.

(47) **Argynnis egleis** Boisduval. Pl. XIII, fig. 13, ♂; fig. 14, ♀, *under side;* fig. 15, ♀ (The Egleis Fritillary).

Butterfly, ♂.—The ground-color of the wings on the upper side is deep fulvous, with rather heavy black markings. The wings on the under side are pale fulvous, mottled with buff on the subapical interspaces of the fore wings. The basal and discal areas of the hind wings are mottled with brown, which in many specimens is of a distinctly purplish shade. In some specimens the inner half of the primaries is rather heavily laved with red. The spots on the under side are either silvered or without silver; in the latter case being pale buff.

♀.—The female is much like the male, but paler. The red on the under side of the primaries is deeper, and the purplish-brown on the inner surface of the secondaries is also darker. Expanse: ♂, 2.25 inches; ♀, 2.50 inches.

Early Stages.—These remain to be ascertained.

Habitat.—This is a common species in California and Nevada.

(48) **Argynnis eurynome** Edwards. Pl. XII, fig. 7, ♂; Pl. XIV, fig. 14, ♀; fig. 15, ♂, *under side* (The Eurynome Silver-spot).

Butterfly, ♂.—The wings on the upper side are bright yellowish-fulvous, but little obscured at the base. The outer margins are edged by two fine lines which are occasionally confluent. The under side of the fore wings is pale buff, laved with cinnamon-brown at the base and along the nervules; the spots on the margin and in the apical area are well silvered. The hind wings on the under side are buff, with the basal and discal areas mottled with pale brown or pale olive-green. The marginal belt is broad and clear buff; all the spots are well silvered.

♀.—The female is like the male, but paler, with the dark markings, especially those of the margin, heavier. The marginal spots inclosed by the lunules are much paler than the ground-color, and in many specimens almost white. On the under side the wings in this sex are like those of the male, but the fore wings are more heavily laved with cinnamon-brown at the base. Expanse: ♂, 1.70–2.00 inches; ♀, 2.00 inches.

Early Stages.—Mr. Edwards, in "The Butterflies of North America," vol. ii, has given us a beautiful figure of the egg of this species. Of the other stages we have no knowledge.

(49) **Argynnis washingtonia** Barnes & McDunnough. Pl. LVI, fig. 8, ♂, *under side,* paratype (The Washington Fritillary).

This species, as our figure shows, is closely related to *A. eurynome,* being mainly distinguished by being darker on the under side of the wings and having the under side of the fore wings flushed with rosy pink and not pale as in typical *eurynome.* It is closely allied in some respects to *A. erinna* Edwards.

Early Stages.—Not described.

Habitat.—Washington, British Columbia.

(50) **Argynnis mormonia** Boisduval. Pl. LXXI, fig. 5, ♂, *under side;* fig. 6, ♀, paratype (The Mormonia Fritillary).

Oberthür in his *Lépidoptérologie Comparée,* Fasc. IX, p. 82, Pl. CCLXI, figs. 2191 and 2193 delineates this species. I reproduce the specimens, which his artist used, and which are now in the U. S. National Museum, being a part of the recently acquired Barnes Collection. I possess a series of specimens taken at Laggan, Alberta, which exactly correspond with these specimens. Boisduval in his description gives Oregon as the locality from which his specimens came. I am inclined to think that *A. mormonia* is simply a somewhat smaller northern race of *A. eurynome* Edwards.

Early Stages.—Unknown.

Habitat.—Northern California to British Columbia and Alberta.

(51) **Argynnis erinna** Edwards. Pl. LVI, fig. 7, ♂, type, *under side* (The Erinna Fritillary).

Erinna was originally described from Spokane Falls. It has been regarded by some writers as a valid species. Edwards originally described it as a variety of *A. eurynome* and I think was perfectly correct in so doing. The form differs from *eurynome* simply in being darker, with less red on the fore wings than in the typical form of *eurynome.* It is a local race of the latter species. In size it does not differ from typical *eurynome.*

Early Stages.—Unknown.

Habitat.—Idaho and Washington.

(52) **Argynnis bischoffi** Edwards. Pl. XI, fig. 7, ♂, type (Bischoff's Fritillary).

Butterfly, ♂.—The fore wings on the upper side are bright reddish-fulvous, the base of the primaries and the inner half of the secondaries being heavily obscured by blackish, so as to conceal the markings. Both wings have moderately heavy black marginal borders. The other markings are as in *A. eurynome.* On the under side the fore wings are buff, laved with reddish at the base. The hind wings are pale buff, with the basal and discal areas mottled with green. The marginal belt is clear buff. In some specimens the spots on the under side are not silvered; in others they are well silvered.

♀.—The female on the upper side is very pale buff, slightly laved with fulvous on the outer margin of both wings. All the markings are heavy; the margins of both wings are solid black, the spots within the lunules being pale and almost white. The fore wings at the base and the inner half of the hind wings are almost solid black. On the under side the wings are very much as in the male, and the same variation as to the silvering of the spots is found. Expanse: ♂, 1.80 inch; ♀, 1.90 inch.

Early Stages.—Unknown.

Habitat.—The types of this species came from St. Michaels, in Alaska. It may be an extreme boreal variety of *A. eurynome.*

(53) **Argynnis clio** Edwards. Pl. XIV, fig. 5, ♂; fig. 6, ♀; fig. 7, ♂, *under side*, type (The Clio Fritillary).

Butterfly.—Closely resembling *A. eurynome* and *A. artonis*. Like *artonis*, the spots on the under side of the wing are without silver. The female very closely resembles the female of *artonis*, and in fact I am unable to distinguish the types of the females of the two species by any marks which seem to be quite satisfactory. Expanse: ♂, 1.75 inch; ♀, 1.75–1.90 inch.

Early Stages.—Unknown.

Habitat.—This species, which is as yet comparatively rare in collections, is found in Montana and the province of Alberta in British America at considerable elevations.

(54) **Argynnis opis** Edwards. Pl. XIV, fig. 8, ♂, *under side*, type (The Opis Fritillary).

Butterfly.—This species, which apparently belongs to the *Eurynome*-group, appears by the location of its markings to be closely related to *eurynome*, but on the upper side the wings of both the male and female are more heavily obscured with fuscous at the base; the dark markings are heavier than in *eurynome*, and in both sexes it is smaller in size, being the smallest of all the species of the genus thus far found in North America. The spots on the under side of the wings are none of them silvered. Expanse: ♂, 1.50 inch; ♀, 1.60 inch.

Early Stages.—Nothing is known of these.

Habitat.—The types came from Bald Mountain, in the Caribou mining district of British Columbia.

(55) **Argynnis artonis** Edwards. Pl. XII, fig. 13, ♂, *under side*, type (The Artonis Fritillary).

Butterfly, ♂.—Closely resembling *A. eurynome* Edwards, from which species it may be distinguished by the entire absence of silvery scales upon the under side of the wings, and also by the fact that the silvery spots on the under side of the hind wings are not compressed and elongated as much as in *eurynome*, and by the further fact that all the dark marginal markings of the under side are obliterated.

♀.—The female does not differ materially from the male, except that the dark markings on the upper side are all much heavier, standing out very distinctly upon the paler ground, and the marginal spots within the lunules are very light in color and relatively large. On the under side the fore wings are laved with red. Expanse: ♂, 1.75–2.00 inches; ♀, 2.00–2.15 inches.

Early Stages.—These still remain to be ascertained.

Habitat.—This interesting butterfly has been found in Colorado, Nevada, Utah, and Arizona.

(56) **Argynnis irene** Boisd. Pl. LVI, fig. 6, paratype of *A. luski* B. & McD. (The Irene Fritillary).

Synonym: *luski* Barnes & McDunnough.

A comparison of the fine figure of the type of *A. irene* Boisd. given by Oberthür in his *Lépidoptérologie Comparée*, Fasc. IX, Pl. CCLXII, fig. 2196, leaves no doubt that the insect named *A. luski* by Barnes and McDunnough is the same as that described by Boisduval in his "Lépidoptères de Californie," 1869, p. 5. A diacritical mark, by which this species may be distinguished from all other species of the genus, is the elongated light spot on the inner margin of the hind wings on the under side, which is similarly developed in no other species. *Irene* was originally described from "California"; *A. luski* from Arizona.

A RACE AFTER A BUTTERFLY

There is much that is pleasing about "first things." I shall never forget the first dollar I earned; the first trout I took with my fly; the first muskalonge I gaffed beside my canoe on a still Canadian lake; the first voyage I made across the Atlantic. So I shall never forget my first capture of a female specimen of *Argynnis diana*.

My home in my boyhood was in North Carolina, in the village of Salem, famous as one of the most successful of the settlements made by the Moravian Brethren under the lead of the good Count Zinzendorf, and well known throughout the Southern States as the seat of an excellent seminary for young ladies. The Civil War broke out, and the hopes cherished of sending me North to be educated were disappointed. I was left to pursue my studies under a tutor, and to roam the neighborhood in quest of insects, of which I gathered a large collection.

One day I spied upon a bed of verbenas a magnificent butterfly with broad expanse of wing and large blue spots upon the secondaries. In breathless haste I rushed into the house and got my net. To the joy of my heart, when I returned to the spot, the beauty was still hovering over the crimson blossoms. But, as I drew near with fell intent, it rose and sailed away. Across the garden, over the fence, across the churchyard, out into the street, with leisurely flight the coveted prize sped its way, while I quickly followed, net in hand. Once upon the dusty street, its flight was accelerated; my rapid walking was converted into a run. Down past the church and—*horribile dictu!*—past the boarding-school that pesky butterfly flew. I would rather have faced a cannonade in those days than a bevy of boarding-school misses, but there was no alternative. There were the dreaded females at the windows (for it was Saturday, and vacation hour), and there was my butterfly. Sweating, blushing, inwardly anathematizing my luck, I rushed past the school, only to be overwhelmed with mortification by the rascally porter of the institution, who was sweeping the pavement, and who bawled out after me: "Oh, it's no use; you can't catch it! It's frightened; you're so ugly!" And now it began to rise in its flight. It was plainly my last chance, for it would in a moment be lost over the housetops. I made an upward leap, and by a fortunate sweep of the net succeeded in capturing my prize.

Many years later, after a long interval in which ornithology and botany had engrossed my mind to the exclusion of entomology, my boyish love for the butterflies was renewed, and I found out the name of the choice thing I had captured on that hot July day on the streets of Salem, and returned to North Carolina for the special purpose of collecting a quantity of these superb insects. My quest was entirely successful, though my specimens were not taken at Salem, but under the shadow of Mount Mitchell, in the flower-spangled valleys which lie at its feet.

Genus BRENTHIS Hübner

"The garden is fragrant everywhere;
In its lily-bugles the gold bee sups,
And butterflies flutter on winglets fair
Round the tremulous meadow buttercups."
MUNKITTRICK.

Butterfly.—Small or medium-sized, very closely approximating in form and color the species of the genus *Argynnis*, in which they are included by many writers. The principal structural difference between the two genera is found in the fact that in the genus *Brenthis* only one of the subcostal nervules arises before or at the end of the cell of the primaries, while in *Argynnis* the two innermost sub-costal nervules thus arise. In *Brenthis* the palpi are not as stout as in *Argynnis*, and the short basal spur or branch of the median vein of the front wings, which is characteristic of the latter genus, is altogether lacking in *Brenthis*.

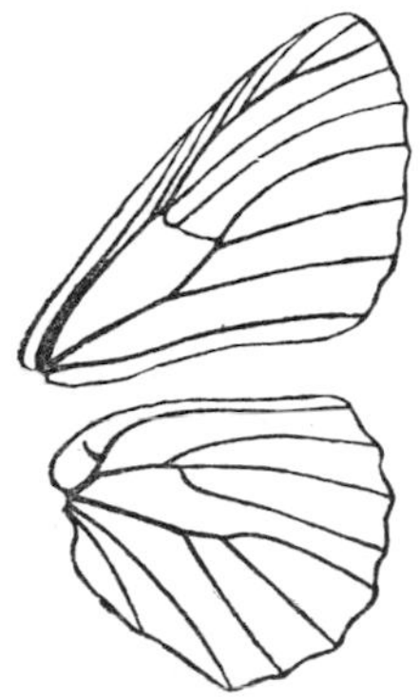

Egg.—Subconical, almost twice as high as wide, truncated at top, and marked with thirteen or fourteen raised longitudinal ridges connected by a multitude of smaller cross-ridges.

FIG. 91.—Neuration of the genus *Brenthis*, enlarged.

Larva.—Not noticeably different in their general appearance from those of the genus *Argynnis*, except that they are smaller and generally not as dark in color as the larvæ of the latter genus. They feed, like the caterpillars of *Argynnis*, upon violets.

Chrysalis.—Pendant, about six-tenths of an inch long, and armed with two rows of sharp conical tubercles on the back.

(1) **Brenthis myrina** (Cramer). Pl. XV, fig. 1, ♂; fig, 2, ♂, *under side*, typical; Pl. V, figs. 12–14, *chrysalis.* Var. **nebraskensis** Holland, Pl. LV, fig. 8, ♂, type. Var. **terræ-novæ** Holland, Pl. LV, fig. 13, ♂, type. Var. **jenningsæ** Holland, Pl. LVI, fig. 9, ♂, type (The Silver-bordered Fritillary).

Butterfly.—In the typical form, which is common in the eastern parts of the United States, the upper side of the wings is fulvous; the black markings are light, the borders heavy. Fore wings on the under side yellowish-fulvous, ferruginous at the tip, with the marginal spots lightly silvered. Hind wings ferruginous, mottled with buff. The spots, which are small, are well silvered. Expanse: ♂, 1.40 inch; ♀, 1.70 inch.

Genus Brenthis

Egg.—Conoidal, about one-third higher than wide, marked by sixteen or seventeen vertical ribs, between which are a number of delicate cross-lines; pale greenish yellow in color.

Caterpillar.—The larva has been carefully studied, and its various stages are fully described in "The Butterflies of New England," by Dr. Scudder. In its final stage it is about seven-eighths of an inch long, dark olive-brown, marked with green, the segments adorned with fleshy tubercles armed with needle-shaped projections; the tubercles on the side of the first thoracic segment being four times as long as the others, cylindrical in form, and blunt at the upper end, the spines projecting upward at an angle of forty-five degrees to the axis of the tubercle.

Chrysalis.—The chrysalis is yellowish-brown, spotted with darker brown spots, those of the thoracic and first and second abdominal segments having the lustre of mother-of-pearl.

This very pretty little species has a wide range, extending from New England to Montana, from Nova Scotia to Alaska, and southward along the ridges of the Alleghanies into Virginia and the mountains of North Carolina.

Numerous varieties of this species have been detected in recent years. The variety *tollandensis* Barnes and Benjamin, which occurs in Colorado, is lighter in color than the typical form, and has the dark spots reduced in size. The variety *nebraskensis* tends greatly to hypertrophy, being much larger than specimens found in the eastern part of the range of the species. The varietal form, *terræ-novæ*, found in Newfoundland, is characterized by having the basal areas of both wings heavily suffused with fuscous. In the variety *jenningsæ*, as shown by the figure we give, the dark markings are much enlarged. The latter variety occurs about Lake Nipigon in Ontario.

(2) **Brenthis andersoni** Dyar. Pl. LXXIV, fig. 7, ♂, type; fig. 8, do., *under side* (Anderson's Fritillary).

This species, which has been regarded by some as a variety of *B. euphrosyne*, a species commonly found in Europe, is represented on our plate by a photograph of the upper and under side of the type, which is in the United States National Museum, and has remained unique until the present day. It is said to have been taken in British Columbia, but until now no other specimens have turned up. It seems in certain particulars to differ from *B. euphrosyne* (Linnæus). Expanse: 1.70 in.

(3) **Brenthis triclaris** (Hübner). Pl. LV, fig. 11, ♂, typical. Var. **alticola** Barnes & McDunnough, Pl. XV, fig. 3, ♂. Var. **dawsoni** Barnes & McDunnough, Pl. LVI, figs. 11 and 12, ♂ and ♀, paratypes (The Triclaris Fritillary).

Butterfly, ♂.—The male above is bright fulvous, with the base of the fore wings and the inner margin of the hind wings heavily obscured with blackish scales. The usual dark markings are finer than in the preceding species; the black marginal borders are not so heavy. The submarginal spots are relatively large and distinct in most specimens, and uniform in size. The light spots of the under side of the median band of the hind wings show through from below on the upper side

106

lighter than the ground-color of the wings. On the under side the fore wings are fulvous, tipped with ferruginous. The hind wings are broadly ferruginous, with a couple of bright-yellow spots near the base and a curved band of yellow spots crossing the median area. The outer margin about the middle is marked with pale fulvous. The spots on the under side are none of them silvered.

♀.—The female is much paler than the male in most cases, and the marginal spots within the lunules are very pale, almost white. The submarginal row of round black spots is relatively large and distinct, quite uniform in size. On the under side the wings are much more conspicuously marked on the secondaries than in the male sex, being crossed by three conspicuous bands of irregularly shaped yellow spots, one at the base and one on either side of the discal area. The submarginal round spots of the upper side reappear on the under side as small, slightly silvered, yellow spots. The marginal spots are bright yellow, slightly glossed with silver. Expanse: ♂, 1.50 inch; ♀, 1.60 inch.

Early Stages.—Unknown.

The typical form is found in Labrador. The variety *alticola*, which is paler, and has the dark spots smaller in size, occurs on the higher peaks of the Rocky Mountains and in Alaska; the variety *dawsoni* turns up near the eastern end of Lake Superior and ranges to Lake Nipigon.

(4) **Brenthis kriemhild** (Strecker). Pl. LVI, fig. 17, ♂, *under side* (paratype of **B. laurenti** Skinner) Pl. LXXIV, fig. 1, ♂, type; fig. 2, do., *under side*; fig. 3, ♂, from Utah; fig. 4, do., *under side*; fig. 5, do, ♀, from Colorado; fig. 6, do., *under side*, types (The Kriemhild Fritillary).

Synonym: *laurenti* Skinner.

This species, which may be easily recognized by the figures of Strecker's types, which we give, is found in the southwestern States and also as far north as Yellowstone Park. There is no silvering of the spots on the under side of the wings. Expanse: 1.5 in.

(5) **Brenthis albequina** Holland. Pl. LV, fig. 19, ♂; fig. 20, ♀; fig. 21, ♂ *under side*, types (The White Horse Fritillary).

This species is most nearly allied to *B. selene* (D. & S.) of Europe, which in turn is not far distant from *B. myrina*. *B. albequina* is easily separable from the latter species, by the fact that the light spot on the under side below the cell of the hind wing near the origin of the first median nervule is divided into two, and does not have the length and breadth of the same spot in other allied species. Expanse: ♂, 1.35–1.45 in.; ♀, 1.75 in.

Habitat.—Southwestern Alaska.

(6) **Brenthis nichollæ** Barnes & Benjamin. Pl. LX, fig. 14, ♂, holotype; fig. 15, ♀, allotype (Mrs. Nicholl's Brenthis).

This species, for the privilege of figuring which I am indebted to the late Dr. William Barnes, is closely allied to *B. dawsoni*, but may at once be distinguished by its smaller size, and the lighter color of the hind margin of the secondaries in the male, and the differences in the macular bands. Expanse: ♂, 1.25 in.; ♀, 1.40 in.

(7) **Brenthis helena** (Edwards). Pl. XVIII, fig. 16, ♂, *under side*; fig. 17, ♂, types (The Helena Fritillary).

Butterfly, ♂.—The wings on the upper side are fulvous, greatly obscured by brown at the base of the fore wings and along the inner margin of the hind wings. The usual black markings are light, and the marginal border is also not so heavily marked as in *B. myrina*. The fore wings on the under side are pale fulvous, laved with ferruginous at the tip. The hind wings are brightly ferruginous, with small yellow marginal spots, and paler spots inclining to buff on the costal border and at the end of the cell, about the region of the median nervules.

♀.—The female is very much like the male on the upper side, but the ground-color is paler. On the under side the wings are somewhat paler, and all the spots and light markings, especially on the secondaries, are far more conspicuous, being bright yellow, and standing out very prominently upon the dark ferruginous ground. Expanse: 1.40 inch.

Early Stages.—The early stages of this insect are not as yet known.

Habitat.—*Helena* appears to be a common species in Colorado, Montana, and New Mexico. It is subject to considerable variation, both in the intensity of the coloring of the under side of the wings, and in the distinctness of the maculation.

Barnes and McDunnough have applied the name *ingens* to certain specimens, which are larger than usual.

(8) **Brenthis montinus** Scudder. Pl. XV, fig. 7, ♂; fig. 8, ♀, *under side* (The White Mountain Fritillary).

Butterfly, ♂.—The upper side is fulvous, closely resembling *B. chariclea*, but the ground-color is darker. The under side of the hind wings is deep ferruginous, mottled with white, the most conspicuous of the white spots being a white bar occurring at the end of the cell, and a small round white spot at the base of the wing. The hind wings have also a marginal row of slightly silvered white spots.

♀.—The female is very much like the male, but the ground-color of the upper side is paler. Expanse: ♂, 1.50 inch; ♀, 1.75 inch.

This interesting butterfly is found on the barren summits of the White Mountains, New Hampshire. It represents the survival of an arctic fauna on these peaks, and, like the arctic flora of the spot where it is found, is a souvenir of the ice-age, which once shrouded the northeastern regions of the United States with glaciers.

(9) **Brenthis chariclea** (Schneider). Pl. XV, fig. 4, ♂. Var. **boisduvali** Duponchel, fig. 5, ♂; fig. 6, ♀, *under side.* Var. **rainieri** Barnes & McDunnough, Pl. LX, fig. 9, ♂, paratype; fig. 10, do., ♀, *under side.* Var. **grandis** Barnes & McDunnough, fig. 7, ♂, paratype; fig. 8, do., ♀, *under side.* Var. **arctica** (Zetterstedt), Pl. LV, fig. 22, ♂; fig. 23, do., ♀. (The Chariclea Fritillary).

This species is circumpolar, being found in one form or another in Europe, Asia, North America, including Greenland. It occurs on the high mountains of British Columbia and of Washington, and upon the loftier peaks of Wyoming, Idaho, and Montana. Various slight varieties have been given names, and some of these are depicted upon our plates. I have never been able to make out any valid distinction between typical *B. chariclea* Schneider, from Scandinavia and Lapland, and *B. boisduvali* Duponchel, originally described from Labrador.

Early Stages.—Little is as yet known of these.

The variety *arctica* Zett., from Greenland is smaller than the typical form and the fore wings appear to be a little more acute at the apex. *B. grœnlandica* Skinner is a synonym for *B. arctica* Zett., as is also *B. obscurata* McLachlan, unless I am greatly mistaken.

(10) **Brenthis butleri** (Edwards). Pl. LV, fig. 16, ♂, paratype; fig. 17, ♀, paratype; fig. 18, ♂, type, *under side* (Butler's Fritillary).

This species, or form, is somewhat closely allied to the preceding, but may be always distinguished by the bright double silvery spots below the cell of the hind wing, near the origin of the first median nervule, which have the form of reversed parentheses—) (, and are usually very bright and conspicuous. The insect occurs abundantly in northwestern Alaska, from Nome northward; and also on the islands and peninsulas north of Hudson Bay.

(11) **Brenthis alaskensis** Holland. Pl. LV, fig. 24, ♂, type; fig. 25, ♀. (The Alaskan Fritillary).

This is the North American form of the European insect, named *B. pales* (Denis & Schiffermüller). It is brighter on the limbal areas of the wings, and darker at their base than the European form, but is otherwise very close to its European congener. The insect is not uncommon in the Yukon Valley.

(12) **Brenthis freija** (Thunberg). Pl. XV, fig. 9, ♂; fig. 10, ♀, *under side;* fig. 11, ♂, from Labrador; fig. 12, ♂, *under side* (dark form from Labrador.) Var. **tarquinius** (Curtis), Pl. LX, fig. 13, ♂, *under side*, from Baffinland (The Lapland Fritillary).

Synonyms: *lapponica* (Esper); *freya* (Godart).

Butterfly.—The wings are pale fulvous, the fore wings at the base and the hind wings on the inner half being deeply obscured with fuscous. The markings are quite heavy. The fore wings on the under side are very pale fulvous, yellowish at the tip, mottled with ferruginous. The hind wings are ferruginous on the under side, mottled with yellow. The spots are quite large, consisting of lines and dashes, and a marginal row of small lunulate spots, pale yellow or white, slightly silvered. Expanse: 1.50 inch.

I am indebted to Dr. J. McDunnough for the privilege of figuring a specimen of the variety of this species named *B. tarquinius* by Curtis. It was captured in Baffinland, and is distinguished from the typical form by the rich maroon tint of the under side of the secondaries.

Habitat.—Circumpolar, being found in Norway, Lapland, northern Russia, and Siberia, through Alaska, British America, and Labrador, occurring also upon the highest peaks of the Rocky Mountains as far south as Colorado.

(13) **Brenthis natazhati** Gibson. Pl. LXXII, fig. 7, ♂; fig. 8, ♀, types, after Gibson (The Natazhati Fritillary).

This species, or form, is closely related to *B. freija*, from which it seems to be mainly different in having the dark spots of the upper side larger and tending to fuse into a dark mass covering the inner two-thirds of both wings on the upper side, while on the under side the ground-color is ochraceous-buff, with the dark markings paler than on the upper side. The silvery spots on this side are dull, the base deeply clouded with blackish, as is also a band following the median row of silvery spots. The species was found at an elevation of 8,600 ft. near Mt. Natazhat. Expanse: ♂, 1.5 in.; ♀, 1.65 in.

(14) **Brenthis polaris** (Boisduval). Pl. LV, fig. 12, ♂, *under side* (The Polar Fritillary).

Butterfly.—The upper side dull fulvous; the markings on the inner half of the wings are confluent, and lost in the brownish vestiture which obscures this portion of the wing. The outer median area is defined by irregular zigzag spots which flow together. Beyond these the submarginal row of small black spots stands out distinctly upon the lighter ground-color of the wings. The outer margin is marked by black spots at the end of the nervules, on the fore wings somewhat widely separated, on the hind wings narrowly separated by the lighter ground-color. On the under side the wings are fulvous, with a marginal row of white checkerings on both wings; hind wing deeply mottled with ferruginous, on which the lighter white markings stand forth conspicuously, forming imperfect antemedian and post-median curved bands. Expanse: ♂, 1.50 inch; ♀, 1.50–2.00 inches.

Early Stages.—Unknown.

Habitat.—Labrador, Greenland, and other portions of arctic America, as far north as latitude 81° 52′.

Alaskan specimens are generally lighter in color on the under side of the secondaries than specimens taken in Labrador. These lighter individuals have been dubbed var. *americana* by Strand.

(15) **Brenthis frigga,** var. **saga** (Staudinger). Pl. XV, fig. 13, ♂; fig. 14, ♀, *under side* (The Frigga Fritillary).

Typical *frigga* described from subarctic Europe and Asia apparently does not occur in our fauna. The variety *saga* Staudinger is, however, not uncommon.

Butterfly, ♂.—The fore wings on the upper side at the base and the hind wings on the inner two-thirds are obscured with brown and the outer margins are more heavily shaded with blackish-brown than in *B. polaris*. On the under side the wings are quite differently marked. The fore wings are fulvous, shaded with brown at the tips, and marked with lighter fulvous on the interspaces beyond the end of the cell. The hind wings are dark ferruginous, shading into purplish-gray on the outer margin, with a whitish quadrate spot on the costa near the base, marked with two dark spots, and a bar of pale, somewhat obscured spots, forming an irregular band across the middle of the hind wings, less conspicuous than in typical *frigga*, to which *B. saga* is very closely related.

♀.—The female does not differ greatly from the male, except that the spots on the under side of the hind wings stand forth more conspicuously, being lighter in color and better defined. Expanse: 1.65–2.00 inches.

This pretty little butterfly occurs in Labrador, across the continent as far west as northern Alaska, and is also occasionally taken upon the alpine summits of the Rocky Mountains as far south as Colorado.

(16) **Brenthis gibsoni** Barnes and Benjamin. Pl. LV, fig. 9, ♂; fig. 10, ♀ (Gibson's Fritillary).

Synonyms: *alaskensis* Lehmann; *lehmanni* Holland.

This butterfly can scarcely be discriminated from *B. frigga* subsp. *saga* Staudinger, except by the fact that it is larger in size, with the basal area on the upper side darker, and the under side of the secondaries near the outer angle having just below the costa a light wedge-shaped pale spot, which does not appear in typical *saga*. Expanse: ♂, 1.5 inch.; ♀, 1.8 inch.

The figures given upon the plate are the types of *B. lehmanni* Holland, which are identical with the insect named *B. gibsoni* by Barnes and Benjamin. The insect is common in the Valley of the Kuskokwim, and also appears to occur on Southhampton Island in Hudson Bay.

(17) **Brenthis epithore** (Edwards). Pl. XV, fig. 17, ♂; fig. 18, ♂, *under side*, types (The Western Meadow-fritillary).

Synonym: *sagata* Barnes & Benjamin.

This species, which is very closely allied to the preceding, and may be only a subarctic form thereof, is common in the mountain valleys of California, and ranges as far east as Colorado. The larva is said to feed on violets. Expanse: ♂, 1.5 inch.; ♀, 1.85 inch.

(18) **Brenthis improba** (Butler). Pl. LV, fig. 27, ♂, typical; Pl. LIX, fig. 23, ♀; Pl. LX, fig. 12, ♂, *under side* (The Dark-winged Fritillary).

This obscurely colored species has been by some writers confounded with the two preceding species, from which it is thoroughly distinct. It inhabits the far north. The male figured on Pl. LV is from northern Alaska; the other male and the female from Baffinland. It has been reported from Nova Zemblya. On the under side the insect is quite differently marked from *B. frigga*, the under side being very dark, with only a quite narrow silvery band on the costa of the secondaries, slightly enlarged near the base, below this line and fusing with it are two light spots. Expanse: ♂, 1.25 inch.; ♀, 1.5 inch.

(19) **Brenthis youngi** Holland. Pl. LV, fig. 28, ♂, *under side*, type (Young's Fritillary).

The insect is bright fulvous on the upper side, except near the bases of the wings, which are clouded with fuscous. On the under side it is, as shown on our plate, pale fulvous with a very narrow edging of silvery on the costa of the hind wing, which is crossed mesially by a narrow, regularly curved band of maroon. Expanse: 1.3 inch.

(20) **Brenthis bellona** (Fabricius). Pl. XV, fig. 16, ♂; Pl. V, figs, 10, 11, chrysalis; var. **toddi,** Pl. LV, fig. 14, ♂; fig. 15, ♀; Ab. **pardopsis,** Holland, Pl. LV, fig. 26 (The Meadow Fritillary).

Butterfly.—This species and its varieties may all be distinguished by the fact that the fore wing at its apex is not pointed, but truncate. Typically pale fulvous on the upper side, with the dark markings on the inner half of the wing narrow but more or less confluent. The dark markings on the outer part of the wing are slight. The fore wings are a little angled on the outer margin below the apex. On the under side the fore wings are pale fulvous, mottled with purple at the tip and on the outer margin. The hind wings on this side are ferruginous, mottled with purple. Expanse: 1.65–1.80 inch.

Egg.—The egg of this species is similar in form, size, color, and markings to the egg of *B. myrina*.

Caterpillar.—The caterpillar also in its early stages closely resembles *myrina*, but in its mature form it differs in not having the spines on the second segment of the body lengthened, as in that species.

Chrysalis.—The chrysalis, which is represented on Plate V, is bluish-gray in color, marked with dark spots. The life-history has been given us by several authors.

This butterfly is very common in the whole of the northern United States, as far south as the mountain-ranges of Virginia, and occurs throughout Quebec, Ontario, and British America, as far west as the foothills of the Rocky Mountains. It flies commonly with *B. myrina*, the only other species of the genus found in the densely populated portions of our territory, from which it may be at once distinguished by the entire absence of the silvered markings which make *B. myrina* so bright and attractive.

The variety *toddi* appears to be the dominant form in eastern Quebec and western Labrador. The form named *kleenei* by Watson is based upon a specimen taken in the Catskill Mts., which is even more melanic than the var. *toddi*, decidedly blacker above and below. I have figured the decidedly curious aberration, which I named some years ago as ab. *pardopsis*, which, while typically marked on the under side, has all the spots of the upper side reduced in size, and not confluent. It is a freak.

(21) **Brenthis alberta** (Edwards). Pl. XV, fig. 15, ♂ (The Alberta Fritillary).

Butterfly.—This, the least attractive in appearance of the species composing the genus, has pale wings with a "washed-out" appearance on the upper side, almost all the dark markings being greatly reduced or obliterated. On the under side the wings are even more obscurely marked than on the upper side. The female is darker than the male, and specimens have a greasy look. Expanse: ♂, 1.55 inch; ♀, 1.65–1.75 inch.

Early Stages.—Unknown, except the egg and the young caterpillar, which have been most beautifully figured by Edwards in Vol. III of "The Butterflies of North America."

(22) **Brenthis distincta** Gibson. Pl. LXXII, fig. 9, ♀, type (After Gibson) (The Distinct Fritillary).

This species, which is evidently near in some respects to the preceding species, is only known to me by the description and figure of the author, who has kindly consented to allow the reproduction of the figure of the type in the Report of the Canadian Arctic Expedition.

(23) **Brenthis astarte** (Doubleday & Hewitson). Pl. XVIII, fig. 14, ♂;
fig. 15, ♀, *under side* (The Astarte Fritillary).

Synonym: *victoria* Edwards.

Butterfly.—This rare insect may at once be distinguished from all others by
the very beautiful markings of the under side of the hind wings, crossed by a band
of irregular, bright-yellow spots, which are narrowly edged with black, and beyond
the black bordered by red. Expanse: ♂, 2.00 inches; ♀, 2.15 inches.

Early Stages.—Unknown.

The first description and figure of this insect were given by Doubleday and
Hewitson. They correctly attributed it to the Rocky Mountains, but Kirby after-
ward gave Jamaica as its habitat, and this led to its subsequent redescription by
Edwards under the name *victoria*. It is found on the high mountains of the
Province of Alberta.

SUSPICIOUS CONDUCT

The entomologist must not expect to be always thoroughly understood. The
ways of scientific men sometimes appear strange, mysterious, bordering even
upon the insane, to those who are uninitiated. A celebrated American naturalist
relates that on one occasion, when chasing butterflies through a meadow belonging
to a farmer, the latter came out and viewed him with manifest anxiety. But when
the nature of the efforts of the man of science had been finally explained, the
farmer heaved a sigh of relief, remarking, in Pennsylvania Dutch, that "he had
surely thought, when he first saw him, that he had just escaped from a lunatic
asylum." The writer, a number of years ago, after having despatched a very
comfortable lunch, sallied forth one afternoon, in quest of insects, and in the
course of his wanderings came upon a refuse-heap by the roadside, opposite a
substantial house, and on this heap discovered an ancient ham, which was surrounded by a multitude of beetles of various species known to be partial to de-
composed, or semi-decomposed, animal matter. He proceeded immediately to
bottle a number of the specimens. While engaged in so doing, the window of the
house across the way was thrown up, and an elderly female thrust her head out,
and in strident voice exclaimed: "Hey, there! What are you doin' with that ham?
I say, don't you know that that ham is spiled?" As he paid no attention to her, she
presently appeared at the door, came across the street, and remarked: "See here,
mister; that ham's spiled; Lucy and me threwed it out, knowin' it was no good.
If you want a good meal of wittles, come into the house, and we will feed you, but
for mercy's sake leave that spiled ham alone." It took considerable effort to assure
her that no designs upon the ham were cherished, and she went away, evidently
completely mystified at the wild conduct of the man who was grubbing in the
rubbish-pile.

Genus MELITÆA* Fabricius

Synonyms: *Cinclidia* Hübner, 1816; *Euphydryas* Scudder, 1872.

(The Checker-spots)

"The fresh young Flie . . . . . .
. . . joy'd to range abroad in fresh attire,
Through the wide compass of the ayrie coast;
And, with unwearied wings, each part t' inquire
Of the wide rule of his renowned sire."

SPENSER.

Butterfly.—Small to medium-sized. Tibiæ and tarsi of the middle and hind pair of legs less strongly armed with spines than in *Argynnis* and *Brenthis*. Palpi not swollen; clothed with long hairs; the third joint finely pointed. Antennæ a little longer than half the length of the costa of the fore wing; the club short, heavy, excavated or spoon-shaped; the subcostal of the fore wing five-branched, the first nervule always rising before the end of the cell, the second at or just before its end. The cell of the primaries is closed, of the secondaries open. The markings of the wings have a different facies from those in the two preceding genera and the spots on the under side are rarely silvered, or, if silvered, the silvering is generally restricted to the submarginal series mainly on the hind wings.

FIG. 92.—Neuration of *Melitæa*.

Egg.—Rounded at the base, subconical, truncated, depressed at the upper end, and fluted by light raised ridges (See text-fig. 8).

Caterpillar.—Cylindrical, in the mature stage armed on each segment with comparatively short spines, thickly covered with diverging hairs or needle-shaped points. In the case of some species, the life-history of which has been worked out, they are known to be gregarious in their early stages, given to separating just before maturity. They feed upon the *Scrophulariaceæ* and other plants.

Chrysalis.—Pendant, rounded at the head, provided with more or less sharply pointed tubercles on the dorsal surface, and generally white, or some shade of light gray, blotched with brown or black, and marked with reddish or orange spots on the dorsal side.

The genus is very extensive and widely distributed over the north temperate zone. A true understanding of the relationships of species can only be reached by the student who has studied the Palearctic as well as the Nearctic forms. Mr. J. D. Gunder of Pasadena has recently published in "The Pan-Pacific Entomologist," Vol. VI, pp. 1–8, an illustrated revision of "The Genus *Euphydryas* Scud. of

---

*In the Annals of the Carnegie Museum Vol. XX, p. 44, I have fully discussed the validity of the genus *Melitæa* and it suffices to say that the proposed genera *Euphydryas* Scudder and *Cinclidia* Hübner only have subgeneric value, while *Lemonias* Hübner being a "stirps-name," and not a generic name, cannot be employed, as has been done in error by a few recent writers.

Boreal America," which illustrates the painstaking diligence of the author. He appears to hold that there are but five true species of *Euphydryas* in our fauna, of one or the other of which the many forms, which have been described, are local races, varieties, or "transitional forms." The five species which he regards as valid in the strict sense are: 1, *E. phaëton* (*recte* phaëtona) (Drury); 2, *E. chalcedona* (Doubl. & Hew.); 3, *E. anicia* (Doubl. & Hew.); 4, *E. editha* (Boisd.); 5, *E. gillettii* Barnes. Under these he arranges all the forms which in past time have been named as species, treating them as variants of the five species above named. His work is interesting and suggestive. There is no doubt whatever that many of the so-called species are varietal forms. Instead, however, of accepting Mr. Gunder's provisional arrangement, I have preferred to adopt the plan now widely prevalent among systematists of arranging the so-called species in "groups." In doing this I have in part followed the order suggested by Gunder.

1. *Phaëtona*-group
Subgenus EUPHYDRYAS Scudder

(1) **Melitæa phaëtona** (Drury). Pl. XVI, fig. 1, ♂; Pl. V, figs. 15, 16, *chrysalis* (The Baltimore).

Butterfly.—The figure given on our plate is that of a typical male. The female is much like the male, but larger. Expanse: ♂, 1. 75–2.00 inches; ♀, 2.00–2.60 inches.

Egg.—A magnified outline of the egg is given in text-figure 8. When first laid it is brownish-yellow, then changes to purplish-crimson, and becomes black just before hatching.

Caterpillar.—The food-plant is *Chelone glabra*, which grows in tufts and patches in swampy places from southern Canada, to as far south as West Virginia and northwestwardly to the Rocky Mountains. The life-history has been described by Edwards, Butt. N. A., Vol. II, and by Scudder, Butt. N. E., Vol. 1. The caterpillars are gregarious and after the third moult weave a web, in which they pass the winter. In the spring they again fall to feeding, as soon as *Chelone glabra* (familiarly known as "Snake-head") begins to send up fresh shoots, and then they scatter and after the fifth moult pupate.

Chrysalis.—This is pendant, pearly-gray, blotched and striped with dark-brown and marked with a few orange-red spots. It is generally found suspended at a considerable distance from the food-plant, for just before pupating the caterpillars wander far away.

This insect is quite local, occurring here and there where the food-plant grows, but in such spots it often appears in swarms.

A number of aberrations, due to the fusing or suppression of the light spots, have been named in recent years. There are many others, to which we may (with gratitude) remark that names have as yet not been given, and which I refuse to name.

2. *Chalcedona*-group

(2) **Melitæa chalcedona** Doubleday & Hewitson. Pl. XVI, fig. 2, ♂; Pl. LIX, fig. 1, ♀ (The Chalcedon Checker-spot).

Butterfly.—This is an extremely variable insect and numerous so-called sub-species, varieties, and aberrational forms have been described and figured. The male figured on Pl. XVI, fig. 2, closely corresponds with the female type depicted by Doubleday & Hewitson, who erroneously gave the habitat of the species as "Haiti." On Pl. LIX, fig. 1, I show a female, which has been closely compared with photographs of the original type and agrees with the same. Expanse: ♂, 1.8–2.5 in.; ♀, 2.25–3 in.

Early Stages.—Described by Edwards "Butt. N. A.," vol. I; "Papilio," vol. IV, p. 63; Wright, "Papilio," vol. III, p. 123; Comstock, "Butt. Calif.," p. 97.

Egg.—Pale yellowish, when first laid, pitted at the base, vertically ribbed above. Caterpillar black, with the bristle-like processes on the segments longer than in *M. phaëtona.*

Chrysalis.—Pale gray, blotched with brown.

The favorite food-plants are the *Scrophulariaceæ,* although it is known also to feed upon the genus *Rosa.*

The species is very common in California in the spring and early summer. It is, as already stated, inordinately subject to variation. In the first edition of this book I spoke of some aberrant forms. Since then names have been applied to these and others by writers. Specimens in which the fore wings are almost entirely black are named var. **supranigrella** Comstock; those with fused and enlarged light spots are called var. **fusimacula** Barnes. Henry Edwards baptized specimens, which have red spots on the margins of both wings and on the fore wing var. **dwinellei** (Pl. LVII, fig. 1). For these and many others the reader is referred to Comstock's "Butterflies of California," and to the papers published in recent years by Mr. J. D. Gunder in the Bulletins of the *Southern California Academy of Sciences, The Entomological News,* and the *Pan-Pacific Entomologist.* They possess interest as possibly showing reversion to, or recession from, an ancestral type in the process of evolution, which is going on. The species is in a state of flux. I have rarely seen a specimen, which absolutely conforms in all minor details to the figure given by Doubleday and Hewitson, which represents the type. I have hundreds of specimens before me and no two are absolutely alike. Minute differences can always be detected.

(3) **Melitæa cooperi** Behr. Pl. LVI, fig. 18, ♂, type; fig. 19, ♀, *under side* type (Cooper's Checker-spot).

Gunder in his recent paper upon the Euphydryads treats this species, or form, as being identical with *M. chalcedona.* I have in my collection the female, which laid the eggs, from which the specimens I figure were bred. This female agrees absolutely with her offspring in form, color, size, and location and shape of the spots. The specimens were sent by Behr to W. H. Edwards as the "types" of Behr's *M. cooperi.* Behr points out in his description that the under side of the wings are more somber in hue, and that the spots are smaller than in *M. chalcedon*. He furthermore informs us that the larva is very different from that of *M. chalcedon*, the caterpillar of *M. chalcedon* being black, while in *M. cooperi* it is yellow. I am aware that larvæ sometimes vary in color, while belonging to the same species, but I prefer to leave the specific identity of this form open to further investigation, and am not quite ready to accept the opinion of Mr. Gunder as final, until the matter shall have been more thoroughly investigated.

(4) **Melitæa colon** Edwards. Pl. XVI, fig. 5, ♂, type (The Colon Checker-spot).

Of the same size and general appearance as *M. chalcedona*, but differing in having the dark band between the extradiscal and submarginal row of light spots on the secondaries solidly black, or with an intercalated row of minute red spots very feebly indicated. Expanse: ♂, 1.75 in.; ♀, 2.50 in.

The types are from the valley of the Columbia River in Oregon. We have a beautiful series of specimens from the same region, in which the black band on the secondaries is absolutely devoid of any red spots.

(5) **Melitæa perdiccas** Edwards. Pl. LVII, fig. 2, ♂; fig. 3, ♀, types (The Perdiccas Checker-spot).

This form, the types of which are figured on the plate, occurs in the neighborhood of Puget Sound. It is smaller than *M. chalcedona* and darker, the light spots being reduced in size. Expanse: ♂, 1.6 in.; ♀, 2.25 in.

(6) **Melitæa macglashani** Rivers. Pl. XVI, fig. 3, ♂ (MacGlashan's Checker-spot).

In this form there is an increase in the size of the light spots. The insect is prevalently broader in expanse of wing than the preceding. The early stages are unknown. The specimen figured came from Truckee, California, the "type-locality," and agrees with the original description. I have a long suite of specimens from Truckee, which, as usual in these things, show small variations. Expanse: ♂, 1.85–2 in.; ♀, 2.25–3.00 in.

(7) **Melitæa truckeënsis** Gunder. Pl. LVII, fig. 17, ♀ (The Truckee Checker-spot).

Synonym: *olancha*, ♀, Comstock (not Wright).

This is a variety of *M. macglashani*, which occurs in considerable numbers at Truckee, California, from which I have a good series. The light spots are more uniform in size and a trifle larger than in typical *M. macglashani*, with which it no doubt interbreeds. Expanse: ♂, 1.75 in.; ♀, 2.25 in.

(8) **Melitæa olancha** Wright. Pl. LVII, fig. 4, ♂; fig. 5, ♀ (The Olancha Checker-spot).

This is a form in which there is a marked tendency to what Mr. Gunder has called "*albifusism*," which is a tendency to an increase in the size of the light spots. It is even more marked in this form than in *M. truckeënsis*. Wright's types were from Mt. Olancha, near Mt. Whitney. The specimens figured on the plate came from a point not far distant in Nevada, and agree with Wright's figures. Expanse: ♂, 1.5 in.; ♀, 2.2 in.

(9) **Melitæa quino** Behr. Pl. LVII, fig. 8, ♂; fig. 9, ♀ (Behr's Checker-spot).

I have followed Gunder in his recent identification of this species. By his kindness I am able to give figures of a male and female from Palm Springs, California. The insect is smaller than *M. olancha* and has more red upon the upper surface. The Mead Collection contains a specimen from Nevada labelled *"quino* Behr," which absolutely agrees with the male specimen figured on our plate. The insects labelled as *M. quino* in the W. H. Edwards Collection, however, do not differ materially from those designated as *M. baroni* by Edwards, who seems, *pro tanto*, to have erred.

For a full discussion of the identity of *M. quino* Behr the reader may consult the paper of Mr. Gunder published in "The Pan-Pacific Entomologist," Vol. V, 1928, pp. 1–5.

The butterfly occurs in early spring in the semi-arid regions of the extreme southern parts of California and Nevada. Expanse: ♂, 1.5 in.; ♀, 1.75 in.

3. *Anicia*-group

(10) **Melitæa anicia** Doubleday & Hewitson. Pl. LVII, fig. 10, ♂, typical; fig. 11, ♀ (Hewitson's Checker-spot).

The male specimen figured on our plate has been compared with the original type in the British Museum and agrees with it. The female also agrees with what is known as that sex of the species. The metropolis of the insect is the Rocky Mountains of Canada. The specimen described by Doubleday & Hewitson was collected by the Earl of Derby in the Canadian Rockies. It occurs about Banff in Alberta and in British Columbia. It also is found at considerable elevations on the mountains of Montana and Idaho.

The late W. H. Edwards regarded the form which he described as *Melitæa brucei* from the high mountains of Colorado as being the same as *M. anicia* D. & H. While there is a close resemblance, there are marked differences between the Coloradan insect and typical *anicia* from Canada. This is especially true of the Coloradan females, some of which are quite melanic and differ in their markings, the light spots being more diffused than in typical *anicia*. Expanse: ♂, 1.25–1.4 in.; ♀, 1.4 in.–1.65 in.

(11) **Melitæa brucei** Edwards. Pl. LIX, fig. 3, ♂; fig. 4, ♀, types (Bruce's Checker-spot).

For purposes of comparison I have shown on the plate specimens of the Coloradan insect, which Edwards regarded as being the same as *anicia*. I am of the opinion that *M. montana* McDunnough, recently described and still more recently figured by Gunder, is very near, if not identical with *M. brucei* Edwards. *M. montana* McDunnough was taken by the author of the species in the Yellowstone Park in Wyoming.

(12) **Melitæa beani** Skinner. Pl. XVIII, fig. 13, ♂, type (Bean's Checker-spot).

This is a small dark form found on the bleak, inhospitable mountain-tops about Laggan, Alberta, and named in honor of its discoverer, Mr. Thos. E. Bean. Dr. Skinner described the form as an alpine variety of *M. anicia*. Mr. Gunder treats it as a valid species and places it in his order of arrangement in the *Editha*-group. His figure of the male is too large. Expanse: ♂, 1.15 in.; ♀, 1.25 in.

(13) **Melitæa helvia** Scudder. Pl. LVII, fig. 12, ♂; fig. 13, ♀ (Scudder's Checker-spot).

This insect, which is recognizable from the figures given on the plate, is, so far as known, the most northern representative of the genus on the continent. It is found in the Yukon Valley in Alaska. The type was destroyed in the Chicago Fire. I have, however, a small series of specimens obtained for me by the late Dr. S. Hall Young, who collected for me in all parts of Alaska. Scudder does not give the sex of the type, but it must have been a male, as his labored description exactly corresponds with that sex. Expanse: ♂, 1.25–1.5 in.; ♀, 1.33–1.6 in.

(14) **Melitæa maria** Skinner. Pl. LVI, fig. 10, ♂, paratype, *under side* (Skinner's Checker-spot).

This species, or variety, is closely allied to *M. bernadetta* Leussler, but the fulvous spots on the upper side are brighter red and give a different facies to the form, when compared with *bernadetta*. On the under side the insect is paler in color than *bernadetta*, and the intramacular bands are not dark, as in the latter species. The type-locality is Park City, Utah, from which place I have a good series. Expanse: ♂, 1.4 in.; ♀, 1.6 in.

(15) **Melitæa bernadetta** Leussler. Pl. LVII, fig. 14, ♂, paratype (Leussler's Checker-spot).

This species, or form, may be recognized by the darker ground-color, which is much blacker than in allied forms, and by the absence of red, this color being confined to a few spots mostly in the costal region of the primaries. The male in the disposition of its markings resembles the female of *M. helvia*, which is, however, far more suffused with fulvous. The metropolis of the species is western Nebraska (Sioux County). Expanse: ♂, 1.5 in.; ♀, 1.8 in.

(16) **Melitæa magdalena** Barnes & McDunnough. Pl. LVI, fig. 23, ♂; fig. 24, ♀, paratypes (McDunnough's Checker-spot).

The figures given on the plate should enable the student to recognize this form. It is darker on the under side than *M. maria* and the dark spots are accentuated, especially on the costal regions of both fore and hind wings. The type-locality is the White Mountains of Arizona. Expanse: ♂, 1.3 in.; ♀, 1.5 in.

(17) **Melitæa carmentis** Barnes & Benjamin. Pl. LVI, fig. 20, ♂; Fig. 21, ♀, paratypes (Benjamin's Checker-spot).

I am indebted to Dr. Barnes for being able to give on the plate recognizable figures of this species, or form, the type-locality of which is southeastern Colorado. On the upper side it is prevalently lighter and more suffused with red than *M. magdalena*. On the under side the intramacular bands, especially those toward the base of the wing, are darker than in *M. maria*. Expanse: ♂, 1.25 in.; ♀, 1.5 in.

4. *Eurytion*-group

This species, which I associate in this group, are all characterized by the more or less extensive prevalence of fulvous spots on the fore wings, giving them a distinctly reddish facies.

(18) **Melitæa eurytion** Mead.* Pl. LVII, fig. 15, ♂; fig. 16, ♀, types (Mead's Checker-spot).

The name *eurytion* was applied by Mead to a form collected by him in north-central Colorado at comparatively low altitudes. Its description in Wheeler's Report on the "Explorations and Surveys West of the One Hundredth Meridian," Vol. V, 1875, Chapter VIII, p. 759, is rather brief and unsatisfactory. What he intended to describe is more satisfactorily rendered to the eye by the types, which are figured on our plate. From these figures it may be seen that the insect is closely related to the form subsequently described by Barnes as *M. capella*, from which it is differentiated by the paler color of the submarginal spots on both the fore and the hind wings. Expanse: ♂, 1.25 in.; ♀, 1.5 in.

(19) **Melitæa capella** Barnes. Pl. LVII, fig. 18, ♂; fig. 19, ♀, paratypes (Barnes' Checker-spot).

M. capella is very close to *M. eurytion* Mead. It was originally described by Barnes from central Colorado and the type-locality is not far from that at which Mead collected *M. eurytion*. The male as well as the female of *M. capella* may be distinguished from *eurytion* by the red suffusion of the upper part of the basal area of the secondaries, in which respect the former differs from *eurytion*, in which the basal area near the costa is black and not red. Expanse: ♂, 1.6 in.; ♀, 1.85 in.

(20) **Melitæa nubigena** Behr. Pl. XVI, figs. 6 and 9, ♂♂, from Colorado; Pl. LIX, fig. 2, ♀, from California, labelled by Hy. Edwards as "type" (The Cloud-born Checker-spot).

The most perplexing problem in the study of the genus *Melitæa* is that of the correct identification of the species named *nubigena* by Behr. The types in Behr's Collection were destroyed in the earthquake and fire which devastated San Francisco in 1906. Behr's short Latin diagnosis is quite unsatisfactory. I have in the collection of W. H. Edwards a specimen ticketted "S. Cala." bearing the note "H. E. sent this as the type of *nubigena*." Henry Edwards ("H. E.") was familiar with Behr's Collection. He was a very close observer and reliable in his determinations. This specimen, I take it, had been compared by him with Dr. Behr's *nubigena*. It comes as near representing the type as anything now extant.

---

*An article recently published, stating that the location of the "Mead Collection" is a matter of uncertainty to entomologists, prompts me to say that more than forty years ago I bought from Theodore L. Mead his entire collection. It contains many of the lepidoptera collected by "The Wheeler Expedition," as well as a vast quantity of material collected by Mead himself. Upon this collection he founded Chapter VIII, upon the lepidoptera published in "Wheeler's Report." Mr. Mead's father-in-law, the late W. H. Edwards, and the late Dr. S. H. Scudder helped Mead in the preparation of his paper. The Mead Collection contains many specimens named and described by Edwards and Scudder bearing their labels, and designated by them as "types." The possession of this collection has enabled the writer to determine with accuracy what Edwards and Scudder regarded as the typical form of many of the species, which they named, and numerous "types" from this collection are figured on the plates of this book.

It agrees especially on the underside with Behr's description, so far as that goes. Messrs. Barnes and McDunnough, who have been followed by Gunder, have regarded a small alticoline variety of *M. rubicunda* Hy. Edw. as being *M. nubigena*. Comstock on the contrary in the "Butterflies of California," Pl. 35, figures specimens which correspond very closely to the insect sent by Henry Edwards to W. H. Edwards as typical *nubigena*. It is exceedingly improbable that Henry Edwards would have confused dwarfed specimens of the species which he himself named *rubicunda* with *M. nubigena* Behr. He was a friend of Dr. Behr and perfectly familiar with his collection. I am inclined, therefore, in view of these facts to agree with Comstock rather than with Barnes and McDunnough.

Some of the specimens labeled *nubigena* in the W. H. Edwards Collection as well as in the Henry Edwards Collection are ticketted as from "Colorado." Gunder seems to hold that not being "topotypical" they do not represent *nubigena*. But the conditions on the high mountains of California and Colorado are essentially the same, and I see no good reason for concluding that the insect may not have a wider range than the Tuolumne Valley in California. Locality is not necessarily a "specific character," though some writers of late seem to think it is.

The matter is still open to discussion. I prefer to follow the elder authors, who were very well informed, and whose opinions I still hold in respect. *Quien sabe?* The early stages have not been described. Expanse: ♂ 1.6 in.; ♀, 1.75 in.

The species is near to *M. eurytion* Mead and *M. capella* Barnes.

(21) **Melitæa colonia** Wright. Pl. LVIII, fig. 2, ♂; fig. 3, ♀ (The Colonia Checker-spot).

This insect, which may be recognized by the figures on the plate, was originally described from Oregon. It has been reported by Barnes and McDunnough as taken in Washington on Mt. Rainier. We have a good series from that locality, but they are prevalently darker above and below, more somber in color, than specimens from Oregon. *M. colonia* is closely related to the following species or form. We do not know its life-history. Expanse: ♂, 1.4 in.; ♀, 1.6 in.

(22) **Melitæa wheeleri** Henry Edwards. Pl. LVIII, fig. 1, ♂, paratype (Wheeler's Checker-spot).

The insect shown on the plate is one of the original lot of specimens from Nevada described by Henry Edwards, bearing the label in his own handwriting, and by him sent to W. H. Edwards, in whose collection it is. It differs from the following species in being smaller, not having a submarginal row of light spots on the secondaries, the spots being bright fulvous throughout on the limbal area. Expanse: ♂, 1.75 in.; ♀, 2 in.

(23) **Melitæa sierra** Wright. Pl. LVII, fig. 6, ♂; fig. 7, ♀ (The Sierra Checker-spot).

Mr. Gunder places this species in the *Chalcedona*-group. I cannot regard this as a natural arrangement. *Sierra* is very closely related in form and coloration to *M. capella* Barnes and *eurytion* Mead.

The species was originally described from the neighborhood of Mt. Whitney, Calif. The female figured was captured in that neighborhood, the male from a point near by in Nevada.

(24) **Melitæa alena** Barnes & Benjamin. Pl. LVII, fig. 20, ♂; fig. 21, ♀, paratypes (The Alena Checker-spot).

The figures on the plate suffice to indicate the differences which exist between this form and its near allies, better than could be done by a lengthy verbal description. The male is darker than the male of *M. capella*. The female has the maculæ of the wings lighter than in the female of the latter, and there is a black submarginal line, which is lost, or at most very faintly indicated, in the female of *M. capella*. The type-locality of *M. alena* is southwestern Utah. Expanse: ♂, 1.5 in.; ♀, 2 in.

(25) **Melitæa irelandi** Gunder. Pl. LVII, fig. 24, ♂, holotype; fig. 25, ♀, allotype (Ireland's Checker-spot).

This insect may easily be recognized from the figures given on the plate. The limbal area of the wings is broadly suffused with bright fulvous and there is an absence of the postdiscal dark transverse band, which characterizes *M. alena* Barnes. The types are from the Sequoia National Park in California. Expanse: ♂, 1.5 in.; ♀, 2 in.

(26) **Melitæa morandi** Gunder. Pl. LVII, fig. 22, ♂, holotype; fig. 23, ♀, allotype (Morand's Checker-spot).

The figures of the original types of this species, or form, are perfectly recognizable. The general coloration is a pale bright fulvous and the basal area is dark fuscous, the characteristic light spots in this area having a tendency to disappear, or being only faintly indicated. The typical locality is Mt. Charleston, in the extreme southern part of Nevada. Expanse: ♂, 1.5 in.; ♀, 1.65 in.

5. *Rubicunda*-group

(27) **Melitæa rubicunda** Henry Edwards. Pl. XVI, fig. 10, ♂, type; Pl. LVIII, fig. 4, ♂, type (The Ruddy Checker-spot).

The species is characterized by having the extradiscal and marginal spots not fulvous, but dark red (crimson). The figures on our plates are taken from specimens communicated by Henry Edwards as "types" to W. H. Edwards. The specimens figured by W. H. Edwards in his "Butt. of N. A." are in my possession, but they are not those indicated as "types," though the differences are so slight as not to be of any consequence, consisting mainly of slight variations in the size of the light spots. Henry Edwards originally described the species from the Sierra Nevada, Mariposa Co., Colorado, as a variety of *M. quino*. The species is widely distributed and ranges from northern to southern California at from moderate to high altitudes. Several aberrant forms have been named, as **foxi** and **albiradiata** by Gunder and **rubrosuffusa** by Comstock. A small dwarfed form found in the Tuolumne Meadows is claimed by some recent writers as being *nubigena* Behr (See No. 20).

(28) **Melitæa aurilacus** (Gunder). Pl. LVII, fig. 28, ♂, holotype; fig. 29, ♀, allotype (Gunder's Checker-spot).

Easily distinguished from *M. rubicunda* by the crimson color of all the outer three rows of lighter spots, especially on the hind wings. The types are from Gold Lake, Sierra County, California. This seems to be a form of *rubicunda* in which red has taken the place of yellow in the submarginal series of spots. I have a male specimen exactly agreeing with the holotype which is labelled "S. Cala." and was placed by W. H. Edwards in his series of *M. rubicunda*. Expanse: ♂, 1.37 in.; ♀, 1.75 in.

6. *Editha*-group

(29) **Melitæa editha** Boisduval. Pl. XVI, fig. 8, ♂; Pl. LVIII, fig. 5, ♂, *under side;* fig. 6, ♀. Var. **hutchinsi** (McDunnough), Pl. LXXIII, fig. 8, ♂; fig. 9, ♀ (Edith's Checker-spot).

This species, which is not uncommon in certain localities in south-central California, may be readily distinguished from its allies by the figures given on our plates. Expanse: ♂, 1.5 in.; ♀, 2 in.

What has been regarded as a varietal form, occurring in Montana and Alberta, showing affiliation also with *M. taylori*, has been given the subspecific name **hutchinsi** by Dr. McDunnough. It is represented on our plate, as cited above, by topotypical material. It is slightly smaller in size than typical *editha* from California, and brighter in color.

(30) **Melitæa taylori** Edwards. Pl. XVI, fig. 16, ♂, type (Taylor's Checker-spot).

This is a northern race, originally described from Vancouver Island, and also occurring on the mainland near by. It is scarcely distinguishable from *M. augusta*. I have a series of specimens reared by Edwards from larvæ sent to him from Vancouver Island. These are all decidedly melanic.

(31) **Melitæa augusta** Edwards. Pl. XVI, fig. 4, ♂; Pl. LVIII, fig. 7, ♀, types. Var. **monoënsis** (Gunder), Pl. LVII, fig. 26, ♂, holotype; fig. 27, ♀, allotype (The Augusta Checker-spot).

Mr. Gunder in his recent revision of the Euphydryads figures as the female "type" a rather atypical female, which is indeed labelled "type" by Edwards, but which does not agree with the run of males and females also labelled "types" by the author of the species. It is a suffused albinic specimen. I have given on the plate a female which is more typical of the species, which is indicated as being a "type," and which agrees more nearly with the male "type." The Edwards Collection contains a number of specimens labelled "*augusta*," which cannot be distinguished from *monoënsis* Gunder, which is a rather well marked race of *augusta*. I have before me specimens intergrading between *augusta* and *monoënsis* Gunder, completely linking the two forms together.

(32) **Melitæa baroni** Edwards. Pl. XVI, fig. 7, ♂; Pl. LVIII, fig. 8, ♀, *under side*, types (Baron's Checker-spot).

This is a common form in Mendocino Co., Calif., whence the types came.

Genus Melitæa

The uniform brick-red of the ground-color of the under side of the wings enables it to be easily discriminated from allied forms. Expanse: ♂, 1.5–1.8 in.; ♀, 1.6–1.9 in. The larval stages have been in part described by Edwards in the "Butt. N. A.," Vol. III, and by Comstock, "Butt. Calif.," p. 101.

7. *Maturna*-group

(33) **Melitæa gillettii** Barnes. Pl. LVI, fig. 22, ♂, paratype (Gillett's Checker-spot).

Synonym: *glacialis* Skinner.

This beautiful and well-marked species is in many respects closely related to *M. maturna* and *M. aurinia*, European forms. *Maturna* has been announced as the type of the non-existent generic name *Lemonias* (Hübner's Tentamen). *Lemonias* is an unpublished stirps- (or family-) name, and has disappeared from the list of generic names in correct use by lepidopterists. The type-locality of *M. gillettii* is the Yellowstone National Park.

8. *Athalia*-group
Subgenus CINCLIDIA Hübner, in part

This group, which includes many palearctic forms, is well represented on the Pacific Coast and in the Rocky Mountains to the east.

(34) **Melitæa gabbi** Behr. Pl. XVI, fig. 15, ♂; Pl. LVIII, fig. 16, ♂, *under side;* fig. 17, ♀ (Gabb's Checker-spot).

Synonym: *sonoræ* Boisduval.

The habitat of this species is in the foothills of the coastal ranges of central and southern California. The general resemblance of the species to the European *M. athalia* was pointed out by Dr. Behr in his original description. I have a male specimen of *M. sonoræ* labelled "type" by Dr. Boisduval in his own handwriting, which was sent by him to W. H. Edwards. This specimen agrees with the figures of *M. sonoræ*, given by Oberthür in the "Lép. Comp." Fasc. IX, Pl. CCLXI, fig. 2189, and agrees with males of *M. gabbi* Behr, which were named by those who had access to Behr's types, before their destruction at the time of the earthquake and fire which overwhelmed San Francisco. A number of aberrant forms have recently been named by Comstock and by Gunder. The species, like all others in the genus, is given to "sporting." Little is as yet known of the early stages. Expanse: ♂, 1.2 in.; ♀, 1.5 in.

(35) **Melitæa palla** Boisduval. Pl. XVI, fig. 13, ♂; fig. 14, ♂, *under side* (From Colorado); Pl. LVIII, fig. 21, ♂; fig. 22, ♀ (typical from California); fig. 23, **M. sterope** Edwards, type, albinic ♀ from Oregon; fig. 24, **M. eremita** Wright, melanic ♀ from California; Pl. XVII, fig. 7, **M. whitneyi** Behr, ♂; fig. 8, ♂, *under side* (The Northern Checker-spot).

The species was originally described by Boisduval from California. It has an extensive range from the western coast as far east as Colorado. It varies considerably. *M. sterope* Edwards, known, so far as I am aware, from the solitary type of the female taken in Oregon, and which is in my possession, is an albinic female of this species. It is very light on the under side. *M. eremita* Wright is a melanic form, the female of which is shown on Pl. LVIII, fig. 24. *M. whitneyi* Behr is a form occurring at relatively high elevations, and prevalently deeper red than those taken at lower elevations. Mead in Chapter VIII of "Wheeler's Report," Henry Edwards (Proc. Cal. Acad. Sci., V, p. 167) and Comstock (Butt. Calif., p. 109) have told all that is known as to the early stages. Expanse: ♂, 1.5 in.; ♀, 1.75 in.

(36) **Melitæa calydon** Mead. Pl. LVIII, fig. 19, ♂; fig. 20, ♀, types (The Calydon Checker-spot).

The type-locality is Turkey Creek Junction, Colorado. The insect is closely related to *M. palla* Behr, which is a Californian form, from which *calydon* differs in having the tints of the upper side of the wings brighter and more diffused fulvous, while the females, so far as shown by the long series before me, show no tendency to dimorphic melanism, which is characteristic of the Californian form. I am happy to be able to figure the species, or variety, which has never before been delineated by any author. It is, as has been suggested by Barnes and Benjamin (Ent. News, XXXVI, 1925, p. 119) the Coloradan form of *M. palla*, though they confess having no knowledge of the location of the "types." We have no knowledge of the early stages. Expanse: ♂, 1.25 in.; ♀, 1.6 in.

(37) **Melitæa damœtas** Skinner. Pl. LVI, fig. 13, ♂, paratype (The Damœtas Checker-spot).

This is a Coloradan form, or species, which is very closely allied to *M. palla*. It is much darker in general color than *M. calydon*, and is closely related to the variety of *palla*, which is known as *M. whitneyi*. It may, however, be distinguished from the latter, by the fact that the outer margin of the upper side of the secondaries is narrowly suffused with fuscous, and the general ground-color is darker, not bright red, as in *M. whitneyi*. A typical specimen collected by Bruce in Colorado at a high elevation was placed by W. H. Edwards under *M. palla*, he having recognized the exceedingly close relationship of the two forms. Early stages unknown. Expanse: 1.25 in.

An aberrant specimen broadly suffused with black has been named *damœtella* by McDunnough.

(38) **Melitæa malcolmi** Comstock. Pl. LVIII, fig. 25, ♂; fig. 26, ♀ (compared with the types by Gunder) (Malcolm's Checker-spot).

On the upper side this form is nearly like *M. palla* in many respects, but on the under side it is much lighter, and, as Dr. Comstock has pointed out, the maculation on this side somewhat resembles that of *M. acasta*. The types were taken on the mountains above the Mammoth Lakes in Mono County, California, whence also came the specimens figured on our plate. Expanse: ♂, 1.45 in.; ♀, 1.6 in.

(39) **Melitæa flavula** Barnes & McDunnough. Pl. LVI, fig. 25, ♂, paratype (The Flavula Checker-spot).

Like the preceding species, or form, closely allied to *M. palla*, but smaller and more somber on the upper side of the wings, and decidedly lighter on the under side; the light transverse bands being pale yellowish, and not shining white, as in *M. acasta*, which on the under side it somewhat recalls. It occurs in Colorado, Utah, and Wyoming. Expanse: ♂, 1.4 in.

(40) **Melitæa hoffmani** Behr. Pl. XVII, fig. 13, ♂; fig. 14, ab. ♀, **hollandæ** Gunder, type (Hoffman's Checker-spot).

In the general style of its markings this species, or form, resembles *M. palla*, from typical examples of which it may be distinguished by the light fulvous outer half of the wings sharply separated from the dark inner area by the dark brown or black extracellular band. The species is very variable. A dark form from northern California has been named **segregata** by Barnes & McDunnough, and on Pl. LVIII, figs. 28 and 29, I am able to show a pair of their paratypes. The aberrant female of this species, which I showed in the first edition of this book, has recently been named **hollandæ** by Gunder. **M. sabina** Wright, figured in his "Butterflies of the West Coast" from a dilapidated female in his possession, which was taken in Arizona, is an extremely light form, in which the dark markings of the wings tend toward obliteration. This specimen is not unlike, and closely matches specimens in the W. H. Edwards Collection, both males, one from California, the other from Oregon. I judge *M. sabina* to be a "freak."

(41) **Melitæa acasta** Edwards. Pl. XVI, fig. 11, ♂; fig. 12, ♂, *under side;* Pl. LVIII, fig. 27, ♀ types (The Acasta Checker-spot).

Prevalently pale fulvous on the upper side. On the under side the light bands and lunular markings are pearly (almost silvery) white. Originally described from Utah, it has been found to occur also in Nevada and Arizona. Specimens from the latter state are generally lighter in color than those from more northern localities. Expanse: ♂, 1.5 in.; ♀, 1.75 in.

(42) **Melitæa neumœgeni** Skinner. Pl. LVI, fig. 16, ♂, *under side*, paratype (Neumoegen's Checker-spot).

This is a smaller species than the preceding, distinguished by the much narrower shining white bands of the secondaries on the under side. It is found in desert places. Originally described from Utah, it has been found to occur also in the arid regions of southeastern California. Comstock has in part described and illustrated the early stages (See *Butterflies of California*, p. 107). Expanse: ♂, 1.25 in.; ♀, 1.5 in.

9. *Harrisi*-group

(43) **Melitæa harrisi** Scudder. Pl. XVII, fig. 5, ♂; fig. 6, ♀, *under side;* Pl. V, figs. 17–18, *chrysalis;* Pl. LIX, fig. 11, var. **albimontana** Avinoff, ♂, type: fig. 12, var. **liggettii** Avinoff, ♂; fig. 13, ♀, types (Harris' Checker-spot).

In the typical form the wings are prevalently bright fulvous, black at the base and on the outer margins. Figs. 5 and 6 on Plate XVII well show the markings of this form on the upper and under sides. A lighter form in which the fulvous areas on the upper side are more widely diffused has received the varietal name *albimontana*. The type is on Pl. LIX, fig. 11. This form is known from northern New Hampshire and Ontario. A very dark form, in which the fulvous spots are greatly reduced, is quite common in the northern parts of western Pennsylvania, and very probably also occurs in the adjacent parts of Ohio. It has been named var. *liggetti* by Avinoff in honor of the successful efforts of Mr. Thomas Liggett of Pittsburgh to secure the only great remaining tract of primitive forest in the State of Pennsylvania, known as "Cook's Forest," as a public park. The types were collected in this forest. The form is highly melanic and somewhat exceeds in size the average of the typical form coming from eastern and more northern localities.

The life-history of the typical form of the insect is well known through the writings of Scudder and others. The egg is yellow. The caterpillar feeds on different species of *Aster* and *Diplopappus umbellatus*. When mature it is reddish fulvous, with a black streak on the back; each segment has one black line in front and two black lines behind the nine sets of spiny tubercles, with which the segments are adorned. The chrysalis is white, or pearly gray, marked with blotches of dark brown, or black.

The species ranges from Nova Scotia westward as far as northern Wisconsin, and southward into northern Illinois, Indiana, and Ohio, and on the Appalachian highlands extends well southward through Pennsylvania into West Virginia.

(44) **M. hanhami** Fletcher. Pl. LXXIV, fig. 9, ♂; fig. 10, ♀, *under side,* type (Hanham's Crescent-spot).

This species is very closely related to the preceding. It is a true *Melitæa* and should not be referred to the genus *Phyciodes*, as has been done by some recent writers. On the under side it closely resembles *M. harrisi*; on the upper side it is characterized by the prevalence, especially on the hind wings, of light yellowish orange markings, which are delimited laterally by the darker nervules, giving the wings a rayed appearance, which is quite distinctive. Expanse: ♂, 1.5 in.; ♀, 1.75 in.

Habitat: Manitoba.

10. *Didyma*-group

As already stated, Scudder, following the Merton Rules, named *didyma* as the species, which according to his opinion should be regarded as the type of the genus *Melitæa* Fabricius. *Didyma*, like all the insects of this group, varies greatly. More than fifty so-called subspecies, varieties, and aberrations have been named in quite recent years by European writers, who are given to making nice discriminations and proclaiming the discovery of and recording "novelties." Indeed it almost begins to appear as if the time is not far off when each individual specimen in the cabinets of collectors will be named, as is the case with human beings, *e. g.* Henry VIII, ♂; Catharine of Aragon, ♀; Anne Boleyn, ♀; Jane Seymour, ♀, etc.

127

Genus Melitæa

The species *didyma* Fabr. is represented in North America by several allied forms. In the order of sequence I include them at this point in our survey of the genus *Melitæa*. It must be borne in mind that in a linear arrangement of species it is impossible to represent in all cases genetic relationships in sequence. The fact is that certain groups are divergent from the stem of evolutionary development. They are "branches" of the tree; off-shoots from the main trunk. This is true of the "*didyma*-group" and of the groups which follow in our plan of arrangement, but the divergence is structurally so slight, that these forms must all be included in the genus.

(45) **Melitæa arachne** Edwards.* Pl. XVII, fig. 11, ♂ *under side;* fig. 12, ♂; Pl. LVIII, fig. 9, ♀; fig. 10, ab. **gunderiæ,** ab. nov., type (The Arachne Checker-spot).

Like many of the group, this species is characterized by the red ground-color of the secondaries on the under side, crossed at the base and about the middle by highly irregular light bands marked externally and internally and often in their middle by minute black points. The figures given will enable the student to recognize the species, which locally is not uncommon in Colorado. It is given to variation, and, though contrary to my general habit, I give on Pl. LVIII, fig. 10, an illustration of one of these, which I dedicate to the good wife of my friend, Mr. J. D. Gunder of Pasadena, California. Expanse: ♂, 1.5 in.; ♀, 1.65 in.

(46) **Melitæa pola** Boisduval. Pl. LVIII, fig. 11, ♀ (identified by Mr. Gunder as the ♀ of *M. monache* Comstock). (The Pola Checker-spot).

Synonym: *monache* Comstock.

Under the specific name *pola* Boisduval described a form, which I am quite unable to distinguish from the insect named *monache* by Comstock. A figure of the male type of *M. pola* is given by Oberthür, "Lépidoptérologie Comparée," Fasc. IX, Pl. CCLXI, fig. 2188. Comparing this closely with the fine figure of the male type of *M. monache* given by Comstock (Butt. of California, Pl. 38, fig. 14) I can detect no essential difference. *M. pola* (? *monache*) is closely allied to the following species, and is no doubt a local race, existing in the desert regions of southeastern California and the adjacent parts of Arizona. Expanse: ♂, 1.25 in.; ♀, 1.5 in.

(47) **Melitæa minuta** Edwards. Pl. LVIII, fig. 12, ♂, *under side;* fig. 13, ♀; Pl. XVI, fig. 22, lightly colored ♀ (The Smaller Checker-spot).

The species was originally described from west-central Texas, where it is found commonly; but it ranges somewhat widely, and we have typical specimens collected in southeastern Colorado. On the under side it is much deeper red than *M. pola*. Expanse: ♂, 1.25 in.; ♀, 1.5 in.

(48) **Melitæa nympha** Edwards. Pl. XVI, fig. 21, ♂; Pl. LVIII, Fig. 14, ♀, types; fig. 15, ♀, *under side* (The Nymph-like Crescent-spot).

This is a well marked species, as the figures show. It is darker on the upper

---

*Dr. McDunnough (Contrib., Vol. III, No. 2, 1916, p. 92) claims that in the Edwards Collection, judging from the locality-labels, the species *arachne* and *minuta* have been reversed. He says that the specimens from Texas should be called *minuta*, and those from Colorado *arachne*. I follow him, but call attention to the fact that *minuta* is also found in Colorado, and is not confined to Texas, as is shown by specimens in my possession.

side than any of its allies in our territory, and the mesial band of the secondaries is always whitish, or white, which is not true of the other species in this group. With over a hundred specimens before me this feature serves to mark them all as distinct, when viewed *en bloc*. It is found in southern Colorado, and Arizona, and is very abundant in the Sierra Madre Mountains in Mexico. Gunder has described an aberration of this species (not of *minuta*) under the name *polingi*. It is suffused with black on the fore wings.

(49) **Melitæa gilensis** Holland. Pl. LVIII, fig. 18, ♂; type (The Gila Checker-spot).

Among the insects in the Mead Collection there has long stood unnamed a specimen, which was taken by the Wheeler Expedition and which is ticketted as from "Fort Gila" in southern Arizona. It comes nearer to the insects included in the *Didyma*-group than any others, and I place it here. The transverse bands and spots on the upper side resemble in a general way those of *M. minuta*, but are fainter, and the ground color is paler, a light buff. On the under side the entire surface is pale whitish, with little contrast between the ground-color and the very narrow transverse bands, which are a shade paler than the ground-color, pearly white, and laterally defined by faint darker lines. The location and outline of these bands recalls that which is found in the species of the *Didyma*-group, but there is an entire absence of the minute black dots, or punctulations, which are so characteristic of all other species of that group. The figure I have given may enable the student to recognize this form. It may be an aberration of *minuta*, but it is, if such, very remarkable. Expanse: ♂, 1.35 in.

11. *Definita*-group

This group is represented in our fauna by but a single species. It represents a transition toward the *Theona*-group. The markings on the under side of the secondaries are very narrow, whereas in the *Theona*-group they are broad.

(50) **Melitæa definita** Aaron. Pl. LVI, fig. 14, ♂; fig. 15, ♂, *under side*, paratypes (Aaron's Checker-spot).

The figures on the plate permit easy identification. The species was originally described from the vicinity of Corpus Christi in Texas. Expanse: ♂, 1.2 in.; ♀, 1.5 in.

12. *Theona*-group

Characterized by the relatively broad and straight mesial band on the under side of the hind wings.

(51) **Melitæa theona** Ménétries. Pl. LIX, fig. 5, ♀ (Ménétries' Checker-spot).

The plate gives a good idea of the general appearance of this form, which is quite dark upon the upper surface. The insect was originally described from Nicaragua, but it ranges northward through Mexico as far as southern Arizona. The female selected for the figure is rather under-sized, but was chosen because it is typically marked and in better condition than others in the possession of the writer. Expanse: ♂, 1.25–1.40 in.; ♀, 1.50–1.65 in.

(52) **Melitæa thekla** Edwards. Pl. XVII, fig. 15, ♂, *under side;* fig. 16, ♂, type (The Thekla Checker-spot).

It may at once be distinguished from *M. theona* by the much lighter, bright fulvous color of both the upper and under sides of the wings. The arrangement of the spots and markings on the under side corresponds to what is seen in *M. theona*, of which it is a subspecies, quite commonly found in Arizona, from which the type came. Expanse: ♂, 1.25 in.; ♀, 1.5 in.

(53) **Melitæa bolli** Edwards. Pl. LIX, fig. 7, ♂; fig. 8, ♀, types (Boll's Checker-spot).

This species, or form, is very close to the preceding. On the upper side the transverse extracellular bands are lighter than in *M. thekla* (often white), and sharply contrasted with the fulvous ground-color of the wings, giving them a different facies from that of the otherwise closely allied form. Expanse: ♂, 1.25–1.5 in.; ♀, 1.5–1.6 in.

Habitat: Arizona.

12. *Leanira*-group

This group is characterized by the broadening of the light transverse markings on the lower side of the secondaries in such a way as to occupy almost the entire surface, leaving only restricted portions of the transverse dark markings, at the end of the cell and sometimes in the submarginal area. The fore wings are generally bright fulvous, the hind wings pale yellow or creamy white. The nervules are always distinctly and sometimes heavily marked with dark brown, or black, giving the hind wings a rayed appearance.

(54) **Melitæa leanira** Boisduval. Pl. XVI, fig. 20, ♂; Pl. LIX, fig. 9, ♂, *under side;* fig. 10, ♀ (The Leanira Checker-spot).

The figures show the insect better than can be done by words. It ranges from the mountains of Arizona to British Columbia. The food-plant of the larva is said to be *Cordylanthus pilosus*, but its life-history has not yet been written. Expanse: ♂, 1.25–1.5 in.; ♀, 1.5–1.75 in.

The variety **obsoleta** Hy. Edw. is a dark form with little fulvous on the upper side, the light spots on this side reduced in size; and with all transverse markings on the under side of the secondaries wanting, or but very feebly indicated.

The variety **leona** Wright on the contrary has the margins of the hind wings on the under side heavily marked with black, the submarginal band of spots solidly black, not pupilled with small white spots, as in the typical form, and a heavy spindle-shaped black band crossing the end of the cell, broken at the end of the cell by a round white spot.

(55) **Melitæa wrighti** Edwards. Pl. XVII, fig. 9, ♂; fig. 10, ♀, *under side*, types (Wright's Checker-spot).

This is a form of the preceding, with much more fulvous on the upper side of the wings. It occurs in southern California, Nevada, and Arizona. It does not differ in size from *M. leanira*. Its life-history remains to be written.

(56) **Melitæa alma** Strecker. Pl. XVII, fig. 1, ♂ (Strecker's Checker-spot). Aberration: **cerrita** Wright.

This species differs from the preceding by having the upper surface of the wings yellowish-ochreous, with but very few dark markings. On the under side the fore wings are pale fulvous, the hind wings pale yellow; the veins and margins black and a transverse double band of black on the outer margin of the median area. The female is like the male, but larger and redder on the upper surface. Expanse: ♂, 1.25 in.; ♀, 1.50 in.

This is a form closely allied to the preceding. It has its metropolis in the arid lands of eastern California, Utah, and Nevada. I have specimens from Death Valley.

(57) **Melitæa fulvia** Edwards. Pl. XVI, fig. 17, ♂, type; Pl. LIX, fig. 6, ♂, *under side* (The Fulvia Checker-spot).

This is another form very closely related to *M. leanira*, but with a much paler upper surface. The light extradiscal spots incline to whitish. On the under side it does not, as the figure shows, materially differ from the allied forms. Expanse: ♂, 1.2 in.; ♀, 1.4 in.

(58) **Melitæa cyneas** Godman & Salvin. Pl. LVIII, fig. 30, ♂; fig. 31, ♀, *under side* (The Cyneas Checker-spot).

This species, or variety, is very closely related to the foregoing. On the upper side of the wings the coloration is very dark, the light spots and bands being much reduced in size. On the under side it is as shown in the figure. Originally described from Mexico, it has been found to occur in southern Texas, whence came the specimens figured on our plate.

13. *Callina*-group

This group contains a number of small forms, all of which are found in Mexico and doubtfully occur within the limits of the United States. They have opaque wings and in their markings recall those of the genus *Phyciodes*, in which they have been placed by a number of recent writers. It is doubtful whether *M. elada* Hew. occurs within our territory, and it is, in my judgment, equally doubtful whether *callina*, attributed to our fauna, occurs within the United States.

(59) **Melitæa callina** Boisduval. Pl. LIX, fig. 21, ♀, type (The Callina Checker-spot).

Oberthür, "Lépidopt. Comp.," Fasc. IX, No. VII, p. 80, states that the female type of this species has disappeared, "disparu," from the Boisduval Collection. I am able to explain its disappearance. Boisduval very kindly sent it to Mr. W. H. Edwards in whose collection, now in my possession, it remains, and I am happy to figure it on the plate, although, as my friend Champion used to say, "it is not a very grand specimen." It corresponds in the markings of the under side very closely with the male, which is figured by Oberthür (*l.c.*) Pl.

CCLXI, fig. 2185. The species was originally described by Boisduval from Sonora, Mexico. It has been confounded with *M. ulrica* Edwards by a number of recent authors. It has nothing whatever to do with the latter species. While attributed to our fauna, there is no evidence, so far as I am aware, that *callina* Boisd. actually occurs within our limits, although it is not impossible that it may turn up in southern Arizona.

14. *Ulrica*-group

This group contains a number of aberrant small forms, which represent a lateral offshoot from the main stem of the genus. They all have semidiaphanous wings. I differ from some recent writers, who have included them in the genus *Phyciodes*, with which from my point of view they have nothing to do. They are found in Texas, in the desert regions of the Great Basin, and the subtropical valleys of Arizona.

(60) **Melitæa ulrica** Edwards. Pl. XVII, fig. 2, ♂, type (The Ulrica Checker-spot).

Synonym: *imitata* Strecker.

In the first edition of this book I followed Skinner in regarding *M. ulrica* Edw. as being identical with the Mexican insect named *elada* by Hewitson, and accordingly figured on Pl. XVII, fig. 2, the type of the former as the latter. I have since been persuaded that they are not identical, and take occasion to correct the error. They are indeed very closely related, but they are not the same, and it is extremely doubtful whether *M. elada* Hew. occurs in the United States, though it is listed as one of our species by many compilers of catalogs and check-lists.

M. ulrica was originally described from San Antonio, Texas. I have in addition to the types a long series of specimens from that locality and points near by, which all agree very closely with the description and with each other. The species is very distantly related to *M. callina* Boisd. Hall in his recent Monograph of the genus *Phyciodes* has sunk *ulrica* as a synonym of *callina* Boisd., but in error, as careful examination of the types on our plates will reveal. They appear distinct. Expanse: ♂, .9 in.; ♀, 1.–1.10 in.

(61) **Melitæa perse** Edwards. Pl. XVI, fig. 19, ♂, type (The Perse Checker-spot).

Closely related to *M. ulrica*, but lighter in color throughout. The marginal crescents on the under side of the primaries are largest at the apex and, rapidly diminishing in size, vanish altogether about the middle of the wing. Expanse: ♂, 1 in.; ♀, 1.10 in. Nothing is known of the life-history of the insect. The species is thus far only known from Arizona.

(62) **Melitæa dymas** Edwards. Pl. XVI, fig. 18, ♀, type (The Dymas Checker-spot).

This is a still lighter form, closely related to the preceding, in which on the upper side almost all the dark transverse marks have disappeared. The habitat of this species is southwestern Texas. Expanse: ♂, .85 in.; ♀, 1.00 in. A variety of this species, with dark outer margins and dark extra-cellular suffusions on the fore and hind wings, has been named *M. senrabii* by Barnes.

(63) **Melitæa chara** Edwards. Pl. XVI, fig. 3, ♂; fig. 4, ♀, *under side,* types (The Chara Checker-spot).

This is a well marked species, distinguished by the light post-discal transverse band on the primaries, slightly less distinct on the upper side, but well marked on the under side, as shown on the plate. Expanse: ♂, 1.00 in.; ♀, 1.25 in. This species is common in Arizona, from which state I have received a long series of specimens.

In concluding this revision of the species of the genus *Melitæa* I cannot refrain from remarking that it seems to me quite evident that the habit of naming slight varieties and aberrations has already been carried in this group to an extreme. It is much to be desired that experiments in breeding species should be seriously taken up. The results would probably tend to simplify the problems, with which we are confronted. Furthermore in the vast territory occupied by the majority of these forms there are so many differences due to environment, ranging from low and high altitudes, from subtropical to arctic conditions on the higher mountains, that too great attention cannot be paid by collectors in the future to the conditions under which their specimens are obtained. Insects bred near the snow-line and insects found near the sea-level not far away, necessarily differ owing to their environment. Conditions in Death Valley, where the thermometer often stands at 120° Fahr. in the shade in the summer months, are very different from those on Mt. Whitney, an alpine peak not far away. Simple facts like these should be borne in mind by students.

COLLECTING IN JAPAN

I was tired of the Seiyo-ken, the only hotel at which foreigners could be entertained without the discomfort of sleeping upon the floor. There are better hotels in Tokyo now. I had looked out for five days from my window upon the stinking canal, through which the tide ebbs and flows in Tsukiji. I felt that, if I stayed longer in the lowlands, I would contract malarial fever or some other uncomfortable ailment, and resolved to betake myself to the mountains, the glorious mountains, which rise all through the interior of the country, wrapped in verdure, their giant summits capped with clouds, many of them the abode of volcanic thunder. So I went by rail to the terminus of the road, got together the coolies to pull and push my jinrikishas, and, accompanied by a troop of native collectors, made my way up the Usui-toge, the pass over which travelers going from western Japan into eastern Japan laboriously crept years ago.

What a sunset when we reached an elevation of three thousand feet above the paddy-fields, which stretch across the Kwanto to the Gulf of Yeddo! What a furious thunderstorm came on just as night closed in! Then at half-past nine the moon struggled out from behind the clouds, and we pushed on up over the muddy roads, until at last a cold breath of night air sweeping from the west began to fan our faces, and we realized that we were at the top of the pass, and before us in the dim moonlight loomed the huge form of Asama-yama, that furious volcano, which more than once has laid the land waste for leagues around, and compared with which Vesuvius is a pygmy. We slept on Japanese mats, and in the morning, the drops glittering on every leaf, we started out to walk through the fields to Oiwake, our baggage going forward, we intending to loiter all day amid the charms of nature. Seven species of lilies bloomed about us in the hedges and the fields; a hundred plants, graceful and beautiful in blossom, scented the air with their perfume, and everywhere were butterflies and bees. Above us hung in the sky a banner, the great cloud which by day and by night issues from the crater of Asama-yama. Five species of Fritillaries flashed their silvery wings by copse and stream; great black Papilios soared across the meadows; blue Lycænas, bright Chrysophani, and a dozen species of Wood-nymphs gamboled over the low herbage and among the grass. Torosan, my chief collector, was in his element. "Dana-san" (*my lord*, or *my master*), "this kind Yokohama no have got." "Dana-san, this kind me no catchee Tokyo side." And so we wandered down the mountain-slope, taking species new alike to American and Japanese, until the sun was sinking in the west. The cloud-banner had grown crimson and purple in the sunset, when we wandered into the hospitable doorway of the wayside inn at Oiwake. There we made our headquarters for the week, and thence we carried away a thousand butterflies and moths and two thousand beetles as the guerdon of our chase.

Genus PHYCIODES Hübner
(Type *Papilio tharos* Drury)

(The Crescent-spots)

"Flusheth the rise with her purple favor,
　　Gloweth the cleft with her golden ring.
'Twixt the two brown butterflies waver
　　Lightly settle, and sleepily swing."
　　　　　　　　　　　JEAN INGELOW.

Butterfly.—The butterflies composing this genus are generally small. Wings on the upper side fulvous, or brown, with black margins, spots, and lines upon the upper side; the under side of the wings reproducing the spots of the upper side in paler tints. Of the spots of the under side of the wings one of the most characteristic is the pale crescent situated on the outer margin of the hind wings, between the ends of the second and third median nervules. This spot is frequently pearly-white, or silvered. Structurally the butterflies of this genus may be distinguished from the preceding genus by the enlarged second joint of the palpi. In the neuration of the wings and in their habits these butterflies closely approximate *Melitæa*.

134

Eggs.—Always higher than broad, with the surface at the base more or less pitted, giving them a thimble-like appearance. On the upper end in some species they have a few short, vertical ridges, radiating from the micropyle.

Caterpillar.—Cylindrical, marked with pale longitudinal stripes upon a darker ground, and adorned with tubercles arranged in regular rows. These tubercles are generally much shorter than in the genus *Melitæa*. The caterpillars do not, so far as is known, weave webs at any time.

Chrysalis.—Pendant, with the head slightly bifid. The dorsal region of the abdomen has short tubercles. The color is generally some shade of pale gray, blotched with black, or dark brown.

Fig. 93.—Neuration of the genus *Phyciodes.*

This genus finds its principal development in South and Central America, which are very rich in species, some of them mimicking in a most marvelous manner the butterflies of the protected genus *Heliconius* and its allies. The species found in the United States and Canada are for the most part not very gaily colored, chaste shades of brown, or yellow, and black predominating.

1. *Tharos*-group

(1) **Phyciodes tharos** (Drury). Plate XVIII, fig. 1, ♂; fig. 2, ♀; var. **marcia**, Edwards, Plate XVIII, fig. 3, ♂; fig. 4, ♀; Plate V, figs. 20–22, *chrysalis* (The Pearl Crescent).

Synonyms: *morpheus* (Fabr.); *cocyta* (Cram.); *tharossa* (Godt); *pulchella* (Boisd.); *pascoënsis* Wright; *camillus* ♂ Wright (not Edw.).

Butterfly.—This very common and well-known little insect scarcely needs to be described. The upper side is bright fulvous, with heavy black borders; all the other dark markings are slight. The wings on the under side are paler, with the dark markings of the upper side showing through, and there are additional markings of brown on the hind wings. Expanse, ♂, 1.25 inch; ♀, 1.65 inch.

Early Stages.—These have been worked out with extreme care by Mr. Edwards, and the reader, who is curious to know about them, should consult "The Butterflies of North America." Dr. Scudder also has minutely and laboriously described the early stages in "The Butterflies of New England." The egg is light greenish-yellow. The caterpillar, which feeds upon various species of aster and allied *Compositæ*, is dark brown after the third moult, its back dotted with yellow, adorned with short, black, bristly spines, which are yellow at the base. The chrysalis is grayish-white, mottled with dark spots and lines.

This species is polymorphic, the winter form *marcia*, which emerges in spring, having the under side brighter, and the light markings more conspicuous on that side than in the summer form, which has been called *morpheus*. Concerning all of this, and the way in which cold affects the color of butterflies, the reader will do well to consult the splendid pages of Edwards and of Scudder.

The pretty little Pearl Crescent ranges from southern Labrador to Florida, in fact, all over North America north of Texas and south of the region of Hudson Bay.

(2) **Phyciodes batesi** (Reakirt). Plate XVII, fig. 35, ♂; fig. 36, ♀, *under side* (Bates' Crescent-spot).

Butterfly, ♂.—On the upper side much like *P. tharos*, with the black markings very heavy. The under side of the hind wings is uniformly pale fulvous or yellow, with a row of faint submarginal brown spots.

♀.—Like the male. Expanse: ♂, 1.25 inch; ♀, 1.50–1.65 inch.

Early Stages.—Unknown.

This species ranges from New York to Virginia, and westward.

(3) **Phyciodes nycteis** (Doubleday and Hewitson). Pl. XVII, fig. 28, ♂, *under side*; fig. 29, ♂; fig. 30, ♀; Pl. V, fig. 19, *chrysalis* (The Nycteis Crescent-spot).

Butterfly.—On the upper side very closely resembling *Melitæa harrisi*, for which it may easily be mistaken upon the wing. The under side of the hind wings is very different, and may at once be distinguished by the lighter color of the base of the wing, and the pale, silvery crescent on the outer margin. Expanse: ♂, 1.25–1.65 in.; ♀, 1.65–2.00 in.

Egg.—The egg is half as high again as broad, marked with sixteen or seventeen vertical ribs above, and pitted about the middle by hexagonal cells. It is pale green in color.

Caterpillar.—The caterpillar undergoes four moults after hatching. In the mature stage it is velvety-black, with a dull orange stripe along the back, and purplish streaks on the sides. The body is studded with whitish spots, each giving rise to a delicate black hair, and is further beset with rather short, black, hairy spines.

Chrysalis.—The chrysalis is pearly-gray, blotched with dark brown.

The life-history of this species has been carefully worked out, and all the details may be found described in minute manner by Edwards and by Scudder.

The varietal form *drusius* Edwards, the types of which I have, has the upper sides of the wings dark, with the fulvous spots much reduced in size. In this respect it resembles the variety of *Melitæa harrisi* named *liggetti* by Avinoff.

The insect ranges from Maine to western North Carolina and thence westward to the Rockies.

(4) **Phyciodes vesta** (Edwards), Pl. XVII, fig. 17, ♂; fig. 18, ♀; fig. 19, ♀, *under side* (The Vesta Crescent-spot).

Butterfly, ♂.—On the upper side it closely resembles the winter form *marcia* of *Phyciodes tharos* (Drury); but the black markings are more evenly distributed. The under side is a pale yellowish-fulvous, and the black markings are slight.

♀.—The female is like the male, but paler. Expanse: ♂, 1.15 in.; ♀, 1.25 in.

The winter and summer forms have been discriminated by Edwards as vars. *hiemalis* and *æstiva*.

Early Stages.—The chrysalis has been described by Edwards in the "Canadian Entomologist," vol. xi, p. 129. This is all we know of the early life of the insect.

It is found in Texas and Mexico.

(5) **Phyciodes phaon** (Edwards). Pl. XVII, fig. 22, ♂; fig. 23, ♀, *under side* (The Phaon Crescent-spot).

Synonym: *gorgone* ♀ Hübner.

Butterfly, ♂.—The ground-color of the male is paler on the upper side than in *Phyciodes tharos*, and the black markings are much heavier. The median band on the fore wings is yellowish. The wings on the under side are yellow, shaded with fulvous on the primaries: on which the dark markings are heavy.

♀.—Like the male. Expanse: ♂, .90 in.; ♀, 1.25 in.

Early Stages.—Unknown.

This insect inhabits the Gulf States, and has been occasionally taken in Kansas.

(6) **Phyciodes thebais** Godman & Salvin. Pl. LIX, fig. 22, ♂, paratype of *P. arida* Skinner (The Thebais Crescent-spot).

Synonym: *arida* Skinner.

It is agreed by students that the insect named *P. arida* by Dr. Skinner is the same as *P. thebais* G. & S. The plate bears a figure of the upper side of a typical specimen of the insect named by Skinner. It occurs in Arizona. It was originally described from Mexico. Expanse: ♂, 1–1.25 in.; ♀, 1.25–1.5 in.

(7) **Phyciodes campestris** (Behr). Pl. XVII, fig. 37, ♂; fig. 38, ♀, *under side* (The Meadow Crescent-spot).

Synonym: *pratensis* (Behr).

Butterfly, ♂.—The butterfly resembles the preceding species on the upper side, but the ground-color is much paler and the black markings are not so heavy. The under side of the wings is pale fulvous, spotted with yellow.

♀.—The female has the black markings of the upper side heavier than the male, and all the spots pale yellow. The markings on the under side are heavier than in the male sex. Expanse: ♂, 1.15 in., ♀, 1.40 in.

Early Stages.—Unknown.

The range of this species is the Pacific coast from Arizona to Alaska.

(8) **Phyciodes orseis** Edwards. Pl. XVII, fig. 31, ♂, type (The Orseis Crescent).

Butterfly, ♂.—The dark markings on the upper side are much heavier than in either of the two preceding species, and the fulvous spots are smaller, the marginal crescents more regular and distinct. The markings on the under side are also much heavier than in *P. batesi* or *P. campestris*.

♀.—The female is like the male, but all the dark markings are heavier and the pale markings lighter. Expanse: ♂, 1.35 in.; ♀, 1.60 in.

Early Stages.—These remain to be described.

Phyciodes orseis ranges from Washington Territory in the north to Mexico in the south.

(9) **Phyciodes camillus** Edwards. Pl. XVII, fig. 32, ♂; fig. 33, ♀; fig. 34, ♂, *under side*, types (The Camillus Crescent).

Butterfly, ♂.—The male is more like *P. campestris*, but the light spots on the primaries are paler, on the secondaries brighter, fulvous. The dark markings on the under side are less pronounced than in *campestris*.

♀.—The female is much like the male. Expanse: ♂, 1.3 in.; ♀, 1.5 in.

Early Stages.—These are wholly unknown.

The species is reported from British Columbia, Colorado, Montana, Kansas, and Texas.

(10) **Phyciodes mylitta** (Edwards). Pl. XVII, fig. 40, ♂, *under side;* fig. 41, ♂, types (The Mylitta Crescent).

Synonyms: *collina* (Behr, not Boisd.); *epula* (Boisd.).

Butterfly, ♂.—Broadly bright fulvous on the upper side, with the dark markings slight; on the under side closely resembling *P. tharos*, var. *marcia*, Edwards.

♀.—The female is like the male, but paler. Expanse: ♂, 1.15 in.; ♀, 1.25–1.5 in.

Early Stages.—These have been described by Mr. Harrison G. Dyar in the "Canadian Entomologist," Vol. xxiii, p. 203. The eggs are laid in clusters upon the thistle (*Carduus*). The caterpillar in its final stage after the fourth moult is black, yellowish below, with a faint twinned yellow dorsal line and faint lines of the same color on the sides. The spines, which are arranged in six rows, are black; those of segments four, five, and six, yellow. The chrysalis is dull wood-brown.

This species has a wide range in the region of the Rocky Mountains, extending from Washington to Arizona, and eastward to Colorado.

(11) **Phyciodes barnesi** Skinner. Pl. XVIII, fig. 5, ♂, type (Barnes' Crescent-spot).

Butterfly, ♂.—Very like the preceding species, with the light fulvous of the upper side of the wings more widely extended, causing the dark markings to be greatly restricted. Expanse, 1.75 in.

The type came from Colorado Springs.

(12) **Phyciodes montana** (Behr). Pl. XVII, fig. 26, ♀, *under side;* fig. 27, ♂ (The Mountain Crescent-spot).

Synonym: *orsa* (Boisd.).

Butterfly.—Upon the upper side the wings are marked much as in *P. camillus*, but are prevalently bright fulvous, with the dark markings quite slight in most specimens. On the under side the wings are pale yellowish fulvous. The female usually has the secondaries crossed by a broad median band of very pale spots. Expanse: ♂, 1.25 in.; ♀, 1.50 in.

Early Stages.—Unknown.

The habitat of this species is the Sierras of California and Nevada.

(13) **Phyciodes picta** (Edwards). Pl. XVII, fig. 20, ♀, *under side;* fig. 21, ♂, types (The Painted Crescent-spot).

Synonym: *canace* Edw.

Butterfly.—The butterfly in both sexes somewhat closely resembles *P. phaon* on the upper side. On the under side the fore wings are red on the median area, with the base, the costa, the apex, and the outer margin pale yellow; the black markings very prominent. The hind wings on the under side are nearly immaculate yellow. Expanse, ♂, .80–1.10 in.; ♀, 1.10–1.25 in.

Early Stages.—These may be found described with minute exactness by Mr. W. H. Edwards in the pages of the "Canadian Entomologist," vol. xvi, pp. 163–167. The egg is yellowish-green. The caterpillar moults five times. When mature it is about six-tenths of an inch long, armed with seven principal rows of short spines, which appear to vary in color in the spring and fall broods, being light brown in the June brood and greenish-yellow in the October brood. The prevalent color of the caterpillar is some shade of yellowish or greenish brown, mottled with lighter and darker tints. The chrysalis is yellowish brown. The food-plants of the caterpillar are various species of *Aster.*

This species is found as far north as Nebraska, and is abundant in Colorado and New Mexico, ranging southward through Arizona into Mexico.

2. *Gorgone*-group

(14) **Phyciodes gorgone** (Hübner). Pl. XVII, fig. 24, ♂; fig. 25, ♂, *under side.* (The Gorgone Crescent-spot).

Synonyms: *ismeria* (Boisd. & Lec.); *carlota* (Reakirt).

Butterfly, ♂.—Easily distinguished from all other allied species by the double row of small light spots on the dark margin of the fore wings on the upper side, and by the silvery, narrow, and greatly bent line of bright silvery spots crossing the middle of the hind wings on the under side.

♀.—The female is like the male, but larger and paler, and all the spots on the upper side are pale fulvous, and not as distinctly white on the outer margin as in the male sex. Expanse, ♂, 1.15–1.35 in;. ♀, 1.35–2.00 in.

Caterpillar.—According to Boisduval and Leconte, it is yellowish, with blackish spines and three longitudinal blackish stripes. The head, the thoracic legs, and the under side are black; the other legs are yellow.

Chrysalis.—According to the same authors, the chrysalis is pale gray, with paler light spots and nearly white dorsal tubercles.

This insect ranges over a wide territory from Canada to the Southern and Western States east of the Rocky Mountains.

This is an aberrant species, the markings on the under side of the secondaries being distinctive. The male was originally figured (?1819) by Hübner associated with a female, which belongs to the species long afterward named *phaon* by Edwards. The male on Hübner's plate has numerical precedence. *P. ismeria* (Boisd. & Lec.) was not published until 1833, and is therefore a synonym.

Genus ANTHANASSA Scudder

Scudder erected this genus in 1872 designating *E. cincta* Edwards as the type. He, however, a few lines below sinks *cincta*, which he evidently did not know, as a synonym of *E. frisia* Poey. I therefore think that *frisia* (Poey) should be accepted as the genotype, more especially as *cincta* is not known.

FIG. 94.—Neuration of *Anthanassa frisia*, enlarged.

Butterfly.—Small butterflies, closely resembling the species of the genus *Phyciodes* in the neuration of the wings, and only differing from them in the outline of the outer margin of the primaries, which are more or less excavated about the middle. In the style of the markings they differ somewhat widely from the butterflies of the genus *Phyciodes*, notably in the absence of the crescents on the underside of the margins of the wings. The wings in the upper side are generally some shade of deep brown or black, marked with spots and bands of white or fulvous, the median band on the hind wings being generally more or less conspicuous. In the pattern of their markings they illustrate a transition from the genus *Phyciodes* to the genus *Chlosyne*.

Egg.—Hitherto undescribed.

Caterpillar.—Cylindrical, with seven rows of spines, one dorsal, and three lateral on each side; the spines are short, blunt, and armed with short bristles. The head is subcordate, with the vertices rounded. It moults four times.

Chrysalis.—Cylindrical, abdomen stout, head-case short, beveled, nearly square at top, the vertices pyramidal. There are three rows of small tubercles on the dorsal side of the abdomen.

The caterpillars, so far as known, feed upon various *Compositæ*, as *Diclippa* and *Actinomeris*.

The genus is well represented in Central and South America. But four species have been attributed to the faunal region covered by this book.

(1) **Anthanassa frisia** (Poey). Pl. XVII, fig. 42, ♂ (The Cuban Crescent).
Synonym: *gyges* Hewitson.

Butterfly.—Upper side reddish-fulvous, clouded with fuscous at the base. On the basal area are waved black lines, separate on the hind wings, more or less blended on the fore wings. The outer border is broadly black. Between this border and the basal third the wing is crossed by irregular black bands, the spaces between which are paler fulvous than the base and the hind wings, those near the outer margin being whitish. These bands are continued broadly across the hind wings. The wings on the under side are fulvous, mottled with dark brown and white, and spotted with conspicuous white spots. The male and the female closely resemble each other. Expanse: 1.40 inch.

The early stages are but little known.

The only locality within the limits of the United States in which this insect has been found is Key West in Florida. It is abundant in the Antilles, Mexico, Central and South America.

(2) **Anthanassa texana** (Edwards). Pl. XVIII, fig. 8, ♂; fig. 9, ♂, *under side;* Pl. LIX, fig. 14, var. **seminole** (Skinner) ♂ (The Texan Anthanassa).

Synonym: *smerdis* (Hewitson).

Butterfly.—Black on the upper side of the wings, shading into reddish-brown on the basal area. The fore wings are spotted on the median and limbal areas with white, and the hind wings are adorned by a conspicuous median band of small white spots. On the under side the fore wings are fulvous at the base, broadly dark brown beyond the middle. The light spots of the upper side reappear on the lower side. The hind wings on the under side are marbled wood-brown on the basal area and the inner margin, darker brown externally. The white macular band of the upper side reappears on this side, but less distinct than above. Expanse: ♂, 1.25–1.50 inch; ♀, 1.60–1.75 inch.

Early Stages.—For the only account of the life-history of this species the reader is referred to the "Canadian Entomologist," vol. xi, p. 127, where the indefatigable Edwards gives us an interesting account of his original observations.

This insect ranges from Texas into Mexico, and eastward to Florida. It has been confounded by some with *Eresia (Anthanassa) ianthe* (Fabr.) and to show the difference between the upper sides of the two species I have given on Pl. XVIII, fig. 10, a representation of what undoubtedly is *ianthe* (Fabr.).

(3) **Anthanassa tulcis** (Bates). Pl. XVII, fig. 39, ♂, type of *punctata* (Edw.). (The Dotted Anthanassa).

Synonym: *punctata* Edwards.

Butterfly.—A lengthy description of this little species is scarcely necessary, as the figure on the plate will suffice for its accurate determination. Nothing is known of its early stages. Expanse: 1.10 in. It is found in New Mexico, Texas, Arizona, and Mexico. Named *punctata* in the first edition of this book I acquiesce in its identification with *tulcis* Bates.

(4) **Anthanassa cincta** (Edwards).? identical with *leucodesma* (Feld.) Pl. LXXIII, fig. 7, ♂.

This species was described and named by Edwards (Proc. Ent. Soc. Phila., Vol. II, 1864, p. 502), from a male specimen. He attributes the species to Texas and Florida. He quotes H. W. Bates as saying: "This species resembles *E. leucodesma* of Felder, a Venezuelan species, but is distinct from it." No specimen labelled *cincta* is in the Edwards Collection, nor in any other collection in the world, so far as I have been able to discover. Hall sinks *cincta* as a synonym of *leucodesma* Felder. *Leucodesma* is abundant in Trinidad and about Panama. Edwards was probably deceived as to the origin of the specimen he described. But I give a figure on Pl. LXXIII of a specimen of *leucodesma* Felder, from the northernmost locality from which I have specimens, and which differ slightly from the typical form delineated by Felder. I do this in order to furnish students in the United States with a clue to help them in determining *cincta* Edw., should they be so lucky as to come across the thing. I do not believe it belongs to the genus *Anthanassa*, of which Scudder made it the type. (See p. 140).

Genus CHLOSYNE Butler
(Type *Papilio janais* Drury)

(The Patched Butterflies)

Butterfly.—Medium-sized or small; rather gaily colored, although the species found in the United States are not very brilliant. Distinguished structurally from

the butterflies of the two preceding genera not only by their larger size and the spindle-shaped third article of the palpi, which in *Anthanassa* and also *Phyciodes* is thin and pointed like a needle, but also by the fact that the lower discocellular vein of the fore wings is generally quite straight and not bowed or angled as in the before-mentioned genera.

Egg.—Similar in appearance to the eggs of the genus *Phyciodes*: obovoid, truncated, and slightly depressed at top, rounded at the bottom; the lower three-fifths with shallow depressions; the upper part with about twenty-four light blunt-edged ribs. The eggs are laid in clusters upon the leaves of *Helianthus*.

Fig. 95.—Neuration of the genus *Chlosyne*, enlarged.

Caterpillar.—Varying in color, generally black, or some shade of red or brown, covered with spines, which are arranged as in the genus *Melitæa* and are thickly beset with diverging bristles. The caterpillar moults four times.

Chrysalis.—Shaped as in the genus *Melitæa*, light in color, blotched with dark brown or black spots and lines.

The genus is well represented in Central and South America. Some of the species are polymorphic, many varieties being produced from a single batch of eggs. The result has been considerable confusion in the specific nomenclature.

(1) **Chlosyne janais** (Drury). Pl. XVIII, fig. 10, ♂ (The Crimson Patch).

Butterfly.—Fore wings black above, spotted with white; hind wings black above, marked in the center with a broad band of crimson. On the under side the markings of the upper side of the fore wings are reproduced. The hind wings on the under side are black at the base and on the outer third; immediately at the base is a yellow bar; across the middle is a broad yellow band laved outwardly by red, upon which are numerous black spots. There is a marginal row of yellow spots and an inner row of smaller white spots on the limbal area. Expanse: 2.50–3.00 inches.

Early Stages.—What is known of these is contained in articles published by Mr. William Schaus, "Papilio," vol. iii, p. 188; and by Henry Edwards, "Entomologica Americana," vol. iii, p. 161, to which the reader may refer.

The habitat of the species is Texas, Mexico, and Central America. The insect is very variable in the markings both of the upper and under sides, and several so-called species are only varietal forms of this.

(2) **Chlosyne erodyle** (Bates). Pl. LIX, fig. 17, ♂. (The Erodyle Patch).

This insect is a rare straggler into our territory along the Texan border, but is abundant further south. Expanse: ♂, 1.6–1.8 in.; ♀, 2 in.

(3) **Chlosyne lacinia** (Geyer). Pl. XVIII, fig. 11, var. **adjutrix** Scudder, ♂. (The Adjutrix Patch).

Butterfly.—*C. lacinia* is a protean species, many varieties being known. Godman and Salvin (Biol. Cent.-Amer., Rhop., III, Pl. 19, figs. 6–17) show twelve different forms, of which the first alone (fig. 6) seems to represent typical *lacinia* (Geyer). In true *C. lacinia* the fore wings are black, marked with small white spots; the hind wings are crossed about the middle by a broad red band, which does not reach the costa, and terminates inwardly about the middle of the inner margin. So far as I know, this form does not occur in the United States, but I have specimens from Mexico, Central America, and Colombia.

The form *adjutrix* is common in the Southwestern States. Expanse: ♂, 1.5 in.; ♀, 1.5–2. in.

(4) **Chlosyne crocale** (Edwards). Pl. XXIV, fig. 8, ♂, *under side;* fig. 9, ♂; Pl. LIX, fig. 18, var. **rufescens** (Edwards) (The Crocale Patch).

In the first edition of this book I treated *C. crocale* as a variant form of *lacinia* (Geyer). In this I was in error. The insect "breeds true" within certain limits, and does not show variation sufficient to cause the belief that it is a form of Geyer's species. The variety *rufescens* (Edwards) has the transverse light band of the hind wing pale orange; the variety *nigrescens* (Cockerell) has this band almost obsolete. The insect is found in California and Arizona. Expanse: ♂, 2 in.; ♀, 2.10 in.

(5) **Chlosyne californica** (Wright). Pl. LIX, fig. 19, ♂; fig. 20, ♀. (The Californian Patch).

In California this form replaces *adjutrix* Scud., which is the usual form east of the Rocky Mountains. The figures we give suffice to show the differences between the two races. Expanse: ♂ and ♀ about 1.5 in.

(6) **Chlosyne endeis** (Godman & Salvin). Pl. LXXVI, figs. 17, 17a (after Godman & Salvin) (The Endeis Patch).

This species has been recently reported as occurring within our borders. I do not possess specimens from within the United States, and have reproduced the figures given by Godman, as being typical.

Genus MICROTIA Bates
(Type *Microtia elva* Bates)

Thus far this genus is only known to consist of a single species, which does not vary greatly throughout its wide range, except that the light transverse bands on the wings are sometimes paler than is shown in the figures we give, being occasionally pale yellow. The insect ranges from Arizona to Colombia. On the under side the wings are marked exactly as on the upper side, except that the general tone of this side is paler than above. The neuration of the wings somewhat enlarged is shown in the cut below, Fig. 96.

(1) **Microtia elva** Bates. Pl. LIX, fig. 15, ♂; fig. 16, ♀, (Bates' Elf).

No description of the butterfly is necessary, as the figures "tell the story." The life-history of the species remains to be written. Expanse: ♂, .75–.9 in.; ♀, 1–1.25 in.

Genus MESTRA Hübner

Synonym: *Cystineura* Boisduval

"And here and yonder a flaky butterfly
  Was doubting in the air."
                                        McDONALD.

Butterfly.—Small butterflies, with elongated fore wings, the hind wings with the outer margin rounded, slightly crenulate. The head is small; the palpi are very delicate and thin, scantily clothed with scales. The costal vein of the fore wing is much swollen near the base. The subcostal vein of this wing sends forth two branches before the end of the cell; the upper discocellular vein is lacking; the middle discocellular is short and bent inwardly; the lower discocellular is almost obliterated, and reaches the median vein at the origin of the second median nervule. In the hind wing the cell is open, and the two radial veins spring from the same point. I put this genus at this point in the series, but think that it should be located nearer the *Satyrinæ*.

FIG. 96.—Neuration of genus *Microtia*, enlarged.

FIG. 97.—Neuration of the genus *Mestra*.

Early Stages.—Very little is as yet definitely ascertained as to these.

But one species is found within the limits covered by this work. Seven species have been described, all of them inhabiting Central or South America.

(1) **Mestra amymone** (Ménétries). Plate XXIV, fig. 7, ♂ (Amymone).

Butterfly.—The fore wings are white on the upper side, dusted with gray at the base, on the costa, the apex, and the outer margin. The hind wings are gray on the basal area, pale yellowish-brown on the limbal area, with a narrow fuscous margin. On the under side the markings of the upper side reappear, the gray tints being replaced by yellow. The hind wings are yellowish, with a white transverse band near the base and an incomplete series of white spots on the limbal area. Expanse: 1.50 inch.

The early stages await description. The insect is found in Texas, straying north to Nebraska, common in Mexico and Central America.

A variety **floridana** (Strecker) occurs in Florida. It differs from typical *amymone* in having the upper side of the wings almost uniformly grayish, with only a trace of fulvous on the upper side of the hind wings. Some writers have identified this with *M. cana* (Erichson) from northern South America.

Genus HYPOLIMNAS Hübner
(The Tropic Queens)

Butterfly.—Eyes naked; palpi produced, rising above the head, heavily scaled; antennæ with a well-developed, finely pointed club. Fore wings with stout costal and median veins; subcostal throwing out five nervules, the first two before the end of the cell, the third midway between the end of the cell and the outer border; the fourth and the fifth diverging from each other midway between the third and the outer border, and both terminating below the apex. The upper discocellular vein wanting; the middle discocellular vein bent inwardly; the lower discocellular very weak, and, in some species, wanting. The cell of the hind wing is lightly closed.

Caterpillar.—Cylindrical, thickest toward the middle; head adorned with two erect rugose spines; the segments have dorsal rows of branching spines, and three lateral rows on either side of the shorter spines. It feeds on various species of malvaceous plants and also on the common Portulaca.

Chrysalis.—Thick, with the head obtusely pointed; abdominal segments adorned with a double row of tubercles; thorax convex.

Fig. 98.—Neuration of the genus *Hypolimnas*.

This genus, which includes a large number of species, reaches its fullest development in the tropics of the Old World, and includes some of the most beautiful, as well as the most singular, forms, which mimic the protected species of the *Danainæ*, or milkweed butterflies, of the Indo-Malayan and Ethiopian regions. In some way one of the most widely spread of these species, which is found throughout the tropics of Asia and Africa, has obtained lodgment upon the soil of the New World, and is occasionally found in Florida, where it is by no means common. It may be that it was introduced from Africa in the time of the slave-trade, having been accidentally brought over by ship. That this is not impossible is shown by the fact that the writer has, on several occasions, obtained in the city of Pittsburgh specimens of rare and beautiful tropical insects, which emerged from chrysalids that were found attached to bunches of bananas brought from Honduras.

(1) **Hypolimnas misippus** (Linnæus). Pl. XXI, fig. 9, ♂ : fig. 10, ♀ (The Mimick).

Butterfly, ♂.—On the upper side the wings are velvety-black, with two conspicuous white spots on the fore wing, and a larger one on the middle of the hind wing, the margins of these spots reflecting iridescent purple. On the under side the wings are white, intricately marked with black lines, and black and reddish-ochraceous spots and shades.

♀ .—The female mimics two or three forms of an Oriental milkweed butterfly, the pattern of the upper side of the wings conforming to that of the variety of the protected species which is commonest in the region where the insect is found. The species mimicked is *Danais chrysippus*, of which at least three varietal forms or local races are known. The American butterfly conforms in the female sex to the typical *D. chrysippus*, to which it presents upon the upper side a startling likeness. On the under side it is marked much as the male. Expanse: ♂, 2.5 in.; ♀ , 3. in.

Early Stages.—What has been said as to the early stages in the description of the genus must suffice for the species. But little is as yet accurately known upon the subject.

The range of *H. misippus* is southern Florida, the Antilles, and the northern parts of South America. It is not common on this side of the Atlantic, but very common in Africa, tropical Asia, and the islands south as far as northern Australia.

FAUNAL REGIONS

That branch of zoölogical science which treats of the geographical distribution of animals is known as zoögeography. None of the zoölogical sciences has contributed more to a knowledge of the facts with which zoögeography deals than the science of entomology.

Various divisions of the surface of the earth, based upon the character of the living beings which inhabit them, have been suggested. At the present time, however, it is agreed that in a general way five major subdivisions are sufficient for the purposes of the science, and we therefore recognize five faunal regions, namely, the *Palæarctic*, which includes the temperate regions of the eastern hemisphere; the *Indo-Malayan*, covering the tropics of Asia and the islands lying south of that great continent, including Australia; the *Ethiopian*, covering the continent of Africa south of the lands bordering on the Mediterranean, and extending northward into the southern part of Arabia; the *Neotropical*, covering the continent of South America, Central America and the islands of the Caribbean Sea and the Gulf of Mexico; and, finally, the *Nearctic*, covering the temperate and polar regions of North America. The butterflies with which this volume deals are mostly nearctic species, only a few species representing the neotropical region being found as stragglers in the extreme southern portion of the United States.

These five faunal regions are characterized by the presence of certain groups of insects, which are more or less peculiar to them. In the Palæarctic Region, for instance, we find a very great development of the *Satyrinæ*, of the genera *Argynnis, Melitæa, Lycæna,* and *Colias.* The genus *Papilio* is but poorly represented, there being only three species found on the entire continent of Europe, and comparatively few in Asia north of the Himalayan mountain-ranges.

As soon as we pass from the boundaries of the Palæarctic Region into India there is discovered a great number of species of the genus *Papilio*. The *Danainæ*, of various genera, swarm, and splendid creatures, magnificent in color, present themselves, replacing among the *Nymphalinæ* the small and obscurely colored forms which are found among the mountains of Europe and on the great Asiatic steppes. In the Indo-Malayan Region one of the most gorgeous of the papilionine genera is known as *Ornithoptera*. These great "bird-wing" butterflies are most brilliant in color in the male, and in the female attain an expanse of wing reaching in some species eight and even nine inches, so that it would be impossible to represent them in their natural dimensions upon a page such as that which is before the reader. One of these giants of the butterfly family, named *Victoria* after her Majesty the Queen of England, is found in the Solomon Islands, and is probably the largest of all known butterflies. One specimen, belonging to the author, has an expanse of wing exceeding nine inches. Among strange comparatively recent discoveries is *Ornithoptera paradisea*, which is found in New Guinea. The male has the hind wings produced in the form of a very delicate and slender tail; the upper surfaces of the wing are broadly marked with shining green and lustrous orange upon a velvety-black ground. The female is black with white spots, slightly marked with yellow, being obscure in color, as is for the most part characteristic of this sex among butterflies, as well as other animals.

The Ethiopian Region is rich in beautiful butterflies of the genus *Callosune*, which are white or yellow, having the tips of the anterior wings marked with crimson or purple. There are many scores of species of these which are found on the grassy park-like lands of southeastern Africa, and they range northward through Abyssinia into Arabia, and a few species even invade the hot lands of the Indian peninsula. In the great forests of the Congo and in fact throughout tropical Africa, the genus *Acræa*, composed of beautiful insects with long, narrow wings like the genus *Heliconius*, but for the most part yellow, rich brown, and red, spotted with black, abound. And here, too, are found some of the noblest species belonging to the great genus *Papilio*, among them that most singular and, until recently, rarest of the genus, *Papilio antimachus* of Drury, one specimen of which, among a dozen or more in the author's possession, has wings which exceed in expanse even those of *Ornithoptera victoria*, though this butterfly, which seems to mimic the genus *Acræa*, has comparatively narrow wings, and they, therefore, do not cover so large an area as *Ornithoptera*.

In the Neotropical Region we are confronted by swarms of butterflies belonging to the *Ithomiinæ*, the *Heliconiinæ*, and the *Acræinæ*, all of which are known to be protected species, and which are mimicked by other species among the butterflies and moths of the region which they frequent. A naturalist familiar with the characteristics of the butterfly-fauna of South America can at a glance determine whether a collection placed before him is from that country or not, merely by his knowledge of the peculiar coloration which is characteristic of the lepidoptera of the region. The most brilliant butterflies of the neotropical fauna are the *Morphos*, glorious insects, the under side of their wings marked with eye-like spots, the upper side resplendent in varying tints of iridescent blue.

In the Nearctic Region there is a remarkable development of the genera *Argynnis*, *Melitæa*, and *Phyciodes*. There are also a great many species of the *Satyrinæ* and of the *Hesperiidæ*, or "skippers." The genus *Colias* is also well represented. The Nearctic Region extends southwardly into northern Mexico, at high elevations, and is even continued along the chain of the Andes, and there are genera found in the vicinity of San Francisco which occur also in Chili and Patagonia. In fact, when we get to the southern extremity both of Africa and of South America we find certain genera characteristic of the north temperate zone, or closely allied to them, well represented.

Genus POLYGONIA Hübner
(Type *Papilio c-aureum* Linnæus)

Synonym: *Grapta* Kirby.

(The Angle-Wings)

Butterfly.—Medium-sized or small, characterized by the more or less deeply excavated inner and outer margins of the fore wings, the tail-like projection of the hind wings at the extremity of the third median nervule, the closed cell of the same wings, and the thick squamation of the palpi on the under side, while on the sides and tops of the palpi there are but few scales. They are tawny on the upper side, spotted and bordered with black; on the under side mimicking the bark of trees and dead leaves, often with a *c*-shaped silvery spot on the hind wings. The insects hibernate in the butterfly form in hollow trees and other hiding-places.

Fig. 99.—Neuration of the genus *Polygonia*.

Egg.—Taller than broad, tapering upward from the base. The summit is broad and flat. The sides are marked by a few equidistant narrow longitudinal ribs, which increase in height to the top. A few delicate cross-lines are interwoven beteween these ribs. They are laid in clusters or in short string-like series (see Fig. 10, p. 4).

Caterpillar.—The head is somewhat quadrate in outline, the body cylindrical, adorned with rows of branching spines (see Pl. III, figs. 23, 27, 31–33, 38).

Chrysalis.—The chrysalids have the head more or less bifid. There is a prominent thoracic tubercle, and a double row of dorsal tubercles on the abdomen. Viewed from the back they are more or less excavated on the sides of the thorax. In color they are generally some shade of wood-brown or greenish.

The caterpillars feed for the most part upon the *Urticaceæ*, plants of the nettle tribe, such as the stinging-nettle, the elm, and the hop-vine, though the *Azalea* and wild currants furnish the food of some species.

The genus is confined mainly to the north temperate zone.

(1) **Polygonia interrogationis** (Fabr.). Pl. I, fig. 3, ♂, *under side;* Pl. XIX, fig. 1, ♂. Form **umbrosa** (Lintner) Pl. XIX, fig. 2, ♀ ; Pl. III, fig. 23, *larva,* from a blown specimen; fig. 27, *larva,* copied from a drawing by Abbot; Pl. IV, figs. 21, 22, 24–26, 40, *chrysalis* (The Question-sign).

Butterfly.—Easily distinguished by its large size, being the largest species of the genus in our fauna. The fore wings are decidedly falcate, or sickle-shaped, bright fulvous on the upper side, spotted and bordered with dark brown and edged with pale blue. On the under side they are mottled brown, shaded with pale purplish, and have a silvery mark shaped like a semicolon on the hind wings. The dimorphic variety *umbrosa,* Lintner, has the upper side of the hind wings almost entirely black, except at the base. Expanse: 2.50 inches.

Early Stages.—These have been frequently described, and the reader who wishes to know all about the minute details of the life-history will do well to consult the pages of Edwards and Scudder, who have written voluminously upon the subject. The food-plants are the elm, the hop-vine, and various species of nettles.

This is one of our commonest butterflies. It is double-brooded in the Middle States. It hibernates as imago, and when the first warm winds of spring begin to blow, it may be found at the sap-pans in the sugar-camps, sipping the sweets which drip from the wounded trunks of the maples. It ranges all over the United States, except the Pacific coast, and is common throughout Canada and Nova Scotia.

(2) **Polygonia comma** (Harris). Pl. XIX, fig. 4, ♂; fig. 3, form **dryas** (Edwards) ♂; Pl. III, fig. 38, *larva;* Pl. IV, figs. 27, 29, 30, 39, 46–48, *chrysalis* (The Comma Butterfly).

Butterfly.—Dimorphic, in the form *dryas* with the hind wings heavily suffused with black, in the typical form predominantly fulvous. Expanse, 1.75–2.00 inches.

The caterpillars feed upon the *Urticaceæ,* and are very common upon the nettle. They vary greatly in color, some being almost snow-white. This species is found throughout Canada and the adjacent provinces, and ranges south to the Carolinas and Texas and over the Northwestern States.

(3) **Polygonia satyrus** (Edwards). Pl. XX, fig. 1, ♀ fig. 2, ♀ *under side;* form **marsyas** (Edwards), Pl. XIX, fig. 14, ♂; fig. 15, ♂, *under side;* Pl. III, fig. 33, *larva;* Pl. IV, figs. 41, 42, *chrysalis.* (The Satyr).

Butterfly.—The species is so accurately depicted in the plates that a description is hardly necessary. The form *marsyas* is smaller, brighter, and with the dark spots on the upper side of the hind wings reduced in size. Expanse: 1.75–2.00 inches.

The food-plant of the caterpillar is the nettle. It occurs occasionally in Ontario, and thence ranges west, being not uncommon from Colorado to California and Oregon. A Californian form, in which the wings on the upper side are prevaiently yellowish fulvous, has been named *chrysoptera* by Wright.

(4) **Polygonia hylas** (Edwards). Pl. XIX, fig. 7, ♂; fig. 8, ♂, *under side* (The Colorado Angle-wing).

Butterfly.—The butterfly closely resembles *P. silenus* on the upper side, but may easily be distinguished by the uniform pale purplish-gray of the lower side of the wings. Expanse: 2.00 inches.

The early stages are unknown. The insect has thus far been found only in Colorado, but no doubt occurs in other States of the Rocky Mountain region.

(5) **Polygonia faunus** (Edwards) Pl. XIX, fig. 12, ♂; fig. 13, ♂, *under side;* Pl. III, fig. 32, *larva;* Pl. IV, figs. 31, 33–35, *chrysalis* (The Faun).

Butterfly.—This species is readily recognized by the deep indentations of the hind wings, the heavy black border, and the dark tints of the under side mottled with paler shades. Expanse: 2.00–2.15 in.

The caterpillar feeds on willows. It is found from New England to the Carolinas, and thence westward to the Pacific.

A varietal form, **P. rusticus** (Edw.), which is found in California and as far north as Vancouver Island, is characterized by having the wings on the upper side lighter and brighter. The male type is shown on Pl. LIX, fig. 26.

(6) **Polygonia zephyrus** (Edwards). Pl. XX, fig. 5, ♂; fig. 6, ♂, *under side* (The Zephyr).

Synonym: *thiodamas* Scudder.

Butterfly.—Fulvous, marked with yellowish toward the outer margins, the dark markings upon which are not as heavy as in the other species of the genus. On the under side the wings are paler than is the case in other species, reddish-brown, marbled with darker brown lines and frecklings. Expanse: 1.75–2.00 inches.

The caterpillar, which feeds upon *Azalea occidentalis*, is described and figured by Edwards in "The Butterflies of North America," vol. i. *Zephyrus* is found throughout the region of the Rocky Mountains, from Colorado to California, and from Oregon to New Mexico.

(7) **Polygonia silvius** (Edwards). Pl. LXXI, fig. 7, ♀, type (The Sylvan Angle-wing).

I figure the upper side of the female labeled as type by W. H. Edwards. After he named and described this species he stated that he was inclined to regard it as a dimorphic form of *rusticus*. It differs, however, on the under side from the species *rusticus*, and much more closely resembles on that side the species *hylas* Edwards. The disposition of the markings is almost precisely that of *hylas*; the color, however, being dark brown, and not silvery gray as in *hylas*. A male exactly corresponding to this female and labeled *silvius* is preserved in the Henry Edwards collection in New York.

There has been some discussion as to the identity of *P. silvius*, but there is not a particle of doubt that the figure given upon our plate is that of the original type. Expanse: 2.15 in.

Habitat.—Northern California, and Oregon.

(8) **Polygonia gracilis** (Grote and Robinson). Pl. XIX, fig. 10, ♂; fig. 11, ♀, *under side* (The Graceful Angle-wing).

Butterfly.—A small species, rather heavily marked with dark brown or blackish on the upper side. The wings on the under side are very dark, crossed about the middle by a pale-gray or white band shading off toward the outer margins. This light band serves as a means of easily identifying the species. Expanse: 1.75 inch.

The early stages are unknown.

The species has been found on the White Mountains in New Hampshire, in Maine, Canada, and British America, as far west as Alaska.

(9) **Polygonia silenus** (Edwards). Pl. XIX, fig. 5, ♂; fig. 6, ♀, *under side* (The Silenus Angle-wing).

Butterfly.—Larger than *gracilis*, and the wings more deeply excised, as in *faunus*. On the under side the wings are very dark, with lighter irrorations, especially on the fore wings. Expanse: 2.00–2.30 inches.

The early stages have never been studied. This species appears to be found only in Oregon, Washington, and British Columbia.

(10) **Polygonia oreas** (Edwards). Pl. LIX, fig. 24, ♂, type; fig. 27, ♂, *under side* (The Oread Angle-wing).

This is another form described from the Pacific coastal region by Edwards, concerning which there has been dispute. It may be only a varietal form of the preceding. There is variation in the dark shades of the under side of the wing. The insect given on Pl. LIX, fig. 27, is paler than the insect figured as *oreas* by Wright.

(11) **Polygonia progne** (Cramer). Pl. XX, fig. 3, ♂; fig. 4, ♂, *under side;* Pl. III, fig. 31, *larva;* Pl. IV, figs. 32, 37, 38, *chrysalis* (Progne).

Synonym: *c-argenteum* Kirby.

Butterfly.—A rather small species, with light-fulvous fore wings, shading into yellow toward the outer margins; the dark markings slight, but deep in color. The secondaries are heavily bordered with black on the outer margin. On the under side the wings are very dark, variegated with paler shades, somewhat as in *P. gracilis.* Expanse: 1.85–2.00 inches.

The early stages have been quite fully described by various authors, and the reader may consult "The Butterflies of New England," vol. i, pp. 266–268, for a full account. The caterpillar feeds on the elm, but more commonly on various species of the *Grossulaceæ*, or currant tribe, wild or domesticated. It ranges from Siberia to Nova Scotia, and southward as far as Pennsylvania.

Genus AGLAIS Dalman

Synonym: *Hamadryas* Barnes & Benjamin (not Boisduval)

(The Tortoise-shells)

Butterfly.—Medium-sized, the wings on the upper side generally some shade of black or brown, marked with red, yellow, or orange. Head moderately large; eyes hairy; palpi more or less heavily scaled; prothoracic legs feeble and hairy; lower discocellular vein of the fore wings, when present, uniting with the third median nervule, not at its origin, but beyond on the curve. Cell of the primaries may or may not be closed; cell of the secondaries open. The fore wings have the outer margin more or less deeply excavated between the extremities of the upper radial and the first median, at which points the wings are rather strongly produced. The hind wings have the outer margin denticulate, strongly produced at the extremity of the third median nervule.

Egg.—Short, ovoid, broad at the base, tapering toward the summit, which is broad and adorned with a few narrow, quite high longitudinal ridges, increasing in height toward the apex. Between these ribs are a few delicate cross-lines. They are generally laid in large clusters upon twigs of the food-plant.

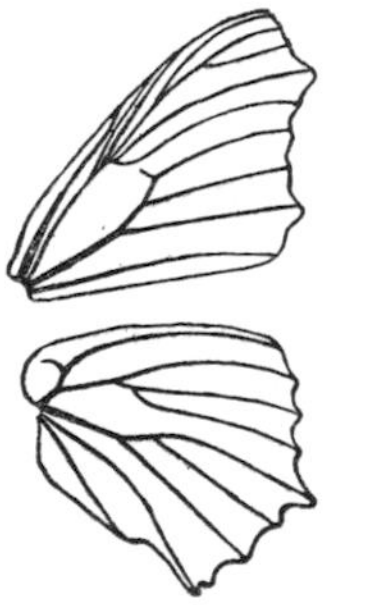

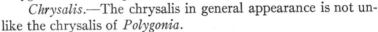

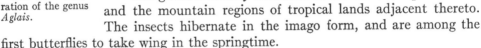

Caterpillar.—Moults four times. In the mature form cylindrical, the segments adorned with long, branching spines arranged in longitudinal rows; the spines much longer, and branching rather than beset with bristles, as in the genus *Polygonia.* It lives upon elms, willows, and poplars.

Chrysalis.—The chrysalis in general appearance is not unlike the chrysalis of *Polygonia.*

The genus is mainly restricted to the north temperate zone and the mountain regions of tropical lands adjacent thereto. The insects hibernate in the imago form, and are among the first butterflies to take wing in the springtime.

Fig. 100.—Neuration of the genus *Aglais.*

(1) **Aglais j-album** Boisduval and Leconte, Pl. XIX, fig. 9, ♀ (The Compton Tortoise).

Butterfly.—No description is required, as the figure on the plate will enable it to be immediately recognized. On the under side of the wings it resembles in color the species of the genus *Polygonia,* from which the straight edge of the inner margin of the primaries at once distinguishes it. It is a very close ally of the European *A. vau-album.* Expanse: 2.60–2.75 inches.

The caterpillar feeds upon various species of willow. It is a Northern form, being found in Pennsylvania upon the summits of the Alleghanies, and thence north to Labrador on the east and Alaska on the west. It is always a rather scarce insect.

(2) **Aglais californica** Boisduval. Pl. XX, fig. 11, ♂ (The California Tortoise-shell).

Butterfly.—On the upper side deep fulvous, mottled with yellow, spotted and bordered with black. On the under side dark brown; pale on the outer half of the primaries, the entire surface marked with dark lines and fine striæ. Expanse: 2.00–2.25 inches.

Early Stages.—The larva and chrysalis have been described by Henry Edwards in the "Proceedings of the California Academy of Sciences," vol. v, p. 171. The caterpillar feeds upon *Ceanothus thyrsiflorus.*

This insect is a close ally of the European *A. xanthomelas.* It ranges from Colorado to California and as far north as Oregon.

152

(3) **Aglais milberti** (Godart). Pl. XX, fig. 10, ♂; Pl. III, fig. 36, *larva;* Pl. IV, figs. 43, 49, 50, *chrysalis* (Milbert's Tortoise-shell).

Synonym: *furcillata* (Say).

Butterfly.—Easily distinguished by the broad yellow submarginal band on both wings, shaded outwardly by red. It is nearly related to the European *A. urticæ.* Expanse: 1.75 inch.

The life-history has been worked out and described by numerous writers. The caterpillars feed upon the nettle (*Urtica*).

This pretty little fly ranges from the mountains of West Virginia northward to Nova Scotia and Newfoundland, thence westward to the Pacific.

(4) **Aglais antiopa** (Linnæus). Pl. I, fig. 6, ♀ ; Pl. III, fig. 28, *larva;* Pl. IV, figs. 51, 58, 59, *chrysalis* (The Mourning-cloak; The Camberwell Beauty).

Butterfly.—This familiar insect needs no description. It is well known to every boy in the north temperate zone. It is one of the commonest as well as one of the most beautiful species of the tribe. A rare aberration, called *hygiæa,* in which the yellow border invades the wing nearly to the middle, obliterating the blue spots, is sometimes found. The author has a fine example of this "freak." Other "freaks" have been named, which are hardly worth mentioning.

The eggs are laid in clusters upon the twigs of the food-plant in spring (see p. 4, Fig. 11). There are at least two broods in the Northern States. The caterpillars feed on willows, elms, and various species of the genus *Populus.*

Genus VANESSA Fabricius

Synonym: *Pyrameis* Hübner.

Butterfly.—The wings in their neuration approach closely to the preceding genus, but are not angulate, and the ornamentation of the under side tends to become ocellate, or marked by eye-like spots, and in many of the species is ocellate.

Egg.—The egg is broadly ovoid.

Caterpillar.—The caterpillar in its mature form is covered with spines, but these are not relatively as large as in *Aglais,* and are not as distinctly branching.

Chrysalis.—The chrysalis approaches in outline the chrysalis of the preceding genus, and is only differentiated by minor structural peculiarities.

The genus includes only a few species, but some of them have a wide range, *Vanessa cardui* being almost cosmopolitan, and having a wider distribution than any other known butterfly.

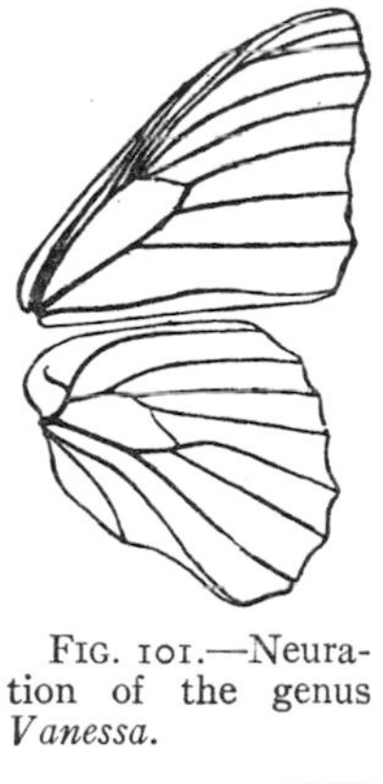

FIG. 101.—Neuration of the genus *Vanessa.*

(1) **Vanessa atalanta** (Linnæus). Pl. XLIII, fig. 4, ♂; Pl. III, fig. 35, *larva;* Pl. IV, figs. 52, 53, 55, *chrysalis.* (The Red Admiral).

This familiar butterfly, which is found throughout North America, Europe, northern Asia, and Africa, needs no description beyond what is furnished on the plates. Expanse: 2.00 in. The food-plants are *Humulus, Bœhmeria,* and *Urtica.*

(2) **Vanessa virginiensis** (Drury). Pl. I, fig. 2, ♂; Pl. XXXIII, fig. 6, ♂, *under side;* Pl. III, fig. 34, *larva;* Pl. IV, figs. 54, 63, 64, *chrysalis* (Hunter's Butterfly).

Synonyms: *huntera* (Fabr.); *iole* (Cram.).

Butterfly.—Marked much like the following species, but easily distinguished at a glance by the two large eye-like spots on the under side of the hind wings. Expanse: 2.00 in.

Early Stages.—These have been frequently described, and are in part well depicted in Plates III and IV. The food-plants are cudweed (*Gnaphalium*) and *Antennaria.*

Hunter's Butterfly ranges from Nova Scotia to Mexico and Central America east of the Sierras.

(3) **Vanessa cardui** (Linnæus). Pl. I, fig. 1, ♂; Pl. III, fig. 37, *larva;* Pl. IV, figs. 60–62, *chrysalis* (The Painted Lady; The Thistle-butterfly).

Butterfly.—This is undoubtedly the most widely distributed of all known butterflies, being found in almost all parts of the temperate regions of the earth and in many tropical lands in both hemispheres. It is easily distinguished from the preceding species by the more numerous and much smaller eye-like spots on the under side of the hind wings. Expanse: 2.00–2.25 in.

Early Stages.—These have been again and again described at great length and with minute particularity by a score of authors. The food-plants of the caterpillar are thistles (*Carduus*), *Urtica, Cnicus,* and *Althœa.*

(4) **Vanessa carye** (Hübner). Pl. XX, fig. 12, ♂. (The West Coast Lady).

Butterfly.—This species is easily distinguished from *P. cardui,* its nearest ally, by the absence of the roseate tint peculiar to that species, the tawnier ground-color of the upper surfaces, and the complete black band which crosses the middle of the cell of the primaries. Expanse, 2.00 inches.

Early Stages.—These have been described by various authors and numerous aberrant forms have been named, described, and figured. This species ranges from Vancouver's Island to Argentina, and is found as far east as Utah.

WIDELY DISTRIBUTED BUTTERFLIES

The primal curse declared that the earth, because of man's sin, should bring forth thorns and thistles, and thistles are almost everywhere. Wherever thistles grow, there is found the thistle-butterfly, or the "Painted Lady," as English collectors are in the habit of calling it, *Vanessa cardui.* All over Europe, all over North America, in Africa,—save in the dense jungles of the Congo,—throughout South America, in far-off Australia, and in many of the islands of the sea this beautiful butterfly is found. At some times it is scarce, and then again there are seasons when it fairly swarms, every thistle-top having one of the gaily colored creatures seated upon its head, and among the thorny environment of the leaves being found the web which the caterpillar weaves. Another butterfly which bids fair ultimately to take possession of the earth is our own *Danais plexippus*, to the wanderings of which allusion has already been made.

Many species are found in the arctic regions both of the Old World and the New. Obscure forms are these, and lowly in their organization, survivors of the ice-age, hovering on the border-line of eternal frost, and pointing to the long-distant time when the great land-masses about the northern pole were knit together, as geologists teach us.

One of the curious phenomena in the distribution of butterflies is the fact that in Florida we find *Hypolimnas misippus*, a species which is exceedingly common in Africa and in the Indo-Malayan subregion. Another curious phenomenon of a like character is the presence in the Canary Islands of a *Vanessa*, which appears to be only a subvariety of the well-known *Vanessa indica*, which is common in India, southern China, and Japan. Away off in southeastern Africa, upon the peaks and foothills which surround the huge volcanic masses of Kilima-Njaro, Kenia, and Ruwenzori, was discovered by the martyred Bishop Hannington a beautiful species of *Argynnis*, representing a genus nowhere else found upon the continent of Africa south of Mediterranean lands. Strange isolation this for a butterfly claiming kin to the fritillaries that sip the sweets from clover-blossoms in the Bernese Oberland, in the valleys of Thibet, and on the prairies of the United States.

Genus JUNONIA Hübner
(Peacock Butterflies)

Butterfly.—Medium-sized butterflies, with eye-like spots upon the upper wings. Their neuration is very much like that of the butterflies belonging to the genus *Vanessa*, to which they are closely allied. The eyes are naked, the fore feet are scantily clothed with hair, and the lower discocellular vein of the fore wing, when present, does not terminate on the arch of the third median nervule before its origin, as in the genus *Aglais*, but immediately at the origin of the third median nervule.

Egg.—Broader than high, the top flattened, marked by ten vertical ribs, very narrow, but not very high. Between the ribs are a few delicate cross-lines.

Caterpillar.—The caterpillar is cylindrical, the segments being adorned with rows of branching spines and longitudinally striped.

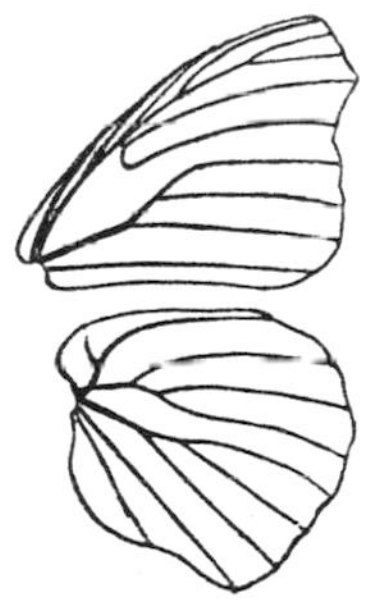

Fig. 102.—Neuration of the genus *Junonia*.

Chrysalis.—The chrysalis is arched on the dorsal surface and marked by two rows of dorsal tubercles, concave on the ventral side. The head is slightly bifid, with the vertices rounded.

There are eighteen or more species which belong to this genus, of which some are neotropical, but the greater number are found in the tropical regions of the

Genus Anartia

Old World. Three forms occur within the limits of the United States, which have by some authors been reckoned as distinct species, and by others are regarded merely as varietal forms.

(1) **Junonia cœnia** Hübner. Pl. XX, fig. 7, ♀ ; Pl. III, figs. 29, 30, *larva;* Pl. IV, figs. 56, 57, 65–67, *chrysalis* (The Buckeye).

Butterfly.—The figure on the plate is far better than any verbal description. On the under side the eye-like spots of the upper side are reproduced, but are much smaller, especially on the hind wings. There is much variety in the ground-color of the wings on the underside. Some specimens are reddish-gray, and some are quite heavily and solidly pinkish-red on the secondaries. Expanse: 2.00–2.25 inches.

Egg.—Dark green.

Caterpillar.—Dark in color, longitudinally striped, and adorned with branching spines, two of which are on the head and point forward.

Chrysalis.—Generally pale wood-brown, strongly arched on the dorsal and concave on the ventral side, always hanging at less than a right angle to the surface from which it depends.

This is a very common butterfly in the Southern States, ranging northward as far as New England, westward to the Pacific, and southward to Colombia. The caterpillar feeds on various species of plantain (*Plantago*), also *Gerardia* and *Antirrhinum.*

(2) **Junonia lavinia** (Cramer). Pl. XX, fig. 8, ♂ (Lavinia).

Butterfly.—This species may be distinguished by the more rounded apex and the more deeply excavated outer margin of the fore wings, and also by the decided elongation of the outer margin of the hind wings at the end of the submedian vein. The wings are paler on the upper side than in the preceding species, and the eye-like spots much smaller. Expanse: 2.00 inches.

The early stages are not accurately known. The insect is common in the Antilles and South America, but is only now and then taken in the extreme southern parts of Texas.

(3) **Junonia genoveva** (Cramer). Pl. XX, fig. 9, ♂ (Genoveva).

Butterfly.—Much darker above than either of the two preceding species. The transverse subapical band is pale yellow, almost white; the ocelli of the wings are more as in *lavinia* than in *cœnia*. Expanse: about 2.00 inches.

This form is confined to the extreme South, occurring in Florida, Texas, and Arizona.

Genus ANARTIA Doubleday

Butterfly.—The head is small; the eyes are round and prominent; the tongue is long; the antennæ are relatively long, having the club short, compressed, and pointed. The palpi have the second joint thick, the third joint gradually tapering and lightly clothed with scales. The fore wings are rounded at the apex, and have the outer and inner margins somewhat excavated. The outer margin of the hind wings is sinuous, produced at the end of the third median nervule. The cell of the hind wing is open. The subcostal nervules in the fore wing are remarkable because of the tendency of the first and second to fuse with the costal vein. The prothoracic feet of the male are small and weak; of the female, stronger.

Early Stages.—Little known.

There are four species belonging to this genus, two of which are found within the limits of the United States.

(1) **Anartia jatrophæ** (Linn. & Johans.) Pl. XX, fig. 13, ♂ (The White Peacock).

Butterfly.—There can be no mistake made in the identification of this species, if the figure we give is consulted. The male and female are much alike. Expanse: 1.75–2.00 inches.

The butterfly is common throughout the tropics of the New World, and is occasionally found in southern Texas and Florida.

FIG. 103.— Neuration of the genus *Anartia.*

(2) **Anartia fatima** (Fabricius). Pl. LIX, fig. 28, ♂. (The Fatima Butterfly).

Readily recognized by the figure we give. The species is well known in Mexico and southward, but only occurs as a straggler on our southern border.

Genus HYPANARTIA Hübner
(The Banded Reds)

FIG. 104.—Neuration of the genus *Hypanartia.*

Butterfly.—Palpi of medium size, well clothed with scales; the second joint moderately thick; the third very little thinner, blunt at the tip. Antennæ with a distinct, short, well-rounded club. The fore wings have the first two subcostal nervules arising before the end of the cell, close to each other. The third sub-costal arises midway between the end of the cell and the origin of the fourth sub-costal. The cell of the fore wing is closed by a stout lower discocellular vein which is more or less continuous with the third median nervule. The hind wing has the cell open or only partially closed.

Early Stages.—But little is known of the early stages of this genus.

The species reckoned as belonging to *Hypanartia* number less than a dozen, most of which are found in tropical America, but, singularly enough, two species occur in tropical and southern Africa, and another has been described from Madagascar.

(1) **Hypanartia lethe** (Fabricius). Pl. XXIV, fig. 10, ♂ (The Lethe Nymph).

This very handsome insect, which is quite common in tropical America, is another straggler into our fauna, being occasionally found in southern Texas. But little is known of its early life-history. Expanse: 2.00 inches.

157

Genus EUNICA Hübner
(The Violet-wings)

Butterfly.—The head is narrow, hairy; the eyes prominent. The antennæ are long and slender, having a greatly enlarged club marked with two grooves. The palpi have the third joint in the case of the female longer than in the case of the male. They are relatively short, thickly clothed with hairs and scales lying closely appressed to the surface. The fore wing has the costal and median vein enlarged and swollen at the base. The subcostal has five nervules, the first two of which arise before the end of the cell, the third midway between the end of the cell and the fourth nervule. The upper discocellular vein is wanting; the middle discocellu-

FIG. 105.—Neuration of the genus *Eunica*.

lar vein is bent inwardly; the lower discocellular vein is somewhat weak and joins the median exactly at the origin of the second median nervule. The cell of the hind wing is lightly closed.

Early Stages.—Very little is known of the early stages of this genus.

The butterflies are characterized by the dark-brown or black ground-color of the upper side, generally glossed with rich blue or purple. On the under side the markings are exceedingly variable and in most cases very beautiful. The genus is characteristic of the neotropical fauna, and there are over sixty species, which have been described. The males are said by Bates, to whom we are indebted for most of our knowledge of these insects, to have the habit of congregating about noon and in the early afternoon in moist places by the banks of streams, returning toward nightfall to the haunts of the females. In this respect they resemble clubmen, who at the same hours are generally to be found congregating where there is something to drink. Only two species are found in our region, and are confined to the hottest parts of Texas and Florida, ranging thence southward over the Antilles and Central America as far as Bolivia.

(1) **Eunica monima** (Cramer). Pl. XXI, fig. 7, ♂; fig. 8, ♀ (The Dingy Purple-wing).

Butterfly.—This obscure little butterfly represents in Florida and Texas the great genus to which it belongs, and gives but a feeble idea of the splendid character of its congeners, among which are some exceedingly beautiful insects. Nothing is known of its life-history. It is common in the Antilles and Mexico.

(2) **Eunica tatila** Herrich-Schæffer. Pl. LIX, fig. 29, ♂. (The Florida Purple-wing).

This species, easily known from our figure, is common in southern Florida. The female is much like the male, but duller in color.

Genus MYSCELIA Doubleday

This genus is characteristic of Central and South America, ranging from the southern borders of the United States to southern Brazil. Two species have been recognized as occurring within our faunal limits. But little is known as yet of the early stages and it is to be hoped that some of our Mexican friends may succeed in developing a knowledge of the egg, larva, and chrysalis. I found a species of the genus on the wing at Cuernavaca in April, and it ought not to be difficult for some of the members of the Instituto de Biologia, who frequent that neighborhood, to work out the life-history.

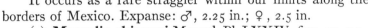

(1) **Myscelia ethusa** (Boisd.). Pl. LX, fig. 3, ♂; fig. 4, ♀. (Boisduval's Myscelia).

Synonym: *cyanecula* Felder.

The insect is delineated in both sexes on our plate and it may thus easily be recognized.

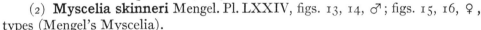

FIG. 106.—Neuration of the genus *Myscelia*.

It occurs as a rare straggler within our limits along the borders of Mexico. Expanse: ♂, 2.25 in.; ♀, 2.5 in.

(2) **Myscelia skinneri** Mengel. Pl. LXXIV, figs. 13, 14, ♂; figs. 15, 16, ♀, types (Mengel's Myscelia).

Like the preceding, this insect is not common within our borders, but appears occasionally along our southern limits adjoining Mexico. It was originally described from the latter country. Expanse: ♂, 2.25 in.; ♀, 2.5 in.

Genus DYNAMINE Hübner

This is a very extensive genus represented by numerous species and varieties, which are found in Mexico, Central and South America. Only one species, *D. dyonis* Hübner, occurs, so far as is known, within the limits of the United States. The neuration is shown in fig. 107, and an examination reveals the fact that these small butterflies structurally, so far as their wings are concerned, belong to that group of the *Nymphalidæ*, which includes the European genus *Limenitis*. The life-history, so far as ascertained, tends to confirm this relationship.

FIG. 107.—Neuration of *Dynamine*.

(1) **Dynamine dyonis** Geyer. Pl. LX, fig. 5, ♂, *under side*. (The Mexican Dynamine).

On the upper side this beautiful butterfly is golden green, marked with black spots at the tip and on the costa as well as the middle and outer margin of the fore wing. The outer border of the hind wing is also irregularly margined with black, most heavily at the upper and at the inner angle. The under side, as our figure shows, is very differ-

159

ently marked, this side being creamy-white with dark bands. On the hind wing there are two conspicuous black ocelli surrounded by fulvous and pupilled with blue. Expanse: 1.5 in.

Genus DIÆTHRIA Billberg

Butterfly.—Small in size, with the upper side of the wings dark in color, marked with bands of shining metallic blue or silvery-green, the under side of the

wings generally more or less brilliantly colored, carmine upon the primaries and silvery-white upon the secondaries, with the apex of the primaries marked with black transverse bands and the body of the secondaries traversed by curiously arranged bands of deep black, these bands inclosing about the middle of the wing circular or pear-shaped spots. All of the subcostal nervules in this genus arise beyond the end of the cell. The costal and the median veins are swollen near the base. The cell in both the fore and hind wings is open.

Fig. 108.—Neuration of the genus *Diæthria.*

Early Stages.—Very little is known of these.

This genus numbers many species, almost all of which are found in South and Central America, only one being known to inhabit the United States, being found in the extreme southern portion of Florida, and there only rarely.

(1) **Diæthria clymena** (Hübner). Pl. XXI, fig. 5, ♂; fig. 6, ♂, *under side* (The Leopard-spot).

Butterfly.—The wings on the upper side are black, the primaries crossed by an oblique iridescent bluish-green band, and the secondaries marked by a similarly colored marginal band. On the under side the primaries are crimson from the base to the outer third, which is white, margined with black, and crossed by an outer narrow black band and an inner broad black band. The secondaries on this side are white, marked about the middle by two large coalescing black spots, and nearer the costa a large pear-shaped spot, both ringed about with black lines. Beyond these black rings are two black bands conformed to the outline of the inner and outer margins of the wing, and, in addition, a fine black marginal line. The costa is edged with crimson. Expanse: 1.75 inch.

Early Stages.—Unknown.

The Leopard-spot is found occasionally in Florida, but quite commonly in the Antilles, Mexico, and Central America.

Genus AGERONIA Hübner
(The Calicoes)

Butterfly.—The antennæ moderately long, delicate, terminated in a gradually thickened club. The eyes are naked; the palpi are compressed, only slightly porrect, not densely covered with scales. The neuration is alike in both sexes, the costal and the median veins greatly thickened toward the base. The first and second subcostals arise from before the end of the cell; the fourth and fifth subcostals arise from a common stem emitted from the third subcostal beyond the end of the cell. The cells in both the fore and hind wings are closed. The butterflies are of medium or large size, curiously marked with checkered spots, blue and white, with broad paler shades on the under side of the secondaries. They are rapid fliers and are said to alight on the trunks of trees with their wings expanded and their heads down. When flying they emit a clicking sound.

FIG. 109.—Neuration of the genus *Ageronia*.

Early Stages.—Very little is known of these.

The chrysalids are slender and have two ear-like tubercles on the head.

This genus is, strictly speaking, neotropical. About twenty-five species have been described from Central and South America, some of them being exceedingly beautiful and rich in color. The two species credited to our fauna are reported as being occasionally found in Texas. I have specimens of one of the species which certainly came from Texas. I cannot be so sure of the other.

(1) **Ageronia feronia** (Linnæus). Pl. XXIV, fig. 4, ♂ (The White-skirted Calico).

Butterfly.—Easily distinguished from the only other species of the genus found in our fauna by the white ground-color of the under side of the hind wings. Expanse: 2.50 inches.

Early Stages.—Unknown.

This remarkable insect is said to be occasionally found in Texas.

(2) **Ageronia fornax** Hübner. Pl. XXIV, fig. 5, ♂, *under side* (The Orange-skirted Calico).

Butterfly.—Closely resembling the preceding species on the upper side, but at once distinguished by the orange-yellow ground-color of the under side of the hind wing. Expanse: 2.60 inches.

Early Stages.—Unknown.

Like its congener, *A. fornax* is reported only from the hotter parts of Texas.

Genus ATHENA Hübner

Synonyms: *Timetes* Boisd.; *Megalura* Blanchard

(The Dagger-wings)

Butterfly.—The palpi are moderately long, thickly clothed with scales, the last joint elongated and pointed. The antennæ have a well-developed club. The fore wings and the hind wings have the cell open. In the fore wing the subcostal vein, which has five branches, emits the first nervule well before the end of the cell, the second a little beyond it, and the third and fourth near together, before the apex of the wing. The third median nervule of the hind wing is greatly pro-

duced and forms the support of the long tail which adorns this wing. Between the end of the submedian vein and the first median nervule is another lobe-like prolongation of the outer margin of the wing. The butterflies are characterized for the most part by dark upper surfaces, with light under surfaces marked with broad bands and lines of varying intensity of color. They are easily distinguished from the butterflies of all other genera of the *Nymphalidæ* by the remarkable tail-like appendages of the hind wing, giving them somewhat the appearance of miniature *Papilionidæ*.

Early Stages.—Nothing of note has been recorded of their early stages, which may be accepted as reliable, and there is an opportunity here for study and research.

Fig. 110.—Neuration of the genus *Athena*.

There are about twenty-five species belonging to the genus, all found within the tropical regions of America. Three species are occasionally taken in the extreme southern portions of Florida and Texas. They are all, however, very common in the Antilles, Mexico, and more southern lands.

(1) **Athena coresia** (Godart). Pl. XXI, fig. 1, ♂; fig. 2, ♂, *under side* (The Waiter).

Butterfly.—Easily recognized by means of our figures, which show that this creature deserves the trivial name I have bestowed upon it. In its dark coat and white vest it gracefully attends the feasts of Flora. Expanse: 2.50 inches.

So far as I am aware, nothing reliable has been recorded as to the early stages of this insect. It is occasionally found in Texas.

(2) **Athena chiron** (Fabricius). Pl. XXI, fig. 4, ♂ (The Many-banded Dagger-wing).

Butterfly.—Easily recognized by means of the figure in the plate. Like the preceding species, this is occasionally found in Texas. It is very common in Mexico, South America, and the Antilles.

(3) **Athena petreus** (Cramer). Pl. XXI, fig. 3, ♂ (The Ruddy Dagger-wing).

Butterfly.—The upper side of the wings is accurately delineated in the plate. On the under side the wings are pale, with the dark bands of the upper side reproduced. Expanse: 2.60 inches.

It occurs in southern Florida and Texas, and elsewhere in tropical America.

Genus BASILARCHIA Scudder
(The White Admirals)

Butterfly.—Head large; the eyes are large, naked; the antennæ are moderately long, with a distinct club; the palpi are compact, stout, produced, densely scaled. The fore wings are subtriangular, the apex well rounded, the lower two thirds of the outer margin slightly excavated. The first two subcostal nervules arise before the end of the cell. The hind wings are rounded, crenulate.

Egg.—Nearly spherical, with the surface pitted with large hexagonal cells (see p. 3, Fig. 1).

Caterpillar.—The caterpillar in its mature state is cylindrical, somewhat thicker before than behind, with the second segment adorned with two prominent rugose club-shaped tubercles. The fifth segment and the ninth and tenth segments also, are ornamented with dorsal prominences (see p. 7, Fig. 20).

Chrysalis.—The chrysalis is suspended by a stout cremaster; the abdominal segments are rounded. On the middle of the dorsum is a prominent projecting boss. The thorax is rounded. The head is rounded or slightly bifid.

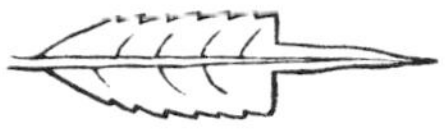

FIG. 111.—Neuration of the genus *Basilarchia*.

FIG. 112.—Leaf cut away at end by caterpillar of *Basilarchia* (Riley).

The caterpillars feed upon the leaves of various species of oak, birch, willow, and linden. The eggs are laid upon the extreme tip of the leaves, and the infant caterpillar, feeding upon the leaf in immediate proximity to the point where it has been hatched, attaches bits of bitten leaf by strands of silk to the midrib, thus stiffening its perch and preventing its curling, as the rib dries. Out of bits of leaves thus detached it constructs a packet of material, which it moves forward along the midrib until it has completed its second moult. By this time winter begins to come on, and it cuts away for itself the material of the leaf on either side of the rib, from the tip toward the base, glues the rib of the leaf to the stem by means of silk, draws together the edges of the remaining portions of the leaf, and constructs a tube-like hibernaculum, or winter quarters, exactly fitting the body, in which it passes the winter.

FIG. 113.—Hibernaculum, or winter quarters, of larva of *Basilarchia*.

There are a number of species of the genus found in the United States, the habits of which have been carefully studied, and they are among our most interesting butterflies, several species being mimicks of protected species. A great many aberrations and so-called "forms" of the various species have been described by Strecker, Nakahara, and others. For the most part they are "freaks," or "sports." We have not space for all of these things, but the zealous student may find an account of them in the writings of these authors.

Genus Basilarchia

(1) **Basilarchia arthemis** (Drury). Pl. XXII, fig. 4, ♂, form **lamina** (Fabricius); fig. 5, ♂, form **proserpina** (Edwards); Pl. III, fig. 26, *larva;* Pl. IV, figs. 14, 23, *chrysalis* (The Banded Purple).

Butterfly.—Easily distinguished in the form *lamina* from *astyanax*, which in other respects it somewhat closely resembles, by the broad white bands crossing both the fore wings and the hind wings, and followed on the secondaries by a submarginal row of red spots shading inwardly into blue. In the form *proserpina* there is a tendency on the part of the white bands to become obsolete, and in some specimens they do entirely disappear. The likeness to *astyanax* in such cases is striking, and the main point by which the forms may then be discriminated is the persistence of the red spots on the upper side of the secondaries; but even these frequently are obsolete. Expanse: 2.50 inches.

Egg.—Grayish-green, with "kite-shaped" cells.

Caterpillar.—Greenish, or olive-brown, blotched with white in its mature form, which is well represented on Plate III. It feeds upon the willow, the hawthorn (*Cratægus*), and probably other plants.

Chrysalis.—The figure on Plate IV is sufficiently exact to obviate the necessity for further description.

This beautiful insect ranges through northern New England and New York, Quebec, Ontario, and the watershed of the Great Lakes, spreading southward at suitable elevations into Pennsylvania. I have taken it about Cresson, Pennsylvania, at an elevation of twenty-five hundred feet above sea-level. It is not uncommon about Meadville, Pennsylvania. The species appears to be, like all the others of the genus, somewhat unstable and plastic, or else hybridization is very frequent. Probably all the species have arisen from a common stock in past ages.

(2) **Basilarchia astyanax** (Fabricius). Pl. XXII, fig. 1, ♂; Pl. III, figs. 17, 21, 25, *larva;* Pl. IV, figs. 12, 13, *chrysalis* (The Red-spotted Purple).

Synonyms: *ephestion* (Stoll); *ursula* (Fabr.); *ephestiæna* (Hbn.).

Butterfly.—This common species is sufficiently characterized by the plate, so far as the upper surface is concerned. On the under side the wings are brownish, banded with black on the margins; the lunules are on this side as above, but the inner band of spots is red. There are two red spots at the base of the fore wings, and four at the base of the hind wings. The palpi are white below, and the abdomen is marked with a lateral white line on each side. Expanse: 3.00–3.25 inches.

Egg.—The egg, which somewhat closely resembles that of *B. archippus* (see p. 3, Fig. 1), is yellowish-green, gradually turning dark brown as the time for the emergence of the caterpillar approaches.

Caterpillar.—The caterpillar is so well delineated on Pl. III, fig. 17, as to obviate the necessity for a lengthy verbal description.

Chrysalis.—What has been said of the caterpillar is also true of the chrysalis (see Pl. IV).

The larva feeds upon the willow, cherry, apple, linden (*Tilia*), huckleberry, currant, and other allied shrubs and trees. The butterfly is somewhat variable, and a number of varietal forms have been described. It ranges generally over the

United States and southern Canada as far as the Rocky Mountains in the West, and occurs at high elevations in Mexico.

(3) **Basilarchia weidemeyeri** (Edwards). Pl. XXII, fig. 6, ♂ (Weidemeyer's Admiral).

Butterfly.—Superficially like *arthemis*, but easily distinguished by the absence of the lunulate marginal bands of blue on the margins of the hind wings and by the presence of a submarginal series of white spots on both wings. Expanse: 3.00 inches.

Early Stages.—These have been described by W. H. Edwards in the "Canadian Entomologist," vol. xxiv, p. 107, and show great likeness to *B. archippus.* The caterpillar feeds upon cottonwood (*Populus*).

The insect is found on the Pacific slope and eastward to Montana, Nebraska, and New Mexico.

(4) **Basilarchia archippus** (Cramer). Pl. VII, fig. 4, ♂; Pl. III, figs. 19, 22, 24, *larva;* Pl. IV, figs. 18–20, *chrysalis;* ab. **pseudodorippus** (Strecker) type, Pl. LIX, fig. 30 (The Viceroy).

Synonym: *disippe* (Godart).

This species mimicks *Danais plexippus* in a remarkable manner, as may be seen by referring to Pl. VII. Expanse: 2.5–2.75 in.

Early Stages.—These have all been carefully studied by numerous writers. The egg is depicted on p. 3, fig. 1. The caterpillar is shown on p. 8, as well as on Pl. III.

The species ranges everywhere from southern Canada and British America into the Gulf States.

(5) **Basilarchia obsoleta** (Edwards). Pl. VII, fig. 5, ♂ (Hulst's Admiral).

Synonym: *hulsti* (Edw.).

Butterfly.—This form is apparently a mimick of *Danais berenice.* The ground-color of the wings is not so bright as in *B. archippus,* and the mesial band of the secondaries on the upper side is relieved by a series of small whitish spots, one on each interspace. The perfect insect can easily be distinguished by its markings. Expanse: 2.50–2.60 inches.

The early stages have not been described. Thus far it is only known from Utah and Arizona.

(6) **Basilarchia lorquini** (Boisduval). Pl. XXII, fig. 3, ♂ (Lorquin's Admiral).

Butterfly.—Easily distinguished from all the other species of the genus by the yellowish-white bar near the end of the cell of the fore wings and the reddish color of the apex and upper margin of the same wings. Expanse: 2.25–2.75 inches.

Early Stages.—These have been partially described by Henry Edwards, and minutely worked out by Dr. Dyar, for whose description the reader may consult the "Canadian Entomologist," vol. xxiii, p. 172. The food-plant of the caterpillar is *Populus,* willows, and the choke-cherry (*Prunus demissa*).

(7) **Basilarchia floridensis** (Strecker). Pl. LXXIII, fig. 1, ♂; fig. 2, ♂ *underside,* type of *B. eros* (Edw.) (The Florida Admiral).

Synonym: *eros* (Edwards).

Genus Heterochroa

This dark-colored species has usually been regarded as a somewhat melanic form of *B. archippus*, but is now accepted in the light of breeding experiments as a valid species. The larva and the chrysalis differ in important respects from those of *B. archippus*. Expanse: ♂, 2.5–2.8 in.; ♀, 3.–3.5 in.

THE BUTTERFLIES' FAD

"I happened one night in my travels
　　To stray into Butterfly Vale,
Where my wondering eyes beheld butterflies
　　With wings that were wide as a sail.
They lived in such houses of grandeur,
　　Their days were successions of joys,
And the very last fad these butterflies had
　　Was making collections of boys.

"There were boys of all sizes and ages
　　Pinned up on their walls. When I said
'Twas a terrible sight to see boys in that plight,
　　I was answered: 'Oh, well, they are dead.
*We catch them alive, but we kill them
　　With ether*—a very nice way:
Just look at this fellow—his hair is so yellow,
　　And his eyes such a beautiful gray.

"'Then there is a droll little darky,
　　As black as the clay at our feet;
He sets off that blond that is pinned just beyond
　　In a way most artistic and neat.
And now let me show you the latest,—
　　A specimen really select,
A boy with a head that is carroty-red
　　And a face that is funnily specked.

"'We cannot decide where to place him;
　　Those spots bar him out of each class;
We think him a treasure to study at leisure
　　And analyze under a glass.'
I seemed to grow cold as I listened
　　To the words that these butterflies spoke;
With fear overcome, I was speechless and dumb,
　　And then with a start—I awoke!"

ELLA WHEELER WILCOX.

Genus HETEROCHROA Boisduval
(The Sisters)

Butterfly.—This genus is very closely allied to the genus *Adelpha* Hübner. By some recent writers it has been sunk as a synonym of the genus *Limenitis* Fabricius. It is also very near to the genus *Basilarchia*, the only structural differences, which can be detected, being that the eyes are hairy, the palpi not so

166

heavily clothed with scales, and the prothoracic legs of the males a trifle smaller than in *Basilarchia*.

Early Stages.—The caterpillar was described by Henry Edwards, and Comstock in his "Butterflies of California" has given fine figures of the chrysalis of *H. californica*. The larva feeds on oaks.

(1) **Heterochroa bredowi** (Geyer).

This is the Mexican form of the insect, which only differs from the form commonly found in the southwestern States of the Union in being more darkly colored, especially on the under side, and having the orange spot of the fore wing smaller. It occasionally turns up in Arizona.

(2) **Heterochroa bredowi** var. **californica** Butler. Pl. XXII, fig. 2, ♀ (The Californian Sister).

Butterfly.—Easily recognized by the large subtriangular patch of orange-red at the apex of the primaries. In its habits and manner of flight it closely resembles the species of the genus *Basilarchia*. Expanse: 2.50–3.00 inches.

The insect is found in California, Nevada, Arizona, and Mexico.

Genus ASTEROCAMPA Roeber

Synonym: *Celtiphaga* Barnes & Lindsey

(The Hackberry Butterflies)

The Hackberry Butterflies have during the past seventy years been shifted by various writers from one genus to another. In the first edition of this book I placed them in the genus *Chlorippe*, following the example of Scudder. They find their final resting-place in the genus *Asterocampa* Roeber, of which *Celtiphaga* Barnes & Lindsey is a synonym.

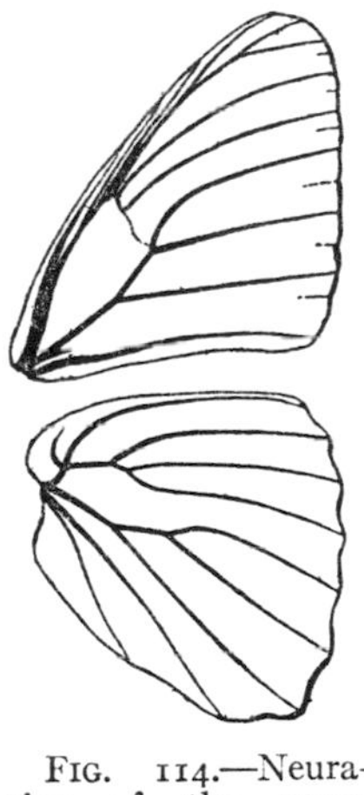

FIG. 115.— Neuration of genus *Astero-campa* ♂.

Butterfly.—Small, some shade of fulvous, spotted and banded with black, with eye-spots on the hind wings, in some species on the fore wings also. Eyes naked; antennæ straight, terminating in a stout oval club; palpi porrect, the two lower joints heavily scaled; costal vein of fore wing stout; first subcostal alone arising before end of cell; cell open in both fore and hind wing.

FIG. 114.—Neura-tion of the genus *Heterochroa*.

Egg.—Nearly globular, summit broad and convex, ornamented with from eighteen to twenty broad vertical ribs, between which are numerous faint cross-lines.

Caterpillar.—Head subquadrate, summit crowned by a pair of stout diverging coronal spines, adorned with radiating spinules, behind on the sides a frill of curved spines. Body cylindrical, thickest at middle, thence tapering forward and backward. Anal prolegs divergent and elongated, as in some genera of the *Satyrinæ*.

Chrysalis.—Compressed laterally, keeled on dorsal side, concave on ventral, head bifid; cremaster presenting the appearance of a flattened disk, the sides studded with hooks, by means of which the chrysalis is attached to the surface, from which it depends in such a manner that the ventral surface is parallel to the plane of support.

The caterpillars feed upon the *Celtis*, or hackberry.

There are a number of so-called species, mainly confined to the southern and western portion of the United States, though some of them range southward into Mexico. Two only are known in the Middle States. None are found on the Pacific slope. The species are double-brooded in the more northern parts of the country, and the caterpillars produced from eggs laid by the second brood hibernate.

(1) **Asterocampa celtis** (Boisduval and Leconte). Pl. XXIII, fig. 3, ♂; fig. 4, ♀ fig. 13, ♂, *under side* (The Hackberry Butterfly).

Butterfly, ♂.—The primaries at the base and the secondaries except at the outer angle pale olive-brown, the rest of the wings black. The dark apical tract of the primaries is marked by two irregular, somewhat broken bands of white spots. There is only one red-ringed eye-spot, which is between the first and second median nervules, near the margin of the fore wing, and there are six such spots on each hind wing. On the under side the ground-color is grayish-purple; the spots and markings of the upper side reappear on this side.

♀.—The female has the wings, as is always the case in this genus, much broader and not so pointed at the apex of the primaries as in the male sex, and the color is much paler. Expanse: ♂: 1.80 inch; ♀, 2.10 inches.

Early Stages.—These are beautifully described and delineated by Edwards in "The Butterflies of North America," vol. ii. The caterpillar feeds on the hackberry (*Celtis occidentalis*).

This species is found generally from southern Pennsylvania, Ohio, Indiana, and Illinois to the Gulf of Mexico.

(2) **Asterocampa montis** (Edwards). Pl. XXII, fig. 7, ♂; fig. 8, ♀. (The Mountain Emperor).

William H. Edwards, when he rearranged his collection before transmitting the same to me, restricted the specific name *montis* to a long series of specimens most of them bred from larvæ obtained in Colorado. They can only be separated from typical *celtis* by the fact that on the primaries there are two ocelli instead of one, as in typical *celtis*, and they are slightly more fulvous than the latter.

(3) **Asterocampa alicia** (Edwards). Pl. XXIII, fig. 9, ♂; fig. 10, ♀ (The Empress Alicia).

Butterfly.—Very bright fawn at the base of the wings, shading into pale buff outwardly. There is but one eye-spot on the primaries. The six eye-spots on the secondaries are black and very conspicuous. The marginal bands are darker and heavier than in many other species of the genus. Expanse: ♂, 2.00 inches; ♀, 2.50 inches.

The early stages are only partially known.

Alicia ranges through the Gulf States from Florida to Texas.

(4) **Asterocampa antonia** (Edwards). Pl. XXIII, fig. 12, ♂ (The Empress Antonia).

Synonym: ? *montis* Edw. (in part).

A. antonia is bright yellowish fulvous on the upper side, closely resembling *alicia;* easily distinguished from that form by the two eye-spots near the margin of the primaries.

Edwards in his final revision of the species, which he had named, labeled in his own handwriting as *antonia*, a specimen which bears the label "Colorado, Dodge, type of *antonia*," and which agrees thoroughly with other specimens, labelled as *antonia* from Texas and Arizona. *Antonia* bears the same relation to *alicia* which *montis* bears to *celtis*. Expanse: 1.75–2.00 in.

Early Stages.—Unknown.

Habitat.—*A. antonia* is found in Texas and Arizona.

(5) **Asterocampa leilia** (Edwards). Pl XXIII, fig. 11, ♂ (The Empress Leilia).

Butterfly.—Like *antonia* this species has two extra-median eye-spots on the primaries, and thus may be distinguished from *celtis*. From *antonia* it may be separated by its larger size and the deeper reddish-brown (fawn) color of the upper surfaces, and the less pronounced basal and median transverse markings. Expanse: ♂, 2.15; ♀, 2.6 in.

Early Stages.—Unknown.

Habitat.—So far we have received this butterfly only from Arizona.

(6) **Asterocampa clyton** (Boisduval and Leconte). Pl. XXIII, fig. 5, ♂; fig. 6, ♀; Pl. III, fig. 20, *larva;* Pl. IV, figs. 15–17, *chrysalis* (The Tawny Emperor).

Synonym: *ocellata* (Edw.)

Butterfly, ♂.—The fore wings without an extra-median eye-spot, and the secondaries broadly obscured with dark brown or blackish, especially on the outer borders, so that the eye-spots are scarcely, if at all, visible.

♀.—Much larger and paler in color than the male, the eye-spots on the secondaries conspicuous. Expanse: ♂, 2.00 inches; ♀, 2.50–2.65 inches.

Early Stages.—The life-history has been carefully worked out, and the reader who wishes to know all about it should consult the writings of Edwards and Scudder.

Habitat.—This species is occasionally found in New England, and ranges thence westward to Michigan, and southward to the Gulf States. It is quite common in the valley of the Ohio.

(7) **Asterocampa flora** (Edwards). Pl. XXIII, fig. 1, ♂; fig. 2, ♀ (The Empress Flora).

Butterfly, ♂.—The ground-color is bright reddish-fulvous on the upper side. The usual markings occur, but there is no eye-spot, or ocellus, on the primaries. The hind wings are not heavily obscured with dark brown, as in *clyton*, and the six ocelli stand forth conspicuously upon the reddish ground. The hind wings are more strongly angulated than in any other species. The borders are quite solidly black.

♀.—The female is much larger than the male, and looks like a very pale female of *clyton*. Expanse: ♂, 1.75 inch; ♀, 2.35 inches.

Early Stages.—The life-history has been described by Edwards in the "Canadian Entomologist," vol. xiii, p. 81. The habits of the insect in its early stages and the appearance of the larva and chrysalis do not differ widely from those of *C. clyton*, its nearest ally.

Habitat.—*Flora* is found in Florida and on the borders of the Gulf to Texas.

(8) **Asterocampa texana** (Skinner). Pl. LX, fig. 6, ♂, paratype (Skinner's Hackberry Butterfly).

This species, or variety, is very closely related to the preceding, as our figure shows. It is to be distinguished from *subpallida* Barnes and McDunnough by the fact that on the underside it preserves the ocelli, while in *subpallida* they, as well as the other transverse markings, are more or less obsolete. *Texana* and *subpallida* are apparently large mutants of *A. flora*, in which the markings of the underside tend to obsolescence.

Genus SMYRNA Hübner

There is only one species of this genus in our fauna.

(1) **Smyrna karwinskii** Geyer. Pl. LXXI, fig. 3, ♂ (Karwinski's Beauty).

The figure we give is sufficiently descriptive of the upper side of the insect. On the lower side the fore wings reproduce the spots of the upper with the tip paler and a small pale triangular mark on the costa, which cuts into the black band which runs from the costa to the inner angle. The cell, which is outwardly defined by a black line, is pale gray and the inner area below the cell is blackish. The hind wing on the under side is prevalently grayish, beautifully marbled and variegated with intricate black lines on the inner two-thirds, beyond which are four ocelli, the uppermost prominent, the one nearest the inner angle the less, and the two intermediate ocelli somewhat indistinct. Expanse: 3.–3.15 in.

The insect is common in Mexico. The specimen figured was taken by the writer at Cuernavaca in the spring of 1930. It is reported as a rare straggler about Brownsville, Texas.

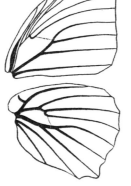

FIG. 116.—Neuration of genus *Smyrna*.

Genus VICTORINA Blanchard
(The Malachites)

Butterfly.—Large butterflies, curiously and conspicuously marked with light-greenish spots upon a darker ground; wings upon the under side marbled with brown about the spots and having a satiny luster. The third median nervule of the fore wing is very strongly bowed upward. The cells of both wings are open. The hind wing is tailed at the end of the third median nervule. The two first sub-costals arise before the end of the cell; the fourth and fifth spring from a common stem which is emitted from the third beyond the end of the cell, as the cut shows.

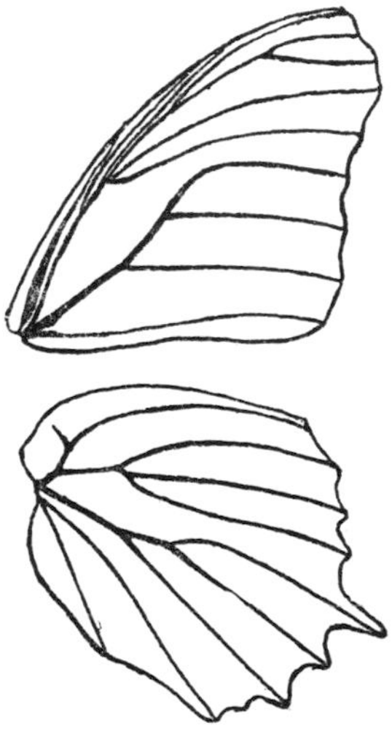

Early Stages.—We know nothing of these.

This genus, in which are reckoned five species, all found in the tropics of the New World, is represented by but a single species in our fauna, which occurs in southwestern Texas and in Florida. It is very common in the West Indies and Central America.

(1) **Victorina steneles** (Linnæus). Plate XXIV, fig. 6, ♂ (The Pearly Malachite).

This splendid insect is occasionally found in southern Florida and the extreme southern part of Texas. It is common throughout tropical America. Nothing has ever been written upon its early stages.

Fig. 117.—Neuration of the genus *Victorina*.

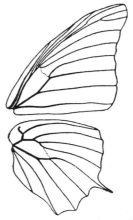

Fig. 118.—Neuration of genus *Coea*.

Genus COËA Hübner

Synonym: *Historis* Barnes & Benjamin (not Hübner).

This genus is monotypic, that is to say, it consists, so far as we know, of only one species. It is closely related to the genus *Charaxes* of the Eastern Hemisphere. As in the case of the preceding species, the figure given will suffice for identification.

(1) **Coëa acheronta** (Fabricius). Pl. LX, fig. 2, ♂ (The Dash-wing).
Synonym: *cadmus* (Cramer); *pherecydes* (Cramer).
The insect which is common in the Antilles, Mexico, and southward, has been reported from southern Florida.

Genus HISTORIS Hübner

Synonym: *Aganisthos* Boisduval.

This is another monotypic genus, which does not call for a lengthy verbal description at this point.

(1) **Historis odia** (Fabricius). Pl. LX, fig. 1, ♂ (The Great Nymph).
Synonyms: *orion* (Fabricius); *danaë* (Cramer).
This striking insect is common in the Antilles, Central and South America,

ranging to southern Brazil. It occurs sparingly in Florida. Some years ago I received a chrysalis from one of my correspondents at Miami, which unfortunately disclosed the butterfly while in transit in the mails. The result was a badly crippled specimen, but it served to show that the species was properly attributed to Florida by Boisduval.

Genus ANÆA Hübner
(The Leaf-wings)

Butterfly.—Medium-sized butterflies, on the upper side of the wings for the most part red or fulvous, on the under side of the wings obscurely mottled on the

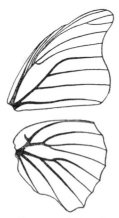

FIG. 119.—Neuration of genus *Historis*, reduced.

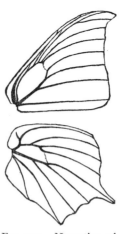

FIG. 120.—Neuration of genus *Anæa*.

secondaries and the costal and apical tracts of the primaries in such a manner as to cause them to appear on this side like rusty and faded leaves. Structurally they are characterized by the somewhat falcate shape of the primaries and the strongly produced outer margin of the secondaries about the termination of the third median nervule. The first and second subcostal nervules coalesce with one another and with the costal vein. The costal margin of the fore wing at the base is strongly angulated, and the posterior margin of the primaries is straight. The cell of the secondaries is very feebly closed.

Egg.—Spherical, flattened at the base and somewhat depressed at the apex, with a few parallel horizontal series of raised points about the summit.

Caterpillar.—Head somewhat globular in appearance; the anterior portion of the first thoracic segment of the body is much smaller in diameter than the head; the body is cylindrical, tapering to a point.

Chrysalis.—Short, stout, with transverse ridges above the wings on the middle of the abdomen, keeled on the sides. The cremaster is small and furnished with a globular tip, the face of which is on the same plane as the ventral surface of the body, causing the chrysalis to hang somewhat obliquely from the surface which supports it.

This is a large genus composed mostly of tropical species, possessed of rather singular habits. The caterpillars in the early stages of their existence have much the same habits as the caterpillars of the genus *Basilarchia*, which have been already described. After passing the third moult they construct for themselves nests by weaving the edges of a leaf together, and thus conceal themselves from sight, emerging in the dusk to feed upon the food-plant. They live upon the

Euphorbiaceæ, the *Lauraceæ*, and the *Piperaceæ*. The insects are double-brooded in the cooler regions of the North, and are probably many-brooded in the tropics.

(1) **Anæa andria** Scudder. Plate XXIV, fig. 1, ♀ (The Goatweed Butter-fly).

Butterfly, ♂.—Solidly bright red above, the outer margins narrowly dusky on the borders. On the under side the wings are gray, dusted with brown scales, causing them to resemble the surface of a dried leaf.

♀.—The female has the upper side paler and marked by pale fulvous bands, as shown in the plate. Expanse: ♂, 2.50 inches; ♀, 3.00 inches.

Early Stages.—In Fig. 21, on p. 8, is a good representation of the mature caterpillar, the nest which it constructs for itself, and the chrysalis. A full account of the life-history may be found in the "Fifth Missouri Report" from the pen of the late C. V. Riley. The caterpillar feeds on *Croton capitatum*.

The insect ranges from Illinois and Nebraska to Texas.

(2) **Anæa morrisoni** Holland (Edw. MS.). Plate XXIV, fig. 2, ♀ (Morrison's Goatweed Butterfly).

Butterfly, ♂.—Much like *P. andria*, but more brilliantly and lustrously red on the upper side, and marked with paler macular bands like the female.

♀.—Differing from the female of *P. andria* in the more macular, or spotted, arrangement of the light bands on the wings, as is well shown in the plate. Expanse: 2.25–2.50 inches.

Early Stages.—Unknown.

This species occurs in Arizona and Mexico. It has recently been erroneously identified by Barnes and Benjamin as being the same as *P. aidea* (Guérin) from Honduras, a smaller and darker insect, from which it is totally distinct in form and maculation.

(3) **Anæa portia** (Fabricius). Plate XXIV, fig. 3, ♂ (Portia).

Butterfly.—Splendid purplish-red on the upper side. On the under side the fore wings are laved with bright yellow on the basal and inner marginal tracts, and the secondaries are dark brown, irrorated with blackish scales arranged in spots and striæ. Expanse: 2.75–3.00 inches.

Early Stages.—Unknown.

Portia occurs in the extreme southern part of Florida and in the Antilles.

FOSSIL INSECTS

Investigations within comparatively recent times have led to the discovery of a host of fossil insects. A few localities in Europe and in North America are rich in such remains, and the number of species that have been described amounts to several thousands. Strangely enough, some of these fossil insects are very closely allied in form to species that are living at the present time, showing the extreme antiquity of many of our genera. One of the comparatively recent discoveries has been the fossil remains of a butterfly which Dr. Scudder, who has described it, declares to be very near to the African *Libythea labdaca*, which differs in certain minor anatomical respects from the American *Libytheas* which are figured in this work; and Dr. Scudder has therefore proposed a new generic name, *Dichora*, meaning "an inhabitant of two lands," which he applies to the African species because related to the extinct American butterfly. The strange discoveries, which have been made by palæontologists as to the huge character of many of the mammals, birds, and reptiles which at one time tenanted the globe, are paralleled by recent discoveries made in insect-bearing strata in France. M. Charles Brongniart of the Paris Museum in publishing an account of the collection which he had made at Commentry, among the creatures which he had collected figures an insect, which is regarded by naturalists as one of the forerunners of our dragonflies, which had an expanse of wing of two feet, a veritable giant in the insect world.

Of fossil butterflies there have thus far been discovered sixteen species. Of these, six belong to the subfamily of the *Nymphalinæ*, and five of the six were found in the fossiliferous strata of Florissant, Colorado. Two species belong to the subfamily *Satyrinæ*, both occurring in deposits found in southern France, and representing genera more nearly allied to those now found in India and America than to the *Satyrinæ* existing at the present time in Europe. One of the fossils to which reference has already been made belongs to the family of the *Libytheidæ*. The remainder represent the families of the *Pieridæ*, the *Papilionidæ*, and the *Hesperiidæ*.

It is remarkable that the butterflies, which have been found in a fossil state, show a very close affinity to genera existing at the present time for the most part in the warmer regions of the earth. Though ages have elapsed since their remains were imbedded in the mud which became transformed into stone, the processes of life have not wrought any marked structural changes in the centuries which have fled. This fixity of type is certainly remarkable in creatures so lowly in their organization.

SUBFAMILY SATYRINÆ (THE SATYRS)

"Aught unsavory or unclean
Hath my insect never seen;
But violets and bilberry bells,
Maple-sap and daffodils,
Grass with green flag half-mast high,
Succory to match the sky,
Columbine with horn of honey,
Scented fern and agrimony,
Clover, catch-fly, adder's-tongue,
And brier-roses dwelt among."

EMERSON.

THE butterflies belonging to this subfamily are, for the most part, of medium size, and are generally obscure in color, being of some shade of brown or gray, though a few species within our territory are brightly colored. Gaily colored species are more numerous in the tropics of both hemispheres. The wings are very generally ornamented, especially upon the under side, by eye-like spots, dark, pupilled in the center with a point of lighter color, and ringed around with one or more light circles. They are possessed of a weak flight, flitting and dancing about among herbage, and often hiding among the weeds and grasses. Many of them are forest-loving insects, though a few inhabit the cold and bleak summits of mountains and grassy patches near the margins of streams in the far North, while some are found on the treeless prairies of the West. In the warmer regions of the Gulf States a few species are found which have the habit of flitting about the grass of the roadsides and in open spaces about houses. The veins of the fore wings are generally swollen at the base; the cell of the hind wing is closed; thus enabling them to be quickly distinguished from other butterflies belonging to the family *Nymphalidæ*.

The eggs, so far as we have knowledge of them, are subspherical, somewhat higher than broad, generally ribbed along the sides, particularly near the apex, and rounded at the base, which is generally broader than the apex.

The caterpillars at the time of emergence from the egg have the head considerably larger than the remainder of the body; but when they have reached maturity they are cylindrical, tapering a little from the middle to either end. They are bifurcated at the anal extremity, a character which enables them to be distinguished at a glance from the larvæ of all other American butterflies except those of the genus *Asterocampa*. They are mostly pale green or light brown in color, ornamented with stripes along the sides. They feed upon grasses and sedges, lying

175

in concealment during the daytime, and emerging at dusk to take their nourishment.

The chrysalids are rather stout in form, but little angulated, and without any marked prominences or projections. They are green or brown in color. Most of them are pendant, but a few forms pupate at the roots of grasses or under stones lying upon the ground.

The butterflies of this subfamily have been arranged, so far as they are represented in the faunal region of which this book treats, in ten genera, which include about seventy species and subspecies. It is quite possible that a number of forms still remain to be discovered and described, though it is also true that some of the so-called species are likely to prove in the end little more than local races, or varieties.

Genus ENODIA Hübner
(The Eyed Nymphs)

"The wild bee and the butterfly
Are bright and happy things to see,
Living beneath a summer sky."
ELIZA COOK.

Butterfly.—Characterized by the stout but not greatly swollen costal vein of the fore wing, by the rather short costal vein of the hind wing, which terminates

before quite reaching the outer angle, by the great length of the lower discocellular vein of the fore wing, and by the prolongation of the outer margin of the hind wing at the end of the third median nervule. The outer margin of the fore wing is either rounded or slightly excavated. The palpi are long and narrow, thickly clothed with hairs below; the antennæ are moderately long, gradually thickening toward the tip, without a well-marked club; the fore legs in both sexes greatly atrophied.

FIG. 121.—Neuration of the genus *Enodia.*

Egg.—Flattened spheroidal, broadly truncated at the base, the surface smooth.

Caterpillar.—Body long, slender, tapering from the middle; the head cleft, each half being produced upward as a conical horn; the anal segment provided with a pair of horns similar to those of the head, produced longitudinally backward.

Chrysalis.—Strongly convex dorsally, concave ventrally, with a stout tubercular eminence on the thorax, without any other projecting tubercles or eminences; light green in color.

This genus is large, and is well represented in Asia and the Indo-Malayan region. I cannot see any good ground for generically separating the two species found in North America from their congeners of Asiatic countries, as has been done by some writers.

(1) **Enodia portlandia** (Fabr.). Pl. XVIII, fig. 20, ♂; Pl. III, fig. 16, *larva;* Pl. IV, fig. 6, *chrysalis* (The Pearly Eye).

Synonym: *andromache* (Hbn.).

Butterfly.—The butterfly, the male of which is well depicted as to its upper side on the plate, does not differ greatly in the sexes. The hind wings on the under side are marked with a series of beautiful ocelli. In the North the insect is single-brooded; in the region of West Virginia and southward it is double-brooded. Expanse: 1.75–2.00 inches.

Early Stages.—The illustrations give a good idea of the mature larva and the chrysalis. The caterpillar, like most of the *Satyrinæ,* feeds upon grasses.

The range of this pretty insect is extensive, it being found from Maine to the Gulf of Mexico, and westward to the Rocky Mountains.

(2) **Enodia creola** (Skinner). Pl. XVIII, fig. 18, ♂; fig. 19, ♀ (The Creole).

Butterfly.—Easily distinguished from the preceding species by the elongated patches of dark raised scales upon the fore wings, situated on the interspaces between the median nervules of the male. The female shown on our plate was taken *in coitu* with the male, and has more yellow upon the upper side of the fore wings than *D. portlandia.* Expanse: 2.25 inches.

Early Stages.—Unknown.

Creola ranges from Florida to Mexico along the Gulf.

Genus SATYRODES Scudder
(The Grass-nymphs)

Butterfly.—The head is moderately large; the eyes are not prominent, hairy; the antennæ are about half as long as the costa of the fore wing, not distinctly clubbed, gradually thickening toward the extremity. The palpi are slender, compressed, hairy below, with the last joint rather short and pointed. The fore and hind wings are evenly rounded on the outer margin. The costal vein of the fore wing is thickened, but not greatly swollen. The first and second subcostals are emitted well before the end of the cell, the third beyond it, and the fourth and fifth from a common stem, both terminating below the apex. The upper discocellular vein is wanting, and the upper radial, therefore, springs from the upper angle of the cell of the fore wing.

Fig. 122.—Neuration of the genus *Satyrodes.* (After Scudder.)

Egg.—Flattened spheroidal, broader than high, flat at the base and rounded above.

Caterpillar.—The head is full, the summit of either half produced upward and forward into a slender, conical horn. The body is nearly cylindrical, tapering backward, the last segment furnished with two pointed, backward projections, resembling the horns of the head.

Chrysalis.—Relatively longer and more slender than in the preceding genus, with the thoracic prominence more acute and the head more sharply pointed.

Genus Euptychia

This genus was erected to receive the single species, which until the present time is its sole representative.

(1) **Satyrodes eurydice** (Linn.-Johans.). Pl. XXV, fig. 1, ♂; Pl. III, fig. 9, larva; Pl. IV, fig. 9, chrysalis. Var **fumosus** Leussler, ♂, paratype, Pl. LXIII, fig. 11.

Synonyms: *canthus* (Linn); *cantheus* (Godart); *transmontana* Gosse; *boisduvalii* (Harris).

Butterfly.—It always haunts meadows and hides among the tufts of tall grasses growing in moist places. It is rather common in New England and the Northern States generally. It is found in Canada and is reported from the cool upper mountain valleys in the Carolinas. It has a weak, jerking flight, and is easily taken when found. Expanse: 1.65–1.90 inch.

Early Stages.—These have been well described by various writers. The caterpillar feeds upon grasses.

The variety *fumosus* described by Leussler from Nebraska is larger than eastern specimens and darker.

Genus EUPTYCHIA* Hübner
(Type *Papilio herse* Cramer)

"Oh! the bonny, bonny dell, whaur the primroses won,
Luikin' oot o' their leaves like wee sons o' the sun;
Whaur the wild roses hing like flickers o' flame,
And fa' at the touch wi' a dainty shame;
Whaur the bee swings ower the white-clovery sod,
And the butterfly flits like a stray thoucht o' God."

MacDonald.

This genus is very extensive, including over two hundred species, most of them found in the tropical regions of America. Only seven species are found in the United States.

Numerous artificial subdivisions of the genus have been suggested, which at best are scarcely of subgeneric value. Weymer, who has recently monographed the genus (*Cf.* Seitz, Grosschmett. d. Erde, Vol. 5, pp. 193–224) has arranged the species in groups, following the precedent set by Rothschild and Jordan in their great monographic revision of the genus *Papilio*. The structural differences in *Euptychia* consist at most of variation in the length of the cell of the hind wing, and slight differences in the outline of that wing quite too insignificant to be regarded as of generic value.

Butterfly.—Eyes hairy. The costal and median veins of the fore wings are much swollen at the base. The palpi are thin, compressed, thickly clothed below with long hairs. The antennæ are comparatively short, gradually thickening toward the outer extremity, and without a well-defined club. Both the fore wing and the hind wing have the outer margin evenly rounded.

*Euptychia Hbn. has page-priority over *Megisto* Hbn. (*Cf.* Hübner, Verz., pp. 53, 54).

Egg.—Globular, flattened at the base, marked with irregular polygonal cells.

Caterpillar.—The head is large, rounded, the two halves produced conically and studded with little conical papillæ. The last segment of the body is bifurcate.

Chrysalis.—Relatively long, strongly produced at the vertex; elevated on the thorax into a blunt tubercular prominence; green in color.

(1) **Euptychia gemma** Hübner. Pl. XXV, fig. 2, ♂, *under side* (The Gemmed Brown).

Butterfly.—Upon the upper side the wings are pale mouse-gray, with a couple of twinned black spots on the outer margin of the hind wings. On the under side the wings are reddish-gray, marked with irregular ferruginous lines. Near the outer margin of the hind wings is a row of silvered spots, the spots corresponding in location to the dark marginal spots being expanded into a violet patch marked in the middle by a twinned black spot centered with silver. Expanse: 1.25–1.35 inch.

Early Stages.—These have been beautifully described and figured by Edwards in the third volume of "The Butterflies of North America."

FIG. 123.—Neuration of genus *Euptychia*.

The egg is somewhat globular, rather higher than wide, flattened at the base, and marked with numerous shallow reticulated depressions. The caterpillar of the spring brood is pale green, of the fall brood pale brown, marked respectively with numerous longitudinal stripes of darker green or brown. It has two long, elevated, horn-like projections upon the head, and on the anal segment two similar projections pointing straight backward. The chrysalis is small, green, or brown, strongly bifid at the head. The caterpillar feeds on grasses.

The insect ranges from West Virginia to Mexico.

(2) **Euptychia henshawi** (Edwards). Pl. XXV, fig. 8, ♂ (Henshaw's Brown).

Butterfly.—Much like *N. gemma*, but considerably larger and decidedly reddish upon the upper side of the wings. Expanse: 1.65 inch.

Early Stages.—Mr. Edwards has figured the egg, which is different in shape from that of the preceding species, being broader than high, subglobular, flattened broadly at the base, green in color, and almost devoid of sculpturings upon its surface. Of the other stages we know nothing.

Henshaw's Butterfly ranges through southern Colorado into Mexico.

(3) **Euptychia phocion** (Fabricius). Pl. XXV, fig. 7, ♂, *under side;* Pl. III, fig. 8, *larva;* Pl. IV, figs. 10 and 11 (The Georgian Satyr).

Synonyms: *areolatus* (Sm. & Abbot); *helcita* (Hbn.).

Butterfly.—The upper side is immaculate gray; beneath pale, with two ferruginous transverse lines. Between these lines is a ferruginous line on each wing, rudely describing a circle. In the circle on the fore wing are three or four eye-spots with a blue pupil and a yellow iris; in the circle on the hind wing are six eye-spots which are oblong and have the pupil oval. Expanse, 1.25 inch.

Early Stages.—These have been fully described, and are not unlike those of other species of the genus. The caterpillar feeds on grasses.

The insect ranges from New Jersey to the Gulf of Mexico as far west as Texas.

(4) **Euptychia euryta** (Fabricius). Pl. XXV, fig. 4, ♂; Pl. III, figs. 3, 6, 10, 13, 14, *larva;* Pl. IV, fig. 28, *chrysalis* (The Little Wood-satyr).

Synonyms: *eurytris* (Fabr.); *eurythris* (Godart); *cymela* (Cramer).

Butterfly.—Easily distinguished from other species in our fauna by the presence of two more or less perfectly developed ocelli on the upper side of the fore wing and also of the hind wing. Expanse: 1.75 inch.

Early Stages.—This is a rather common butterfly, the larval stages of which have been fully described by various authors. The egg is even taller in proportion to its breadth than that of *E. gemma*, which it otherwise closely resembles in outline and sculpturing. The caterpillar is pale brown, conformed in general form to that of other species of the genus, but somewhat stouter. It feeds on grasses. The chrysalis is pale brown, mottled with darker brown.

The insect ranges through Canada and the United States to Nebraska, Kansas, and Texas.

(5) **Euptychia mitchelli** (French). Pl. XXV, fig. 6, ♂, *under side* (Mitchell's Satyr).

Butterfly.—Easily distinguished from the other species of the genus by the eye-spots on the under side of the wings, four on each of the primaries and six on each of the secondaries, arranged in a straight series on the outer third, well removed from the margin. These spots are black, ringed about with yellow and pupilled with blue.

Early Stages.—Unknown.

The species is local, and thus far is recorded only from northern New Jersey, near Lake Hopatcong, the State of Michigan, and Portage County, Ohio. No doubt it occurs elsewhere, but has been overlooked by collectors.

(6) **Euptychia sosybia** (Fabricius). Pl. XXV, fig, 5. ♂, *under side* (The Carolinian Satyr).

Butterfly.—One of the smallest species of the genus. The upper surface is immaculate dark mouse-gray, without an ocellus on the upper side. On the under side the wings are paler, with three transverse undulatory lines, one defining the basal, the other the median area, and one just within the margin. Between the last two are rows of ocelli. The spots in these rows are obscure, except the first on the primaries and the second and last two on the secondaries, which are black, ringed about with yellow and pupilled with blue.

The female is like the male, but a trifle larger.

Early Stages.—These have been described by Edwards, French, and Scudder, and do not differ strikingly from those of other species.

The insect ranges from the latitude of New Jersey southward, throughout the southern half of the Mississippi Valley. It is common in western North Carolina.

It has been erroneously confounded with *hermes* (Fabr.), an allied, but distinct, species from Mexico and Central America.

(7) **Euptychia rubricata** Edwards. Pl. XXV, fig. 3, ♂. (The Red Satyr).

Butterfly.—Easily distinguished by its much redder color from all its congeners, among which it has its closest ally in *E. euryta*. It has an eye-spot near the apex of the fore wing, and one near the anal angle of the hind wing. The basal area of the primaries beneath is bright reddish; the secondaries on this side are gray, crossed by two transverse lines as in the preceding species, and a double submarginal line. On the fore wings the double submarginal line is repeated, and in addition there is another line which runs upward from just before the inner angle to the costa, at about one-third of its length from the apex. The eye-spots of the upper side re-appear below, and in addition there is another near the outer angle of the secondaries, and a few silvery well-defined ocelli between the two on the secondaries.

Early Stages.—Unknown.

The Red Satyr is found in Texas, Arizona, Mexico, and Central America.

Genus PARAMECERA Butler

There is only one species of this genus thus far known. It is not distantly related to *Euptychia*, but may easily be distinguished by the large patch of dark raised scales in the region of the median nervules on the fore wing. On the under side it is paler, more or less ruddy, and the fore wings are crossed by two dark bands and have a large apical pupilled eye-spot, followed below by a blind, much smaller, eye-spot. The hind wings are ornamented by a pale mesial band bordered by darker lines and a submarginal row of eye-spots of which the two or three near the anal angle are the darkest.

(1) **Paramecera xicaque** (Reakirt). Pl. LX, fig. 11, ♂ (Reakirt's Satyr).

The insect has an expanse ranging from 1.35–1.75 in.

Its life history is unknown. It occurs in southern Arizona and southward.

Genus CŒNONYMPHA Westwood
(The Ringlets)

"There is a difference between a grub and a butterfly; yet your butterfly was a grub."—SHAKESPEARE.

Butterfly.—Small butterflies. The subcostal, median, and submedian veins are all strongly swollen at the base. The palpi are very heavily clothed with hairs, the last joint quite long and porrect. The antennæ are short, delicate, gradually but distinctly clubbed. The eyes are naked. Both wings on the outer margin are evenly rounded.

Egg.—Conical, truncated, flat on the top, rounded at the base, with the sides marked with numerous low, narrow ribs, between which are slight cross-lines, especially toward the apex.

Genus Cœnonympha

Caterpillar.—The head is globular; the body cylindrical, tapering gradually backward, furnished in the last segment with two small horizontal cone-shaped projections.

Chrysalis.—Ventrally straight, dorsally convex, strongly produced in a rounded, somewhat keeled eminence over the thorax; pointed at the end. Generally green or light drab in color, with dark markings on the sides of the wing-cases.

Fig. 124.—Neuration of the genus *Cœnonympha.*

This genus is distributed throughout the temperate regions both of the Old and the New World, and includes in our fauna a number of forms, the most of which occur in the northern and western parts of the continent.

(1) **Cœnonympha california** Doubleday & Hewitson. Pl. XXV, fig. 14, ♀ Form **galactinus** Boisduval, Pl. XXV, fig. 9, ♂. Form **eryngii** Henry Edwards, Pl. XXV, fig. 10, ♂ (The California Ringlet).

Butterfly.—This little species is to be distinguished from its near allies by the white, or whitish, color of the upper side of the wings. According to W. H. Edwards and Henry Edwards the form *galactinus* is the spring form; Comstock and Skinner say that it is the summer form, and that *califvrnia* is the spring form. Comstock says that *eryngii* is a local race of the summer brood.

The form *galactinus* has the wings darker on the under side and the marginal eye-spots somewhat more developed than in *california*. The form *eryngii* is slightly tinged with yellow above, and on the under side the maculation is faint and the eye-spots obsolete. The form *siskiyouensis* Comstock has the same tint on the upper side as *eryngii*, while the dark areas of the hind wings on the under side are grayish, not tinged with ferruginous, otherwise like *california*, according to the figures given by Comstock.

Early Stages.—For a full knowledge of these the reader must consult the fine plate given by Edwards in Vol. III of "The Butterflies of North America" and the brief account with illustrations furnished by Comstock in "The Butterflies of California."

The species ranges from British Columbia to the mountains of Central California and eastward for a considerable distance. It has been taken in Nevada.

(2) **Cœnonympha kodiak** Edwards. Pl. XXV, fig. 22, ♀, *upper side*, type (The Alaskan Ringlet).

Butterfly.—Grayish white on both the upper and under sides, darker than *C. californica*. The basal area of the primaries on the under side is solidly dark stone-gray.

Early Stages.—Nothing so far is known of these.

It is found on the Island of Kodiak. It must not be confused with the next species.

(3) **Cœnonympha yukonensis** Holland. Pl. LX, fig. 21, ♂; fig. 22, ♀, *under side*, types (The Yukon Ringlet).

Butterfly.—Readily distinguished from *C. kodiak* by the ochraceous color of the upper side, and the red color of the basal area of the fore wings on the lower side, which are not stone-gray, as in *C. kodiak*, and still further distinguished by the white color of the fringes especially of the hind wings.

The Yukon Ringlet is remarkably constant in color and markings throughout its range. Since giving the original description I have received many scores of specimens from all parts of Alaska and the Yukon, some of them hundreds of miles apart, and I discover little or no variation. Expanse: ♂, 1.1–1.2 in.; ♀, 1.2–1.3 in.

(4) **Cœnonympha inornata** Edwards. Pl. XXV, fig. 29, ♂, type; fig. 13, ♂, *under side;* Var. **benjamini** McDunnough. Pl. LX, fig. 19, ♂, paratype, *under side;* fig. 20, ♀, paratype (The Prairie Ringlet). Var. **columbiana** McD., Pl. LX, fig. 17, ♀, paratype; fig. 18, ♂, paratype, *under side* (The Columbian Ringlet). Var. **insulana** McD., Pl. LX, fig. 23, ♀, paratype; fig. 24, ♂, paratype, *under side* (The Vancouver Ringlet). (The Inornate Ringlet).

Synonym: *quebecensis* Barnes and Benjamin.

Butterfly.—The wings on the upper side are more or less ochreous on the disk, with the costæ and the outer margins, especially of the hind wings, dark brown. No apical ocellus is visible upon the upper side of typical *inornata* from Winnipeg, but sometimes, though not invariably, appears on the lower side. One of the original types from Winnipeg has a small apical ocellus on the lower side of the right wing and none on the left. Specimens from Newfoundland and Labrador are generally much darker than those from Winnipeg and further west and south. I have in fact a melanic specimen from southern Labrador in which the dark fuscous color of the outer margin has spread over the entire wing to the exclusion of the ochreous tint, which normally appears upon the disk, and on the lower side this same color prevails, with no trace whatever of ocelli or lighter markings. It is a freak. On the under side the wings in typical specimens are marked much as on the upper side as far as the termen of the discal area, which is defined outwardly by a pale yellowish narrow transverse band.

A decidedly larger, more brightly colored, and conspicuously marked form, which is not uncommon in the regions lying west and south of the belt occupied by typical *inornata*, has recently been set off as a variety by Dr. McDunnough under the name *benjamini* (The Prairie Ringlet). Still another form, which occurs in British Columbia, has been named by the same author var. *columbiana*. The form found on Vancouver Island, which Edwards regarded as the same as *C. ampelos*, has been given the varietal name *insulana* by McDunnough. W. H. Edwards described the larval stages of this form as those of *C. ampelos* in the Canadian Entomologist, vol. xix, p. 41. I am indebted to Dr. McDunnough for the privilege of figuring paratypes of these varieties.

C. inornata in its typical form ranges from Winnipeg, the type locality, through northern Ontario and Quebec to Labrador and Newfoundland, as has been already intimated. It also occurs upon the high mountains of Colorado. In its various varietal forms it extends across the continent as far as British Columbia. Some writers have endeavored to identify it with the European *C. niphon* Rott., but this is undoubtedly an error.

(5) **Cœnonympha ampelos** Edwards. Pl. LX, fig. 16, ♀, specimen from Oregon (topotypical); Pl. XXV, figs. 21 and 30, from Vancouver, labelled *ampelos* by W. H. Edwards.

The original description given by Edwards, Trans. Amer. Ent. Soc., III, Jan. 1871, p. 213, is as follows:

"Male.—Expands 1.3 inch. Upper side bright, glossy ochraceous; immaculate; fringes concolored.

"Under side nearly same shade, paler and changing to buff at apex of primaries; on secondaries slightly paler at outer angle and elsewhere much powdered with brown atoms, a pale straight ray from costal edge of primaries nearly crosses the wing; secondaries have a similar ray, tortuous, interrupted in the upper median interspaces, not quite reaching the abdominal margin; both wings immaculate.

"Body fuscous covered with ochraceous hairs; beneath yellowish and grey; palpi grey; antennæ annulated black and white; club black, tip ferruginous.

"Female.—Same size, slightly paler; otherwise like male.

"From 1♂, 1♀. Oregon. Allied to *inornata*, Edw."

In a mysterious way the two original types from Oregon many years ago disappeared from the Edwards Collection. Dr. McDunnough (Can. Ent., Vol. LX, 1928, p. 273) announces that he has found the female type in the Canadian National Collection at Ottawa. Through his kindness I am able to figure a specimen from Salem, Oregon, which in the matter of locality agrees with the description of Edwards, and otherwise suits what Edwards wrote in his first description of the species. Edwards regarded the insects which he obtained in large numbers from Vancouver Island, and some of which he bred, as being the same as the insect which he originally described from Oregon. An author is generally supposed to know the species which he has named and described, but to err is human, and it is possible that in this case Edwards made a mistake. Dr. McDunnough has given the name *insulana* to the form commonly found on Vancouver Island (See *antea* under *C. inornata.*) In the present case I simply submit the evidence as it lies before me, according to which, following Dr. McDunnough, we **should** restrict the name *ampelos* to specimens from Oregon, and name what Edwards called and figured as *ampelos* as *insulana* McDunnough.

(6) **Cœnonympha elko** Edwards. Pl. XXV, fig. 25, ♀, *under side;* fig. 26, ♂. types (The Elko Ringlet).

Butterfly.—Yellow on both sides of the wings, lower side paler than the upper; basal area very lightly clouded with fuscous.

Early Stages.—Unknown.

Originally described from Elko, Nevada, this species, or variety, is known to range northward into Washington and Montana. I have a long series from Spokane Falls labelled by Edwards. Skinner sank the name *elko* as a synonym of *ampelos*, but the two forms seem to me, as names go in this genus, to be sufficiently distinct, to merit separation.

(7) **Cœnonympha ochracea** Edwards. Pl. XXV, fig. 11, ♂; fig. 12, ♂, *under side* (The Ochre Ringlet).

Butterfly.—Glossy ochraceous yellow above without markings, save a few dark scales at the apex and along the outer margin and the apical ocellus, which faintly shows through from below. On the under side the fore wing colored as on the upper side with a distinct apical ocellus, and a submarginal row of pale spots; hind wings at base dark fuscous marked by a discal and submarginal series of pale spots, the submarginal series sometimes being faintly pupilled.

Early Stages.—Unknown.

The type in the collection of W. H. Edwards is from Winnipeg. The insect has a wide range from British America to Nevada and Arizona on the mountains, and occurs abundantly in Colorado. It has been reported from Kansas, but I have no specimens from the western part of that state. It varies greatly in size and markings.

(8) **Cœnonympha brenda** Edwards. Pl. XXV, fig. 27, ♀, *under side;* fig. 31, ♂; Pl. LXXIV, figs. 11, 12, type of *C. brenda*, both sides, courtesy Field Mus. Nat. Hist. (The Utah Ringlet).

Butterfly.—Generally larger than the other species of the genus found in North America. Easily distinguished by the marginal row of ocelli on the secondaries, which are always present, though often "blind," that is to say, without a distinct dark pupil. Expanse: ♂, 1.25–1.5 in.; ♀, 1.7–1.85 in.

Early Stages.—Unknown.

In the first edition of this book I applied the specific name *pamphiloides* Reakirt to this form, of which numerous specimens are in the collection of W. H. Edwards, labeled "*pamphiloides*" by him. Since I first wrote, it has been generally agreed that Reakirt, misled by a wrong locality-label, redescribed the European *C. pamphilus* Linn. under the name *pamphiloides*. In reality there is no such species as *pamphiloides* in North America, and the name *pamphiloides* is a mere synonym for the European *pamphilus*, which also does not occur in America.

(9) **Cœnonympha furcæ** Barnes & Benjamin. Pl. LX, fig. 25, ♂; fig. 26, ♀, *under side* (The Grand Canyon Ringlet).

Butterfly.—This delicate little species is very pale yellowish, almost white, on the upper side of the wings, with the darker markings of the lower side showing through on the upper side. The fore wings have a distinct eye-spot near the apex. The other markings, especially those of the lower side recall in their disposition and form those of the preceding species, but the hind wings are prevalently stone-gray. Expanse: ♂, 1.15 in.; ♀, 1.25 in.

The insect has only recently been described. The specimens shown on our plate were caught by the author early in June, 1927, while visiting the Grand Canyon. The insects have the habit of darting into the air from spots where they seemed to congregate, three or four together, and then quickly settling again near the same spot, whence they have flown. At first sight I mistook them for small Hesperids, so quick was their flight, but was soon undeceived.

(10) **Cœnonympha haydeni** Edwards. Pl. XXV, fig. 24, ♂, *under side* (Hayden's Ringlet).

Butterfly.—Dark immaculate mouse-gray on the upper side. On the under side the wings are pale hoary gray, with the hind wings adorned by a marginal series of small ocelli, black, ringed about with yellow and pupilled with pale blue.

Early Stages.—Unknown.

Hayden's Ringlet is found in Montana, Idaho, Wyoming, and Colorado.

Genus NEOMINOIS Scudder

Butterfly.—Medium-sized, with the costa and inner margin of the fore wing straight, the outer margin of the same wing evenly rounded. The hind wings have the outer margin evenly rounded, and the costal margin quite strongly produced, or bent at an angle, just above the origin of the costal vein. The inner margin is straight. The costal vein of the fore wing is slightly swollen. The costal margin at the extremity of the second costal nervule is slightly bent inward; the upper discocellular vein is wanting; the lower radial vein is emitted from the lower discocellular a little below the point at which it unites with the middle discocellular. The middle discocellular of the hind wing appears as an inward continuation of the lower radial for some distance, when it bends upward suddenly to the origin of the upper radial. The head is small; the antennæ are short, with a thin, gradually developed club; the palpi are slender, compressed, well clothed with long hairs below.

Fig. 125.—Neuration of the genus *Neominois*, enlarged.

Egg.—Somewhat barrel-shaped, broader at the base than at the top, with the summit rounded. The sides are ornamented with fourteen or fifteen vertical raised ridges, which are quite broad, and sometimes fork or run into each other. On the sides these ridges seem to be regularly excised at their bases, and between them on the surface are many horizontal raised cross-lines, giving the depressed surface the appearance of being filled with shallow cells.

Caterpillar.—The mature caterpillar has the head globular, the body cylindrical, gradually tapering backward, and provided with two very short conical anal projections.

Chrysalis.—Formed under the surface of the earth; rounded, somewhat carinate, or keel-shaped, where the wing-cases unite on the ventral side. The head is rounded, the thorax strongly arched, the dorsal side of the abdomen very convex. On either side of the head are small clusters of fine processes shaped somewhat like an Indian club, the thickened part studded with little spur-like projections. These can only be seen under the microscope.

But two species of the genus **are** known within our faunal limits.

(1) **Neominois ridingsi** Edwards. Pl. XXV, fig. 15, ♂ (Ridings' Satyr).

Butterfly.—The upper side is well depicted in the plate. The under side is paler than the upper side, and the basal and median areas of both wings are profusely mottled with narrow pale-brown striæ, the secondaries crossed by a darker mesial band, the outer margin of which is sharply indented. Expanse: 1.50 inch.

Early Stages.—These have been beautifully ascertained, described, and figured by Edwards in the third volume of "The Butterflies of North America." The egg, larva, and chrysalis agree with the generic description already given, which is based upon the researches of Edwards.

It is found in the Mountain States of the Pacific coast.

(2) **Neominois dionysius** Scudder. Pl. XXV, fig. 16, ♂ (Scudder's Satyr).

Butterfly.—Distinguished from the preceding species by the larger and paler submarginal markings on the upper side of the wings and the pale color of the basal tract in both wings. On the under side the median band of the secondaries is narrower and more irregularly curved than in *ridingsi*, with the dentations of the outer margin more sharply produced. Expanse: 1.90 inch.

Early Stages.—Nothing has been written on the early stages, but no doubt they agree closely with those of the other species.

It is found in Utah, Colorado, and Arizona.

"Hast thou heard the butterflies,
What they say betwixt their wings?"
TENNYSON, *Adeline.*

Genus CERCYONIS Scudder
(Type *Papilio alope* Fabr.)

(The Wood-nymphs)

"Fluttering, like some vain, painted butterfly,
From glade to glade along the forest path."
ARNOLD, *Light of Asia.*

Butterfly.—Of medium size; wings marked with eye-like spots. Upon the upper surface generally obscurely colored, of some shade of gray or brown, occasionally banded with some shade of yellow. On the under side the wings are generally beautifully striated and spotted, with the eye-like spots usually ranged on the hind wings in two groups of three spots, one near the costa, the other near the lower angle. The costal vein at the base is greatly swollen; the median and submedian veins less so. The first and second subcostal nervules arise very near the end of the cell, slightly before it. The outer margin of the fore wing is evenly rounded; the outer margin of the hind wing often somewhat scalloped; the head small, the eyes of moderate size, full, naked; the antennæ gradually thickening to a broadly rounded club, which is slightly depressed; the palpi slender, compressed, profusely clothed beneath with long hairs. The fore legs are very small.

Genus Cercyonis

Egg.—Short, barrel-shaped, greatly diminishing in size on the upper half, truncated at the summit; the sides furnished with a large number of vertical ribs, not very high, with numerous delicate cross-lines between them. At the summit the ribs are connected by a waved, raised elevation.

Caterpillar.—Head globular; body cylindrical, tapering from the middle forward and backward; provided with short and slender diverging anal horns.

Chrysalis.—Shaped very much as in the genus *Enodia* from which it is hardly distinguishable. Generally green in color.

This genus, which is very near, if not identical with, the genus *Satyrus* of Europe, includes a number of so-called species, which are more or less subject to varietal modifications. In the following pages I give a number of the forms, which by some writers have been treated as species. An intensive study has forced upon my mind the conviction that many of these forms are merely local races of the species *alope* (Fabr.) widely diffused over the continent and under varying conditions producing more or less inconstant mutational forms.

Fig. 126.—Neuration of the genus *Cercyonis*. (After Scudder.)

(1) **Cercyonis pegala** (Fabricius). Pl. XXVI, fig. 18, ♀, *under side* (The Southern Wood-nymph).

Butterfly.—The largest species of the genus in our fauna, easily recognized by the broad yellow submarginal band on the primaries, marked with a single eye-spot in the male and two eye-spots in the female. The plate gives a correct idea of the under side of the wings. Expanse: 2.75 inches.

Early Stages.—These have only been partially ascertained. The caterpillar, like all others of the genus, feeds on grasses.

This insect is found in the Gulf States and as far north as New Jersey.

(2) **Cercyonis alope** (Fabr.). Pl. XXVI, fig. 1, ♂; fig. 2, ♀; Pl. III, fig. 18, *larva.* Var. **maritima** (Edw.) Pl. LXIII, fig. 15, ♂. Var. **texana** (Edw.) Pl. LXIII, fig. 21, ♂, *under side*, type (The Common Wood-Nymph).

Butterfly.—Closely resembling the preceding species, but somewhat smaller in size. The figures on Pl. XXVI correctly represent the typical form. This is a protean species, widely spread over the continent, the varieties found in the eastern and southern States being characterized more or less by the presence of a well-defined yellowish band on the primaries, while in those from the north and west this band tends to become more or less obsolete. In West Virginia and the mountains southward this band is often pale whitish yellow. The number of the ocelli is not constant, and specimens constantly turn up in which they tend to disappear. The industry of observers and collectors has provided us with numerous varietal names. *C. maritima* (Edw.) common on the Atlantic seaboard from New Jersey to Nova Scotia is relatively small in size, dark, with the yellow band on the fore wings bright and sharply defined. *C. texana* (Edw.) from the south is generally larger than the New England form, browner on the under side, the yellow band and the dark markings more prominent.

(a) **Cercyonis alope,** form **nephele** (Kirby). Pl. XXVI, fig. 3, ♂; fig. 4, ♀, *underside;* Pl. IV, figs. 7, 8, *chrysalis* (The Clouded Wood-nymph).

This form, long held to be a species, is now known to be only a melanic variety, characterized by the partial or entire suppression of the yellow band on the primaries and a diminution of the size of the eye-spots. It is found on the mountains of Pennsylvania, New York, and New England, and throughout Canada, ranging far north and west.

(b) **Cercyonis alope,** form **olympa** (Edw.). Pl. XXVI, fig. 9, ♂; fig. 10, ♀ *under side,* types (The Olympian Wood-nymph).

Synonym: *ino* Hall.

Common in the region west of the Mississippi and thence ranging to the Pacific coast. It cannot be distinguished from *C. nephele,* except by the locality-labels, upon which some recent writers appear to found their so-called "species."

(c) **Cercyonis alope,** form **boöpis** (Behr). Pl. LXIII, fig. 18, ♂; fig. 17, ♀, *under side* (The Ox-eyed Wood-nymph).

This variety, closely allied to the preceding, occurs in central and northern California, and is abundant north of San Francisco Bay. The ocelli on the under side of the secondaries tend to disappear. A trifling variety, in which the hind wings on the under side are hoary, dusted with white scales, was named var. *incana* by Edwards.

(d) **Cercyonis alope** form **baroni** (Edw.). Pl. XXVI, fig. 15, ♂; fig. 16, ♀, *under side,* types (Baron's Satyr).

This occurs in northern California and Oregon. The eye-spots on the under side do not tend to disappear as much as in the variety *boöpis,* which it otherwise closely resembles, and from which it is hard to separate it, except with the help of locality labels.

(e) **Cercyonis alope,** var. **ariane** (Boisd.). Pl. XXVI, fig. 5, ♂; fig. 6, ♀, *under side,* dark form, from near San Francisco, Pl. LXIII, fig. 20, ♀, *under side,* lighter form from Oregon (The Ariane Satyr).

This insect is no doubt only a race of *C. alope.* The ocelli persist in the males, but tend to disappear in the females. There is considerable difference in the hue of the ground-color of the under side of the wings. In the southern parts of the range the ground-color is darker and browner than in the north. On Pl. LXIII, fig. 20, I show the under side of a female from Oregon, which is paler than the specimens shown on Pl. XXVI, which are from central California. This female corresponds closely with the figure of the type of the female of *ariane,* published by Oberthür.

(f) **Cercyonis alope** var. **gabbi** (Edw.). Pl. XXVI, fig. 17, ♀, *under side,* type (Gabb's Satyr).

This variety is larger than the last three mentioned, and has a more southern range. All the specimens in the Edwards Collection are labelled as having been taken in Utah. It also turns up in southern California. It is nearly allied to the variety named *texana* (Edw.), of which it is no doubt a race, with a "washed-out" style of coloration.

Genus Cercyonis

A remarkable variety of the female, dubbed *stephensi* by Wright, is characterized by being pale fawn, with both the fore and hind wings girdled by broad bands of pale yellow. It is figured by Wright and by Comstock. It is a rare "freak."

(g) **Cercyonis alope** var. **wheeleri** (Edw.). Pl. LXIII, fig. 16, ♀, type, *under side* (Wheeler's Satyr).

The original types of this so-called species, taken by the Wheeler Expedition in Arizona, are in my possession. There is a male and two females, one of which is figured upon the plate. It is hard to discover any material difference between the insect named *C. gabbi* (Edw.) and *C. wheeleri* (Edw.). The only distinction worth mentioning is the fact that the three specimens have the upper ocellus of the primaries twinned, *i.e.* composed of two eye-spots fusing with each other. But this is a small distinction upon which to found a species. This phenomenon often occurs in specimens of *C. alope*, and is shown in one of the specimens labelled *gabbi* by Edwards himself. The form *wheeleri*, like *gabbi*, seems to me to be merely a local race of the insect which is represented further east by the var. *texana*, and still further east by typical *alope*, and *pegala*, which latter is possibly only a form of *alope*.

(3) **Cercyonis meadi** (Edwards) Pl. XXVI, fig. 13, ♀ ; fig. 14, ♂. *under side* (Mead's Satyr).

Butterfly.—This well-marked species is comparatively small, and may easily be distinguished from all others by the bright red on the limbal area above and on the middle area of the primaries below. Expanse: 1.60–1.75 inch.

Early Stages.—These have been described and figured by Edwards in "The Butterflies of North America," vol. iii. The caterpillar is green, marked by paler stripes and lozenge-shaped spots of pale green on the side. The chrysalis is pale green. The egg is pale saffron. The caterpillars feed on grass.

Mead's Satyr ranges through Colorado, Montana, Utah, and Arizona.

(4) **Cercyonis sthenele** (Boisduval) Pl. XXVI, fig. 20, ♂, *under side* (The Least Wood-nymph).

Butterfly.—Quite small. The female is paler and the ocelli are larger and more distinct than in *C. charon* and allied forms. The distinguishing feature is the irregular, dark, twice-strangulated median band on the under side of the secondaries, bordered on both sides by light almost white shades. Expanse: 1.4–1.5 in.

The species was originally described from the vicinity of San Francisco, where it was abundant on the hills, upon which that city has grown up. It is now believed to be extinct, no specimens having been collected for many years past, although diligently sought. There are five specimens in the Edwards Collection in my possession.*

---

*Weymer (Seitz, Vol. V, p. 229) says that the insect figured on Pl. 50 d, and labelled "*silvestris*," is in reality *sthenele*. It is more likely a poor figure of *œta*, as shown by the zig-zag, inwardly pointing transverse markings of the secondaries.

(5) **Cercyonis silvestris** (Edwards). Pl. LXIII, fig. 12, ♀ ; fig. 13, ♀ ; *under side*; fig. 14, ♂ (The Sylvan Satyr).

Synonym: *phocus* (Edwards); *okius* (Oberthür).

Butterfly.—This is a small species, the males dusky on the upper side, the patch of dark androconia below the cell well marked. The females are paler. The ocelli on the underside tend to become obsolete. It is very near *C. paula* (Edw.), but quite distinct.

I possess the types of the species named *C. phocus* (Edwards). On their labels W. H. Edwards, the author of both species, has written the words "—silvestris Edw." He decided that in naming *phocus* he had perpetrated a synonym, and I think he was right in so deciding. I cannot for the life of me see any material difference between the two insects.

(6) **Cercyonis paula** (Edwards). Pl. XXVI, fig. 19, ♂, *under side;* Pl. LXIII, fig. 19, ♀ , type; fig. 23, ♀ , *under side* (The Small Wood-nymph).

Butterfly.—A small species, grayish brown above, the females lighter than the males. The fore wings with two pupillate ocelli, one near the apex, and one near the inner angle, the latter inconspicuous in the male, more conspicuous in the female. On the under side the wings are lighter, marked with numerous minute striæ; the secondaries are crossed by a broad darker median band defined inwardly and outwardly by narrow dark lines. The outer third is paler, now and then almost white, mottled with darker spots and lines, generally with two ocelli near the inner angle on this side. Expanse: 1.75–2.00 in.

Early Stages.—Unknown.

C. paula occurs in Nevada (type locality), northern California, Oregon, and Washington. Some writers have regarded it as a variety of *sthenele*, but, in spite of resemblances, it is probably quite distinct.

(7) **Cercyonis œta** (Boisduval). Pl. XXVI, fig. 7, ♂; fig. 8, ♀ , *under side;* Pl. LXIII, fig. 22, ♂, *under side* (The Least Satyr).

Butterfly.—This is another small species, as to the identity of which there has been some dispute. It is characterized by its relatively small size; the prevalent, though not invariable, absence of the lower ocellus on the upper side of the fore wings in the male, and the peculiar zigzag and broken outline of the mesial band on the under side of the secondaries. This is shown in our figure of the under side of the male, which corresponds exactly with the figure given by Barnes & McDunnough (Cont. Nat. Hist. Am. Lep., III, No. 2, PL. VIII, fig. 7). This specimen is one of the long series of *Satyrus œtus*, so determined and labelled by W. H. Edwards, which includes the original type of the species, so labelled by Boisduval in his own hand-writing, and sent by him to W. H. Edwards long before the Boisduval Collection passed into the ownership of M. Charles Oberthür. Expanse: 1.6–2. in.

This insect, the preliminary stages of which are unknown, inhabits the high sierras of California and the Rocky Mountains eastward. It is closely related to *C. charon*, but the latter is much darker and invariably has two ocelli on the forewing.

(8) **Cercyonis charon** (Edwards). *Pl. XXVI, fig. 11, ♂; fig. 12, ♀; Pl. LXIII, fig. 24, ♂, type, *under side*; fig. 25, ♀, type, *under side* (The Dark Wood-nymph).

Butterfly.—The male is very dark, almost black, in color; the female is somewhat paler. There are two eye-spots on the fore wings in the usual location, indistinct on the upper, distinct on the lower side of the wings. The under sides of the wings are variable. In the type they are dark; in other specimens they are a little paler. Both the fore and hind wings are abundantly and evenly marked by little striæ, and crossed on either side of the median area by obscure, irregular, transverse dark lines, which in some specimens are lost in the dark ground-color. Expanse: 1.50–1.75 in.

Early Stages.—These have been described and beautifully figured by Edwards. The caterpillar is green, cylindrical, tapering before and behind, marked with longitudinal pale yellow lines. The chrysalis is green, or black, striped with narrow white lines. The egg is somewhat firkin-shaped, flat at the top and base, vertically ribbed, and honey-yellow. The larva feeds on grasses. *C. charon* is found in the Rocky Mountains of the Northwest, ranging from British Columbia as far south as the high mountains of New Mexico.

(9) **Cercyonis behri** Grinnell. Pl. LXXI, fig. 9, ♂; fig. 10, ♀, *under side* (Behr's Satyr).

Butterfly.—It gives me great pleasure to figure this species from specimens from the collection of the late Dr. Barnes, now belonging to the U. S. National Museum. It was originally described from the vicinity of San Francisco, where it has apparently become extinct. The specimens figured on our plate are from Provo, Utah. They seem to agree quite well with the original description, and the species apparently has a quite wide distribution.

Genus ŒNEIS Hübner

Synonym: *Chionobas* Boisd.

(The Arctics)

"To reside
In thrilling region of thick-ribbed ice."
SHAKESPEARE.

Butterfly.—The antennæ are short, eyes of moderate size; front full, protuberant; palpi slender; fore wings somewhat produced at tip, with outer margins rounded and hind margins very slightly, if at all, sinuate. The nervules of fore wings slightly dilated toward the base; hind wings elongated, oval, with the outer margins evenly rounded. The color of these butterflies is some shade of brown,

*The figures on Pl. XXVI are not dark enough through fault of the engraver. They should be almost black.

or smoky gray; the outer margin is generally lighter than the base of the wing, and is often marked with ocelli, sometimes pupilled with white. Wings generally marbled and mottled on the under side, and sometimes crossed on the middle of the hind wings by a broad band of darker color. The fringes are dark, sometimes checkered with white.

Egg.—Ovate-spherical, higher than broad, marked on the side from the apex to the base with raised sculptured ridges; deposited, so far as we have been able to learn, on dried grass and the stems of plants in proximity to the growing plants upon which the young caterpillars are destined to feed.

Caterpillar.—Head on emergence from the egg somewhat larger than the rest of the body, but, as the larva passes successive moults and attains maturity, the relative thickness of the body increases, and the adult larva tapers a little from about the middle in either direction. The larvæ are pale green or brown, marked by darker stripes upon the back and on the sides, the markings on the sides being in most species more conspicuous than those on the back. The species all feed on grasses.

Chrysalis.—Stout, very slightly angulated, formed, so far as we know, unattached, under stones and at the roots of grasses. When pupating, the caterpillar often makes for itself a slight depression or cell in the soil, in

Fig. 127.—Neuration of the genus *Œneis*, enlarged.

which a few threads of silk have been deposited, though not enough to justify us in calling the structure a cocoon.

This genus is composed of butterflies which are mainly arctic in their habitat, or dwell upon the summits of lofty mountains, where the summer is but brief. Only a few species are found at comparatively low elevations, and these in British America, or the parts of the United States immediately contiguous to the Canadian line. The most widely known of all the species up to this time is the White Mountain Butterfly, *Œneis semidea* (Say) a colony of which has existed probably ever since the glacial period upon the loftiest summits of the White Mountains in New Hampshire. A number of species are found in the region of the Rocky Mountains. One species, *Œneis jutta* (Hübner) occurs in Maine, Nova Scotia, and parts adjacent and varietal forms thereof in Labrador and Alaska. There are in all over thirty species of this genus recognized by authors as occurring in our fauna. In their early stages all of the species show a close likeness to one another.

(1) **Œneis nevadensis** (Felder). Pl. LXII, fig. 1, ♂; fig. 2, do., *under side* (Felder's Arctic).

This species, with which *Œ. gigas* Butler has been confounded by some authors, may be distinguished from the latter by its smaller size, the paler ground-color of the fore wings, and the different markings of the under side. Expanse: ♂, 2.25 in.; ♀, 2.35 in.

(2) **Œneis gigas** Butler. Pl. XXVII, fig. 1, ♂; fig. 2, ♀; Pl. LXII, fig. 3, ♂, *under side* (The Greater Arctic).

Synonym: *californica* (Boisd.)

Butterfly.—This, one of the largest species in the genus, ranges from British Columbia southward at higher elevations. The butterfly hides among the dark mosses and upon the trunks of prostrate trees. The males are vigilant and inquisitive, and dart out suddenly when alarmed, or attracted by passing insects. The females have a slower and more leisurely flight and are more readily taken. Expanse: 2.10–2.50 in.

Early Stages.—Edwards has figured the egg and the caterpillar in its first three stages, but the remaining life-history of the species awaits investigation.

(3) **Œneis iduna** (Edwards.) Pl. XXVII, fig. 4, ♂; Pl. LXII, fig. 6, ♂, *under side*, types (The Iduna Arctic).

Butterfly.—This insect, some specimens of which even exceed *Œ. gigas* in size, is found on the Coast Ranges and southward to Mendocino County in California. It is decidedly lighter on the outer third of the wings than the preceding species, the male being prevalently a pale yellowish-brown, with the basal and median areas of the fore wing darker brown. On the under side the wings are somewhat lighter than in the preceding species, with the maculations fewer and the transverse lines defining the median bar distinctly marked. Expanse: 2.00–2.30 in.

Early Stages.—These have been most beautifully delineated by Edwards in the third volume of "The Butterflies of North America."

(4) **Œneis macouni** (Edwards.) Pl. XXVII, fig. 3, ♂; Pl. LXII, fig. 5, ♂, *under side*, types (Macoun's Arctic).

Butterfly.—This species is closely allied to *Œneis gigas*, but may be distinguished by the absence of the bar of raised scales which is found in the male sex about the lower part of the cell of the fore wing in most of the species of the genus. It has thus far been found only on the north shore of Lake Superior and at the eastern base of the Rocky Mountains in the territory of Alberta. Expanse, 2.00–2.25 inches.

FIG. 128.—Caterpillars of *Œneis macouni* (Riley).

Early Stages.—For a knowledge of these in all their minute details the reader is again referred to the pages of the indefatigable Edwards.

(5) **Œneis ivallda** (Mead). Pl. XXVII, fig. 9, ♂; Pl. LXII, fig. 4, ♀, types (Mead's Arctic).

Butterfly.—This species is easily distinguished from all others by the peculiar pale ashen color of the upper side of the wings. It is not a common species, and is apparently restricted to the highest mountains of California and Nevada, principally about Lake Tahoe, though it probably occurs elsewhere. Expanse: 1.90–2.10 in.

Early Stages.—Only the egg and young larva have been described by W. H. Edwards.

(6) **Œneis chryxus** (Westwood). Pl. XXVII, fig. 10, ♂; Pl. LXII, fig. 9, ♂, *under side*, from Banff, Alberta; fig. 7, var. **calais** (Scud.) ♀, type, from Rupert House; fig. 8, ♀, *under side* (The Chryxus Arctic).

Butterfly.—Widely distributed from the higher mountains in the southwestern states through British Columbia and the region of Hudson Bay to Alaska. It varies greatly. Specimens from the southern limits of its range being often much lighter in color than those from more northern regions. There is also a great variation in the number and size of the ocelli, some specimens being devoid of them and others having many. The life-history is fully recorded in the pages of Edwards. Most authors agree in regarding *Œneis calais* Scudder as a varietal form of *chryxus*. It gives me pleasure to figure the type of *calais* on our plate. Expanse: 1.60–1.75 in.

(7) **Œneis nahanni** Dyar. Pl. LXXV, figs. 10, 10a. ♂, type (Dyar's Arctic).

Butterfly.—This species is unknown to me, except by the types, the male of which I figure through the courtesy of the United States National Museum. The original description given by Dr. Dyar is as follows:

"Blackish above, washed with ferruginous brown, the veins darker, the markings of underside showing. A small ocellus or none above vein 5 on fore wings, two to five on hind wings, the one above vein 5 largest, the rest small or absent. Hind wings below black and white coarsely strigose, somewhat as in *uhleri* Reakirt and *varuna* Edwards, but much more densely, the white of the wing being largely obscured. Median band weakly indicated; ocelli black with white pupils; fore wings shaded with red over the disk."

"One ♂, one ♀, Nahanni Mts., Mackenzie, 2,500 ft., July 16, 1903."

Judging from the description and the types this is a form not distantly related to *Œ. chryxus*, and has no near relationship to *Œ. varuna* and *uhleri*, with which the author made comparison.

(8) **Œneis jutta** (Hübner). Pl. XXVII, fig. 5, ♀. Var. **alaskensis** Holland, Pl. LXII, fig. 10, ♂, fig. 11, ♀, types (The Nova Scotian Arctic).

Butterfly.—This species, which is found in Europe, is not uncommon in the State of Maine as far south as Bangor, and occurs also in Nova Scotia, ranging thence westward to Ottawa and the Hudson Bay country. The varietal form *alaskensis* is smaller, duller in color, and with more translucent wings than is the case in European and Nova Scotian examples. It is not uncommon in the Yukon Valley. Expanse: 1.80–2.10 in.

Early Stages.—For a thorough knowledge of these the reader may consult the pages of Scudder and Edwards.

Genus Œneis

(9) **Œneis uhleri** (Reakirt). Pl. XXVII, fig. 12, ♂; Pl. LXII, fig. 12, ♂, *under side* (Uhler's Arctic).

Butterfly.—This species is found in Colorado. It is generally redder on the upper side than *Œ. varuna* and the females are often richly ornamented with eye-spots on the outer borders of both the fore and the hind wings. The species has been beautifully described and delineated by Edwards in the third volume of the "Butterflies of North America," and it would be difficult to add to what he has given us. Expanse: 1.45–1.55 in.

The type of var. *obscura* figured by Edwards is in my possession. It simply differs by being darker on the upper side.

(10) **Œneis varuna** (Edwards). Pl. XXVII, fig. 8, ♂; Pl. LXII, fig. 13, ♂; fig. 14, ♀, types from North Dakota (The Varuna Arctic).

Butterfly.—This species is smaller than those which thus far have been mentioned. It has been well figured by Edwards. It is found in the prairie lands of North Dakota, Montana, and the parts of Canada adjacent, and is not uncommon about Calgary, Alberta. There is considerable variation. Often specimens are light on the upper side of the wings, and almost immaculate, while frequently, as shown in the types, they are highly ornamented with ocelli. On the underside the species is marked very much as in *Œ. uhleri*. Expanse: 1.50–1.60 in.

Early Stages.—Little of these is as yet known.

(11) **Œneis daura** (Strecker). Pl. LXXVI, fig. 20, ♀, type; fig. 20a, do. *under side* (Strecker's Arctic).

So far as I know, the only specimen in existence of this species or form, is the type, a female, in the Field Museum of Natural History in Chicago, to the Director of which I am indebted for the photograph which is reproduced on the plate. Strecker informs us that the specimen was taken on Mt. Graham, Arizona. It is wonderfully like the female of *Œ. alberta*, which is common in Alberta. Can there have been a mistake made as to the locality at which the specimen is said to have been captured? Alberta is far from Arizona and collectors in the latter region have never found *Œ. daura* in Arizona since Strecker wrote, so far as I know.

(12) **Œneis alberta** Elwes. Pl. LXII, fig. 15, ♂; fig. 16, ♀ (The Albertan Arctic).

Butterfly.—Quite variable in the color of the upper side, ranging from pale gray to darker shades and often reddish upon the hind wings. The females are generally paler than the males. The species has been fully described and well delineated, and its life-history worked out by Edwards in "The Butterflies of North America," Vol. III. It is common in the Province of Alberta. Expanse: ♂, 1.4–1.6 in.; ♀, 1.4–1.8 in.

A variety of this species has been named *oslari* by Skinner. It occurs in Colorado, is a little larger than typical *alberta*, which it closely resembles upon the under side; the wings on the upper side are smoky brown, with a reddish brown extra-mesial band running from near the costa to the inner margin of the primaries. Expanse: ♂, 1.6 in., ♀, 1.8 in.

(13) **Œneis caryi** Dyar. Pl. LXXV, figs. 11, 11a. ♂, type (Cary's Arctic).

Butterfly.—This species, like *Œ. nahanni* is unknown to me except from the type, a figure of which we give. The original description is as follows:

"Gray brown above, washed with dark ferruginous red submarginally on fore wings, over most of surface of hind wings; two large black ocelli on fore wings above veins 2 and 5 respectively, one on the hind wings near anal angle, the three minutely white pupilled and repeated below. Fore wings below reddish on the disk and inner margin; hind wings contrastingly marbled in black and white, the median band strongly white edged.

"One ♂, Smith Landing, Athabasca, June 13, 1903. *Type.*—No. 8046, U. S. National Museum.

"Near *norna* Thunberg, but the red color of the wings is much darker and more rust-colored than in this form or in *katahdin* Newcomb."

This insect is not far from *Œ. taygete* Geyer, but the mesial band on the under side of the secondaries is not as well defined as in typical *Œ. taygete.*

(14) **Œneis cairnesi** Gibson. Pl. LXXII, fig. 6, ♂, type; Pl. LXXV, fig. 20, ♂, type, *under side.* (After Gibson: Canad. Arct. Exped., Pt. i, Pl. IV, f. 6; Pl. II, f. 7).

This is apparently another species, or form, belonging to the *Taygete*-group, in which the wings are laved on the upper side with fulvous. The insect is only known to me through the description and figures of Dr. Gibson, which he has kindly allowed me to reproduce. Expanse: 1.75 in.

(15) **Œneis taygete** Geyer: Pl. XXVII, fig. 6, ♂ (The Labrador Arctic).
Synonym: *boötes* (Boisduval).

Butterfly.—The wings are not very translucent, fulvous (some males fuscous); and the broad mesial band on the under side of the hind wings is generally well defined and strongly directed outwardly just below the costa. Expanse: 1.75 in.

Early Stages.—Unknown.

Habitat: The species is very common in Labrador, and we have a long series from both the eastern and western coast of the peninsula. The specimen figured on our plate is from Nain, Labrador. It appears to be common about Lake Athabasca, from which region we have numerous specimens.

(16) **Œneis katahdin** (Newcomb). Pl. LXII, fig. 19, ♂; fig. 20, ♀, *under side,* types (The Katahdin Arctic).

The specimens we figure were obtained from the author of the species and were labelled by him as "type." They undoubtedly are at least paratypes. The upper side of the wings is somewhat broadly laved with fulvous, shading into gray. On the upper side the marginal markings of the hind wings in both sexes are dark and coalesce. Expanse: ♂, 1.5 in.; ♀, 1.65 in.

(17) **Œneis norna** (Thunberg). Pl. LXII, fig. 17, typical, ♂, *under side;* fig. 18, ♀; fig. 22, ♂, var. from Finland, *under side* (The Norna Arctic).
Synonym: *semidea* Gibson (in part) not Say.

This species ranges from northern Europe through Siberia into Alaska and eastward, and in its wide range has developed many varietal forms. Our plate shows the male and the female figured by Edwards in "The Butterflies of North America," which are matched by specimens from the Great Slave Lake. The female is from Nushagak, Alaska, the male being a specimen from Finland, obtained from the late Dr. Otto Staudinger, and pronounced by him as being typical. The insect figured by Dr. Gibson (Canad. Arctic Exped., Pl. II, fig. 3) and pronounced by him to be a form of *semidea* (Say) is a form of *norna* (Thunberg), not uncommon in Finland, a Finnish specimen of which is shown on Pl. LXII, fig. 22. The specimen agrees well with Gibson's figure. It represents one of several varieties sent me by Dr. Staudinger.

It may not be improper to call the attention of students to the fact that the male figured on our plate, which is the male used by Edwards, was not quite accurately delineated by Mrs. Peart, who, deft draughtswoman as she was, failed in certain minor details to catch the exact features of the specimen before her. The most accomplished artist is not as accurate as sunlight.

The figures on our plate are of natural size.

(18) **Œneis polixenes** (Fabr.) Pl. LXIII, fig. 6, ♂, *under side;* fig. 7, ♀ (The Fabrician Arctic).

Synonym: *crambis* (Edw.) (?Freyer).

I follow recent usage in applying the name *polixenes* (Fabr.) to what W. H. Edwards described and figured as *Œ. crambis*. The question of the proper name of the species is involved in more or less controversy, into which I will not go. The insect is not uncommon in Labrador. It is not what European students are in the habit of calling *crambis*. The life-history is only partly known.

(19) **Œneis peartiæ** (Edwards). Pl. LXII, fig. 21, ♂, type; Pl. LXXII, fig. 4, ♀, *under side,* after Gibson, Can. Arct. Exped., Pl. IV, fig. 5. (Mrs. Peart's Arctic).

This is a small species with blackish semitransparent wings, the hind wings marked with a dark curved mesial band on the under side. It is still a great rarity. It is found in the far north. The only specimen I possess is the male type, shown on the plate.

(20) **Œneis brucei** (Edwards). Pl. XXVII, fig. 7, ♂, type; var. **yukonensis** Gibson, Pl. LXXII, fig. 3, ♂, type, *under side,* after Gibson (Bruce's Arctic).

Butterfly.—Wings transparent, permitting the label to be read through them; a well defined dark band on the under side of the secondaries. The variety *yukonensis* Gibson is smaller in size and the mesial band of the hind wings below defined on either side by more white than in specimens from Colorado.

Early Stages.—All we know of them has been given by Edwards.

The insect has a wide range from the alpine summits of Colorado to the mountains of Yukon Territory.

(21) **Œneis beani** Elwes. Pl. LXIII, fig. 4, ♂; fig. 5, ♀, *under side* (Bean's Arctic).

Synonym: *subhyalina* Edwards (not Curtis).

Butterfly.—This insect is found on high mountain peaks near Laggan, Alberta. Its wings are more or less diaphanous and pale smoky gray. This fact led W. H. Edwards to identify it with *Œ. subhyalina* Curtis, from which it is evidently different, not having the costa on the upper side "freckled with black and white," a feature emphasized by Curtis.

Early Stages.—Unknown.

(22) **Œneis assimilis** Butler. Pl. LXII, fig. 23, ♂; fig. 24, ♂, *under side* (Butler's Arctic).

Butterfly.—This species, or form, is characterized by the even marbling of the lower side of the wings and the absence of a well defined mesial band on the under side of the secondaries. It resembles the preceding species, but is lighter in color on the upper side, and on the under side has the costa of the fore wing freckled with white and dark brown, which is not the case in *Œ. beani*.

Early Stages.—Unknown.

(23) **Œneis subhyalina** (Curtis). Pl. LXIII, fig. 27, ♂; fig. 26, ♂, *under side* (Curtis' Arctic).

Probably no species has given rise to more discussion than this, described from a single specimen captured one hundred years ago by Sir John Ross.

The insect was described, but not figured, by Curtis in 1835. He does not give the sex of the type. His statement that the insect on the *upper side* has the costa "freckled with white and black" puts it beyond doubt that it is allied to the species *semidea* Say. The only other species likely to have been taken by Ross in which the costa is sometimes (but rarely) freckled with black and white on the upper side of the costa is *Erebia discoidalis* Kirby, but the rest of the description of Curtis fails entirely to apply to this. After reflection and careful study I am led to believe that *Œ. subhyalina* (Curtis) is a form of *semidea* (Say) not uncommon in Labrador and the North West Territory, the wings of which are translucent, so that the markings of the under side can be seen through from above, and which are really subhyaline. I figure a pair of such specimens, believing that they really represent what Curtis described. They are different from typical *semidea* (Say) in having translucent wings and much less darkly marked at the base of the secondaries on the under side. In our figure of the male the spots of the lower side show clearly on the upper side, the wings being quite diaphanous, or sub-hyaline.

(24) **Œneis œno** (Boisd. ?) Pl. LXII, fig. 25, ♂, being the insect figured as *œno* by Edwards; fig. 26, ♂, *under side*.

Butterfly.—This is a species about which there has been much discussion. Various insects have had this name applied to them. In Vol. III of his great work Edwards figured what he believed to be *œno*, but some students are inclined to think that the learned author was mistaken in his identification.

Dr. McDunnough gave the name **lucilla** to pale specimens, which McDunnough regarded as the form, which Edwards had described, figured, and named as *œno*. But McDunnough's figures of *lucilla*, which are before me, do not agree with the specimens figured by Edwards as *œno*, which are also before me, as I write. The insects named *œno* by Edwards are darker and differently marked on the under side from the insects named *lucilla* by McDunnough.

I am not sure of the identity of the butterfly named *œno* by Boisduval, but am sure that what Edwards figured and described under this name, agrees more closely with the description and figures of Boisduval than do the specimens called *lucilla* by McDunnough. Both *œno* Boisduval (*fide* Edwards) and *lucilla* McDunnough, seem to me to be western varieties of *Œneis semidea* (Say). The subject requires further study and more material than has thus far been at command.

(25) **Œneis semidea** (Say). Pl. XXVII, fig. 11, ♂; Pl. III, figs. 1, 2, 4, 7, 15, *larva;* Pl. IV, figs. 4, 5, *chrysalis;* Pl. LXIII, fig. 8, ♂, *under side;* Var. **arctica** Gibson, Pl. LXXII, fig. 5 (After Gibson). (The White Mountain Butterfly).

This butterfly, originally described by Say from the subarctic summits of the White Mountains in New Hampshire, is believed to have a wide distribution, and in various varietal forms ranges probably as far as Siberia. The form found on the highest summits of the mountains of Colorado was identified by Edwards as *œno* (Boisduval). Specimens much lighter on the under side were yclept *lucilla* by Barnes & McDunnough. The basal area of the wings in specimens from New Hampshire and Labrador is generally more solidly black than in specimens from the western mountains. The variety *arctica* Gibson is a dwarf form from the high North. The variety *nigra* (Edwards) is founded upon a specimen from Mt. Washington, which is quite uniformly black on the under side of the hind wing.

(26) **Œneis simulans** Gibson. Pl. LXXV, fig. 19, ♂, *under side*, type (The Mimicking Arctic).

I do not know this insect, except from the description and figure of the author of the species, whose kind permission I have to reproduce the figure on the plate. It is said by the author not to be superficially separable from *Œ. semidea* (Say) var. *arctica* Gibson, but to differ in the form of the genitalia.

It probably is a form of *semidea*, which in its wide range has developed numerous mutations.

(27) **Œneis gibsoni** Holland, sp. nov. Pl. LXIII, fig. 10, ♂, holotype; fig. 9, ♀, allotype (Gibson's Arctic).

What I take to be the insect, the female of which is figured as a form of *semidea* by Gibson in the Report of the Canadian Arctic Expedition, Pl. II, fig. 7, is represented in my collection by three males and one female taken in the Kuskokwim Valley. That the males belong with the females is beyond a doubt, in spite of the fact that they differ from each other in the superficial appearance of the under side of the wings. The heavy marginal markings of the under side of the male are distinctive, and the sexes were taken *in consortio*. I name the insert in honor of Dr. Arthur Gibson, who has contributed much to our knowledge of the genus *Œneis*. The figures on the plate serve better than a detailed verbal description to show how the thing appears. Expanse: 1.75–2 in.

(28) **Œneis semplei** Holland. Pl. LXIII, fig. 1, ♂; fig. 2, ♀; fig. 3, ♂, *under side*, types (Semple's Arctic).

The specimens represented by the figures on our plate reveal a somewhat close resemblance to *Œ. semidea* (Say). The female, however, is wholly unlike any female specimen of *semidea* known to the author, who has seen hundreds of specimens. The ocelli on the fore and hind wings are characteristic. The specimens were taken in the month of July on the east coast of Hudson Bay, 1926, at the point where Little Cape Jones River empties into the bay, by one of the John B. Semple Expeditions of the Carnegie Museum.

The figure of the under side of a typical male specimen of *semidea* from Mt. Washington (see Pl. LXIII, fig. 8) enables a comparison between the under sides of the two species. It is noticeable that the markings of the under side of these two forms while having a general resemblance are different in the direction of the white spots on the costa of the fore wing. The presence of two dark cloudings running inwardly from the costa of the fore wing on the under side, one at the end of the cell and the other near the base differs from *semidea;* whereas in the latter there is a dark submarginal line running from the apex to the middle of the outer margin or the wing, which line is entirely absent in *semplei.*

After carefully studying the matter, the author regards this as a valid species, which he names after that excellent friend of the Carnegie Museum, Mr. John B. Semple, whose kindness in financing numerous ornithological expeditions to the northern parts of America is gratefully appreciated.

In concluding what I have said as to the species of *Œneis* I may remark that in my judgment the nomenclature has been somewhat confused by the fact that the older authors persisted in trying to fit to American forms the names given to insects of European origin. I doubt the actual identity of a number of the species from Scandinavia, Lapland, and northern Siberia with those occurring in the New World. The nomenclature is still badly "messed," and it will require more material and study before it is properly disentangled. Besides these things vary greatly and the markings of the under side of the hind wings furnish only a relatively good clue to relationships. The genitalia, resorted to by some recent authors, in my judgment after careful study, seem almost worthless for discrimination. The genitalia vary as much as the other parts of the insect, as shown by actual tests. So-called "fundamentalists" may be pleased with the "Lock and Key" theory of genitalic structure, by which the Maker is thought by them to have fixed the limits of the procreative ability of the lower forms, but my studies tend to show that many forms interbreed in spite of the "Lock and Key" arrangement. Nature is in a constant flux. A couple of dissections of a species do not disprove the statement.

Genus EREBIA Dalman
(The Alpines)

"Then we gather, as we travel,
  Bits of moss and dirty gravel,
    And we chip off little specimens of stone;
  And we carry home as prizes
  Funny bugs of handy sizes,
    Just to give the day a scientific tone."
                    CHARLES EDWARD CARRYL.

Butterfly.—Medium-sized or small butterflies, dark in color; wings usually marked with eye-like spots; antennæ short, with a gradually thickened club;

Genus Erebia

eyes naked. The costal vein of the fore wing is generally strongly swollen at the base. The subcostal vein is five-branched; the first two nervules generally emitted before the end of the cell; the third nearer the fourth than the end of the cell; the fourth and fifth nervules spring from a common stem, the fourth terminating immediately on the apex. The lower radial is frequently projected inwardly into the cell from the point where it intersects the union of the middle and lower

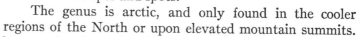

discocellular veins. The outer margins of both wings are evenly rounded.

Egg.—Subconical, flattened at the base and at the top, the sides marked by numerous raised vertical ridges, which occasionally branch or intersect each other.

Caterpillar.—The head is globular, the body cylindrical, tapering gradually backward from the head, the last segment slightly bifurcate.

Chrysalis.—The chrysalis is formed about the roots of grass and on the surface of the ground, either lying loosely there or surrounded by a few strands of silk. The chrysalis is convex, both ventrally and dorsally, humped on the thorax, produced at the head; all the projections well rounded; generally some shade of light brown or ashen-gray, with darker stripes and spots.

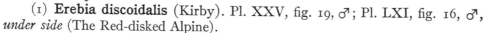

FIG. 129.—Neuration of the genus *Erebia*, enlarged.

The genus is arctic, and only found in the cooler regions of the North or upon elevated mountain summits. A few species range downward to lower levels in more temperate climates, but these are exceptional cases.

(1) **Erebia discoidalis** (Kirby). Pl. XXV, fig. 19, ♂; Pl. LXI, fig. 16, ♂, *under side* (The Red-disked Alpine).

Butterfly.—Easily distinguished by the plain black wings relieved by a reddish brown shade on the disk of the primaries on the upper side, by the white freckles on the costa of the fore wing, and by the peculiar markings of the under side. Expanse: 1.75–1.9 in.

Early Stages.—Hitherto undescribed.

The species is widely distributed from the region of Hudson Bay to the Pacific in Alaska. We have it abundantly from the Yukon Valley.

(2) **Erebia fasciata** Butler. Pl. LXI, fig. 5, ♂; fig. 6, ♀, *under side*, paratypes (The Banded Alpine).

Butterfly.—The male on the upper side is black. The female on the upper side is paler, tinged with reddish. The markings of the under side are very distinct, and are well shown in our figure. Expanse: 2.00–2.10 in.

Early Stages.—Hitherto undescribed.

The species has been reported from Victoria Island and the neighborhood of Point Barrow. The specimens figured on our plate are two of the nine specimens upon which Butler founded his description and are simply labeled "Arctic America."

(3) **Erebia avinoffi** Holland. Pl. LXI, fig. 7, ♀, type; fig. 8, ♂, allotype, fig. 9, ♀, paratype, *under side* (Avinoff's Alpine).

This species, which is quite distinct from *Erebia fasciata* Butler, was evidently confused with the latter by Elwes and Edwards. It is distinguished by the invariable presence on the upper side of the fore wings of a broad well defined band of rufous and by the narrow mesial pale band on the under side of the secondaries, which is enlarged laterally along the costa. Expanse: ♂, 1.75 in.; ♀, 2 in.

The type is a female from Kotzebue Sound; the allotypes, ♂♂ were taken at Indian Cape on the eastern side of Behring Strait.

(4) **Erebia rossi** (Curtis). Pl. LXXIII, fig. 3, ♂; fig. 4, ♀, *under side*. Var. **kuskoquima** Holland, Pl. LXI, fig. 21, ♂; fig. 22, ♀; fig. 23, ♀, *under side* (Ross' Alpine).

Butterfly.—The typical form of this species, originally described from Boothia Felix, occurs on the eastern side of the continent. We have a small series collected by G. M. Sutton on Southampton Island. It ranges thence northward. The insect as we pass westward toward the Pacific, gradually becomes lighter in color, especially in the female sex. The extradiscal band on the lower side of the secondaries, which in the typical form is obscure, is lighter and in the females the light spots on the upper and under sides of the hind wings increase in size and number. To this western varietal race figured on our plates I have given the sub-specific name *kuskoquima*, as it occurs quite abundantly in the Kuskokwim Valley.

A closely allied form is found in eastern Siberia. Expanse: ♂, 1.5–1.75 in.; ♀, 1.5–1.85.

(5) **Erebia steckeri** Holland. Pl. LXI, fig. 1, ♂, fig. 2, ♂, *under side;* fig. 3, ♀, fig. 4, ♀, *under side*, types (Stecker's Alpine).

Butterfly.—This beautiful species belongs to the *Disa*-group, but is at once distinguished by the very deep black mesial band on the under side of the secondaries, followed outwardly by a paler gray band, and preceded at the base by gray. The figures given on the plate will serve to readily distinguish this species, from *E. fasciata*, which it somewhat resembles on the secondaries, by the invariable presence of the four red ocelli on the primaries pupilled with black, and centered with white. Expanse: ♂, 1.65 in.; ♀, 1.75 in.

The species is represented in my collection by numerous specimens collected for me by the Rev. A. Stecker, in charge of the Moravian Mission to the Esquimaux on the Kuskokwim River, in whose honor I name it.

(6) **Erebia disa**, var. **mancinus** Doubleday & Hewitson. Pl. XXV, fig. 23, ♂; Pl. LXI, fig. 17, ♂, *under side* (The Mancinus Alpine).

Butterfly.—The wings are dark brown on the upper side. On the outer third below the apex are three or four black ocelli, broadly ringed with red and pupilled with white. The upper ocellus is generally bipupilled, that is to say, the black spot is twinned, and there are two small light spots in it. On the under side the fore wings are deep chestnut. The hind wings are broadly sown with gray scales, giving them a hoary appearance, and there are two minute light spots before the outer margin; one not far from the costa before the upper angle, the other near the end

Genus **Erebia**

of the cell. The female does not differ from the male, except that the ocelli on the fore wings are larger and more conspicuous. Expanse: ♂, 1.75 in., ♀ 1.9 in.

Early Stages.—Unknown.

This species is found in Alaska and on the mountains of British Columbia.

(7) **Erebia vidleri** Elwes. Pl. LXI, fig. 18, ♂; fig. 19, ♀, *under side* (Vidler's Alpine).

Butterfly.—Dark blackish brown on the upper side of the wings. The fore wings marked externally by a moderately broad bright reddish band diminishing in width from the costa toward the lower angle. On either side of the first radial are two black ocelli pupilled with white and at the lower end of the light band between the first and second median nervules is a small black ocellus also pupilled with white. On the under side the wings are much paler than on the upper side and the marginal band of the secondaries is bright yellowish red, with the spots repeated as on the upper side. The hind wing is traversed by a grayish white postmedian curved band, in which both between the second and the third median nervules is a minute ocellus; the fringes both on the upper and under side are checkered with white. Expanse: ♂ and ♀, 1.75 in.

Early Stages.—Unknown.

The habitat of this species is British Columbia, whence many specimens have been obtained.

(8) **Erebia epipsodea** Butler. Pl. XXV, fig. 28, ♂; Pl. LXI, fig. 26, ♀, from Montana; fig. 27, ♂, *under side* from Montana; fig. 24, ♂, from Yukon; fig. 25, ♂, from Yukon, *under side* (The Common Alpine).

Synonym: *rhodia* Edwards.

Butterfly.—The wings are dark brown on the upper side, with three or four black ocelli, pupilled with white, and broadly surrounded by red, located near the outer margin of the fore wings, and with three or four similar ocelli located on the upper side of the hind wings. The spots on the upper side reappear on the under side, and in addition the hind wings are traversed by a broad curved median blackish band, which is most distinct in specimens from southern parts of the range of the species, but in those coming from the more northern portions of the country is lost in the deeper black ground-color, which is characteristic of specimens collected in Alaska and the far northern British Possessions.

Early Stages.—These have been carefully described by Edwards in "The Butterflies of North America," Vol. III, and by H. H. Lyman in the "Canadian Entomologist," Vol. XXVIII, p. 274. The caterpillar feeds on grasses.

The species ranges from New Mexico (at high elevations) northward to Alaska, whence we have obtained it in large numbers, the northern specimens being always darker in color than those from further south. Pl. LXI, fig. 24, shows the under side of an Alaskan specimen.

(9) **Erebia brucei** Elwes. Pl. LXI, fig. 20, ♀. (Bruce's Alpine).

Synonym: *sineocellata* Skinner.

Butterfly.—This has been regarded by many authors as a variety of *E. epipsodea*. It is characterized by the almost entire obsolescence of the rufous marginal

204

spots and the ocelli on both the upper and lower sides of the wings. So far as known this insect only occurs at very high altitudes in Colorado. The specimen figured on our plate was taken by Bruce on one of the lofty peaks near Cashier Valley, Colorado, at an elevation of 13,000 feet above sea-level. Expanse: ♂, 1.45.; ♀, 1.55 in.

(10) **Erebia youngi** Holland. Pl. LXI, fig. 28, ♂, type; fig. 29, ♀, type; fig. 30, ♀, *under side*, paratype (Young's Alpine).

Butterfly.—This small species is represented by the specimens upon which the original description of the species was based. The types were collected in Alaska between Forty-Mile and Mission Creeks by the late Dr. S. Hall Young. The female somewhat closely resembles the species from Asia named *E. fletcheri* by Elwes (Trans. Ent. Soc. London, 1899, p. 347), but, judging from the figure which he gives on Pl. XII, fig. 4, it is abundantly distinct, being smaller in size and the markings on the under side of the secondaries being different. My original comparison of the species with *E. dabanensis* Erschoff was not quite fortunate, as the resemblance to the figure which Erschoff gives of his unique type (*Cf.* "Mémoires sur les Lépidoptères," Vol. II, Pl. XVI, fig. 1), is not very close, and only superficial. The figures given by Elwes of what he conceived to be *E. dabanensis* Erschoff do not exactly accord with Erschoff's description and figure (*Cf.* Trans. Ent. Soc. Lond., 1899, Pl. XII, figs. 5–8).

(11) **Erebia magdalena** Strecker. Pl. XXV, fig. 17, ♂. (Strecker's Alpine).

Butterfly.—Uniformly dark blackish-brown on both sides of the wings, with no spots or markings.

Early Stages.— These have been partially described and figured by Edwards.

This species was described from Colorado at an elevation of from ten to twelve thousand feet above sea-level, and has also been reported from Alaska.

(12) **Erebia tyndarus** (Esper). Pl. XXV, fig. 20, ♂ (type of *E. callias* Edw.) (The Colorado Alpine).

Synonym: *callias* Edwards.

Butterfly.—Pale brown on the upper side, with a more or less indistinctly defined broad transverse band of reddish on the outer third of the fore wings. At the apical end of this band are two black ocelli, pupilled with white. The fore wings on the under side are reddish, with the costa and outer margin grayish. The ocelli on this side are as on the upper side. The hind wings are gray, dusted with brown scales and crossed by narrow, irregular, dark-brown subbasal, median, and submarginal lines.

Early Stages.—Unknown.

This species is not uncommon on the mountains of Colorado and New Mexico. It has been regarded as a variety of the European *E. tyndarus*, but I fail entirely to see after examining large series of *tyndarus* from Europe that it is separable from that species.

(13) **Erebia sophia** Strecker. Pl. XXV, fig. 18, *ethela* Edwards, ♀, type; Pl. LXI, fig. 10, *ethela* Edwards, ♂, type, *under side;* fig. 11, do., ♀, *under side;* fig.

12, *sophia*, ♀, *under side*, from Yukon; fig. 13, var. **alasкensis** Holland, ♂, type; figs. 14, 15, do., ♂♂, *under side*.

Synonym: *ethela* Edwards.

At the time I first published this book I was in agreement with Dr. Henry Skinner in regarding *E. ethela* Edw. as being identical with *E. sophia* Strecker. In fact I figured the upper side of the female type of *E. ethela* Edw. under the name *E. sophia*. I have not essentially changed my opinion, in spite of the fact that I have since accumulated much material bearing upon the problem, and have designated a certain Alaskan form as a variety or subspecies.

The type of *E. sophia* Strecker was a female specimen taken by an Esquimau near Fort Churchill. On Pl. LXI, fig. 12, I show the under side of a female taken at Eagle City, Alaska, which agrees with the type of *E. sophia* and does not differ on either side from the female type of *E. ethela* Edw., the upper side of which is shown on Pl. XXV, fig. 18. I also show the under side of the male type of *E. ethela* Edw., which may be matched by specimens from Alaska.

There is, however, a large percentage of Alaskan specimens, which I have seen, which deviate from the typical form of the male sex of *E. ethela* in being much darker upon the lower side of the wings, and having the submarginal spots greatly reduced in size on the lower side of the wings, and even in some cases entirely wanting, except the three subapical spots of the primaries. This variant form is represented on Pl. LXI, figs. 13, 14, 15. To this form in 1900 I gave the varietal name *alaskensis*. Females closely corresponding to these males in the markings of the under side, but grading into females like the one shown on Pl. LXI, fig. 12, were taken at Eagle, Alaska, at the same time; so that I am forced to the conclusion that we are dealing in this case with an insect which is subject to considerable variation.

Fig. 130.—Neuration of the genus *Gyrocheilus*.

The Coloradan specimens to which W. H. Edwards applied the specific name *ethela* are in my possession. They came from very high altitudes, and are brighter than Alaskan specimens, which, except occasionally, show a marked tendency toward the obsolescence of the lighter markings both above and below.

Genus GYROCHEILUS, Butler

Butterfly.—Medium-sized butterflies, dark in color, with light eye-like spots on the primaries and brown borders on the secondaries. The antennæ are short, with a gradually tapering club; the palpi are long, slender, compressed, well clothed with scales on the lower surface. The costa of the fore wings is strongly arched, the outer margin evenly rounded, the outer margin of the hind wings regularly scalloped. The costal vein of the primaries is somewhat thickly swollen at the base.

Early Stages.—Unknown.

(1) **Gyrocheilus tritonia** Edwards, Plate XVIII, fig. 21, ♂ (Tritonia).

Butterfly.—The wings of the upper side are dark brown, with a submarginal row of white-centered ocelli below the apex of the primaries. The secondaries are marked with a submarginal band of red. On the under side the fore wings are as on the upper side. The hind wings have the submarginal band purplish red, irrorated with whitish and dark brown scales, on the inner edge relieved by a number of imperfectly developed ocelli, which are partially ringed about on the side of the base by pale yellow.

Early Stages.—Unknown.

Tritonia occurs in southern Arizona and northern Mexico, and is a local race of *G. patrobas* (Hew.), found further South.

IN THE FACE OF THE COLD

When the full moon hangs high overhead, the snow creaks underfoot, the north wind roars with furious blast, and the trees of the forests crack in the frost with a report like that of cannon, then, hanging in its little nest on the bare branches of the wind-tossed trees, the tiny caterpillar of the Viceroy keeps the spark of life where men freeze and die. Nothing in the realm of nature is more wonderful than the manner in which some of the most minute animal forms resist cold. The genera *Erebia* and *Œneis*, and many species of the genus *Brenthis*, are, as we have already learned, inhabitants of the arctic regions, or of lofty Alpine summits, the climate of which is arctic. Their caterpillars often hibernate in a temperature of from forty to fifty, and even seventy, degrees below zero, Fahrenheit.

It has been alleged that caterpillars freeze in the winter and thaw out in the spring, at that time regaining their vitality. Thus far the writer is unable to ascertain that any experiments or observations have positively decided for or against this view. A number of recorded cases in which caterpillars are positively stated to have been frozen and to have afterward been found to be full of vitality when thawed are open to question.

The most circumstantial account is that by Commander James Ross, R. N., F. R. S., quoted by Curtis in the Entomological Appendix to the "Narrative" of Sir John Ross's second voyage to the arctic regions. The specimens upon which the observations were made were the caterpillars of *Laria rossi*, a moth which is found abundantly in the arctic regions of North America. I quote from the account: "About thirty of the caterpillars were put into a box in the middle of September, and after being exposed to the severe winter temperature of the next three months, they were brought into a warm cabin, where, in less than two hours, every one of them returned to life, and continued for a whole day walking about; they were again exposed to the air at a temperature of about forty degrees below zero, and became immediately hard-frozen; in this state they remained a week, and on being brought again into the cabin, only twenty-three came to life; these were, at the end of four hours, put out once more into the air and again hard-frozen; after another week they were again brought in, when only eleven were restored to life; a fourth time they were exposed to the winter temperature, and only two returned to life on being again brought into the cabin; these two survived the winter, and in May an imperfect *Laria* was produced from one, and six flies from the other.''

The foregoing account seems to verify more thoroughly the stories that have been told than anything else I have been able to discover within the limits of entomological literature, but does not conclude argument. It would be interesting in these days, when methods of artificial freezing have been so highly perfected, to undertake a series of experiments to prove or disprove, as the case may be, the view which has been held since the time of the ancients. There is here a field for nice investigation on the part of some reader of this book. In making the experiment it probably would be well to select the larvæ of species which are known to hibernate during the winter and to be capable of withstanding a great degree of cold.

The effect of cold suddenly applied to the chrysalids of butterflies at the moment of pupation is often to produce remarkable changes in the markings. The spots upon the wings of butterflies emerging from chrysalids thus treated are frequently rendered more or less indistinct and blurred. The dark markings are intensified in color and enlarged; the pale markings are also in some cases ascertained to experience enlargement. Many of the strange and really beautiful aberrations known to collectors have no doubt been produced by the action of frost, which has occurred at the season when the larva was pupating. The species believed by the writer to be most prolific in aberrations are species, which pupate early in the spring from caterpillars which have hibernated, or which pupate late in the autumn. Some are species found at considerable altitudes above sea-level, where late frosts and early frosts are apt to occur. A number of very beautiful experiments upon the effect of cold upon the color of butterflies have been made in recent years, and some very curious phenomena have been observed. The writer has in his collection a considerable number of strikingly aberrant specimens which emerged from chrysalids treated to a sudden artificial lowering of the temperature at the critical period of pupation.

FAMILY II

LIBYTHEIDÆ (THE SNOUT–BUTTERFLIES)

"What more felicitie can fall to creature
 Than to enjoy delight with libertie,
And to be Lord of all the workes of Nature,
 To raigne in th' aire from th' earth to highest skie,
To feed on flowres and weeds of glorious feature,
 To take whatever thing doth please the eie?"

SPENSER.

Butterfly.—The butterflies of this family are very readily distinguished from all others by their long projecting palpi, and by the fact that the males have four feet adapted to walking, while the females have six, in which respect they approach the *Riodinidæ*.

Only one genus is represented in our faunal region, the genus *Libythea*.

Genus LIBYTHEA Fabricius
(The Snout-butterflies)

Butterfly.—Rather small in size, with the eyes moderately large; the antennæ with a distinct club at the end; the palpi with the last joint extremely long and heavily clothed with hair. The fore wings have the outer margin strongly excised between the first median nervule and the lower radial vein; at the end of the radial veins the wing is strongly produced outwardly; the inner margin is bowed out toward the base before the inner angle. The costa of the hind wing is bent upward at the base and excised before the outer angle; the wing is produced at the end of the subcostal vein, the third median nervule, and the extremity of the submedian vein. There is also a slight projection at the extremity of the first median nervule. Of these projections the one at the extremity of the third median nervule is the most pronounced. The cell of the primaries and of the secondaries is lightly closed.

FIG. 131. — Neuration of the genus *Libythea*.

Egg.—The egg is ovoid, nearly twice as high as wide, with narrow vertical ridges on the sides, every other ridge much higher than its mate and increasing in height toward the vertex, where they abruptly terminate, their extremities ranging around the small depressed micropyle. Between these ridges are minute cross-lines.

Genus Libythea

Caterpillar.—The caterpillar has the head small, the anterior segments greatly swollen and overarching the head. The remainder of the body is cylindrical.

Chrysalis.—The chrysalis is of a somewhat singular shape, the abdomen conical, the head sharply pointed, a raised ridge running from the extremity of the head to the middle of the first abdominal segment on either side, and between these ridges is the slightly projecting thoracic tubercle. On the ventral side the outline is nearly straight.

The caterpillar feeds upon *Celtis occidentalis*. Two species are accounted as belonging to our fauna. It is, however, doubtful whether these species are in reality such, and there is reason to think them in fact to be merely varietal forms, or races, no structural difference being apparent in any of them, and the only differences consisting in the ground-color of the wings.

(1) **Libythea bachmanni** Kirtland. Pl. XXVIII, fig. 1, ♂; fig. 2, ♂, *under side;* Pl. V, figs. 23, 24, *chrysalis* (The Snout-butterfly).

Butterfly.—Mainly distinguished from the following species by the redder color of the light spots on the upper side of the wings. Expanse: 1.75 inch.

Early Stages.—The generic description must suffice for these. They have been frequently described.

The butterfly ranges from New England and Ontario southward and westward over the whole country as far as New Mexico and Arizona.

(2) **Libythea carinenta** (Cramer). Pl. XXVIII, fig. 3, ♂ (The Southern Snout-butterfly).

Synonyms: *motya* Boisd. & Lec.; *larvata* Strecker.

Butterfly.—Much like the preceding species, but distinguished from it by the paler yellowish-fulvous coloration of the upper side of the wings. Expanse: 1.75 inch.

Early Stages.—These have not been carefully described as yet.

L. carinenta ranges from New Mexico into South America.

―――――――――

"We are not the only tenants of our farms—the fields and hedges, woods and waters, all around us, teem with a complex, rich, and interesting life. But nature will speak only to those who listen with love and sympathy."

SIR JOHN LUBBOCK.

From Introduction to "Tenants of an Old Farm," by Henry C. McCook, D. D.

FAMILY III

RIODINIDÆ (THE METAL–MARKS)

(*Erycinidæ* of many authors)

"I wonder what it is that baby dreams.
  Do memories haunt him of some glad place
  Butterfly-haunted, halcyon with flowers,
  Where once, before he found this earth of ours,
  He walked with glory filling his sweet face?"

Edgar Fawcett.

Butterfly.—Small, the males having four ambulatory feet, the females six, in which respect they resemble the *Libytheidæ*, from which they may readily be distinguished by the small palpi. There is great variety in the shape and neuration of the wings. Some of the genera of this subfamily (not all) have the precostal vein on the extreme inner margin of the wing free at its end, and projecting, so as to form a short frenulum, as in many genera of the moths. In addition the costal vein sends up a branch at the point from which the precostal is usually emitted. This apparent doubling of the precostal is found in no other group of butterflies, and is a strong diacritical mark by which they may be recognized. They are said to carry their wings expanded when at rest, and frequently alight on the under surface of leaves, in this respect somewhat approaching in their habit the Pyralid moths. Many of the species are most gorgeously colored; but those which are found within our region are for the most part not gaily marked. They may be distinguished from the *Lycænidæ* not only by the peculiar neuration and manner of carrying the wings, but by the relatively longer and more slender antennæ.

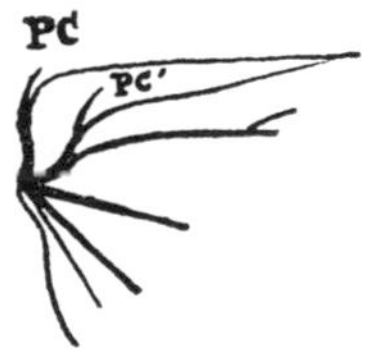

Fig. 132.—Neuration of base of hind wing of the genus *Apodemia*: *PC*, precostal vein; *PC'*, second precostal vein.

Early Stages.—Comparatively little is known of these, though in certain respects the larvæ and the chrysalis show a relationship to the *Lycænidæ*, with which some writers have in fact grouped them, but erroneously, as the writer believes.

Almost all of the species are American, and the family attains its highest development in the tropical regions of South America.

Genus APODEMIA Felder

(Type *Lemonias mormo* Felder)

Butterfly.—Small, brightly colored, the sexes often differing greatly in appearance from each other. The eyes are naked. The palpi are produced, porrect;

the last joint is short, thin, pointed, and depressed. The antennæ are moderately long, provided with a gradually thickening, inconspicuous club. The upper discocellular vein is wanting in the fore wing. The middle and lower discocellulars are of equal length. The hind wing has the end of the cell obliquely terminated by the middle and lower discocellular veins. The apex of the fore wing is somewhat pointed, the outward margin straight. The outward margin of the hind wing is evenly rounded.

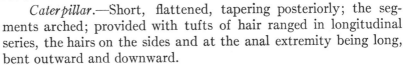

FIG. 133.—Neuration of the genus *Apodemia*.

Egg.—Flattened, turban-shaped, with a small, depressed, circular micropyle, the whole surface covered with minute hexagonal reticulations.

Caterpillar.—Short, flattened, tapering posteriorly; the segments arched; provided with tufts of hair ranged in longitudinal series, the hairs on the sides and at the anal extremity being long, bent outward and downward.

Chrysalis.—Short, suspended at the anal extremity, and held in position by a silk girdle, but not closely appressed to the surface upon which pupation has taken place; thickly covered with short, projecting hair.

The citadel of this genus is Mexico; though a few species are found as far south as Brazil. It is represented in our fauna by a few species, which occur in California, Arizona, Texas, New Mexico, and southern Colorado.

(1) **Apodemia mormo** (Felder). Plate XXVIII, fig. 7, ♂, *under side* (The Mormon).

Butterfly.—The wings on the upper side are dark ashen-gray, with the primaries from the base to the limbal area, and inwardly as far as the bottom of the cell and the first median nervule, red. The wings are profusely marked with white spots variously disposed. The under side is accurately depicted in our plate. Expanse: 1.10 inch.

Early Stages.—These have not been studied, but are probably similar to those of *A. virgulti.*

The Mormon is found in Utah, New Mexico, Arizona, and California. A pale variety occurring in arid localities in southwestern California has been named var. *deserti* by Barnes and McDunnough.

(2) **Apodemia virgulti** (Behr). Pl. XXVIII, fig. 6, ♂, (Behr's Metal-mark).

Butterfly.—Much like the preceding species on the upper side, but smaller and darker. The hind wings on the under side are much darker than in *A. mormo* and the pearly-white spots relatively smaller, forming a different pattern, and standing out very distinctly on the dark ground. Expanse: .9–1.10 in.

Early Stages.—These have been fully described by Coolidge in the Trans. Am. Ent. Soc., Vol. V, p. 324, and by Comstock in "The Butterflies of California," p. 150. Some writers maintain that *A. virgulti* is a form of *A. mormo*, but this remains to be proved by breeding.

Virgulti is common in southern California and Mexico.

(3) **Apodemia cythera** (Edwards). Pl. XXVIII, fig. 4, ♀, *under side;* fig. 5, ♂, types (The Cythera Metal-mark).

Butterfly.—Distinguished from *L. mormo* by the red submarginal band on the secondaries on the upper side, the greater prevalence of red on the primaries, and by the tendency of the spots on the under side of the secondaries, just after the costa, to fuse and form an elongate pearly-white ray. The submarginal spots on the lower side of the fore wings are smaller than in *mormo*. The sexes do not differ except in size. Expanse: 1.00–1.30 inch.

Early Stages.—Unknown.

Cythera is found in Arizona and Mexico. Comstock and others have treated this as a form of *mormo*, but without the test of breeding.

(4) **Apodemia duryi** (Edwards) Pl. XXVIII, fig. 10, ♀, type (Dury's Metal-mark).

Some authors are inclined to the view that this insect is the same as the species named *mejicanus* by Dr. Behr. Edwards named the species in honor of Mr. Charles Dury of Cincinnati.

Early Stages.—Unknown.

The type specimen, which is figured on the plate, came from New Mexico. The insect occurs in Arizona, and is not uncommon in Mexico.

(5) **Apodemia palmeri** (Edwards). Pl. XXVIII, fig. 11, ♂, type (Palmer's Metal-mark).

Butterfly.—Smaller than any of the preceding species. The ground-color of the wings is mouse-gray, spotted with white; on the under side the wings are whitish-gray, laved with pale red at the base of the fore wings. The white spots of the upper side reappear on the under side. Expanse: .75–.95 in.

Early Stages.—These are, so far as they have been worked out by Edwards, quite similar in many respects to those of *Polystigma nais*.

The range of the species is from Utah through Arizona into Mexico.

(6) **Apodemia marginalis** (Skinner). Pl. LXIV, fig. 1, paratype (Skinner's Metal-mark).

Under this name Dr. Henry Skinner described an insect, which he regarded as being either a new species, or a very striking variety of *A. palmeri*. The wings are relatively widely margined on the upper side with red, and the maculation is somewhat different on both sides of the wings from that of *A. palmeri*, giving them a different appearance. Only the test of breeding will show that it is a variety of *A. palmeri*, and we prefer to treat it as distinct. Expanse: .9 in.

Early Stages.—These are unknown, though Comstock states that the larva is said to feed upon *Beloperone californica*.

The insect has thus far only been reported from the Imperial Valley in California.

(7) **Apodemia hepburni** Godman and Salvin. Pl. LXXVI, figs. 10, 10a, ♂, (after Godman and Salvin). (Hepburn's Metal-mark).

This insect, which by Barnes and Benjamin has been treated as a "form" of *A. palmeri* Edwards, is by them included in our fauna. It was originally described from Chihuahua, Mexico. While superficially resembling *A. palmeri*, it may be distinguished by its more pointed fore wings, by the absence of almost all the light

213

markings on the upper side, except at the end of the cells, and the subapical band of the fore wing; and by the pattern of the transverse markings of the under side of the wings, which is different from that of *A. palmeri*, and more closely analogous in outline (though much paler) to the pattern of the markings shown on the under side of *A. phyciodoides* (Barnes and Benjamin).

(8) **Apodemia phyciodoides** Barnes and Benjamin. Pl. LXXVI, fig. 5, ♂, holotype; fig. 5a, ♂, do. *under side;* fig. 6, ♀, allotype; fig. 6a, ♀, do. *under side.*

We give on the plate figures of the upper and under side of the types of the male and the female of this form, which has been recently described by Barnes and Benjamin from Cochise County, Arizona. It appears to belong to the same group as *A. hepburni* and *A. walkeri* Godman and Salvin. The ground-color of the upper side of the wings is bright fulvous, as in many species of *Phyciodes*, with dark transverse lines and spots. On the under side the markings are dark brown on a light background, which on the fore wing is pale yellowish red; on the hind wing creamy white. Expanse: male, .7 in.; female, 1.10 in.

Early Stages.—Unknown.

(9) **Apodemia multiplaga** Schaus. Pl. LXXVI, figs. 4, 4a, ♂. (paratype) (Schaus' Metal-mark).

This species, originally described from Mexico, has been found to occur in southern Texas. It may easily be recognized by the figures on the plate. Expanse: 1 15 in.

Early Stages.—Unknown.

Genus POLYSTIGMA Godman and Salvin

This genus was erected by the authors "because of the remarkable development of the front legs of the male, which are perfect, that is to say they possess terminal claws. . . . There is a spine beneath at the end of the tip, another near the proximal end of the first tarsal joint, and another on what appears to be the fourth joint. The terminal joint of the front leg of the female is as long as the second joint and all the tarsal joints, as well as the distal end of the tip is strongly spinous beneath. This nearly perfect structure of the front leg of the male we have not found in any other Erycinid [Riodinid]; it, in fact, forms an exception to the definition of the family, so far as the development of the tarsi is concerned." (*Biol. Cent.-Amer.; Lep. Rhop.*, Vol. I, p. 469).

(5) **Polystigma nais** (Edwards). Pl. XXVIII, fig. 8, ♂, fig. 9, ♀. (The Nais Metal-mark).

Butterfly.—The ground-color of the upper side is bright red, clouded with fuscous on the base of the hind wings and bordered with the same color. There is a small precostal white spot on the primaries near the apex. The wings are profusely marked with small black spots arranged in transverse series and bands. The fringes are checkered with white. On the under side the wings are pale reddish, mottled with buff on the secondaries. The black spots and markings of the upper side reappear on the under side and stand out boldly on the lighter ground-color. Expanse, 1.00–1.25 inch.

Early Stages.—These are beautifully delineated in "The Butterflies of North America," Vol. II. The egg is pale green, turban-shaped, covered with hexagonal reticulations. The caterpillar is rather stout and short, the first segment projecting over the head. The body is somewhat flattened and tapering behind, covered with tufts of hairs projecting outward and downward on all sides, only the two rows of short tufts on the back sending their hairs upward. The color is mouse-gray striped longitudinally on the back with yellowish-white, the tufts more or less ringed about at their base with circles of the same color. The chrysalis is blackish-brown, attached at the anal end, held in place by a girdle, but not closely appressed to the surface on which pupation has taken place, and thickly studded with small projecting hairs. The larva lives on the wild plum.

Nais occurs from Colorado to Mexico east of the Rocky Mountains.

Genus EMESIS Fabricius

Butterfly.—Medium in size, the sexes not greatly differing from each other in coloration, generally being of some shade of brown, or fulvous, with darker markings; on the underside paler, tending to yellow or orange or even white. The antennæ are moderately long and slender. The palpi are moderately long and are so closely appressed to the front as scarcely to be visible when viewed from above. The wings are not indented or scalloped, subtriangular in outline in the males, broader and more rounded in the females. In the males the apex of the fore wing is generally produced and in some species tends to become slightly falcate at the tip. The legs are well developed, not hairy. Many of the species are feeble in flight and have the habit of concealing themselves on the under side of leaves, where they sit with their wings expanded. Some species, however, fly freely in the open, haunting flowers.

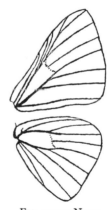

FIG. 134.—Neuration of genus *Emesis*, enlarged.

Early Stages.—Little is known about these, except that the chrysalid is suspended by its cremaster from a small button of silk spun by the caterpillar.

The genus is well represented in tropical America. But two species are known to occur on the Mexican border of the United States.

(1) **Emesis ares** (Edwards). Pl. XXVIII, fig. 17, ♂, fig. 18, ♀, types (The Ares Butterfly).

Butterfly.—The upper side of both sexes of the male and female types are delineated on the plates. On the under side the wings are pale red, marked with a few black spots, representing on the under side the markings of the upper side. Of these, the spots of the median and submarginal bands are most conspicuous. Expanse: 1.00–1.35 in.

(2) **Emesis cleis** (Edwards). Pl. XXVIII, fig. 19, ♂; fig. 20, ♀, types (The Cleis Butterfly).

Like the preceding form this is sufficiently well delineated upon the plate by figures of the types not to call for lengthy description. On the underside it closely resembles *E. ares*.

Both *E. ares* and *E. cleis* (Edwards) resemble *E. zela* Butler, but the latter is a much darker and somewhat smaller insect, which occurs in Venezuela.

The two species figured in this book range from Arizona to Central Mexico.

Genus LASAIA Bates

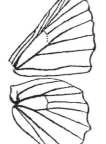

This genus, which ranges in its distribution from Paraguay northward, contains about a dozen species and named varieties.

The butterflies are rather small in size, with slightly crenulated wings, and in the male sex on the upper side are of some shade of metallic or bronzy green. The females gray or dull brown. Two species have been credited to our fauna, of these *L. sula* Staudinger is said by Stichel to range to Texas. Barnes and McDunnough list *L. narses* as also occurring within our border. Of this species I figure specimens, which so well represent the genus, that it does not seem necessary to enter upon a detailed description of its features.

FIG. 135.—Neuration of genus *Lasaia*, enlarged.

(1) **Lasaia narses** Staudinger. Pl. LXIV, fig. 2, ♂; fig. 3, ♀, paratypes, received by the author from Dr. Staudinger of Dresden, who named the species.

The insect is said to fly in the vicinity of Brownsville, Texas. It is rather common further south. *L. sula* is not known to me by material coming from any point in the United States.

Genus CARIA Hübner

Body robust; costa of the fore wing bent inwardly about the middle. The accompanying cut shows the neuration. There is very little difference between the forms which have been classified under this genus and those which have been assigned to the genus *Symmachia* Hübner. The chief distinction pointed out by Godman is in the form of the genitalia. The genus ranges from Paraguay in the south to Arizona, and contains about a dozen species, all of which except *C. ino* are characterized by having patches of velvety green scales variously disposed upon the upper surface of the wings and minute silvery marginal spots on the under side of the wings. The compilers of check-lists have credited the species *domitianus* Fabricius and the species *ino* Godman and

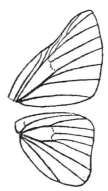

FIG. 136.—Neuration of genus *Caria*, enlarged.

Salvin to our fauna, and the species *melicerta* Schaus, described from Mexico has recently been treated as a synonym of *ino*. The author is at variance with the views indicated. On Pl. LXXVI, figs. 1–3 are given photographic representations of the three species; figs. 2 and 2a representing the type of **C. melicerta** Schaus. **C. domitianus** (figs. 1, 1a) is characterized by a large subtriangular patch of raised velvety green scales upon the upper side of the fore wings. **C. ino** Godman and Salvin (figs. 3, 3a) is altogether without any velvety green scales on the upper side of the fore wing. *C. melicerta* Schaus is characterized by a small patch of velvety green scales on the costal margin at the point where the costa is bent inwardly. *C. melicerta* is intermediate between *C. domitianus* and *C. ino*, and, as far as we know, is confined to the eastern parts of the Mexican and possibly the adjoining Texan area bordering the Gulf; while *C. ino* is found on the Pacific side of Mexico, and may occur in western Arizona.

Genus CALEPHELIS Grote and Robinson

(Type *C. virginiensis* (Gray), misidentified as *cænius* (L.) by G. & R.)

Synonym: *Lephelisca* Barnes and Lindsay.

Butterfly.—Small, dark brown, or reddish in color, lighter below; metallic spots upon the under side of the wings. Head relatively small; eyes naked; antennæ relatively long, slender, with an elongated club, rounded at end. Palpi very short; the third joint minute, pointed. Fig. 137 shows the neuration.

Early Stages.—Unknown.

(1) **Calephelis virginiensis** (Gray). Plate XXVIII, fig. 16, ♂. (The Little Metal-mark).

In the first edition of this book this species was given as *C. cænius* Linnæus, by which name it was known for the greater part of a century. Recent researches have revealed the fact that the insect named *cæneus* by Linnæus came from Guiana and belongs to the genus *Emesis*, so the name may not be applied to our insect; and, we must accept the name given to it by Gray in 1832, and adopted by Guérin in 1844.

Butterfly.—Very small, reddish-brown on the upper side, brighter red on the under side. On both the upper and under sides the wings are profusely spotted with small steely-blue metallic markings, arranged in more or less regular transverse series, especially on the outer margin. Expanse: .75 inch.

Early Stages.—The life-history is unknown.

Fig. 137.— Neuration of the genus *Calephelis*, enlarged.

Virginiensis is common in Florida, and ranges thence northward to Virginia and westward into the valley of the Mississippi. It is common in parts of Ohio.

(2) **Calephelis borealis** Grote and Robinson. Plate XXVIII, fig. 12, ♂, *under side;* fig. 13, ♂ (The Northern Metal-mark).

Butterfly.—Nearly twice as large as the preceding species. The wings on the upper side are sooty-brown, spotted with black, and marked by a marginal and submarginal series of small metallic spots. On the under side the wings are light red, spotted with a multitude of small black spots arranged in regular series. The two rows of metallic spots near the margins are repeated more distinctly on this side. Expanse: 1.15 inch.

Early Stages.—Unknown.

This rare insect has been taken from New York to Virginia, and as far west as Michigan and Illinois. The only specimen I have ever seen in life I took at the White Sulphur Springs in West Virginia. It settled on the under side of a twig of black birch, with expanded wings, just over my head, and by a lucky stroke of the net I swept it in.

(3) **Calephelis nemesis** (Edwards). Plate XXVIII, fig. 15, ♂, type (The Dusky Metal-mark).

Butterfly.—Very small—as small as *cœnius*—but with the fore wings at the apex decidedly pointed in the male sex. The wings are dusky-brown above, lighter obscure reddish below. Both the primaries and the secondaries on the upper side are crossed by a dark median band, broader on the primaries at the costa. The metallic markings are quite small and indistinct. Expanse: .85 inch.

Early Stages.—Unknown.

Nemesis occurs in Texas, Arizona, and southern California.

(4) **Calephelis australis** (Edwards). Plate XXVIII, fig. 14, ♂, type (The Southern Metal-mark).

Butterfly.—The wings in the male sex are more pointed at the apex than in the preceding species, and in both sexes are smaller in expanse. The color of the upper side of the wings is dusky, on the under side pale yellowish-red. On both sides the wings are obscurely marked with dark spots arranged in transverse series. The marginal and submarginal metallic bands of spots are as in the preceding species. Expanse: 1.00 inch.

Early Stages.—Unknown.

Australis ranges from Texas, Arizona, and California into Mexico. Comstock regards *australis* as a form of *nemesis*. They are at least closely related.

(5) **Calephelis perditalis** Barnes and McDunnough. Pl. LXXVI, figs. 7, 7a, ♂; 8, 8a, ♀, paratypes (Barnes' Metal-mark).

Butterfly.—This species is nearly of the same size as *C. nemesis* Edwards, and like that species has the fringes of the fore wing checkered with white just below the apex and near the inner angle, which is not true of *C. virginiensis;* it differs from *C. nemesis* in having the apex of the fore wing rounded and not pointed. On the underside the metallic post-median band of markings is wider and more distinct than in either *nemesis* or *virginiensis.* Expanse: .8–.9 inch.

We have females in which the ground-color on the upper side is pale luteous, differing from the typical form in thus being much lighter on the upper surface.

The species occurs at various localities in Texas. The types are from San Benito, Texas. We also have it from San Antonio and Comfort, Texas.

(6) **Calephelis louisiana** Holland. Plate LXXVI, fig. 9, ♂, type; 9a, do., *under side* (The Louisiana Metal-mark).

The color of the wings on the *upper side* is dull brown, interrupted on the fore wings by a band of dark luteous, which extends from the base, parallel with the costa, to the outer margin; a similarly colored light transverse band crosses the hind wing, about its middle, parallel to the outer margin, sending an outward ray-like projection from about its middle toward the outer margin. The thorax and abdomen on the upper side have the same color as the wings. On the *under side* the prevalent color is light red, paler than in *C. virginiensis*, and in tint agreeing with *C. perditalis*. The dark markings and metallic spots are disposed much as in *C. virginiensis* and *C. borealis*, but the postmedian band is formed of relatively wider spots, increasing in size toward the costa of the fore wing, in certain lights showing dark reflections. Thorax and abdomen on this side concolorous; legs testaceous, tibiæ whitish. Expanse: .75 in.

The type shown on the plate, was taken at Opelousas, Louisiana, by G. R. Pilate.

(7) **Calephelis wrighti** Holland. Pl. LXXVI, figs. 11, 11a, types (After Wright) (Wright's Metal-mark).

Synonym: *nemesis* Wright (not Edwards).

This insect, the original colored figures of which are reproduced in black and white from photographs taken of the figures given by Wright (Butt. West Coast, Pl. XXVI, figs. 303 and 303c) is certainly not *C. nemesis* Edw., nor *C. australis* Edw. I have named it in honor of my correspondent, the late W. G. Wright, from whom in the old days I bought nearly everything he had for sale in the line of butterflies. The types are in the Museum of the California Academy of Science. For a more detailed description the reader may consult the Annals of the Carnegie Museum, Vol. XX, pp. 5–6. This is a species which should be found about Mendocino, California.

UNCLE JOTHAM'S BOARDER

"I've kep' summer boarders for years, and allowed
    I knowed all the sorts that there be;
But there come an old feller this season along,
    That turned out a beater for me.
Whatever that feller was arter, I vow
    I hain't got the slightest idee.

"He had an old bait-net of thin, rotten stuff
    That a minner could bite his way through;
But he never went fishin'—at least, in the way
    That fishermen gen'ally do;
But he carried that bait-net wherever he went;
    The handle was j'inted in two.

"And the bottles and boxes that chap fetched along!
    Why, a doctor would never want more;
If they held pills and physic, he'd got full enough
    To fit out a medicine-store.
And he'd got heaps of pins, dreffle lengthy and slim,
    Allers droppin' about on the floor.

"Well, true as I live, that old feller just spent
    His hull days in loafin' about
And pickin' up hoppers and roaches and flies—
    Not to use for his bait to ketch trout,
But to kill and stick pins in and squint at and all.
    He was crazy 's a coot, th' ain't no doubt.

"He 'd see a poor miller a-flyin' along,—
    The commonest, every-day kind,—
And he 'd waddle on arter it, fat as he was,
    And follower up softly behind,
Till he 'd flop that-air bait-net right over its head,
    And I 'd laugh till nigh out of my mind.

"Why, he 'd lay on the ground for an hour at a stretch
    And scratch in the dirt like a hen;
He 'd scrape all the bark off the bushes and trees,
    And turn the stones over; and then
He 'd peek under logs, or he 'd pry into holes.
    I 'm glad there ain't no more sech men.

"My wife see a box in his bedroom, one day,
    Jest swarmin' with live caterpillars;
He fed 'em on leaves off of all kinds of trees—
    The ellums and birches and willers;
And he 'd got piles of boxes, chock-full to the top
    With crickets and bees and moth-millers.

"I asked him, one time, what his business might be.
    Of course, I fust made some apology.
He tried to explain, but such awful big words!
    Sorto' forren, outlandish, and collegey.
'S near 's I can tell, 'stead of enterin' a trade,
    He was tryin' to jest enter *mology*.

"And Hannah, my wife, says she 's heerd o' sech things;
    She guesses his brain warn't so meller.
There 's a thing they call Nat'ral Histerry, she says,
    And, whatever the folks there may tell her,
Till it 's settled she 's wrong she 'll jest hold that-air man
    Was a Nat'ral Histerrical feller."
               ANNIE TRUMBULL SLOSSON.

MIMICRY

Protective mimicry as it occurs in animals may be the simulation in form or color, or both, of natural objects, or it may be the simulation of the form and color of another animal, which for some reason enjoys immunity from the attacks of species which ordinarily prey upon its kind. Of course this mimicry is unconscious and is the result of a slow process of development which has, no doubt, gone on for ages.

Remarkable instances of mimicry, in which things are simulated, are found in the insect world. The "walking-sticks," as they are called, creatures which resemble the twigs of trees; the "leaf-insects," in which the foliage of plants is apparently reproduced in animate forms; the "leaf-butterfly" of India, in which the form and the color and even the venation of leaves are reproduced, are illustrations of mimicry which are familiar to all who have given any attention to the subject.

Repulsive objects are frequently mimicked. A spider has been lately described from the Indo-Malayan region, which, as it rests upon the leaves, exactly resembles a patch of bird-lime. The resemblance is so exact as to deceive the most sagacious, and the discovery of the creature was due to the fact that the naturalist, who happened to see it, observed to his surprise that what he was positive was a mass of ordure was actually in motion. A similar case of mimicry is observable among some of the small Acontiid moths of North America. One of these is pure white, with the tips of the fore wings dark greenish-brown. It sits on the upper side of leaves, with its fore wings folded over, or rolled about the hind wings, and in this attitude it so nearly approximates in appearance the ordure of a sparrow as to have often deceived me when collecting.

BY THE BY!

The word "butterfly" does not occur in the Bible. There is mention of flies, ants, locusts, and moths, but there is no allusion to our favorites of the air. That may be because the butterflies of Palestine and adjacent countries are not numerous, or strikingly beautiful. It does not follow from this omission that we are doing devilish work, when we study these forms of insect life, though the word Beelzebub, regarded by the ancient Jews as the prince of devils, means "the lord of flies."

There are many things that the writers of the Old and New Testament knew nothing about. America, Australia, and New Zealand were entirely unknown to them. There is no reference to giraffes or walruses. Nothing is said about microscopes, telescopes, locomotives, steamships, submarines (unless there is a reference to the latter in the story of Jonah). Of course there is no reference to aeroplanes. There is not a single reference to such things as telegraphy by wire, or wireless, and of course there is no reference to radios, or talking movies. The Bible is not a scientific manual, but teaches the rules of good conduct as between man and man, and man and his Maker. The saying of the old woman: "If it isn't in the Bible, I won't believe it," was the height of foolishness.

FAMILY IV

LYCÆNIDÆ (HAIR-STREAKS, COPPERS, AND BLUES)

"Mark, while he moves amid the sunny beam,
O'er his soft wings the varying lusters gleam.
Launched into air, on purple plumes he soars,
Gay nature's face with wanton glance explores;
Proud of his varying beauties, wings his way,
And spoils the fairest flowers, himself more fair than they."
Quoted as from Haworth by Scudder.

Butterfly.—Small, in both sexes having all feet adapted to walking. There is exceeding diversity of form in the various genera composing this family. Many of the genera are characterized by the brilliant blue on the upper side of the wings; in other genera shades of coppery-red predominate. The Hair-streaks frequently have the hind wings adorned with one or more slender, elongated tails.

These differences at an early day led to the classification of these butterflies in three groups, popularly known as "The Blues," "The Coppers," and "The Hair-streaks." Dennis and Schiffermueller, two Austrian monks, who published a list of the butterflies found in the neighborhood of Vienna, adopted this arrangement in the year 1776, and it is therefore as as old as the American Republic, and has outlasted almost every government on the globe. Some writers in quite recent years have tried to upset this old system, but in this book I follow it, as have almost all writers who have studied and written about butterflies for the past one hundred and fifty years.

In Africa and Asia there are numerous genera of *Lycænidæ*, which wonderfully mimic protected species which belong to the *Acræidæ*.

Egg.—The eggs are for the most part flattened or turban-shaped, curiously and beautifully adorned with ridges, minute eminences, and reticulations. Some of them under the microscope strongly resemble the shells of "sea-biscuits" with the rays removed (see p. 4, fig. 7).

Caterpillar.—The caterpillars are for the most part slug-shaped, flattened. They are vegetable feeders, save the larvæ of two or three genera, which are aphidivorous, feeding upon mealy bugs or plant-lice.

Chrysalis.—The chrysalids are short, compressed, attached at the anal extremity, with a girdle or cincture about the middle, closely fastened to the surface upon which pupation takes place.

222

SUBFAMILY THECLINÆ (THE HAIR-STREAKS)

Genus EUMÆUS Hübner

Butterfly.—Medium-sized or small; dark in color, with the under side and the borders of the upper sides beautifully adorned with spots having metallic luster. The palpi are divergent, longer in the female than in the male. The antennæ are stout, rather short, with a gradually thickened club. The eyes are naked. The veins on the fore wing are stout. The hind wings are not tailed. The accompanying cut gives a clear idea of the neuration.

Fig. 138. — Neuration of the genus *Eumæus*, reduced.

Three species are reckoned as belonging to the genus, two of them being found in the extreme southern limits of our fauna.

(1) **Eumæus atala** (Poey). Pl. XXVIII, fig. 22, ♂, *under side.*

Easily distinguished from *E. minyas* Hübner by its smaller size and the fact that the iridescent blue of the upper side of the fore wing is confined to the costal region. Expanse: 1.65–1.75 in.

Early Stages.—These have been fully described by Scudder (Mem. Bost. Soc. Nat. Hist., II, p. 413) and by Schwarz ("Insect Life," I, p. 39). The larva feeds upon the "coontie," *Zamia integrifolia*, and the insect swarms in the region of the Everglades of Florida.

(2) **Eumæus minyas** (Hübner). Pl. LXIV, fig. 4, ♂; fig. 5, ♀ *under side.*
Synonym: *toxea* (Godart).

This is a larger species than the preceding. The wings above are greenish-blue with the veins broadly marked with black. The figures on the plate give a good idea of the markings. Common from southern Texas to northern Argentina. Expanse: ♂, 1.5–2. in.; ♀, 2.25–2.5 in.

A form in which the greenish blue of the upper side is replaced by deep cobalt-blue has been named *costaricensis* by Draudt.

Genus THECLA Fabricius
(The Hair-streaks)

"These be the pretty genii of the flow'rs,
Daintily fed with honey and pure dew."
HOOD.

Butterfly.—Small or medium-sized; on the upper side often colored brilliantly with iridescent blue or green, sometimes dark brown or reddish; on the under side marked with lines and spots variously disposed, sometimes obscure in color, very frequently most brilliantly colored.

Various subdivisions based upon the neuration of the wings have been made in the genus in recent years, and these subdivisions are entitled to be accepted by those who are engaged in a comparative study of the species belonging to this great group. Inasmuch, however, as most American writers have heretofore classified all of these insects in the genus *Thecla*, the author has resolved not to depart from familiar usage, and will therefore only indicate these subdivisions as subgeneric, representing groups. In the arrangement of the species I have to some extent followed the order given by Draudt in his monograph of the American species published in Seitz' "Gross-Schmetterlinge der Erde," Vol. V, pp. 739–812. The collocation of a large number of distantly related species in the subgenus *Strymon*, adopted by some recent makers of check-lists, does not seem to me to be natural.

Fig. 139. — Neuration of *Thecla edwardsi*. (After Scudder.) Typical neuration of the genus *Thecla*.

Egg.—Considerable diversity exists in the form of the eggs of the various species included under this genus as treated in this book, but all of them may be said to be turban-shaped, more or less depressed at the upper extremity, with their surfaces beautifully adorned with minute projections arranged in geometric patterns.

Caterpillar.—The caterpillars are slug-shaped, their heads minute, the body abruptly tapering at the anal extremity. They feed upon the tender leaves of the ends of branches, some of them upon the leaves of flowers of various species.

Chrysalis.—What has been said concerning the chrysalids of the family applies likewise to the chrysalids of this and the succeeding genera. They lie closely appressed to the surface upon which they are formed, and are held in place by an attachment at the anal extremity, as well as by a slight girdle of silk about the middle. In color they are generally some shade of brown.

1. The *Halesus*-group

Subgenus ATLIDES Hübner

(1) **Thecla halesus** (Cramer). Pl. XXIX, fig. 9, ♂. (The Great Purple Hair-streak).

Synonyms: *dolichos* (Hübner); *juanita* (Scudder).

Butterfly.—The hind wings have a long tail, and are lobed at the anal angle. The wings are fuscous, iridescent bluish-green at the base. The body is bluish-green above. On the under side the thorax is black, spotted with white, the abdomen bright orange-red. The wings on the under side are evenly warm sepia, spotted with crimson at their bases, glossed with a ray of metallic green on the fore wings in the male sex, and in both sexes splendidly adorned at the anal angle by series of metallic-green and iridescent blue and red spots. Expanse: 1.35–1.50 inch.

Early Stages.—All we know of them is derived from the drawings of Abbot, published by Boisduval and Leconte, and this is but little. The caterpillar is said by Abbot to feed on various oaks.

It is very common in Central America and Mexico; is not scarce in the hot parts of the Gulf States; and is even reported as having been captured in southern Illinois. It also occurs in Arizona and southern California.

2   The *Crysalus*-group

Subgenus HYPAUROTIS Scudder

(2) **Thecla crysalus,** Edwards. Pl. XXIX, fig. 11, ♂ (The Colorado Hairstreak).

Butterfly.—The wings on the upper side are royal purple, broadly margined with black. On the fore wings a broad oblique black band runs from the middle of the costa to the middle of the outer margin. At the inner angles of both wings are conspicuous orange spots. On the under side the wings are fawn, marked with white lines edged with brown. The orange spots reappear on this side, but at the anal angle of the hind wings are transformed to red eye-spots, pupilled with black and margined with metallic green. The hind wings are tailed. Expanse: 1.50 inch.

The variety **citima** Henry Edwards differs in being without the orange spots and having the ground-color of the under side ashen-gray. Specimens connecting the typical with the varietal form are in my possession.

Early Stages.—Unknown.

Found in southern Colorado, Utah, Arizona, and southern California.

3.   The *Irus*-group

Subgenus INCISALIA Scudder

(3) **Thecla augustinus** Westwood. Plate XXX, fig. 15, ♂ (The Brown Elfin).

Synonyms: *augustus* Kirby (not Fabr.); *crœsioides* Scudder.

Butterfly.—Brown on the upper side; paler on the under side. The fore wings are marked by a straight incomplete median band, and the hind wings by an irregularly curved median band or line. Back of these lines toward the base both wings are darker brown. Expanse: .90 inch.

Early Stages.—These are not well known. Henry Edwards describes the caterpillar as "carmine-red, covered with very short hair, each segment involute above, with deep double foveæ." The chrysalis is described by the same observer as being "pitchy-brown, covered with very short bristly hair, the wing-cases paler." The food-plant is unknown.

This species is boreal in its haunts, and is found in New England and northward and westward into the British possessions.

Genus Thecla

(4) **Thecla iroides** Boisduval. Pl. LXIV, fig. 6, ♂, fig. 7, ♂, *under side* (The Western Elfin).

This species is difficult at first sight to discriminate from *T. augustinus*, but is distinguished by the fact that the outer margin of the hind wing is evenly rounded and does not project as strongly outwardly at the end of the second median nervule as in *T. augustinus;* the wings on the upper side are generally paler in tint and not as dark brown as in that species. It is the form of *augustinus* which prevails on the Pacific coast. The larva feeds on *Sedum*. The insect flies in early spring near sea-level; at a later date on the mountains. All we know of the early stages was published in 1878 by Henry Edwards.

(5) **Thecla irus** (Godart). Pl. XXX, fig. 12, ♂; Pl. V, figs. 32–34, *chrysalis* (The Hoary Elfin).

Synonym: *arsace* Boisduval.

Butterfly.—The outer margin of the hind wings has short projections at the ends of the median nervules; grayish-brown on the upper side. The wings on the under side are of the same color as above, paler on the outer margins, and darker toward the base. The species is subject to considerable variation. The hind wings above are often marked with reddish near the anal angle and the outer margin below with hoary-purple. Usually small crescentic spots appear on the outer margin of the hind wings, or they may be absent. Expanse: 1.10 in.

Early Stages.—An epitome of all that is known is to be found in "The Butterflies of New England." The caterpillar feeds on young plums just after the leaves of the blossom have dropped away. The species is rather rare, but has been found from east to west in the latitude of New England.

(6) **Thecla hadros** Cook & Watson. Pl. LXIV, fig. 46, ♂, paratype (The Hadros Elfin).

This species like the preceding has very short tail-like projections at the end of the first and second median nervules of the hind wing. It is larger in size than the preceding species. On the upper side the color is uniformly deep chestnut-brown; on the under side blackish, with a deep black ocellus near the anal angle. Its habitat is Texas. Expanse: 1.2–1.3 in.

(7) **Thecla henrici** Grote and Robinson. Pl. XXX, fig. 21, ♀ (Henry's Hair-streak).

Butterfly.—The outline of the wings is as in *T. irus*. The outer half of the wings broadly reddish-brown. The secondaries on the under side are broadly blackish-brown on the basal half, with the outer margin paler. The division between the dark and light shades is irregular and very sharply defined, often indicated by a more or less perfect irregularly curved median white line. Expanse: 1.00–1.10 in.

Early Stages.—These have been described by Edwards in the "American Naturalist," Vol. XVI, p. 123. The habits of the larva are identical with those of *T. irus*.

It occurs from Maine to West Virginia, but is not common.

(8) **Thecla mossi** Henry Edwards. Pl. LXIV, fig. 10, ♂, compared with type (Dr. Moss' Elfin).

This species in outline is like the preceding, with the upper side dark grayish-brown; fringes white. On the under side the wings are of the same tint outwardly, but paler, darkening toward the base. Both wings are crossed about the middle by a sinuous, very narrow white line, bent outwardly beyond the cell, most strongly on the hind wing; the line is defined inwardly by a narrow dark line and the wings toward the base are very dark brown. Expanse: .8–.9 in. *Habitat*: Vancouver Island.

(9) **Thecla polios** Cook and Watson. Pl. LXIV, fig. 9, ♂, paratype (The Polios Elfin).

Hind wings not tailed, but faintly crenulate, dark purplish fuliginous in color, with deep black marginal spots at the end of the nervules, between which the fringes are whitish. On the under side the wings are outwardly hoary purple, this tint on the fore wing confined to the outer margin; on the hind wing covering the outer third. About the middle of both wings there is a very narrow white line, incomplete on the fore wing, but complete on the hind wing, on which it is twice strongly bent outwardly beyond the cell. Inwardly this line is succeeded by broad dark maroon shades. Near the upper angles of both wings there are similar dark maroon cloudings and the same deep color appears at the base of both wings, deepest on the hind wings. The fringes are white, interrupted with black at the ends of the nervules. This insect is known from the coast of New Jersey. Expanse: .9 in.

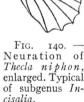

(10) **Thecla fotis** Strecker. Pl. LXIV, fig. 11, ♂, *under side* (Strecker's Elfin).

Hind wing rather strongly lobed at anal angle.

The color of the upper side is dark grayish fawn with a faint purplish iridescence. The figure shows the markings of the under side, which are characteristic. It occurs in Arizona. Expanse: .8–.9 in.

Fig. 140. — Neuration of *Thecla niphon*, enlarged. Typical of subgenus *Incisalia*.

(11) **Thecla eryphon** Boisduval. Pl. XXX, fig. 17, ♀, *under side* (Eryphon).

Butterfly.—Closely resembling the following species both on the upper and under side of the wings, but easily distinguished by the fact that, on the under side of the fore wings, the inner of the two dark bands on the outer third of the wing is not sharply angulated below the third median nervule, as in *T. niphon*, but is more even, and in general parallel with the submarginal line. Expanse: 1.15 inch.

Early Stages.—These have not been described.

Eryphon replaces the Eastern *T. niphon* on the Pacific coast.

(12) **Thecla niphon** (Hübner). Pl. XXX, fig. 11, ♀; fig. 22, ♀, *under side;* Pl. V, figs. 38, 40, *chrysalis* (The Banded Elfin).

Butterfly.—Reddish-brown on the upper side. The under side is accurately depicted on the plate. Expanse: 1.10 inch.

Early Stages.—These have been elaborately described by Scudder in his great work. The caterpillars feed upon pine.

The Banded Elfin is found from Nova Scotia to Colorado, in the Northern States, where its food-plant occurs, but is never abundant.

4. The *Dolylas*-group Draudt

Subgenus DOLYMORPHA Holland

Thecla jada is the only representative in our fauna, so far as we know, of a large group found in Mexico and southward in which the hind wings are greatly elongated and lobed at the end; the first submedian vein of the secondaries at its end is bent outwardly at right angles to its axis and forms a small projecting tail. These butterflies are all of some shade of blue or violet on the upper side with the costa and apical region more or less broadly black; on the under side the wings are light in color, some shade of white, light yellow, light gray, or light brown, crossed by darker bands. For this group I venture to propose the subgeneric name *Dolymorpha**.

(13) **Thecla jada** Hewitson. Pl. LXIV, fig. 12, ♂; fig. 13, ♂, *under side* (The Jada Hair-streak).

This is a rare straggler into our territory upon our southwestern borders. The figures we give will suffice for its determination by those who are so fortunate as to capture it. It is not rare in Mexico.

5. The *Dumetorum*-group

Subgenus CALLOPHRYS Billberg

The most striking and obvious feature of this group is the fact that on the underside the wings are of some shade of green. I arbitrarily include *Thecla pastor* Butler and Druce, which has the hind wings lobed at the anal angle and with short projections at the tip of the median nervules of the hind wings, much as in the subgenus *Incisalia*. It is put by Draudt in his *Amyntor*-group, "the species of which are all brilliantly blue on the upper side in the male sex." The other species in our fauna are dull in color on the upper side with the hind wings only feebly produced at the ends of the median nervules.

(14) **Thecla pastor** (Butler and Druce). Pl. LXIV, fig. 14, ♂, fig. 15, ♀, *under side* (The Morpho-blue Elfin).

Butterfly.—♂. The wings are deep blue above, bordered on the costa and outer margin with black. ♀, Dull greenish-blue above, with the costa and outer third of the fore wing broadly black. On the under side in both sexes the wings are dull yellowish green. The figures on the plate will help the student to recognize this species. Expanse: ♂ and ♀ about 1.25 in.

---

*Compounded of the first two syllables of *Dolylas* and μδρφη.

The insect is not rare at high elevations in Central America and occurs as an infrequent straggler in Arizona.

(15) **Thecla dumetorum** Boisduval. Pl. XXX, fig. 1, ♂; fig. 2, ♂, *under side* (The Green White-spotted Hair-streak).

Butterfly.—Dark fawn-color above, sometimes tinged externally with reddish. On the under side both wings are green, the primaries having a short straight band of white spots on the outer third, and the secondaries a small white spot on the costa beyond the middle, and two or three conspicuous white spots near the anal angle. Expanse: 1.10 inch.

A variety which lacks the white spots on the under side of the wings has been called **perplexa** by Barnes and Benjamin.

Early Stages.—The larva feeds on *Hosackia, Eriogonum,* and *Syrmatium.* The caterpillar and chrysalis have been described by Williams (Ent. News, XXI, p. 36), and of the variety **perplexa** by Coolidge (Trans. Am. Ent. Soc., Vol. L, p. 329).

(16) **Thecla affinis** Edwards. Pl. XXX, fig. 3, ♀, *under side,* type (The Green-winged Hair-streak).

Butterfly.—On the upper side closely resembling the preceding species. On the under side the wings are uniformly bright green. Expanse: 1.00 in.

Early Stages.—These await description.

The types came from Utah. I also have specimens from California.

(17) **Thecla sheridani** Edwards. Pl. LXIV, fig. 16, ♂, *under side,* type (Sheridan's Hair-streak).

The males are darker on the upper side than in *affinis,* the fringes are white. Easily distinguished by the straight white line which crosses the middle of the hind wing.

Early Stages.—Undescribed, but probably much the same as in the two foregoing species. Expanse: 1–1.2 in.

Habitat: Colorado and Wyoming.

A slight variety has been called **neoperplexa** by Barnes and Benjamin.

(18) **Thecla apama** Edwards. Pl. LXIV, fig. 17, ♂, *under side,* type (The Apama Hair-streak).

The fore wing in this species is fuscous above and reddish on the under side, except the costa, which is green like the hind wing. An irregular wavy red line more or less parallel to the outer border traverses the hind wing below. Specimens lacking this line are the var. **homoperplexa** of Barnes and Benjamin. Expanse: .9–1.10 in.

6. *Polibetes*-group

Subgenus EUPSYCHE Scudder

(19) **Thecla m-album** Boisduval and Leconte. Pl. XXIX, fig. 10, ♂ (The White-M Hair-streak).

Butterfly.—Iridescent blue at the base of the wings on the upper side. On the under side the fore wing is crossed by a submarginal and a median line of white, shaded with brown, the median line most distinct. This line is continued upon the hind wings, and near the anal angle is zigzagged, so as to present the appearance of an inverted M. Near the outer angle of the M-spot is a rounded crimson patch. The anal angle is deep black, glossed with iridescent blue. Expanse: 1.35–1.45 in.

Early Stages.—All we know of this pretty species is based upon the account and drawings of Abbot made in the Eighteenth Century. We need better information. According to Abbot, the caterpillar feeds on *Astragalus* and different oaks.

This insect has been taken as far north as Jersey City and Wisconsin, and ranges southward as far as Venezuela. Its citadel is found in the live-oak hummocks of the Gulf States and the oak forests on the highlands of Mexico and more southern countries.

7. The *Xami*-group Draudt

Subgenus MITOURA Scudder

(20) **Thecla spinetorum** Boisduval. Pl. XXIX, fig. 21, ♀ (The Thicket Hair-streak).

Synonyms: *ninus* Edw.; *cuyamaca* Wright.

Butterfly.—Dark blackish on the upper side, with both wings at the base shot with bluish-green. On the under side the wings are pale reddish-brown. Expanse: 1.15 in.

Early Stages: Little is known of these.

Habitat.—Reported, so far, from Colorado, California, and Washington.

(21) **Thecla johnsoni** Skinner. Pl. LXXV, figs. 1, 2, type (Johnson's Hair-streak).

The butterfly is bluish black on the upper side, on the under side the ground-color is dark brown. It is a rare species in collections and is only known from Vancouver Island and British Columbia.

(22) **Thecla nelsoni** Boisduval. Pl. XXX, fig. 8, ♀, *under side;* fig. 13, ♀ (Nelson's Hair-streak).

Butterfly.—Bright fulvous on the upper side, with the costa, the outer margins, the base, and the veins of both fore and hind wings fuscous. On the under side the wings are paler red, with an incomplete narrow white line shaded with deep red just beyond the median area, and not reaching the inner margin. This line is repeated on the hind wing as an irregularly curved median line. Between it and the outer margin on this wing are a few dark lunules near the anal angle. Expanse: 1.00 inch.

An aberrant specimen with the under side wholly brown was dubbed *exoleta* by Henry Edwards. A variety with the under side paler chestnut-brown, and the markings less distinct has been yclept *muiri* by the same author.

Early Stages.—Unknown.

Habitat.—The species is found in California and Colorado.

(23) **Thecla xami** Reakirt. Pl. LXIV, fig. 20, ♂, *under side* (The Xami Hair-streak).

Synonym: *blenina* Hewiston.

Butterfly.—Pale brown on the upper side with the outer margins fuscous. On the under side the wings are pale shining gray, tending to lilac, with the white crosslines sharp and distinct. Expanse: 1.12 in.

Early Stages.—Unknown.

Habitat.—Found in Arizona and southward.

(24) **Thecla siva** Edwards. Pl. XXX, fig. 9, ♂, *under side*, type (The Juniper Hair-streak).

Synonym: *rhodope* Grote and Robinson.

Brown on the upper side, in some specimens bright fulvous, the outer margins bordered with deep brown. On the under side the wings are darker lilaceous than in the preceding species, dusted with greenish scales at the base of the fore wings and on the hind wings. The transverse markings are much the same as in *T. xami*. A variety, which is prevalently a little darker than the typical form, has been named *juniperaria* by Comstock, and he has given us an account of the egg, larva, and chrysalis (*Butt. Calif.*, pp. 165–6). Expanse: 1 in.

The insect is not uncommon in the juniper groves of California.

(25) **Thecla loki** Skinner. Pl. LXIV, fig. 18, ♂, paratype, *under side* (Skinner's Hair-streak).

This species may be discriminated from others by the submarginal row of dark spots on the hind wing below, which are continuous across the wing. Expanse: 1 in.

Habitat.—It is said to be confined in its range to the San Diego Mountains, but probably is not wanting in the Sierra Madre of northern Mexico.

(26) **Thecla gryneus** (Hübner). Pl. XXIX, fig. 32, ♂, *under side;* var. **castalis** Edwards, Pl. XXIX, fig. 29, ♂, Pl. V, figs. 30, 31, *chrysalis* (The Olive Hair-streak).

Synonyms: *damon* (Cram.) not D. & S.; *damastus* (Godart); *auburniana* Harris, in part.

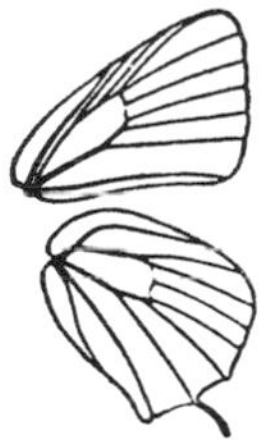

Fig. 141.— Neuration of *Thecla gryneus*, enlarged. Type of subgenus *Mitoura*, Scudder.

Butterfly.—On the upper side bright fulvous, with the costa, the outer margins, and the veins of both wings blackish, darkest at the apex. On the under side the wings are greenish, crossed on the fore wing by a straight, incomplete white line, and on the hind wing by a similar irregular line. Both of these lines are margined internally by brown. There are a couple of short white lines on the hind wing near the base, and the usual crescentic spots and markings on the outer border and at the anal angle. Expanse: .90–1.00 inch.

Early Stages.—These have been described by several authors. The caterpillar feeds on the red cedar (*Juniperus virginiana* Linnæus). It is double-brooded in the North and triple-brooded in the South.

Gryneus ranges from Ontario to Texas over the entire eastern half of the

United States. **T. castalis** Edw. is a slight variety, in which there is more red on the upper sides of the wings, and scarcely perceptible modifications of the light spots on the under side.

(27) **Thecla simæthis** (Drury). Pl. XXIX, fig. 39, ♂, *under side* (The Simæthis Hair-streak).

Butterfly.—Resembling the preceding species, but the white band on the secondaries is straight, and the outer margins are heavily marked with brown. Expanse: .85–1.00 in.

Early Stages.—Unknown.

(28) **Thecla telea** Hewitson. Pl. LXIV, fig. 22, ♂; fig. 23, do., *under side* (The Telea Hair-streak).

Butterfly.—On the upper side brilliant shining blue. On the under side prevalently green with dark red markings on the outer margin and the anal angle of the hind wing.

This is a Mexican species, which strays over our southern borders in Texas and Arizona. Expanse: .75 in.

(29) **Thecla adenostomatis** Henry Edwards. Pl. XXIX, fig. 25, ♂, paratype (The Gray Hair-streak).

Butterfly.—Mouse-gray on the upper side, with a few white lines on the outer margin near the anal angle; hoary-gray on the under side, darker on the median and basal areas. The limbal area is defined inwardly by a fine white line, is paler than the rest of the wing, and on the secondaries is marked by a full, regularly curved submarginal series of small dark lunules. Expanse: 1.30 inch.

Early Stages.—Undescribed.

Habitat.—California.

(30) **Thecla sæpium** Boisduval. Pl. XXIX, fig. 33, ♂; fig. 34, ♀ *under side*; **chlorophora** Wats. & Comst., Pl. LXV, fig. 17, ♂, paratype, *under side* (The Hedge-row Hair-streak).

Butterfly.—Somewhat resembling the preceding species in general appearance, but with the wings on the upper side reddish brown, and on the lower side paler than in that species. The lines on the under side of the wings are externally defined by white, and the anal spots are better defined and developed than in *T. adenostomatis*. Expanse: 1.2 in.

Early Stages.—Unknown.

Habitat.—The species is common in southern California and ranges as far east as Utah. Henry Edwards applied the varietal name *fulvescens* to individuals which are paler above and below than the run of specimens; and the name *chlorophora* was given by Watson & Comstock to those which are darker.

(31) **Thecla chalcis** Behr. Pl. XXIX, fig. 36, ♂; fig. 37, ♀, *underside* (The Bronzed Hair-streak).

Synonym: *provo* Watson & Comstock.

With the types of *T. chalcis* and *T. provo* before me I find them to be identical in every respect. They only differ from *sæpium* Bvd. in having the upper surface of the wings a little more lustrous in certain lights, showing a slightly purplish sheen, which is not apparent in a series of many specimens of *sæpium* before me. I am more than ever convinced that *T. chalcis* is simply a color-phase of *T. sæpium*. Expanse: 1.–1.10 in.

Early Stages.—Unknown.

Habitat.—The types of *T. chalcis* are from California; the types of *T. provo* are from Utah.

(32) **Thecla auretorum** Boisduval. Pl. LXXVI, fig. 14, ♂; type, after Oberthür; Pl. LXV, fig. 14, *T. tetra* Edw. ♂, type (The Gold-hunters Hair-streak).

Synonym: *tetra* Edwards.

This rare form, of the early stages of which nothing is known, is from southern California. On the under side near the anal angle there is a small red ocellus pupilled with black, and faint suggestions of the same ornament appear on the upper side, the ground-color of which is rather dark purplish fuscous. I figure one of the types of *tetra* Edwards, which has long been accepted by authors as synonymous with *auretorum*, and which agrees with the figure of the type of *auretorum* given by Oberthür (Lép. Comp., Fasc. IX, Pl. CCXXXV, fig. 1921). Expanse: 1 in.

(33) **Thecla tacita** Hy. Edwards. Pl. XXIX, fig. 30; Pl. LXIV, fig. 19, ♂, type (The Tacit Hair-streak).

This rare little insect has been erroneously regarded by some writers as identical with the foregoing species. We show the type of the species so labelled by Henry Edwards in his own handwriting. Above it is a very pale iridescent yellowish lilac with dark borders on both wings; below the wings are pale grayish white, with two small yellow lunules near the anal angle, and entirely without the dark marks at the end of the cell found in *auretorum*. Expanse: 1.10 in.

Early Stages.—Unknown.

Habitat.—Southern California.

(34) **Thecla spadix** Hy. Edwards. Pl. LXV, fig. 6, ♂; fig. 7, ♀; fig. 8, ♂ *under side* (The Nut-brown Hair-streak).

This species plainly belongs in this group. The male on the upper side is dark, fuscous brown. The female is somewhat paler, with the disk of the wing fulvous. In both sexes the under side is dark grayish brown, with some obscure traces of transverse lines, and darker lunules near the anal angle. Expanse: 1.00 in.

Early Stages.—Unknown.

Habitat.—Southern California.

8. The *Grunus*-group Draudt

Subgenus HABRODAIS Scudder

(35) **Thecla grunus** Boisduval. Pl. XXIX, fig. 12, ♂ (Boisduval's Hair-streak).

Butterfly.—The wings are brown on the upper side, lighter on the disk; in some specimens, more frequently of the female sex, bright orange-tawny. On the under side the wings are pale tawny, with transverse marginal and submarginal series of small dark spots on both wings. Two or three of the marginal spots near the anal angle are black, each crowned with a metallic green crescent. Expanse: 1.10–1.20 inch.

Early Stages.—These have in part been described by Dyar, "Canadian Entomologist," vol. XXV, p. 94. The caterpillar is short, flattened, the segments arched, the body tapering backward, bluish-green, covered with little dark warty prominences bearing tufts of hairs, obscurely striped longitudinally with broken, pale lines, and having a diamond-shaped shield back of the head. The chrysalis is thick and conformed to the generic type of structure. The color is pale green, striped and dotted with pale yellow on the abdomen. The caterpillar feeds in the Yosemite Valley upon the young leaves of the live-oak (*Quercus chrysolepis*).

The insect is found in California and Nevada.

9. The *Calanus*-group Draudt

Genus THECLA Fabricius

Type *betulæ* Schiffermueller

This is the typical group of the genus, made up of what have been sometimes called *par excellence* "The tailed Theclas." They have a short tail at the end of the second median nervule of the hind wing, and a longer tail at the end of the first median nervule of the same wing. Furthermore they all have a small oval sex-brand near the costa of the fore wing at the end of the cell, or tufts of androconia at the same place. This feature is, however, not absolutely peculiar to this group, as it appears in some others. Many species are found in the palearctic region, but not as many as in the New World. Here belong some of our commonest as well as some of our rarest species.

(36) **Thecla edwardsi** Saunders. Pl. XXIX, fig. 27, ♀, *underside;* Pl. V, fig. 29, *chrysalis* (Edwards' Hair-streak).

Butterfly.—Dark plumbeous-brown on the upper side, with a pale sex-mark on the fore wing of the male. On the under side the wings are paler and a trifle warmer brown, with their outer halves marked with two rows of dark spots defined inwardly or outwardly with white lines. The usual black spots, green scales, and red crescents are found near the anal angle on the under side.

Early Stages.—For all that is known of these the reader will do well to consult the pages of Scudder. The caterpillar feeds on oaks.

The species ranges from Quebec westward to Colorado and Nebraska, being found commonly in New England.

(37) **Thecla calanus** (Hübner). Pl. XXIX, fig. 26, ♂; Pl. V, figs. 25, 27, *chrysalis* (The Banded Hair-streak).

Synonyms: *falacer* (Godt.); *lorata* G. & R.; *inorata* G. & R.

Butterfly.—On the upper side resembling the preceding species very closely, but a trifle darker, and warmer brown. On the under side the wings are marked by fine white lines on the outer half, which are not broken, as in *edwardsi*, but form continuous bands. Expanse, 1.15 inch.

The form *lorata* G. & R. is a "faked" specimen. I am informed by Mr. Watson of the American Museum that he has bred specimens of what is called *inorata* from eggs of typical *T. calanus*. It represents specimens in which the submarginal band on the lower side of the primaries is a little broader and darker than usual.

Early Stages.—The caterpillar feeds on oaks. The life-history is described with minute exactness by Scudder in "The Butterflies of New England," vol. ii, p. 888.

This insect has a wide range, being found from the province of Quebec to Texas and Colorado. It is common in western Pennsylvania.

(38) **Thecla melinus** (Hübner). Pl. XXIX, fig. 31, ♂; Pl. XXXII, fig. 20, ♂; Pl. LXIV, fig. 26, var. **pudica,** ♂, *under side.* Pl. V, fig. 39, *chrysalis* (The Common Hair-streak).

Synonyms: *hyperici* Bvd. & Lec.; *humuli* Harris.

Butterfly.—Much confusion has arisen from the fact that this insect has received a number of names and has also been confounded with others. This common little butterfly may easily be recognized by its plain slaty upper surface, adorned by a large black spot, crowned with crimson between the origin of the two tails of the secondaries. Expanse: 1.10–1.20 inch.

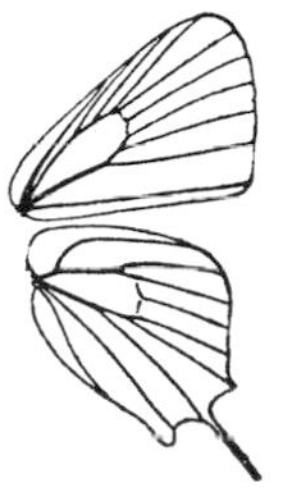

The variety *pudica* Hy. Edwards, which is not uncommon in California and Arizona, differs from the typical form by being paler, sometimes white, on the under side.

Early Stages.—These are in part well known. The caterpillar feeds on the hop-vine. *Melinus* is found all over temperate North America, and ranges southward into Mexico and Central America at suitable elevations.

FIG. 142.— Neuration of *Thecla melinus.* (After Scudder.)

(39) **Thecla ontario** Edwards. Pl. LXXVI, figs. 12, 12a, after Edwards (The Ontario Hair-streak).

This species is very rare. It was originally described from a solitary female. It may be only an aberrant form of another species, possibly of the preceding. The specimen figured by Edwards was not in his collection when I received it. There is a ragged specimen in the United States National Museum.

(40) **Thecla liparops** Boisduval & Leconte. Pl. XXIX, fig. 28, ♀, *under side;* Pl. V, fig. 28, *chrysalis* (The Striped Hair-streak).

Synonym: *strigosa* Harris.

Butterfly.—Dark brown on the upper side, grayish below. The lines are arranged much as in *T. edwardsi*, but are farther apart, often very narrow, scarcely defining the dark bands between them. The spots at the anal angle are obscure and blackish. Expanse, 1.15 inch.

Early Stages.—Much like those of the allied species. Scudder, in "The Butterflies of New England," gives a full account of them. The caterpillar feeds on a variety of plants—oaks, willows, the wild plum, and other rosaceous plants, as well as on the *Ericaceæ*.

It ranges through the northern Atlantic States and Quebec to Colorado and Montana, but is local in its habits, and nowhere common.

(41) **Thecla martialis** Herrich-Schæffer. Pl. XXX, fig. 18, ♀, *under side* (The Martial Hair-streak).

Butterfly.—The insect figured on the plate, which may easily be recognized by its under side, was determined by Dr. Skinner to be the above species. My specimens coming from the Edwards collection are labeled *Thecla acis*, ♀. They were taken at Key West. A comparison with the under side of *T. acis* (see Plate XXIX, fig. 38) will reveal the great difference. On the upper side the wings are black, at the base of the fore wings and on the disk of the hind wings deep blue. Expanse: 1.00 in.

Early Stages.—Unknown.

Habitat.—Southern Florida and Cuba.

(42) **Thecla acis** (Drury). Pl. XXIX, fig. 38, ♀, *under side* (Drury's Hair-streak).

Butterfly.—The upper side of the wings is dark brown. The under side is shown in the plate. Expanse: .90 inch.

Early Stages.—Unknown.

This very pretty species is found in the extreme southern portions of Florida and in the Antilles.

(43) **Thecla wittfeldi** Edwards. Pl. XXIX, fig. 19, ♀; fig. 20, ♂, *under side*, types (Wittfeld's Hair-streak).

Butterfly.—The figures on the plate give a correct idea of both the upper and under sides of this insect. It is much darker in ground-color than any of its congeners. Expanse: 1.25–1.35 inch.

Early Stages.—Unknown.

The types which are in my possession came from the Indian River district in Florida. The locality where they were found has been built over in recent years. The species is thought by some to be extinct.

(44) **Thecla alcestis** Edwards. Pl. XXIX, fig. 14, ♀; Pl. LXV, fig. 12, ♂, *under side* (The Alcestis Hair-streak).

Butterfly.—Uniformly brownish gray on the upper side of the wings, with the usual oval sex-mark on the fore wing of the male, and a few bluish scales near the anal angle. The ground-color of the wings on the under side is much redder than above; a white bar closes the cell of both wings; both wings are crossed by two white lines. The anal angle is marked with black, followed outwardly by a broad patch of iridescent greenish-blue scales. Between the end of the submarginal vein and the first median nervule is a black spot surmounted with carmine, edged inwardly with black; three or four carmine crescents similarly edged, but rapidly diminishing in size, extend as a transverse submarginal band toward the costa. Expanse: 1.25 inch.

Early Stages.—Unknown.

Alcestis is found in Texas and Arizona.

(45) **Thecla oslari** Dyar. Pl. LXV, fig. 13, ♂, type, *under side* (Oslar's Hair-streak).

Very closely related to *T. alcestis*, from which it does not greatly differ in color on the upper side, except in being somewhat paler gray, inclining to bluish. On the under side of the primaries the whitish subterminal band, which is always conspicuous in *T. alcestis*, is wanting and the ground-color is paler. Expanse: 1 in.

Habitat: Arizona about Tucson.

(46) **Thecla acadica** Edwards. Pl. XXIX, fig. 15, ♂; Pl. V, fig. 35, chrysalis (The Acadian Hair-streak).

Synonym: *souhegan* Whitney.

Butterfly.—The male is pale slaty-gray above, with some ill-defined orange spots near the anal angle, the usual oval sex-mark on the fore wing. The female is like the male above; but the orange spots at the anal angle of the hind wings are broader, and in some specimens similar spots appear on the fore wings near the inner angle. On the under side in both sexes the wings are pale wood-brown, adorned by a black bar at the end of the cells, submarginal and median bands of small black spots surrounded with white, and on the secondaries by a submarginal series of red crescents diminishing in size from the anal angle toward the outer angle. Near the anal angle are two black spots separated by a broad patch of bluish-green scales. Expanse: 1.15–1.25 inch.

Early Stages.—For a knowledge of what is known of these the reader may consult the pages of Scudder and Edwards. The caterpillar feeds upon willows.

T. souhegan Whitney only differs from typical *acadica* in being lighter on the under side of the wings; **coolinensis** Watson and Comstock from Coolin, Idaho, has dull orange spots rather than orange-red spots, as in *acadica*; **montanensis** Watson and Comstock is lighter on the under side than typical *acadica* and the extra-discal row of spots on the primaries is arranged in a straighter line. It requires a very critical eye to detect these slight differences from typical *acadica*.

It is found all over the Northern States, ranging from Quebec to Vancouver's Island.

(47) **Thecla californica** Edwards. Pl. LXIV, fig. 24, ♂, type; fig. 25, ♀, type, *under side* (The Californian Hair-streak).

On the upper side the fore wings are somewhat broadly marked with red at the inner angle, and the hind wings have the lower outer margin broadly red. There is considerable individual variation in the extent of the red markings.

This is a very common species in California and is found abundantly on the foothills and mountains of the Pacific seaboard. Expanse: ♂, 1.1 in.; ♀, 1.25 in.

Early Stages.—Unknown.

(48) **Thecla sylvinus** Boisduval. Pl. LXXVI, fig. 12, type. After Oberthür (Lép. Comp., Pl. CCXXXV, fig. 1920).

The species is not uncommon in California. The larval food-plant is willow, and it frequents the neighborhood of water-courses.

(49) **Thecla dryope** Edwards. Pl. LXIV, fig. 27, ♂, type; fig. 28, ♂, *under side* (The Dryope Hair-streak).

There has been some discussion as to the validity of this species and it has been claimed that it is the same as *sylvinus* Boisd. lacking the short upper tail on the secondaries. However, there are traces of the existence of such a short tail on specimens labelled *dryope* by Edwards, and the species is no doubt valid.

(50) **Thecla itys** Edwards. Pl. XXIX, fig. 17, ♀, type, Pl. LXIV, fig. 31, ♂ (The Itys Hair-streak).

The female on our plate is one of the original types taken at Prescott, Arizona; the male is from Utah. The species is still rare in collections.

(51) **Thecla putnami** Henry Edwards. Pl. LXIV, fig. 33, ♂; fig. 34, ♀, *under side* (Putnam's Hair-streak).

T. putnami is paler on the upper side than *T. itys*. *T. desertorum* Grinnell seems to be the same as *putnami*, but somewhat lighter on the upper side than the common run of *putnami*.

(52) **Thecla favonius** Smith and Abbot. Pl. XXIX, fig. 22, ♂. (The Southern Hair-streak).

Butterfly.—The wings are dusky-brown above, with a small pale oval sex-mark in the male near the upper edge of the cell in the primaries. On either side of the second median nervule, near the outer margin of both wings, are bright orange-red patches, most conspicuous in the female. The hind wings near the anal angle are blackish, margined with a fine white line. On the under side the wings are marked much as in *m-album*, but in the region of the median nervules, midway between their origin and termination, is a rather broad transverse carmine streak, edged inwardly with dark lines. This is largest and most conspicuous in the female sex. Expanse: 1.00–1.15 inch.

Early Stages.—These have been described, in part, by Smith and Abbot and Packard. The caterpillar feeds on oaks.

Favonius is found in the Gulf States, and as far north as South Carolina.

(53) **Thecla autolycus** Edwards. Pl. XXIX, fig. 13, ♀; Pl. LXV, fig. 11, ♂, *under side;* Pl. LXV, fig. 15, var. **ilavia** Beutenmueller (The Texas Hair-streak).

Butterfly.—On the upper side resembling *favonius*, but with the orange-red spots on the wings much broader, ranging from the lower radial vein to the sub-median in the fore wings. The carmine spots on the under side of the wings are not arranged across the median nervules, as in *favonius*, but are in the vicinity of the anal angle, crowning the black crescents near the inner end of the outer margin. Expanse: 1.15–1.30 inch.

The variety *ilavia* Beutenmueller is characterized by the light yellow ground-color of the under side of the wings, which in the typical form is dark brown.

Early Stages.—Unknown.

This species is found in Texas, and is also said to have been found in Missouri and Kansas.

10. The *Cecrops*-group, Draudt

(54) **Thecla cecrops** (Fabric.). Pl. XXX, fig. 7, ♂; Pl. XXIX, fig. 18, ♀, *under side* (The Cecrops Hair-streak).

Synonyms: *pœas* (Hübner); *beon* (Godart).

Butterfly.—Dark brown, glossed at the base of the wings and in the inner margin of the secondaries with blue. The under side is well delineated on the plate. Expanse: 1.00 in.

Early Stages.—These await description.

Cecrops is common in the Southern States, and has been taken as far north as West Virginia, Kentucky, and southern Indiana.

11. The *Læta*-group

Subgenus ERORA Scudder

(55) **Thecla læta** Edwards. Pl. XXIX, fig. 23, ♂; fig. 24, ♂, *under side* (The Early Hair-streak).

Butterfly.—The wings brown, glossed with bright blue above; on the under side pale fawn, with a band of pale-red spots on both wings about the middle and a few similar spots on the outer and inner margins of the hind wings. Expanse: .75 in.

Early Stages.—Only the egg, described and figured by Scudder, is known.

It ranges from Quebec to southern New Jersey, and westward to West Virginia, and has been taken on Mount Graham, Arizona. It appears in early spring. It is still rare in collections.

12. The *Fuliginosa*-group

Subgenus SATYRIUM Scudder

(56) **Thecla fuliginosa** (Edwards). Pl. XXX, fig. 16, ♂, type, *under side;* Pl. LXXIII, fig. 17, ♂; fig. 18, ♀; fig. 19, ♀, *under side*, types (The Sooty Gossamer-wing).

Synonym: *suasa* (Boisduval).

Butterfly.—Dark brownish gray on the upper side in both sexes. On the under side the figure on the plate gives a correct representation of the color and markings. Expanse: 1.10 in.

Early Stages.—Unknown.

The species occurs in Utah, Nevada, northern California, Oregon, and Washington.

Originally described under the generic name *Lycœna*, the insect is now recognized by many writers, following Scudder, as belonging to the *Theclinœ*.

13. The *Columella*-group

Subgenus CALLICISTA Grote

(57) **Thecla columella** (Fabr.). Pl. LXIV, fig. 35, ♂; fig. 36, ♀, *under side* (The Antillean Hair-streak).

Synonyms: *eurytulus* (Hübn.); *cybira* Hew.; *salona* Hew.; *istapa* Reak.; *ocellifera* (Grote); *modesta* (Maynard); *laceyi* (Barnes).

This insect has been blessed with many names. The males always have a raised tuft of black androconia at the end of the cell of the fore wing. The females are also dark at this point, but the scales are not raised into an elevated tuft.

Thecla laceyi was described by Barnes from a single female specimen taken in Texas (*Cf.* Canad. Ent., XLII, 1910, p. 365). The type to this day remains unique in the Barnes Collection, where I have recently critically examined it. I am convinced that it is an aberration of *T. columella* in which the spots on the underside of the secondaries have run together thus forming transverse lines and the ground color is a trifle darker than in the usual run of flown specimens. Expanse: ♂ and ♀ ; .9–1. in.

Habitat: Southern Florida and southern Texas.
Very abundant in Cuba and Central America.

14. The *Leda*-group, Draudt

(58) **Thecla leda** Edwards. Pl. LXIV, fig. 37, ♂; fig. 38, ♀, types (The Leda Hair-streak).

Butterfly.—♂. Wings on the upper side fuscous shot with light blue at the base of the primaries and on the inner half of the secondaries. A tuft of black androconia at the end of the cell of the fore wing. On the under side the wings are pale gray, the cells at their ends with a faint dark bar, followed by fine and somewhat irregular discal and submarginal transverse lines, the space between which is paler in tint than the rest of the wings, especially on the hind wing. The outer margins are narrowly laved with yellowish. At the anal angle of the hind wing are two small black spots capped with orange-yellow; fringes fuscous.

♀. Marked like the male, but much darker on the upper side, the blue areas contrasting strongly with black. The upper side of the head and thorax are concolorous with the wings; the abdomen in both sexes paler, yellowish. Expanse: 1 in.

Early Stages.—Unknown.

Habitat.—Arizona and Mexico.

(59) **Thecla ines** Edwards. Pl. XXIX, fig. 35, ♂, type. (The Ines Hair-streak).

Butterfly.—Closely related to the preceding, but with the blue areas of the wings deeper blue, more sharply defined on the upper side, and solidly covering the whole hind wing, and not merely its inner half as in the case of *T. leda*. On the under side the light band between the distal and submarginal lines of the hind wing is white, strongly contrasting with the darker slaty ground-color of this side. Some recent check-lists represent this species as being a subspecies of *T. leda*, but this is very doubtful, as they are found at the same localities at the same time. Expanse: .75 in.

(60) **Thecla clytie** Edwards. Pl. XXX, fig. 6, ♀, type (The Clytie Hair-streak).

Butterfly.—The figure well represents the upper side of the female. The male on the upper side is deeper blue, and has a small tuft of black androconia at the end of the cell. On the under side in both sexes the wings are white with the usual spots and transverse lines very faint; those at the anal angle being very minute. Expanse: .8–.9 in.

Early Stages.—Unknown.

Habitat.—Texas, Arizona, and Mexico.

(61) **Thecla avalona** Wright. Pl. LXV, fig. 9, ♂, paratype (The Catalina Hair-streak).

This species is a rarity, and is only found on the hills of Catalina Island off the coast of California. Our figure gives a good representation of the upper surface of the male. The lower side is quite evenly bluish gray, with only very faint traces of transverse lines beyond the cells. There are two quite minute black ocelli at the usual points on the margin of the under side of the hind wing near the anal angle. Expanse: 1 in.

Early Stages.—The egg has been described by Karl Coolidge in the Bulletin of the Brooklyn Ent. Soc., Vol. XVIII, p. 160.

15. The *Critola*-group Draudt

(62) **Thecla critola** Hewitson. Pl. LXXVI, figs. 13, 13a, ♂, type (after Hewitson).

Butterfly.—This striking little insect may at once be recognized by the round black spot on the fore wing. Dr. Dyar, who was the first to announce its presence in our fauna, informs us that this spot is not composed of androconia, but of ordinary scales, deep black in color. Expanse: 1 in.

Hewitson's figure makes the contrast between the black spot and the surrounding blue too strong. The blue in life is darker, as shown by specimens in my cabinet.

16. The *Behri*-group Draudt

Subgenus CALLIPSYCHE Scudder

(63) **Thecla behri** Edwards. Pl. XXX, fig. 4, ♂; fig. 5, do., *under side*, types (Behr's Hair-streak).

Butterfly.—Both sides are well displayed on the plate, and therefore need no particular description. Expanse: 1.10 in.

Early Stages.—Unknown.

Genus Thecla

This species is found in northern California and Oregon, and eastward to Colorado.

17. Endymion-group Draudt

(64) **Thecla endymion** (Cramer). Pl. LXIV, fig. 32 (The Endymion Hair-streak).

Synonyms: *tyrtæus* (Fabr.); *xenophon* (Donovan); *hugon* (Godart).*

This insect under the name *hugon* Godart has long been listed as occurring within the United States. It is found in the Antilles, and may occur within our fauna on the Keys of Florida, which have not been thoroughly explored. The specimen on our Plate is from Haiti. It is a great rarity. The wings are colored much as in *T. behri* on the upper side, but are tailed. On the under side they are quite different, and the markings are somewhat like those in the *Calanus*-group.

18. The *Titus*-group Draudt

Subgenus STRYMON Hübner

FIG. 143. — Neuration of *Thecla titus*, enlarged. Typical of subgenus *Strymon* Hübner.

(65) **Thecla titus** (Fabricius). Pl. XXX, fig. 10, ♂; fig. 14, ♂, *under side;* Pl. V, fig. 37, *chrysalis* (The Coral Hair-streak).

Synonym: *mopsus* (Hübner) (Type of genus *Strymon* Hübner).

Butterfly.—This somewhat aberrant form is uniformly gray-brown on the upper side. Some specimens of the female have a few red spots at the anal angle of the hind wing. On the under side the wings are colored as on the upper side; but the hind wings have a conspicuous submarginal band of coral-red spots on their outer third. Expanse, 1.30 inch.

Specimens lacking the red spots have been dubbed var. *immaculosus* by Comstock.

Early Stages.—These have been well described by several authors. The fullest account is given by Scudder. The caterpillar feeds on the leaves of the wild cherry and the wild plum.

The insect occurs from the Atlantic to the Pacific, from Maine to Georgia. It is not very common.

19. The *Azia*-group Draudt

(66) **Thecla azia** Hewitson. Pl. LXIV, fig. 29, ♂; fig. 30, do., *under side* (The Azia Hair-streak).

Butterfly.—This small species has the upper side somewhat bluish fuscous, with a tuft of black androconia at the end of the cell of the fore wing; on the under side it is fulvous gray. Expanse: .75 in.

*I give the synonymy as stated by Draudt.

Early Stages.—Unknown.
Habitat.—Texas, Arizona, and Mexico.

20.   Of Uncertain Location

(67) **Thecla heathi** Fletcher. Pl. LXXVI, fig. 16, ? sex (after Fletcher).

This insect, so far as is known, is represented by the unique type, described and figured in the "Canadian Entomologist," vol. xxxvi, p. 125. The type is in the United States National Museum. It has been placed in various positions in "check-lists" by their authors.

The insect appears to me to be very probably a hybrid between *T. titus* and some other species, or a singular aberration of *T. titus*.

"Come hither, my sparrows,
My little arrows.
If a tear or a smile
Will a man beguile,
If an amorous delay
Clouds a sunshiny day,
If the step of a foot
Smites the heart to its root,
'Tis the marriage ring
Makes each fairy a king."

So a fairy sung.
From the leaves I sprung;
He leap'd from the spray
To flee away;
But in my hat caught
He soon shall be taught.
Let him laugh, let him cry,
He's my butterfly;
For I've pulled out the sting
Of the marriage ring.
                    WILLIAM BLAKE.

SUBFAMILY SPALGINÆ Holland

(Type *Spalgis epius* Westwood)

This subfamily of the *Lycænidæ* is proposed by me, not only upon the ground of the structural affinities of the imagines, or perfect winged insects, but upon the structure of the larvæ, more particularly the chrysalids, and the habits of the larvæ. The genera so far included in the group by me are the genus *Spalgis* of the eastern hemisphere, and *Feniseca* of the western hemisphere. There may be other genera, which later will be found to be properly included. The *Gerydinæ*, of the larval stages of which next to nothing is known, are, however, structurally quite different in important respects. The genus *Spalgis* ranges in Asia from Burmah to Ceylon, and in Africa is represented by several species, which occur in the tropical regions of the western coast. The genus *Feniseca*, which I include in this subfamily, has a moderately wide distribution in the eastern parts of boreal America. There is nothing really very remarkable in this in the light of what, as paleontologists, we know of the distribution of animals. Some genera, now extinct in North America, still exist in tropical Africa.

Butterfly.—Both *Spalgis* and *Feniseca* agree in the structural features of the imago, and particularly in having the third to the fifth subcostal nervules of the fore wing arising from a common stalk, the third at a point about one-third of its length beyond the end of the cell.

Larva.—The larvæ are oblong-oval, flattened dorsally, the segments covered with bristles or bristly hairs, arranged in dense series on the summit of each segment. The caterpillars are carnivorous, feeding upon scale-insects, with the exuviæ of which they are covered in life.

Chrysalis.—All the species have chrysalids, which are peculiar in that, when viewed dorsally, they present a grotesque likeness to the features of an ape, or a human being. This is shown in the figures which I give. (See Pl. LXXVI, figs. 21–23).

Genus FENISECA Grote
(The Harvesters)

"Upon his painted wings, the butterfly
Roam'd, a gay blossom of the sunny sky."
WILLIS G. CLARK.

Butterfly.—Small, bright orange-yellow, on the upper side spotted with black, on the under side more or less mottled and shaded with gray and brown, the mark-

244

ings of the upper side reappearing. The cut shows the neuration, which need not be minutely described.

Egg.—Subglobular, much wider than high, its surface smooth marked with a multitude of very fine and indistinct raised ridges, giving it the appearance of being covered by very delicate polygonal cells.

Caterpillar.—In its mature stage the caterpillar is short, slug-shaped, covered with a multitude of bristling hairs, upon which it gathers the white exudations or scales of the mealy bugs, upon which it feeds.

Chrysalis.—Small, brown in color; when viewed dorsally showing a remarkable and striking likeness to the face of a monkey, or baboon.

But one species of the genus is known.

(1) **Feniseca tarquinius** Fabricius, Pl. XXVIII, fig. 21, ♂; Pl. V, figs. 45, 46, and Pl. LXXVI, fig. 23, *chrysalis* (The Harvester).

Fig. 144.—Neuration of the genus *Feniseca*, enlarged.

Butterfly.—The upper side of the wings is well depicted in the plate. There is considerable variation, however, in the size of the black markings upon the upper surface, and I have specimens in which they almost entirely disappear. On the under side the wings are paler; the spots of the upper side reappear, and, in addition, the hind wings are mottled profusely with small pale-brown spots. Expanse: 1.30 inch.

Early Stages.—What has been said of these in the description of the genus will suffice for the species.

This curious little insect, which finds its nearest allies in Asia and Africa, ranges all over the Atlantic States from Nova Scotia to the Carolinas, and throughout the valley of the Mississippi.

"Loose to the wind their airy garments flew,
Thin glittering textures of the flimy dew,
Dipt in the richest tincture of the skies,
Where light disports in ever mingling dyes,
While every beam new transient colours flings,
Colours that change whene'er they wave their wings."

POPE. (*Rape of the Lock.*)

SUBFAMILY CHRYSOPHANINÆ* (THE COPPERS)

Genus CHRYSOPHANUS Hübner

"Atoms of color thou hast called to life
(We name them butterflies) float lazily
On clover swings, their drop of honey made
By thee, dear queen, already for their need."
MARY BUTTS.

Butterfly.—Small butterflies, with the upper side of the wings some shade of coppery-red or orange, frequently glossed with purple. On the under side the wings are marked with a multitude of small spots and lines. The neuration of the wing is shown in Fig. 145, on the following page, and needs no further description.

Egg.—The eggs are hemispherical, flattened on the base, the upper surface deeply pitted with polygonal or somewhat circular depressions.

Caterpillar.—The caterpillars, so far as known, are decidedly slug-shaped, thickest in the middle, tapering forward and backward, and having a very small head.

Chrysalis.—The chrysalids are small, rounded at either end, and held in place by a girdle of silk a little forward of the middle.

This genus is found in the temperate regions of both the New and the Old World, and also in South Africa.

1. The *Arota*-group

Subgenus THARSALEA Scudder
(Tailed Chrysophani)

(1) **Chrysophanus arota** (Boisduval). Pl. XXIX, fig. 1, ♂; fig. 2, ♀ (The Arota Copper).

Butterfly.—The plate gives a good idea of the upper side of the wings in both

---

*Dr. Aurivillius (Rhopalocera Æthiopica, p. 382) points out that the generic name *Heodes* was applied by Dalman to a species of this group before the name *Chrysophanus* was applied to another species, and claims that the generic name of the complex should therefore be *Heodes*. Not necessarily. Scudder has shown that typical *Chrysophanus* differs materially from typical *Heodes*. I use *Heodes* in a subgeneric sense in this volume.

I am after careful study utterly opposed to the substitution of the generic name *Lycæna* for *Chrysophanus*, based upon the mistake made by Curtis in 1824, who either did not know, or had forgotten, that the species *phlæas*, which he made the type of *Lycæna*, had long before been legitimately removed from the Fabrician complex of species named *Lycæna* by Fabricius, and transferred to *Heodes* by Dalman, and to *Chrysophanus* by Hübner. Curtis was in error, and those, who advocate following him, are in error also.

246

sexes. On the under side the fore wings are pale gray in the male and pale red in the female, with the outer margin lavender. The spots of the upper side reappear on the disk. The hind wings on the under side are purplish-gray on the inner two thirds and paler gray on the outer third, with many black spots on the disk, margined with white. Expanse: 1.10–1.25 inch.

Comstock has given the subspecific name **nubila** to specimens found about Los Angeles, which are darker than usual, with a wider marginal band in the male and the red spots in the female suffused with fuscous.

FIG. 145.—Neuration of *Chrysophanus thoë*, enlarged. Typical of the genus.

Early Stages.—These have been partially described by Dyar in the "Canadian Entomologist," vol. xxiii, p. 204. The caterpillar feeds on the wild gooseberry (*Ribes*).

Arota is a Californian species.

(2) **Chrysophanus virginiensis** Edwards. Pl. XXVIII fig. 23, ♂; fig. 24, ♀ (The Nevada Copper).

Butterfly.—Allied to the preceding species, but easily distinguished by the submarginal white bands of crescent-shaped spots on the under side. These are particularly distinct on the hind wings. Expanse: 1.25–1.30 inch.

Early Stages.—Unknown.

Virginiensis, so named because the first specimens came from Virginia City, is found in California, Nevada, and Colorado.

(3) Chrysophanus hermes Edwards. Pl. LXIV, fig. 50, ♂; type (The Hermes Copper).

Synonym: *del-sud* Wright.

This small form may easily be known from the figure on the plate. The female is like the male, but frequently yellower on the upper side, the dark spots often much reduced in size. It so far has only been taken in the vicinity of San Diego, California, and nothing is known of its larval history.

2. The *Xanthoides*-group

Subgenus GÆIDES Scudder

(4) **Chrysophanus xanthoides** (Boisduval). Pl. XXVIII, fig. 29, ♂; fig. 30, ♀ (The Great Copper).

Butterfly.—The student will easily recognize it by the figure. It is one of the largest species of the genus in North America. The under side is creamy-white, spotted with distinct small black spots, in large part reproducing the spots of the upper side. Expanse: 1.50–1.65 in.

(5) **Chrysophanus editha** Mead. Pl. XXVIII, fig. 26, ♂; fig. 27, ♀, types (Edith's Copper).

Butterfly.—This is a much smaller species than the last, which it somewhat resembles on the upper side. On the under side it is wholly unlike *xanthoides*, the wings being pale pearly-gray, pale ochreous on the outer margins, the spots of the fore wings black and of the hind wings ochreous, narrowly margined with white or fine black lines. Expanse: 1.10–1.25 inch.

Early Stages.—Entirely unknown.

This species is found in Nevada.

(6) **Chrysophanus gorgon** (Boisduval). Pl. XXVIII, fig. 35, ♂; fig. 36, ♀. (The Gorgon Copper).

Butterfly.—Somewhat like the preceding species, but with the fore wings of the male redder on the upper side, and of the female more broadly mottled with pale red, the spots in some specimens inclining to buff. The under side of the wings is white, marked with the usual series of black spots. The secondaries have a marginal series of elongated pale-red spots, tipped at either end with black. Expanse: 1.25–1.30 inch.

Early Stages.—We as yet know nothing of these.

Gorgon is found in California and Nevada.

(7) **Chrysophanus dione** Scudder. Pl. LXV, fig. 4, ♂; fig. 5, ♀ (The Dione Copper).

Butterfly.—This is a large species, in which the male and the female are alike in having the upper surface uniformly lustrous fuscous. It is near to *xanthoides*, and some writers have claimed that it is only a variety of the latter species. Expanse: ♂, 1.6 in.; ♀, 1.7 in.

Early Stages.—Little is known of these.

Habitat.—The Upper Mississippi Valley east of the Rocky Mountains.

3. The *Thoë*-group

Genus CHRYSOPHANUS Hübner

(8) **Chrysophanus thoë** (Boisduval). Pl. XXVIII, fig. 31, ♂; fig. 32, ♀; Pl. V, fig. 50, *chrysalis* (The Bronze Copper).

Butterfly.—The plate makes a description of the upper side of the wings unnecessary. On the under side the fore wing in both sexes is bright tawny-red, pale gray at the apex; the hind wings are bluish-gray, with a broad band of carmine on the outer margin. Both wings are profusely adorned with small black spots. Expanse: 1.30–1.40 inch.

Early Stages.—These are only partially known. The caterpillar feeds on *Rumex.*

It is not uncommon in northern Indiana, Illinois, and Pennsylvania, and ranges from Maine to Kansas and Colorado.

(9) **Chrysophanus mariposa** (Reakirt). Pl. XXVIII, fig. 37, ♂; fig. 38, ♀. (Reakirt's Copper).

Synonym: *zeroë* Boisd.

Butterfly.—Small, with a broad dusky band on the hind wing of the male and on the fore wing of the female. The male is purplish-red above, the female bright red, with the usual spots. On the under side the ground-color of the fore wings is pale red, of the hind wings clear ashen-gray, with the characteristic markings of the genus. Expanse: 1.10 inch.

Early Stages.—Undescribed.

The insect ranges from British Columbia into northern California, Montana, and Colorado.

(10) **Chrysophanus nivalis** (Boisduval). Pl. LXV, fig. 1, ♂; fig. 2, ♀ ; fig. 3, ♂, *under side*. The specimens figured are the types of *C. ianthe* Edw. (The Snowy Copper).

Synonym: *ianthe* Edwards.

Butterfly.—The under side of the hind wing of the male, devoid of the usual spots and markings found in other species, enables it to be readily recognized. Expanse: ♂, and ♀ , 1.25 in.

Early Stages.—Unknown.

Habitat.—The Sierras of California and Wyoming.

(11) **Chrysophanus helloides** (Boisduval). Pl. XXVIII, fig. 33, ♂; fig. 34, ♀ ; var. **florus** Edw. Pl. LXIV, fig. 44, ♂, type (The Purplish Copper).

Synonym: *castro* Reakirt.

Butterfly.—The male has the fore wings broadly shot with iridescent purple. The female is well delineated in the plate. On the under side the fore wings are pale red, the hind wings reddish-gray, with a marginal row of brick-red crescents. The usual black spots are found on both wings. Expanse: 1.15–1.30 inch.

The variety *florus* Edwards is prevalently darker on the upper side. It is a melanic form.

Early Stages.—We know next to nothing of these.

The Purplish Copper is found in the Northwestern States from northern Illinois and Iowa to Vancouver Island.

(12) **Chrysophanus dorcas** (Kirby). Pl. LXIV, fig. 43, ♂ (The Dorcas Copper).

Butterfly.—This is a species found in the north. It is said to occur in northern Michigan and ranges thence as far as Alaska to the northwest and Labrador to the northeast. The specimen figured on the plate was taken at Winnipeg. The female is darker, and suffused with blackish with the red spots of the hind wing obscured.

Early Stages.—Unknown.

(13) **Chrysophanus charlottensis** Holland. Pl. LXIV, fig. 47, ♂; fig. 48, ♂, *under side;* fig. 49, ♀ types (Queen Charlotte's Copper).

Butterfly.—This unique little species fully described by me in the "Annals of the Carnegie Museum," Vol. XX, p. 5, is here represented by figures, which should enable its instant recognition. It is quite different on the under side from any other species, and I only provisionally place it here.

Early Stages.—Unknown.

Habitat.—Queen Charlotte Island.

4. The *Epixanthe*-group

Subgenus EPIDEMIA Scudder

(14) **Chrysophanus epixanthe** (Boisd. & Lec.). Pl. LXVIII, fig. 10, ♂ : fig. 4, ♀ ; fig. 12, ♀ , *under side* (The Epixanthe Copper).

Butterfly.—One of the smallest species of the genus in North America. On the upper side the wings are dark fulvous, with the usual black spots of the primaries and secondaries well defined. The female on the upper side, especially of the fore wing, is a little paler than the male. The hind wings at the anal angle are always marked with orange, and not infrequently this orange spot is followed upwardly by other similar spots, forming a narrow orange marginal band, diminishing in width toward the outer angle. On the under side in both sexes the color of the fore wings is pale red, shading externally into pale fuscous. The hind wings below are pale gray, somewhat broadly suffused outwardly with pale fuscous. The dark spots on the under side of the fore wing are relatively large, dark, and clearly defined; on the under side of the hind wings they are very small and tend to become obsolete. Expanse: ♂ and ♀ , .85–1. in.

Early Stages.—Nothing is known of these.

Habitat: New England, thence westward and northward as far as Michigan. I have found the insect quite common about Magnolia, Massachusetts. It is quite distinct from the following species.

(15) **Chrysophanus amicetus** Scudder (Boisd., *MS*.). Pl. XXVIII, fig. 28, ♂; Pl. LXIV, fig. 41, ♂; fig. 42, ♀ , *under side* (The Newfoundland Copper).

Synonym: *phædrus* Hall.

Butterfly.—This delicate little species has been confounded by myself and others with the preceding species, from which it is totally distinct. It differs from *C. epixanthe* in having the wings less densely scaled, and the fore wings less sharply pointed at the apex, more delicate in structure. On the upper side the wings are broadly suffused with purple margined externally rather broadly with dark fuscous. There are never more than two dark spots visible on the upper side of the fore wings, invariably one at the end of the cell, sometimes followed internally in the cell by a second; on the hind wing there is a black spot or bar at the end of the cell. There is never any trace of orange maculation at the anal angle or the outer margin of the secondaries. On the under side the ground-color is pure shining white, immaculate on the secondaries, but on the primaries marked with excessively small dark points, representing the discal and submarginal spots which are generally found in this genus. Fringes short, very pale gray.

Expanse: ♂ and ♀ , .87 in.

Early Stages.—Awaiting study.

Habitat.—Newfoundland and northern Nova Scotia. I have long possessed a fine series of this species collected in Newfoundland by Mead.

5. The *Heodes*-group

Genus HEODES Dalman
(Type *phlæas* (Linnæus)

(16) **Chrysophanus hypophlæas** Boisduval. Pl. XXVIII, fig. 25, ♂; Pl. V, fig. 49, chrysalis; Pl. LXIV, fig. 45, var. **fasciata** Strkr., paratype (The American Copper.)

Synonym: *americanus* Harris.

Butterfly.—This is one of the commonest butterflies in the United States. The figure will serve to recall it to the mind of every reader. It is abundant everywhere, except in the Gulf States; and ranges as far north as Manitoba. Expanse: 1.00 in.

Early Stages.—These have often been described. The caterpillar, which is small and slug-shaped, feeds upon the common sorrel (*Rumex acetosella*).

A number of aberrations and so-called varieties have been named. One of these called *fasciata* Strecker is represented by a specimen bought from H. Strecker by the author years ago. In it the spots of the fore wing coalesce. Others have been named because one or the other, or all of the black spots, except that at the end of the cell of the fore wing, are lacking. That spot never "goes out."

The variety *arethusa* Dod is a form in which the red markings are obscured and the ground color on the upper side is gray with a somewhat bluish tint. On the under side the spots are very much as in typical *hypophlæas*.

(17) **Chrysophanus fieldeni** McLachlan. Pl. LXVIII, fig. 5, ♂; fig. 6, ♀, *under side* (The Arctic Copper).

Butterfly.—This species is more nearly allied to *C. phlæas* of Europe and Siberia than to *C. hypophlæas*. It differs strikingly from the latter in having the red surfaces of the fore wings brilliantly metallic in lustre. McLachlan described them as being "brassy." In *hypophlæas* the wings never show a bright metallic sheen, but are, as artists say, "mat in color." The spots of the fore wings are located as in *C. phlæas*, but smaller. The hind wings on the upper side are deep velvety black, with a broad orange-red submarginal band, above and very close to which in some specimens there appear two or three very minute spots of brilliant blue. On the under side the fore wings are pale red, bordered on the external margin with a relatively wide band of purplish gray; the spots of the upper side being rather faintly reproduced. The hind wings on the lower side are evenly purplish gray, in shade and color corresponding to the outer marginal band of the fore wings, with scarcely a trace of the orange-red marginal band, which is so conspicuous upon the upper side of the wing. Expanse: ♂, .9 in.; ♀, 1 in.

The Carnegie Museum has a fine series of this species collected in July and early August on Southhampton Island in Hudson Bay by G. M. Sutton. It ranges northward on the western side of Davis Strait on the islands and peninsulas as far as 82° N.

After careful study I regard the insect as representing a valid species, as species go in this genus; though I have seen a few specimens labelled C. *phlœas* from central Siberia, which come close to it.

6. The *Cupreus*-group

(18) **Chrysophanus cupreus** Edwards. Pl. LXIV, fig. 39, ♂; fig. 40, ♀, types (The Lustrous Copper).

Butterfly.—This handsome little creature is found in the Sierras of California from Tulare to Shasta and ranges thence northward into Oregon.

Early Stages.—Hitherto undescribed.

(19) **Chrysophanus snowi** Edwards. Pl. XXIX, fig. 7, ♂; fig. 8, ♀, types (Snow's Copper).

Butterfly.—This is a medium-sized species, easily recognized by the even, rather wide black border on both wings on the upper side, and the dirty-gray color of the hind wings on the under side. Expanse: 1.15–1.25 in.

Early Stages.—Unknown.

Snow's Copper, which is named in honor of the late Chancellor of the University of Kansas, occurs in Colorado at high elevations, and is reported from Alberta and British Columbia.

(20) **Chrysophanus rubidus** Behr. Pl. XXIX, fig. 5, ♂; fig. 6, ♀ (The Ruddy Copper).

Butterfly.—This is a rather large species. The male on the upper side is prevalently pale, lustrous red, with a narrow black marginal band and uniformly conspicuous white fringes. The upper side of the female is accurately depicted in the plate. On the under side the wings are shining white, the secondaries immaculate. Expanse: 1.30–1.50 in.

Early Stages.—These are altogether unknown.

This exceedingly beautiful species is found in Oregon, Nevada, and Montana.

(21) **Chrysophanus sirius** Edwards. Pl. XXIX, fig. 3, ♂; fig. 4, ♀, types (The Sirius Copper).

Butterfly.—The male closely resembles the preceding species on the upper side, but is brighter red, especially along the nervules of the fore wings. The female on the upper side is dusky. On the under side the wings are whitish or pale gray, but the hind wings are spotted, bearing the characteristic markings of the genus. Expanse: 1.20–1.30 in.

Early Stages.—Unknown.

The species has been found from Fort McCleod in British America, as far south as Arizona, among the North American Cordilleras.

7. The *Heteronea*-group

This group is the connecting link between *Chrysophanus* and the true *Lycœninæ*.

(22) **Chrysophanus heteronea** (Boisduval). Pl. XXXI, fig. 13, ♂; fig. 14, ♀; Pl. XXXII, fig. 19, ♀, *under side* (The Varied Blue).

Butterfly.—On the upper side the male is blue, the female brown. On the under side the wings are white, with faint pale-brown spots on the hind wings and distinct black spots on the fore wings. The male looks like a large *Lycæna*. The female is not unlike the females of other species of *Chrysophanus*. This species and the next represent a bridging over of the gap between the Coppers and the Blues. Expanse: 1.25–1.40 in.

Early Stages.—These await description.

Heteronea ranges at suitable elevations among the mountains from Colorado to California.

(23) **Chrysophanus clara** Henry Edwards. Pl. XXX, fig. 26, ♀, type (The Bright Blue).

Butterfly.—The figure in the plate is that of the type of the female. The male is pale lustrous purplish blue, with a narrow black margin. *Clara* is closely related to *Heteronea*, but is smaller.

Early Stages.—Undescribed.

Habitat.—The insect so far is only known from the Tehachapi and Teton ranges of southern California, and is restricted there to a few localities. It is rare in collections.

THE UTILITY OF ENTOMOLOGY

All the forces of nature are interdependent. Many plants would not bear seeds or fruit were it not for the activity of insects, which cause the pollen to be deposited upon the pistil and the seed-vessel to be fertilized. Attempts were made many years ago to grow clover in Australia, but the clover did not make seed. All the seed required for planting had to be imported at much expense from Europe. It was finally ascertained that the reason why the clover failed to make seed was because throughout Australia there were no bumblebees. Bumblebees were introduced, and now clover grows luxuriantly in Australia, making seed abundantly; and Australian meats, carried in the cold-storage rooms of great ocean steamers, are used to feed the people of Manila, Hong-Kong, Yokohama, and even London.

A few years ago the orange-groves in southern California became infested with a scale-insect, which threatened to ruin them and to bring orange-growing in that part of the land to an unprofitable end. The matter received the careful attention of the chief entomologist of the United States Department of Agriculture, the lamented Professor C. V. Riley. In the course of the studies which he and his associates prosecuted, it was ascertained that the same scale-insect which was ruining the orange-groves of California is found in the orange-groves of Queensland, but that in Queensland this insect did comparatively small injury to the trees. Investigation disclosed the fact that in Queensland the scale-insect was kept down by the ravages of a parasitic insect which preyed upon it. This parasite, by order of the chief entomologist, was immediately imported, in considerable numbers, into southern California, and let loose among the orange-groves. The result has been most beneficial.

These are two illustrations, from among hundreds which might be cited, of the very practical value of entomological knowledge.

The annual loss suffered by agricultural communities through ignorance of entomological facts is very great. Every plant has its insect enemy, or, more correctly, its insect lover, which feeds upon it, delights in its luxuriance, but makes short work, it may be of leaves, it may be of flowers, it may be of fruit. It has been estimated that every known species of plant has five or six species of insects which habitually feed upon it. Where the plant is one that is valuable to man and is grown for his use, the horticulturist or the farmer finds himself confronted, presently, by the ravages of these creatures, and unless he has correct information as to the best manner in which to combat them, he is likely to suffer losses of a serious character. We all have read of the havoc wrought by the Kansas locust, or grasshopper, and of the ruin brought about by insects of the same class in Asia and in Africa. We all have heard of the Hessian fly, or the weevil, and of the army-worm. The legislature of Massachusetts has in recent years spent millions of dollars in the attempt to exterminate the gipsy-moth. The caterpillar of the cabbage-butterfly ruins every year material enough to supply sauer-kraut to half of the people. The codling-moth, the little pinkish caterpillar of which worms its way through apples, is estimated to destroy five millions of dollars' worth of apples every year within the limits of the United States. And what shall we say of the potato-bug, that prettily striped beetle, which, starting from the far West, has taken possession of the potato-fields of the continent, and for the extermination of which there is annually spent, by the agricultural communities of the United States, several millions of dollars in labor and in poisons?

A few facts like these serve to show that the study of entomology is not a study which deserves to be placed in the category of useless pursuits. Viewed merely from a utilitarian standpoint, this study is one of the most important, far outranking in its actual value to communities the study of many branches of zoölogical science, which some people affect to regard as of a higher order.

The legislature of Pennsylvania acted wisely in passing a law which demands that in every high school established within the State there shall be at least one teacher capable of giving instruction in botany and in entomology. The importance of entomology, while not perceived by the masses as yet, has been recognized by almost all the legislatures of the States; and not only the general government of the United States, but the governments of the individual commonwealths, are at the present time employing a number of carefully trained men, whose business is to ascertain the facts and instruct the people as to the best manner in which to ward off the attacks of the insect swarms, which are respecters neither of size nor beauty in the vegetable world, attacking alike the majestic oak and the lowliest mosses.

SUBFAMILY LYCÆNINÆ (THE BLUES)

The genus *Lycæna* was set up by Fabricius in 1807 for a number of species, some of them belonging to the *Theclinæ*, others to what we know as the *Chryso-phaninæ*, and still others to what we designate as *Lycæninæ*. Denis and Schiffer-mueller in 1776 recognized the "Hair-streaks," the "Coppers," and the "Blues," as natural divisions. They were followed by Geoffroy St. Hilaire and by Oken, who in 1815 restricted the term *Lycæna* to what we know as "The Blues." For a period of years the usage of different authors varied, but for eighty years, following the example of Westwood, almost all authors have accepted the grouping originated by Denis and Schiffermueller and followed by Geoffroy and Oken. The majority have applied the name *Lycæna* to the "Blues." Arguments against this usage have cropped up now and then and a lot of ink has been spilt in endeavoring to show that established custom is wrong. The nomenclature in use for nearly a century, and only opposed by a few, remains in vogue with the vast majority of authors and students. I shall not depart from it. What is the use?

Our Anglo-Saxon ancestors used to call dogs *tykes*. "Tyke" has priority over the word "dog." But "I'll be dog-goned" if I throw "dog" out of my vocabulary in favor of "tyke," except as an opprobrious epithet, which it has come to be. Darkness had priority over light according to Genesis, but I do not intend to call "white" *black*, even if darkness went before light. "The law of priority" should be respected, but like other rules, its application should be coupled with regard to historic fact and the teachings of common sense.

Genus LYCÆNA Fabricius

(Type according to some authors *L. endymion* W. V.; according to others *L. arion* Linnæus).

"Bright butterflies
Fluttered their vans, azure and green and gold."
SIR EDWIN ARNOLD.

Butterfly.—Generally small, for the most part blue on the upper side of the wings, white, gray, or brown on the under side, variously marked with spots and lines.

What has been said in reference to the subdivision of the genus *Thecla* may be repeated in regard to the genus which we are considering. It has been in recent years subdivided by writers, and many of their subdivisions are defensible from a narrow systematic standpoint. Nevertheless, owing to the close resemblance, which prevails throughout the group, in this book, which is intended not merely for scientific, but popular use, the author has deemed it best only to indicate the subdivisions, which have been made, as subgeneric, which they really, for the most part, are.

Eggs.—The eggs are flattened, turban-shaped (See p. 4, fig. 7).

Caterpillar.—Slug-shaped, as in the preceding genera, feeding upon the petals and bracts of flowers, or upon delicate terminal leaves.

Chrysalis.—Closely resembling the chrysalids of the preceding genera, *Thecla* and *Chrysophanus.*

The *Lycæninæ* are very widely distributed in the temperate regions of both hemispheres. Many species are found in the cold north, or upon the summits of high mountains. A few are found in the tropics. The *Theclinæ*, on the contrary, are common in temperate regions, and still commoner in tropical areas, only a very few species ranging to the far north, or alpine summits.

Subgenus LYCÆNOPSIS Felder

(1) **Lycæna pseudargiolus** Boisd. & Leconte. Pl. XXXI, fig. 6, ♂; fig. 7, ♀; Pl. XXX, fig. 32, ♂, *under side;* Pl. V, figs. 36, 43, 44, *chrysalis.* Var. **lucia** Kirby, Pl. XXXI, fig. 1, ♂; Pl. XXX, fig. 20, ♂, *under side.* Var. **marginata** Edw., Pl. XXXI, fig. 2, ♂; fig. 3, ♀; Pl. XXX, fig. 19, ♂, *under side.* Var. **violacea** Edwards. Pl. XXXI, fig. 5, ♂. Var. **nigra** Edwards. Pl. XXXI, fig. 4, ♂. Var. **neglecta** Edwards, Pl. XXXI, fig. 8, ♂; fig. 9, ♀ Var. **arizonensis** Edwards, Pl. XXXI, fig. 10. Var. **echo** Edwards, Pl. LXVII, fig. 13, ♀. Var. **gazora** Boisduval, Pl. LXVII, fig. 10, ♂.

Butterfly.—The insect is very polymorphic, as the careful researches of Edwards and others have clearly shown. The variety *lucia* is common in the cold north and is produced by over-wintering chrysalids as far south as the mountains of West Virginia. It is characterized by the broad irregular dark blotch in the middle of the secondaries on the under side. The variety *marginata* is also a truly boreal form, in which the outer margins on the under side are heavily banded with dark fulvous. It occurs from Canada to Alaska, and on the high and cold mountains of the New England and Middle States. The variety *violacea* is the early spring form found in more southern localities. Var. *nigra* is a melanic form found from Virginia to Colorado. The variety *neglecta* is smaller than typical *pseudargiolus*, and has the dark spots on the under side more distinct and the hind wings, especially in the female, paler. The variety *arizonensis* is, as its name shows, the form which occurs in the southwestern states. The variety *echo* occurs in southern California and northern Mexico. It is larger in size than the varieties from the far north and the black spots, while distinct, do not tend to fuse. The variety *gazora* is not un-

Fig. 146. — Neuration of *L. pseudargiolus*, enlarged. Typical of subgenus *Lycænopsis.*

common in Mexico, and occurs as a straggler on our southern border. Expanse: .75–1.5 in.

Early Stages.—These have been worked out in the case of the species and most of the varieties and are well described by Edwards, Scudder, and other authors. The larva feeds upon the petals of the flowers of various species of *Cornus* (Dog-wood, Bunch-berry).

Habitat.—This is the most widely distributed Lycænid on the continent. It ranges in its various varietal forms from Alaska to Mexico, and from the Atlantic to the Pacific.

Subgenus PHÆDROTES Scudder

(2) **Lycæna piasus** Boisduval. Pl. XXXI, fig. 19, ♂; fig. 20, ♀; Pl. XXX, fig. 44, ♀, *under side*. Var. **catalina** Reakirt = *rhæa* Boisduval, Pl. LXVI, fig. 47, ♂, *under side*. Var. **daunia** Edwards, Pl. LXVI, fig. 45, ♂. *under side* (The Arrow-head Blue.)

Synonyms: *sagittigera* Felder; ? *viaca* Edw.; *lorquini* Behr (not H.-S.)

Butterfly.—This beautiful insect, like many others of the group is polymorphic. The large form figured on Pl. XXXI is true *piasus* Boisd. The smaller forms, *catalina* Reakirt and *daunia* Edwards, are very close to each other, only differing in the fact that the ground-color of the wings in the latter is somewhat darker than in the former, and the marginal spots of the fore wing are not as much inwardly bounded by white sagittate markings as in *catalina*. Expanse: 1.3–1.45 in.

Early Stages.—The egg has been figured by Comstock in his "Butterflies of California," p. 196. The food-plant is lupine.

Habitat.—The large typical form is not uncommon in central and northern California and Oregon. The varieties *catalina* and *daunia* occur in southern California.

Genus LYCÆNA Fabricius

(Type *P. endymion* W. V.; or *P. arion* Linn.)

(3) **Lycæna maricopa** Reakirt. Pl. LXVI, fig. 1, ♂, *under side* (The Maricopa Blue).

Synonyms: *pardalis* Behr; *erymus* Boisd.

♂. On the upper side deep purplish blue, with lighter bluish scales toward the base of both wings; margins of the primaries quite broadly dark fuscous, with only traces of this darker coloring on the outer margins of the hind wings. Fringes uniformly fulvous white. On the under side the figure given on our plate gives a correct idea of the disposition of the markings. The female does not materially differ in coloration from the male on the under side, but is dark brownish on the upper side, with only slight traces of bluish scaling toward the base of the wings, and with a black discal bar at the end of the cell of the fore wing.

Early Stages.—Unknown.

Habitat.—Central California.

(4) **Lycæna icarioides** Boisduval. Pl. XXX, fig. 29, ♂, *under side;* Pl. LXV, fig. 18, ♂; Pl. LXV, fig. 19, ♂, type of **mintha.** (Boisduval's Blue).

Synonyms: *phileros* Boisd.; *mintha* Edwards.

Butterfly.—On the upper side closely resembles the preceding species in both sexes, but the female has the outer borders of the wings more extensively black. On the under side it may be distinguished by invariably having two rows of black submarginal spots on the hind wings, which are quite regular, but not as strongly defined as is the single line in *maricopa.* Expanse: 1.12 – 1.25 in.

Early Stages.—Unknown.

This species is found in northern California and ranges as far as British Columbia. In the southern part of the range it occurs at moderate elevations, but in the north at low levels. The types of *mintha* Edwards, which are in my possession, are undoubtedly only slightly smaller specimens of *icarioides.*

(5) **Lycæna fulla** Edwards. Pl. XXX, fig. 24, ♂; fig. 25, ♀; Pl. LXV, fig. 22, ♂, type, *under side* (The Evius Blue).

Synonym: *evius* Boisduval.

This species, which occurs abundantly in the southern mountain ranges of California may be a race of *L. icarioides*, but is sufficiently distinct in its markings to justify giving it a name. Expanse: 1.10 in. – 1.2 in.

(6) **Lycæna lycea** Edwards. Pl. XXXII, fig. 18, ♂, type, *under side;* Pl. LXV, fig. 20, ♂, *type;* fig. 21, ♀, typical (The Lycea Blue).

Synonym: *rapahoe* Reakirt.

Butterfly.—The perfect insect is very nearly as large as *C. heteronea*, which superficially it resembles. The male is lilac-blue on the upper side, with margins dusky. The black spots of the under side do not show through on the upper side. The female is dusky, with the wings shot with blue at their bases, more especially the fore wings. On the under side the wings are white. The spots on this side are well delineated in our figure in Plate XXXII. Expanse: 1.30 in.

Early Stages.—These await description.

The butterfly is found on the Rocky Mountains from New Mexico to Montana.

(7) **Lycæna blackmorei** Barnes & McDunnough. Pl. LXV, fig. 25, ♂; fig. 26, ♀; fig. 27, ♂, *under side*, paratypes (Blackmore's Blue).

Butterfly.—Originally described as a subspecies of *L. icarioides*, this form is distinguished on the upper side by the more silvery blue of the wings and the more diffuse, dark margin of the primaries in the male, and the brighter blue of the basal area and the deeper black of the outer borders in the female. On the under side the species closely resembles *fulla*, but is whiter with the dark markings less distinct. Expanse: ♂, 1.15 in.; ♀, 1.25 in.

Habitat.—Vancouver Island.

(8) **Lycæna amica** Edwards. Pl. LXV, fig. 28, ♂; fig. 29, ♂, *under side* (The Amica Blue).

Butterfly.—On the upper side the male closely resembles *blackmorei*, but the blue color is deeper and the margin of the hind wings is marked at the tips of the veins by inwardly projecting dark rays. On the under side the fore wings are marked as in *blackmorei*, but the hind wings have a regular submarginal band of small dark spots and a semicircular series of postcellular spots, which do not occur in *blackmorei*, the hind wings of which are immaculate. Expanse: 1 in.

Habitat.—The insect was originally described from the Mackenzie River. The original type is lost, but the specimens figured on the plate are from the far north of British America and agree so well with the original description that their identity cannot be doubted.

(9) **Lycæna ardea** Edwards. Pl. LXV, fig. 23, ♂, type; fig. 24, ♂, *under side* (The Ardea Blue).

Butterfly.—♂. On the upper side pale blue, in certain lights tending to grayish. The primaries are somewhat broadly margined with dark fuscous; the secondaries have only a fine fuscous line surrounding them. The fringes are white. On the under side the wings are grayish white, with a small discal dot at the end of the cell, followed outwardly by an irregularly curved postmedian series of small black spots margined with white. The hind wings on the lower side are devoid of markings except a white blotch near the end of the cell. (The figure of the under side on our plate is a trifle too light and should be grayer). Expanse: 1.1–1.2 in.

The insect occurs in Nevada.

(10) **Lycæna insulana** Blackmore. Pl. LXV, fig. 30, ♂; fig. 31, ♂, *under side*, paratypes (The Island Blue).

Butterfly.—This species is very near to *amica* Edw., but is much paler shining blue on the upper side, with pale submarginal spots on the outer border between the nervules. On the under side the markings are almost identical with those of *L. amica*. Expanse: 1 in.

Habitat.—Vancouver Island.

(11) **Lycæna pheres** Boisd. Pl. XXX, fig. 37, ♂; Pl. LXV, fig. 35, ♂, from San Francisco; P. XXX, fig. 42, ♀, *under side* (The Pheres Blue).

Butterfly.—The male is pale shining blue above, with dusky borders. The female is dusky, with a little blue at the base of the wings on the same side. Below, the spots on the fore wings are strongly defined; on the hind wings they are white on a pale stone-gray ground. Expanse: 1.20 in.

Early Stages.—We know next to nothing of these.

Dr. McDunnough having taken exception (Cont. Nat. Hist. Lep., III, p. 115) to the tint of the male figured on Pl. XXX, I have depicted on P. LXV a male taken at San Francisco, the type-locality.

The butterfly has a wide range in California and locally varies in tint.

(12) **Lycæna pembina** Edwards. Pl. LXV, fig. 36, ♂, fig. 37, ♀; fig. 38, ♂, *under side* (The Pembina Blue).

Butterfly.—The species was named by Edwards from specimens taken near Winnipeg, which he informs us were lost while in transit to a student on the Pacific Coast. The butterfly has turned up since at the type-locality and appears to be not uncommon in parts of Alberta, British Columbia, and the adjacent parts of the United States. The figures on our plate will enable its easy determination by students. Expanse: 1 in.

Early Stages.—Unknown.

(13) **Lycæna helios** Edwards. Pl. LXV, fig. 40, ♂ *under side* (The Helios Blue).

Butterfly.—The male on the upper side is dull purplish blue; the margin of the fore wings fuscous, of the secondaries only with a narrow dark lining; fringes long, grayish white, toward the apex of fore wing fuscous. The female above is darker than the male, with the border of the hind wings marked with ill defined oval blotches in the interspaces; body above blue, on the under side blackish gray. The figure on our plate gives a clear conception of the markings of the under side. Expanse: 1.1–1.25 in.

Early Stages.—Unknown.

The specimen figured on the plate is labelled *"helios"* in the handwriting of Edwards, and is the only specimen in his collection so labelled. It is not one of the original types, which were "from California," but is from Arizona. The insect is on the under side near to *pembina*, but broader of wing, darker in tint, and quite different in the color of the thorax and abdomen.

(14) **Lycæna columbia** Skinner. Pl. LXVI, fig. 2, ♂, paratype; fig. 3, ♂ *under side* (The Columbia Blue).

Butterfly.—On the upper side bright blue with the outer margins of both the fore and hind wings somewhat broadly margined with black; fringes white. On the under side the ground-color of the wings is slaty gray. The disposition of the markings is clearly shown on our plate. Expanse: ♂, 1.25, in.; ♀, 1.3 in.

Habitat.—Washington, British Columbia, and northern California.

(15) **Lycæna oro** Scudder. Pl. LXVI, fig. 4, ♂; fig. 5, ♀; fig. 6, ♂, *under side* (The Oro Blue).

Butterfly.—The insect is smaller and more delicate in structure than the preceding species. The male is of a somewhat tenderer blue with narrow black borders; the female has the costal and outer borders bounded by brown. The wings reveal a certain amount of translucency so that it is possible in proper light to faintly see from above the spots on the under side, especially in worn specimens. The markings of the lower side are disposed much as in *L. antiacis*, which is a much larger species. Expanse: 1–1.2 in.

Habitat.—Colorado.

(16) **Lycæna behri** Edwards. Pl. XXX, fig. 35, ♂, *under side;* fig. 36, ♂; fig. 41, ♀ (Behr's Blue).

Butterfly.—The male is shining blue above, with narrow dark margins; the female is dark on the upper side with only a few blue scales at the base of the wings. The maculation of the under side of the wings is clearly shown in the figure on our plate. Expanse: 1.1–1.25 in.

Early Stages.—These are in part described by F. X. Williams in "The Entomological News," XIX, p. 482, and by Comstock in his "Butterflies of California," p. 195.

Habitat.—Central California.

In southern California there is a race of this species, smaller in size, in which the dark spots on the under side tend to fade away. This is the variety named *australis* by Grinnell.

(17) **Lycæna antiacis** Boisduval. Pl. LXVI, fig. 9, ♂, *under side* (The Eyed Blue.)

Butterfly.—On the upper side the male is pale lilac-blue, the female dusky, marked with blue at the base of the wings. On the under side the wings are brown. There is a single quite regular band of large-sized black spots on the fore wing beyond the middle, and a triply festooned curved band of similar spots on the hind wing. These spots are all margined with white. Expanse: 1.15–1.25 in.

Early Stages.—These await description.

The insect is found in central California, and is by some writers regarded as an aberrant form of the next species but the test of breeding has not been applied.

(18) **Lycæna xerces** Boisduval. Pl. XXX, fig. 43, ♂, *under side;* Pl. LXV, fig. 41, ♂, *under side;* Pl. LXVI, fig. 10, ♂; fig. 11, ♀, form **mertila** Edwards; Pl. LXV, fig. 43, ♀, form **polyphemus** Boisd.; Pl. LXV, fig. 42, ♂, *under side* (The Xerces Blue).

Butterfly.—The normal and commonest form of this species is *polyphemus*, in which the spots on the lower side are pupilled with black. Typical *xerces* Boisd., which was described before Boisduval named *polyphemus* has the spots on the under side without dark pupils, as the figure on our plate shows. The variety named *mertila* by Edwards is smaller in size and has a whitish streak in the cell of the fore wing on the under side. Expanse: varying from 1.25 to 1.45 in.

Early Stages.—These are described by Comstock, "Butterflies of California," p. 190, after the observations of F. X. Williams published in "The Entomological News," Vol. XIX, p. 476. The food-plant of the larvæ is *Lotus*.

Habitat.—The insect in its various forms has a wide range in northern California.

(19) **Lycæna sæpiolus** Boisduval. Pl. XXXI, fig. 15, ♂; fig. 16, ♀; Pl. LXV, fig. 39, ♀, blue form. Dimorphic form **dædalus** Behr, Pl. XXXI, fig. 11, ♂; fig. 12, ♀; Pl. XXX, fig. 28, ♀, *under side,* = **æhaja** Behr (The Greenish Blue).

Butterfly.—This is a polymorphic species. The male on the upper side has the wings blue, shot in certain lights with brilliant green. The female on the same side is dusky, with greenish blue scales at the base of the wings, and often with reddish markings on the outer border of the hind wings. But bluish females are not as frequently found as those which are brown, suffused with red, both on the fore and hind wings. Dr. Behr, not recognizing the fact that the reddish females were dimorphic, gave the name *daedalus* to specimens which had such females, and those females, which were very red, he further named as a separate species, calling them *aehaja*. In the lapse of time the matter has been solved, and we now know that these forms all belong to the species first named *sæpiolus* by Boisduval. The illustrations on our plates will easily enable the student to identify the species and its forms. Expanse: .75–1.2 in.

Early Stages.—These are as yet not known.

Habitat.—The species has a wide range through California and eastward to the region of the Rocky Mountains, and even as far as Nebraska.

(20) **Lycæna hilda** Grinnell. Pl. LXV, fig. 32, ♂; fig. 33, ♀; fig. 34, ♂, *under side* (The Hilda Blue).

Butterfly.—The figures we give will take the place of a lengthy description. The insect is regarded by some as a geographical race of the preceding species, but it seems to the writer very distinct, and having little to do with *sæpiolus*.

Early Stages.—Unknown.

Habitat.—The San Jacinto and nearby mountain ranges of southern California.

Subgenus GLAUCOPSYCHE Scudder

(Type *L. lygdamus* Doubleday.)

(21) **Lycæna lygdamus** Doubleday. Pl. XXXI, fig. 17, ♂; fig. 18, ♀; Pl. XXX, fig. 50, ♀, *under side* (The Silvery Blue).

Butterfly.—The male has the upper side of the wings pale silvery-blue, narrowly edged with black; the wings of the female on the upper side are darker blue, dusky on the borders, with a dark spot at the end of the cell of the primaries. On the under side the wings are pale chocolate-brown, with a submarginal band of black spots, margined with white, on both wings, as well as a spot at the end of the cells, and one or two on the costa of the secondaries. Expanse: .85–1.10 inch.

Early Stages.—These are yet to be ascertained.

The insect is reported from Michigan to Georgia.

(22) **Lycæna couperi** Grote. Pl. XXX, fig. 34, ♂, *under side;* Pl. LXVI, fig. 7, ♂; fig. 8, ♀. (Couper's Blue.)

Butterfly.—The wings of the male above are pale shining blue, with a narrow black border; of the female darker blue, broadly margined externally with dusky. On the under side the wings are dark brownish-gray, with the spots arranged much as in *L. antiacis*, but with those of the hind wings generally white, and without a dark pupil. The series on the fore wing is usually distinctly pupilled with black. Expanse: 1.25 in.

Early Stages.—Unknown.

The species is found in Newfoundland, Labrador, Anticosti, and westward and northward. It is a boreal form.

(23) **Lycæna afra** Edwards. Pl. LXXIII, fig. 13, ♂; fig. 14, ♀, *under side*, type (The Afra Blue).

Butterfly.—This species has by some writers been treated as the same as *L. couperi*, but is quite distinct, differing in the darker color and markings of the lower side of the wings. (Compare Pl. XXX, fig. 34, with the figures on P. LXXIII, above cited). Expanse: .8–.9 in.

Early Stages.—Unknown.

Habitat.—Saskatchewan and territories west and north as far as southern Alaska.

Subgenus LYCÆIDES Hübner

(Type *L. argus* (Linn.))

(24) **Lycæna scudderi** Edwards. Pl. XXX, fig. 48, ♂; fig. 49, ♀ ; Pl. LXVI, fig. 12, ♂, type, *under side;* Pl. V, fig. 41, chrysalis (Scudder's Blue).

Butterfly.—The commonest eastern representative of the group, to which the species belongs. On the upper side the male is difficult to distinguish from *L. melissa.* The female is darker than the male, and has only a few orange crescents on the outer margin of the hind wing. On the under side the wings are shining white; the spots are much reduced in size, the large orange spots found in *L. melissa* are replaced by quite small yellowish or ochreous spots, and the patches of metallic scales, defining them externally, are very minute. Expanse: 1.00–1.20 in.

Early Stages.—These are accurately described by Dr. Scudder in his great work, "The Butterflies of New England," and by others. The caterpillar feeds upon the lupine, and probably other leguminous plants.

It is widely distributed through the basin of the St. Lawrence, the region of the Great Lakes, and northward as far as British Columbia, being also found on the Catskill Mountains. I have found it very common at times about Saratoga, New York.

(25) **Lycæna kodiak** Edwards. Pl. LXVI, fig. 13, ♂; fig. 14, ♀ ; fig. 15, ♂, *under side* (The Kodiak Blue).

Butterfly.—This is the subarctic race of *L. scudderi,* which is characterized by being smaller than typical *scudderi,* darker in color on the under side of the wings, with the orange spots more or less suffused with gray, and the fine marginal row of minute black spots lacking on the primaries. Expanse: .9–1.1 in.

Early Stages.—Unknown.

Habitat.—Originally described from Kodiak Island, the species is widely diffused through Alaska and the northwestern parts of British America.

(26) **Lycæna aster** Edwards. Pl. XXX, fig. 40, ♂; fig. 46, ♀ ; fig. 47, ♂, *under side* (The Aster Blue).

Butterfly.—The male looks like a dwarfed specimen of *L. scudderi.* The female is dull bluish-gray above, with black spots on the outer margins of the wing, most distinct on the secondaries. Below, instead of a marginal band of orange spots, a diffuse band of blue spots, paler than the surrounding parts of the wing. Expanse: .95–1.00 in.

Early Stages.—These furnish a field for investigation.

The insect is reported thus far only from Newfoundland, from which locality I obtained through the purchase of the Mead collection a large and interesting series.

Genus Lycæna

(27) **Lycæna annetta** Edwards. Pl. XXXII, fig. 13, ♂, type; fig. 14, ♀, type; Pl. LXVI, fig. 16, ♂, type, *under side* (The Annetta Blue).

Butterfly.—The male on the upper side is pale blue, paler than *L. melissa;* the female on the upper side is still paler than the male with the outer borders rather broadly whitish, ornamented by a marginal series of dark spots. The figures on our plates give a good idea of the appearance of both sexes. Expanse: 1.15 in.

Early Stages.—Unknown.

Habitat.—Thus far only known from the Salt Lake Valley in Utah.

(28) **Lycæna melissa** Edwards. Pl. XXXI, fig. 25, ♂; fig. 26, ♀; Pl. LXVI, fig. 17, ♀, *under side*, types (The Orange-margined Blue).

Butterfly.—The male on the upper side is pale blue, with a narrow black marginal line and white fringes. The female is brown or lilac-gray, with a series of orange-red crescents on the margins of both wings. On the under side the wings are stone-gray, with the usual spots, and on the secondaries the orange-colored marginal spots are oblong, tipped inwardly with black and outwardly by a series of metallic-green maculations. Expanse: .90–1.15 inch.

Early Stages.—We know very little about these.

Habitat.—It ranges from Kansas to California, and northward to Montana.

(29) **Lycæna lotis** Lintner. Pl. LXVI, fig. 18, ♂; fig. 19, ♀; fig. 20, ♂, *under side* (The Lotis Blue).

Butterfly.—This is regarded by some as a varietal or local race of the preceding species, from which it differs by being larger, with the orange band on the hind wings of the female broader, the under side whiter, with spots larger and more widely separated than in *L. melissa*.

Early Stages.—Unknown.

Habitat.—It was originally described from Mendocino County in southern California, and is quite abundant in the mountains of that region.

(30) **Lycæna anna** Edwards. Pl. LXVI, fig. 21, ♂, type; fig. 22, ♀, type; fig. 23, ♂, paratype, *under side* (The Anna Blue).

Synonyms: *cajona* Reakirt; *argyrotoxus* Behr; *philemon* Boisd.

Butterfly.—On the upper side the species in both sexes somewhat closely resembles *L. melissa*, but on the under side the wings are much paler. The dark spots are greatly reduced in size and the submarginal spots on the hind wing reduced, showing very little of the orange maculation, which is conspicuous in *L. melissa*. Expanse: 1.3–1.45 in.

Early Stages.—Not known.

Habitat.—The species ranges from the central part of southern California northward as far as British Columbia.

(31) **Lycæna acmon** Doubleday & Hewitson. Pl. XXXI, fig. 27, ♂; fig. 28, ♀; Pl. LXVI, fig. 24, ♀, *under side;* fig. 25, ♀, var., *under side.* Var. **lupini** Boisd., Pl. LXVI, fig. 26, ♂; fig. 27, ♀; fig. 28, ♂, *under side.* Var. **chlorina** Skinner, Pl. LXVI, fig. 29, ♂, paratype; fig. 30, ♀, paratype (The Acmon Blue).

Synonym: *antægon* Boisd.

Butterfly.—This species is easily discriminated by the orange subterminal band on the upper side of the hind wings of both sexes bordered externally by black points on the interspaces. The form *lupini* differs from the typical form in having the outer orange band on the upper side of the secondaries narrower and sometimes not continuous, but composed of a series of small orange crescents. The spots on the under side are generally smaller than in typical *acmon*. The male is slightly shaded with green, while the female very nearly corresponds in all respects to the typical female of *acmon*.

There are a number of other varieties or subspecies, as *cottlei* Grinnell, in which the blue of the upper side is deeper in both sexes, especially in the female, and also the orange outer margin of the secondaries is broader than usual. The var. *monticola* Clemence is closely related, being lustrous blue, like *cottlei*, but larger in size and bluer at the bases of the fore wings than outwardly. There are other subspecific forms which can only be discriminated by extremely minute distinctions, to which authors have called attention.

Early Stages.—The egg has been well figured by Comstock, "Butterflies of California," p. 188, and the caterpillar (as *antægon*) was partially described by Henry Edwards in the "Proc. of Calif. Acad. of Sci.," 1875.

Habitat.—The species is widely distributed from Arizona to British Columbia and eastward through the Rocky Mountain region.

(32) **Lycæna emigdionis** Grinnell. Pl. LXVI, fig. 31, ♂; fig. 32, ♀; fig. 33, ♂, *under side* (The San Emigdio Blue).

Butterfly.—This species may be distinguished from *acmon* by the orange band of the secondaries, which is not sharply defined, but merges inwardly into the ground-color. On the under side there are two lines of large submarginal black spots.

Early Stages.—Undescribed.

Habitat.—The insect is found in the Mohave region and on the southern edge of the San Joaquin Valley in California.

(33) **Lycæna neurona** Skinner. Pl. LXVI, fig. 34, ♂, paratype (The Veined Blue).

Butterfly.—This species is distinguished by the fact that in both sexes the wings on the upper side are not blue, but dark blackish, marked by bright red stripes on the outer parts of the fore wings. Expanse: .8–1 in.

Early Stages.—Unknown.

Habitat.—The southern Sierra Nevadas of California, and the Tehachapi and San Bernardino Mountains.

(34) **Lycæna battoides** Behr. Pl. XXXII, fig. 11, ♂; Pl. LXVI, fig. 35, ♀, *under side*. Var. **oregonensis** Barnes & McDunnough, Pl. LXVI, fig. 36, ♂, paratype, *under side*. Var. **bernardino** Barnes & McDunnough, Pl. LXVI, fig. 37, ♂, paratype, *under side* (The Square-spotted Blue).

Butterfly.—Easily recognized by the fact that the spots on the under side of the wings are quadrangular, or squarish. In typical *battoides* the extra-discal spots on the under side of the hind wings tend to run into the inner row of submarginal spots. The outer row of submarginal spots, while minute, are distinctly shown. In the variety *oregonensis* the extra-discal spots do not fuse with the inner submarginal series; and the males have a wider dark marginal band on the upper sides of the wings. In the variety *bernardino* the spots on the lower side are much reduced in size, and the ground-color of the lower side of the wings is almost white. Expanse: 1–1.1 in.

Early Stages.—These have not thus far been studied.

Habitat.—The typical form occurs on the mountains of central California and is on the wing in July. The variety *oregonensis* was originally described from specimens taken at Crater Lake, Oregon. The variety *bernardino* is found on the mountains of southern California.

(35) **Lycæna glaucon** Edwards. Pl. XXX, fig. 31, ♀, *under side;* fig. 39, ♂, type. Var. **intermedia** Barnes & McDunnough, Pl. LXVI, fig. 38, ♂, paratype (The Glaucous Blue).

Butterfly.—Violet-blue on the upper side, with even marginal bands of black on both wings. On the under side there is a submarinal band of orange spots on the hind wings, more distinct in the female than in the male. In the variety *intermedia* the marginal bands on the upper side are broader than in the typical form, and on the under side the orange band of the secondaries is broken up into small lunules. Expanse: 1 in.

Early Stages.—Unknown.

Habitat.—From California to Colorado. The variety *intermedia* was originally described from the upper part of the Sacramento Valley.

(36) **Lycæna enoptes** Boisduval. Pl. XXX, fig. 30, ♂, *under side;* fig. 51, ♂. Var. **ancilla** Barnes & McDunnough, Pl. LXVI, fig. 41, ♂; fig. 42, ♀, fig. 43, ♂, *under side;* paratypes (The Dotted Blue).

Butterfly.—The wings on the upper side are purplish-blue—pale in the male, darker in the female—bordered with dusky, more heavily in the female than in the male. The fringes are white, checkered with dusky at the ends of the veins. The female sometimes has the hind wings marked on the upper side with red marginal spots on the inner half of the border. On the under side the wings are pale bluish-gray, marked with a profusion of small black spots, those on the outer margin arranged in two parallel lines, between which, on the hind wings, are red spots. The variety *ancilla* Barnes & McDunnough from Eureka, Utah, is to be distinguished by the fact that the orange spots between the two outer submarginal rows of black spots on the under side of the hind wings are continuous as a band, and are not broken into separate spots, as in typical *enoptes.*

The distinction between *L. glaucon, battoides,* and *enoptes,* and their varieties has been rather finely drawn by recent writers, and it is difficult to make out the differences. Expanse: about 1 in.

Early Stages.—Unknown.

Habitat.—The species ranges from California to Colorado.

(37) **Lycæna mohave** Watson & Comstock. Pl. LXVI, fig. 44, ♂, type, *under side* (The Mohave Blue).

Butterfly.—This is a smaller insect than the preceding. In color it is much grayer on the under side, and with scarcely distinguishable traces of the orange maculation near the outer borders of the hind wings on the under side. It may be a dwarfed form of *L. enoptes* found in the Mohave Desert, where it occurs. Expanse: .8 in.

Early Stages.—Unknown.

(38) **Lycæna rita** Barnes & McDunnough. Pl. LXVI, fig. 39, ♂, paratype; fig. 40, ♂, paratype, *under side* (The Rita Blue).

Butterfly.—This is closely related to *L. battoides* var. *bernardino*, but the blue in the male is clearer and brighter, and the ground-color of the under side is whiter. It is not the same as *L. mohave*, with which it has been confused by some writers, and it may be worth while to mention here that the male figured by Comstock in his "Butterflies of California" is not the male of this species, which has no red submarginally. Expanse: .9 in.

Early Stages.—Unknown.

Habitat.—The southern Mohave Desert, California; Arizona.

(39) **Lycæna spaldingi** Barnes & McDunnough. Pl. LXVI, fig. 46, ♂, paratype, *under side* (Spalding's Blue).

Butterfly.—Closely related to *L. enoptes*, but with a blotch of orange on the under side of the fore wings near the inner angle. Expanse: .9 in.

Early Stages.—Unknown.

Habitat.—Colorado.

(40) **Lycæna speciosa** Henry Edwards. Pl. XXXII, fig. 1, ♂; fig. 2, ♀, paratype, *under side* (The Small Blue).

Butterfly.—Quite small; the male pale blue above, edged with dusky; the female dusky, with the inner two thirds shot with blue. The maculation of the under side is as represented on the plate. Expanse: .8 in.

Early Stages.—Unknown.

Habitat.—Mohave desert, southern Calfornia.

(41) **Lycæna yukona** Holland. Pl. LXVII, fig. 7, ♂; fig. 8, ♀; fig. 9, ♂, *under side*, typical (The Yukon Blue).

Butterfly.—This species is very close to that varietal form of *L. optilete* Knoch, which is known as *cyparissus* Hübner. It, however, consistently differs by having but one red spot near the anal angle of the secondaries on the under side, whereas in *L. cyparissus* there are invariably two such spots, and in *optilete* a marginal series. Expanse: .8–.9 in.

Early Stages.—Unknown.

Habitat.—The species ranges from the region of Great Slave Lake westward into Alaska in the valley of the Yukon.

(42) **Lycæna shasta** Edwards. Pl. XXXI, fig. 23, ♂; fig. 24, ♀; Pl. LXVII, fig. 6, ♂, *under side* (The Shasta Blue).

Synonyms: *zelmira* Felder; *calchas* Behr; *nivium* Boisd.

Butterfly.—The figures on the plate give a fairly good idea of the upper side of this species in both sexes, though the male is not quite so dark a blue, as is represented. On the under side the wings have the usual black spots, on a dirty gray ground, and in addition, on the hind wings there are a number of small marginal spots surmounted by metallic-colored bluish-green scales, which help to easily identify the species.

A variety, named *L. shasta comstocki* by C. L. Fox, has been dubbed *The Yosemite Blue*. It is darker than the typical form, the female has no blue scales and is adorned on the hind wings by a marginal row of reddish spots. Expanse: about 1 in.

Early Stages.—Awaiting description.

Habitat.—The high cold summits of the mountains of California, Washington, ranging east to Colorado. The variety *comstocki* is found about the glaciers at the head of the Yosemite Valley. A rather small variety called *minnehaha* by Scudder is found on the high mountains of Colorado.

Subgenus PHILOTES Scudder

(43) **Lycæna sonorensis** Felder. Pl. XXXI, fig. 21, ♂; fig. 22, ♀; Pl. LXVI, fig. 45, ♂, *under side* (The Sonora Blue).

Synonym: *regia* Boisduval.

Butterfly.—Easily distinguished from all other species by the red spots in the region of the median nervules on the upper side. Expanse: .87 in.

Early Stages.—Unknown.

This lovely little insect is found rather abundantly in southern California and northern Mexico.

A variety, in which there is more white than usual on the under side has been called *sonoralba* by Watson & Comstock.

Subgenus AGRIADES Hübner

(44) **Lycæna podarce** Felder. Pl. XXXII, fig. 15, ♂; fig. 16, ♀; Pl. LXVI, fig. 50, ♂, *under side* (The Gray Blue).

Synonyms: *tehama* Reakirt; *cilla* Behr; *nestos* Boisd.; *orbitulus* Strecker. (not Esper, nor De Prunner).

Butterfly.—The male is grayish-blue above, with dusky margins, lighter on the disk of both the fore and hind wings. There are a few dark marginal crescents on the hind wings. On the under side the wings are very pale, profusely spotted; the spot at the end of the cell of the secondaries being large and whitish, without a pupil, the rest being black, ringed about with white. The female is dark brown above, the fore wings having a black spot ringed about with yellowish at the end of the cell. Expanse: 1.05 in.

Early Stages.—These have never been described.

The species is reported from California, Nevada, and Colorado. It is alpine in its habits. The insect figured as *podarce* by Wright is not this species.

(45) **Lycæna aquilo** (Boisduval). Pl. XXXII, fig. 9, ♂; fig. 10, ♂, *under side*. Var. **suttoni** Holland, Pl. LXVIII, fig. 7, ♂; fig. 8, ♀; fig. 9, ♂, *under side;* types (The Labrador Blue).

Synonym: *franklini* Curtis.

Butterfly.—The male is shining bluish gray on the upper side; the female a little darker, with pale spots and striations. On the under side the wings are marked with black spots, which on the hind wings toward the base are broad and diffuse, almost entirely covering the inner half of the wings, but not reaching the costa. There is considerable variation in the markings of the lower side in specimens from different localities. The Carnegie Museum has a good series from Southampton Island in Hudson Bay, in which all the markings are more sharply defined and blacker than in specimens from Labrador, reaching the costa of the hind wing on the under side. To this form I have given the subspecific name **suttoni**. Expanse: .8 in.

Habitat.—The species ranges from northern Labrador to the north and west over a wide area.

(46) **Lycæna rustica** Edwards. Pl. XXXII, fig. 17, ♂, *under side* (The Rustic Blue).

Butterfly.—Much like the preceding species, but a third larger and paler blue on the upper side of the wings of the male. On the under side the disposition of the spots and markings is much as in *L. aquilo*, but on the secondaries the dark spots and shades are all replaced by white on a pale-gray ground. Expanse: .90–1.00 in.

Early Stages.—We are in complete ignorance as to these.

The butterfly is found in British America and on the Western Cordilleras.

Subgenus EVERES Hübner

(47) **Lycæna amyntula** Boisduval. Pl. XXXII, fig. 7, ♂; fig. 8, ♀. (The Western Tailed Blue).

Butterfly.—Closely resembling *L. comyntas*, of which it may be only a slightly modified western form, and, until the test of breeding has been applied, we cannot be sure of this. The figures in the plate give a very good representation of the upper side of the wings of this species.

Early Stages.—But little has been found out concerning these.

It ranges from the eastern foothills of the Rocky Mountains to the Pacific in California, British America, and through the northern tier of Western States.

(48) **Lycæna comyntas** (Godart). Pl. XXXI, fig. 29, ♂; fig. 30, ♀; Pl. XXXII, fig. 12, ♂, *under side;* Pl. V, figs. 42, 47, 48, *chrysalis.* Var. **herri** Grinnell, Pl. LXVII, fig. 11, ♂; fig. 12, ♀, *under side,* typical (The Eastern Tailed Blue).

Butterfly.—The blue of the upper side of the male in the plate is too dark; but the female and the under side of the wings are accurately delineated. The species is generally tailed, but specimens without tails occur. The variety *herri* differs from the typical form in having a rather well marked black border on the outer margins of the wings above. It is found in Arizona. Expanse: 1.00–1.10 in.

Genus Lycæna

Early Stages.—These are well known and have been fully described. The caterpillar feeds on leguminous plants.

This delicate little species ranges from the valley of the Saskatchewan to Costa Rica, and from the Atlantic to the foothills of the Western Cordilleras. It is common in the Middle and Western States, flitting about roadsides and weedy forest paths.

FIG. 147. — Neuration of *Lycæna comyntas*, enlarged. Typical of the subgenus *Everes*, Hübner.

Subgenus HEMIARGUS Hübner

(Type *hanno* Stoll)

(49) **Lycæna catilina** (Fabricius). Pl. XXXI, fig. 31, ♀ ; Pl. XXX, fig. 45, ♂, *under side* (The Indian River Blue).

Synonym: *ammon* of many authors.

Butterfly.—The male is brilliant lilac-blue on the upper side; the female shining violet-blue, with very dark and wide black borders on the fore wings and one or two conspicuous black eye-spots near the anal angle of the hind wings, each surmounted by a carmine crescent. The figure in Pl. XXX gives a correct representation of the under side. Expanse: .95–1.10 in.

Early Stages.—Unknown.

This beautiful little insect is not uncommon in southern Florida, and also occurs in the Antilles and tropical America. It is closely related to *L. ammon* Lucas, with which I, in common with others, confused it. *L. ammon* seems to slightly differ and is an Antillean insect.

(50) **Lycæna hanno** (Stoll). Pl. XXXII, fig. 3, ♂, *under side* (The Florida Blue).

Synonym: *antibubastus* Hübner.

Butterfly.—The male on the upper side is purplish blue, with a narrow black line on the outer borders; fringes white. The female is darker. On the under side the hind wings are more or less broadly margined with fuscous followed inwardly by a pale more diffuse band of lighter color, in some specimens nearly white. This pale band is lacking on the primaries. On the under side the hind wings have two small dark spots on the costa, one near the base, one near the middle. They are not as large as the spots found in the next species.

(51) **Lycæna filenus** Poey. Pl. LXVIII, fig. 2, ♂ ; fig. 3, ♀ ; fig. 4, ♂, *under side* (The Filenus Blue).

Synonyms: *pseudoptiletes* Boisd. & Lec.; *astenidas* Lucas; *astenıaıa* Bethune-Baker.

Butterfly.—This species has often been confounded by writers with the preceding species, which in many respects it resembles. On the upper side the male near the base of the fore wings and on the inner half of the hind wings is blue; outwardly on the fore wings dark fuscous, almost black and on the costa and outwardly on the hind wings of the same color; fringes whitish. There are two or three dark blotches near the anal angle on the upper side capped with orange lunules. On the under side both the fore and the hind wings in both sexes are traversed by two curved fuscous lines, both defined externally by a series of clear white spots. The basal area in both wings is pale gray, the hind wings having three black spots, two of which are on the costa, and the third which is smaller at the base of the cell. These spots are large, distinct, and partially margined with white. At the anal angle of the hind wings there are two large ocelli, sometimes a third. The one nearest the anal angle being the largest is pupilled with blue; above these spots there is an orange red shade. Expanse: ♂, .75 in.; ♀, .8 in.

Early Stages.—Unknown.

Habitat.—This species, which is not uncommon in Cuba, has been found on the Indian River and elsewhere in southern Florida.

(52) **Lycæna gyas** Edwards. Pl. LXVII, fig. 1, ♂; fig. 2, ♀; fig. 3, ♂, *under side*. Var. **zachæina** Butler & Druce: Pl. LXVII, fig. 4, ♂; fig. 5, do., *under side* (The Gyas Blue).

Butterfly.—The male on the upper side is quite pale lilac-blue, with the apex of the fore wing laved with pale fuscous. The female on the upper side is darker. In both sexes there is a trace of the dark ocellus near the anal angle, which is conspicuous on the under side. On the under side the markings are as shown on our plate. The variety *zachæina* Butl. & Druce, is brighter more shining blue on the upper side. Expanse: .65–.75 in.

Early Stages.—Unknown.

Habitat.—Arizona, Mexico.

This species has in part been confused by some writers with the following.

(53) **Lycæna isola** Reakirt. Pl. XXX, fig. 35, ♂, *under side;* fig. 38, ♀. (Reakirt's Blue).

Synonym: *alce* Edwards.

Butterfly.—The male on the upper side is pale lilac-blue, with the outer borders and the ends of the veins narrowly dusky. The female is brownish-gray on the upper side, with the wings at their base glossed with blue. In both sexes there is a rather conspicuous black spot on the margin of the hind wings between the first and second median nervules. The under side depicted on our plate, to which the student may refer, does not show the dark shade on the outer margin as well as might be. It is very like *hanno* on the outer border beneath. Expanse: 1 in.

Early Stages.—Unknown.

The species occurs in Texas. Arizona, and Mexico.

Subgenus ZIZERA Moore

(54) **Lycæna** (*Zizera?*) **cyna** Edwards. Pl. LXVI, fig. 51, paratype; Pl. LXVIII, fig. 1, ♀, type, from San Antonio, Texas, *under side* (The Cyna Blue).

Butterfly.—This delicate little insect, originally described from San Antonio, is by me provisionally referred to the genus *Zizera*, which is widely distributed in southern Asia and Africa. It has nothing to do with the species included in the genus *Hemiargus*, as has been pointed out by Bethune-Baker. It differs in outline and structure. The fore wings are relatively long and slender, the hind wing short, both wings well rounded externally. On the upper side they are pale lilac-blue laved with pale fuscous outwardly; on the under side they are very pale gray with ashen fringes, a minute spot in the middle of the cell and a bar at the end of the cell of the fore wing; both wings traversed by a curved extra-discal band of very minute gray spots. Expanse: .65–.75 in.

Early Stages.—Unknown.

Habitat.—The species ranges from Texas to Arizona.

Subgenus LEPTOTES Scudder

(Type *Lycæna theonus* Lucas)

(55) **Lycæna marina** Reakirt, Pl. XXXI, fig. 32, ♂; Pl. XXX, fig. 27, ♀, *under side* (The Marine Blue).

Butterfly.—The male, on the upper side, is pale lilac-blue, the dark bands of the lower side appearing faintly on the upper side. The female is dark brown on the upper side, with the wings at the base shot with bright lilac-blue; the dark bands on the disk in this sex are prominent, especially on the fore wings. The under side of the wings is accurately depicted in Pl. XXX and therefore requires no description. Expanse: 1.10 in.

Early Stages.—Unknown.

Marina is found in Texas, Arizona, southern California, and southward.

(56) **Lycæna theona** Lucas. Pl. XXXII, fig. 6, ♀. (The West Indian Blue). Synonym: *floridensis* Morrison.

Butterfly.—The male is shining lavender-blue, this color glossing the dark outer borders of the wings; the female is white, with the outer costal borders heavily blackish, the primaries shot with shining sky-blue toward the base. On the under side the wings are crossed by dark bands of spots, arranged much as in *L. marina*, but darker. The hind wings near the anal angle have conspicuous eye-spots both above and below. Expanse: .80 in.

Early Stages.—Unknown.

This lovely insect is found in the Gulf States and all over the hot lands of the New World.

Subgenus BREPHIDIUM Boisduval

(Type *Lycæna exilis* Boisduval)

(57) **Lycæna isophthalma** Herrich-Schäffer. Pl. XXXII, fig. 4, ♂. (The Dwarf Blue).

Synonym: *pseudofea* Morrison.

Butterfly.—Light brown on the upper side in both sexes, with the outer margin of the hind wings set with a row of dark spots, which on the under side are defined by circlets of metallic scales. The under side is pale brown, profusely marked by light spots and short bands. Expanse: .75 in.

Early Stages.—Up to this time we have learned very little concerning them. The species occurs in the Gulf States and the Antilles.

(58) **Lycæna exilis** Boisduval. Pl. XXXII, fig. 5, ♂ (The Pygmy Blue). Synonym: *fea* Edwards.

Butterfly.—On the upper side this, which is the smallest of North American butterflies, very closely resembles the foregoing species, but may be instantly distinguished by the white spot at the inner angle of the fore wing and the white fringes of the same wing near the apex. The hind wings on the under side are set with a marginal series of dark spots ringed about with metallic scales. Expanse: .65 in.

Early Stages.—Unknown.

The Pygmy is found in the Gulf States, southern California, and throughout tropical America.

SIZE

Size, like wealth, is only relative. The farmer who owns a hundred acres appears rich to the laborer whom he employs to cut his wheat; but many a millionaire spends in one month as much as would purchase two such farms. The earth seems great to us, and the sun still greater; but we know there are suns the diameter of which is equal to the distance from the earth to the sun, in which both earth and sun would be swallowed up as mere drops in an ocean of fire. In the animal kingdom there are vast disparities in size, and these disparities are revealed in the lower as well as in the higher classes. In the class of mammals we find tiny mice and great whales; in the insect world we find beetles which are microscopic in size, and, not distantly related to them, beetles as large as a clenched fist. The disparity between a field-mouse and a sulphur-bottomed whale is no greater than the disparity in size which exists between the smallest and the largest of the beetle tribe. And so it is with the lepidoptera. It would take several thousands of the Pygmy Blue, *Lycæna exilis*, to equal in weight one of the great bird-wing butterflies of the Australian tropics. The greatest disparity in size in the order of the lepidoptera is not, however, shown in the butterflies, but among the moths. There are moths the wings of which do not cover more than three sixteenths of an inch in expanse, and there are moths with great bulky bodies and wings spreading from eight to ten inches. It would require ten thousand of the former to equal in weight one of the latter, and the disproportion in size is as great as that which exists between a shrew and a hippopotamus, or between a minnow and a basking-shark.

It is said that, taking the sulphur-bottomed whale as the representative of the most colossal development of flesh and blood now existing on land or in the sea, and then with the microscope reaching down into the realm of protozoan life, the common blow-fly will be ascertained to occupy the middle point on the descending scale. Man is, therefore, not only mentally, but even physically, a great creature, though he sometimes stands amazed at what he regards as the huge proportions of other creatures belonging to the vertebrates.

FAMILY V.

PIERIDÆ (THE SULPHURS AND WHITES)

> "Fly, white butterflies, out to sea,
>   Frail pale wings for the winds to try;
>   Small white wings that we scarce can see,
>   Fly.
>   Here and there may a chance-caught eye
>   Note, in a score of you, twain or three
>   Brighter or darker of tinge or dye;
>   Some fly light as a laugh of glee,
>   Some fly soft as a long, low sigh:
>   All to the haven where each would be,—
>   Fly."
>
> SWINBURNE.

Butterfly.—Provided with six ambulatory feet; for the most part medium-sized or small; white, or yellow in color, with dark marginal markings. In many genera the subcostal vein of the fore wing has five, or in some cases six nervules, and the upper radial is lacking in this wing.

Early Stages.—The eggs are spindle-shaped, marked with vertical ridges and cross-lines. The caterpillars are long, slender, smooth, without osmateria, or scent-organs. They are generally green in color, longitudinally striped with darker or paler lines. The chrysalids in all the genera are more or less elongate, often laterally compressed, attached at the anal extremity and held in place by a girdle of silk about the middle, but never appressed to the surface, upon which pupation takes place, as in the *Riodinidæ* and *Lycænidæ*. They are generally more or less pointed at the head, with the wing cases in many genera greatly developed on the ventral side forming a broad keel-shaped projection.

This family is large, and greatly developed in the tropics of both hemispheres. Some of the genera are very widely distributed in temperate regions, especially *Pieris* and *Colias*.

Genus DISMORPHIA Hübner

"I saw him run after a gilded butterfly; and when he caught it, he let it go again; and after it again; and over and over he comes, and up again; catched it again." SHAKESPEARE, *Coriolanus*.

Butterfly.—Medium-sized, varying in the form of the wings, some species resembling other *Pierinæ* in outline and color; but more frequently mimicking the Ithomiid and Heliconiid butterflies. Some of them represent a commingling of the features of the genus *Pieris* and the above mentioned protected groups. Eyes not prominent. Palpi quite small, basal joint long, middle joint oval, third joint small, oval, or slightly club-shaped. Antennæ long, thin, terminating in a gradually enlarged spindle-shaped club. Fore wings sometimes oval, more frequently elongated, narrow, twice, or even three times as long as broad, especially in the male sex; apex pointed, falcate, or rounded; cell long and narrow; first subcostal nervule rising either before or after the end of the cell, and in numerous cases, as shown in the cut, coalescing with the costal vein.

FIG. 148.—Neuration of the genus *Dismorphia*.

Early Stages.—Of the early stages of these interesting insects we have no satisfactory knowledge.

The species of the genus belong exclusively to the tropical regions of the New World. There are about a hundred species, which have already been named and described, and undoubtedly there are many more which remain to be discovered. These insects can always be distinguished from the protected genera which they mimic by the possession of six well-developed ambulatory feet in both sexes, the protected genera being possessed of only four feet adapted to walking.

(1) **Dismorphia melite** (Linnæus). Pl. XXXVII, fig. 17, ♂; fig. 18, ♀ (The Mime).

Butterfly.—The figures on the plate make a description of the upper side unnecessary. On the under side the wings of the male are shining white, except the costa, which is evenly dull ochreous from the base to the apex. The hind wings are ochreous, mottled with pale brown. The female on the under side has the fore wings very pale yellow, with the black spots of the upper side reproduced; the hind wings are deeper yellow, mottled with pale-brown spots and crossed by a moderately broad transverse pale-brown band of the same color.

Early Stages.—Unknown.

The species is credited to our fauna on the authority of Reakirt. It is abundant in Mexico. It mimicks certain forms of *Ithomiinæ*.

Genus NEOPHASIA Behr

"It was an hour of universal joy.
  The lark was up and at the gate of heaven,
  Singing, as sure to enter when he came;
  The butterfly was basking in my path,
  His radiant wings unfolded."

ROGERS.

Butterfly.—Medium-sized, white in color, more nearly related in the structure of its wings to the European genus *Aporia* than to any other of the American Pierid genera. The upper radial is lacking, and the subcostal is provided with five

275

branches, the first emitted well before the end of the cell; the second likewise emitted before the end of the cell and terminating at the apex; the third, fourth, and fifth rising from a common stalk at the outer upper angle of the cell.

Early Stages.—The egg is flask-shaped, fluted on the sides, recalling the shape of the "pearl-top" lamp-chimney. The caterpillar, in its mature form, is about an inch long. The body is cylindrical, terminating in two short anal tails. The color is dark green, with a broad white band on each side, and a narrow band of white on the back. The feet are black, and the prolegs greenish-yellow. The chrysalis is dark green, striped with white, resembling the chrysalids of the genus *Colias*, but somewhat slenderer. The caterpillar feeds upon conifers.

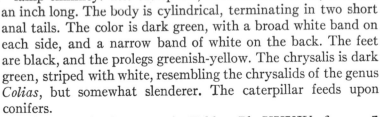

FIG. 149.—Neuration of the genus *Neophasia*.

(1) **Neophasia menapia** Felder. Pl. XXXIV, fig. 7, ♂ (The Pine White).

Butterfly.—The insect on the under side sometimes has the outer margin of the secondaries marked with spots of bright pinkish-red, resembling in this style of coloration certain species of the genus *Delias* of the Indo-Malayan fauna.

Early Stages.—These have been thoroughly described by Edwards in his third volume. The caterpillar infests the pine-trees and firs of the northern Pacific States. The larva lets itself down by a silken thread, often a hundred feet in length, and pupates on the ferns and shrubbery at the foot of the trees. It sometimes works great damage to the pine woods. The butterflies often appear in great swarms. One of my friends tells me that they occasionally appear in cloud-like masses, and after laying their eggs die, covering the ground like drifted snow.

(2) **Neophasia terlooti** Behr. Pl. LXXI, fig. 12, ♂; fig. 13, dimorphic ♀, **princetonia** Poling (Terloot's White).

Synonym: *epyaxa* Strecker.

Butterfly, ♂.—More heavily marked with black on the fore wings than is the case in *N. menapia*. The females are dimorphic, some of them being marked very much like the males, but with the black areas heavier; others are as shown on our plate, having the ground-color deep red. Expanse: ♂, 2 in.; ♀, 2.2 in.

Early Stages.—Not much has as yet been written about these. The larvæ feed on the leaves of coniferous trees.

Habitat.—Southern California, Arizona, northern Mexico.

The caterpillars of a Mexican butterfly, not distantly related to Terloot's White, weave nests, somewhat resembling those of the Web-worm, which are common by the roadsides in New England. The Mexican Indians collect these nests and, frying the caterpillars in lard or butter, eat them as a delicacy. The scientific name of the insect is *Eucheira socialis* Westwood. A friend once sent me a barrel full of these nests from Mexico. I did not eat the caterpillars, but I preserved scores of the butterflies, and many larvæ and chrysalids.

Genus MELETE Swainson

Synonym: *Daptonoura* Butler

"The virtuoso thus, at noon,
Broiling beneath a July sun,
The gilded butterfly pursues
O'er hedge and ditch, through gaps and mews;
And, after many a vain essay
To capitvate the tempting prey,
Gives him at length the lucky pat,
And has him safe beneath his hat;
Then lifts it gently from the ground;
But, ah! 't is lost as soon as found.
Culprit his liberty regains,
Flits out of sight, and mocks his pains."

COWPER.

The species included in this genus are neotropical. They were formerly classified in the genus *Tachyris* Wallace, or in the genus *Daptonoura* Butler. All the species, belonging to the former genus are now known to be old world forms. The genus *Daptonoura* of Butler unfortunately falls as a synonym of the genus *Melete* Swainson. There is only one species of the genus which occurs within the limits of the United States, *M. ilaire* (Godart).

(1) **Melete ilaire** (Godart). Pl. XXXV, fig. 4, ♂; fig. 5, ♀ (form **neumœgeni**) (The Florida White).

Butterfly.—The hind wings of the male on the under side, which is not shown in the plate, are very pale saffron. The under side of the wings in the female is pearly-white, marked with bright orange-yellow at the base of the primaries. A melanic form of the female, shown in fig. 5, is common in Florida. It was named *neumœgeni* by Skinner and rebaptized *hollandi* by Roeber.

Early Stages.—We know, as yet, but little of these.

The insect is abundant in the tropics of America.

Genus ASCIA Scopoli

(Type *Papilio monuste* Linnæus)

This genus is separable from the genus *Pieris* Schrank, the type of which is *Papilio rapæ* Linnæus. Though the two genera are closely related to each other, *Ascia* may be at once distinguished from *Pieris* by the fact that the costal vein of the fore wing in the former genus terminates far beyond the end of the cell; while in the latter genus it terminates before reaching the end of the cell. The genus is intermediate between *Melete* Swainson and *Pieris* Schrank. It is mainly tropical. But two species belonging to it are found within the limits of the United States, *monuste* (Linnæus) and *amaryllis* (Fabricius).

(1) **Ascia monuste** Linnæus. Pl. XXXV, fig. 1, ♂; fig. 2, ♀. Pl. LXVII, fig. 15, ♂; fig. 16, dimorphic ♀, **phileta** (Fabr.); fig. 17, var. **crameri** Holland, ♂; fig. 18, var. **raza** Klots, ♂, paratype (The Great Southern White).

Butterfly.—This species in its wide range exists in many varietal forms. The male figured on Pl. LXVII, fig. 15, is a typical male corresponding almost exactly

with the illustration given by Kleemann (*Beiträge*, etc., Tom. I, Pl. III, fig. 3), except that it lacks the black spots at the end of the veins on the secondaries. It is more albinic than the specimen figured by Kleemann. The male figured on our plate, fig. 17, corresponds more nearly with the figure given by Cramer (Pap. Exot., Pl. CXLI, fig. F). To this form, which is common in Florida, I venture to apply the varietal or subspecific name *crameri*. The females are very variable in their markings. On Pl. LXVII, fig. 16, I show a female which was taken in *copula* with the male figured (fig. 15). It is a dimorphic female representing the form named *phileta* by Fabricius. This dimorphic female varies extensively in the ground-color of the upper surface, which ranges from a pale gray to the deep color shown in the specimen represented upon our plate. The female shown on Pl. XXXV, fig. 2, has the black spot at the end of the cell of the fore wing

Fig. 150.—Neuration of the genus *Melete*.

united with the dark margin of the fore wing. Specimens frequently occur in which this black spot is not united with the black superior border. On the under side there is a great variety in maculation. In the specimen represented on Pl. LXVII, fig. 15, there are only a few traces of the darker markings on the under side of the hind wings which appear so prominently in the variety *raza* Klots. In the specimen depicted on the same plate, fig. 17, var. *crameri*, the dark spots are indicated, but are quite pale fulvous and more or less obsolete in the limbal area. The variety *raza* Klots is more or less widely distributed through the American tropics, and we have in our collection numerous specimens from the province of Minas Geraes in Brazil, which are identical with the insect, a paratype of which we figure on Pl. LXVII, fig. 18.

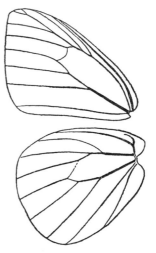

Fig. 151.—Neuration of genus *Ascia*, enlarged.

There is a great deal of variety in size in the species. In the variety *crameri* the specimens generally run larger than in typical *monuste*. The females are not always as large in expanse of wings as the males. In general the insects ♂ and ♀, have an expanse of from 2 in. to 2.5 in.

Early Stages.—What we know of these is derived principally from Abbot through Boisduval, and there is opportunity here for much closer investigation than has been made in times past.

Habitat.—The species has a wide range through subtropical and tropical America, and is not uncommon in the Gulf States.

(2) **Ascia amaryllis** var. **josepha** Godman & Salvin. Pl. LXVII, fig. 14, ♂. (The Amaryllis White).

This form of the species *amaryllis*, which is only distinguished from the typical form by the absence of a black spot at the end of the cell of the secondaries and by the reduced side of the black spot at the end of the cell of the primaries, is well represented upon our plate and hardly needs further description. Expanse: ♂, 2.5 in.; ♀, 2.75 in.

Early Stages.—Awaiting study.

Habitat.—It has been reported as occurring in Florida and on the Mexican border of the United States. The insect is common further southward.

Genus PIERIS Schrank
(Type *Papilio rapæ* Linn.)
The Whites

> "And there, like a dream in a swoon, I swear
>   I saw Pan lying,— his limbs in the dew
> And the shade, and his face in the dazzle and glare
>   Of the glad sunshine; while everywhere,
>   Over, across, and around him blew
>   Filmy dragon-flies hither and there,
>   And little white butterflies, two and two,
>   In eddies of odorous air."
>   JAMES WHITCOMB RILEY.

Butterfly.—Medium-sized, white in color, marked in many species on both the upper and under sides with dark brown. Antennæ distinctly clubbed, moderate in length; palpi short, delicate, compressed, with the terminal joint quite short and pointed. Costal vein of the primaries terminating before reaching the end of the cell; subcostal of primaries has four branches, the first arising before the end of the cell, the second at its upper outer angle, and the third and fourth from a common stem emitted at the same point. The outer margin of the primaries is straight, the outer margin of the secondaries more or less evenly rounded.

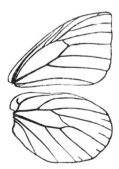

FIG. 152.—Neuration of genus *Pieris*.

Egg.—Spindle-shaped, with vertical raised ridges.

Caterpillar.—Elongate, the head hemispherical, very slightly, if at all, larger in diameter than the body. The caterpillars feed upon cruciferous plants.

Chrysalis.—Attached by the anal extremity, and held in place by a silk girdle; slightly concave on the ventral side; convex on the dorsal side, with a distinct or pointed hump-like projection on the thorax. At the point where the thoracic and abdominal segments unite in some species there is in addition a distinct keel-shaped eminence, and at the head the chrysalis is furnished with a short conical projection.

(1) **Pieris beckeri** Edwards. Pl. XXXIV, fig. 8, ♂; fig. 9, ♀ (Becker's White).

Butterfly.—This species, through the green markings of the under side of the hind wings, concentrated in broad blotches on the disk, recalls somewhat the species of the genus *Euchloë*, and by these markings it may easily be discriminated from all other allied species.

Early Stages.—These have been in part described by Edwards in the second volume of "The Butterflies of North America."

The species ranges from Oregon to central California, and eastward to Colorado.

(2) **Pieris occidentalis** Reakirt. Pl. XXXIV, fig. 13, ♂. Var. **calyce** Edwards, Pl. LXVII, fig. 26, ♂, type. Var. **nelsoni** Edwards. Pl. LXVII, fig. 29, type (The Western White).

Butterfly.—Not unlike the preceding species on the upper side, but easily distinguished by the markings of the under side of the wings, which are not concentrated in blotches, but form more or less broad longitudinal rays on either side of the veins from the base to the outer margin. It gives me pleasure to figure on Pl. LXVII the types of two forms named by W. H. Edwards, which recent studies indicate are to be accepted as subspecies of *P. occidentalis*. *P. calyce* was described by Edwards from Nevada. It also occurs in California at high elevations in the mountains, and is regarded as a spring form. *P. nelsoni* was first described from St. Michaels. It has a wide range in Alaska. Expanse: ♂, 1.75 in.; ♀, 1.8–1.9 in.; var. *calyce*, expanse: 1.4 in.; var. *nelsoni*, expanse: 1.6 in.

Early Stages.—Little as yet has been written upon these.

Habitat.—*P. occidentalis* and its varieties has a wide range in the mountain states of the western part of the continent, and northward to Alaska, where it replaces the eastern species *P. protodice*.

(3) **Pieris protodice** Boisduval and Leconte, Pl. XXXIV, fig. 10, ♂; fig. 11, ♀; Pl. II, fig. 7, *larva;* Pl. V, figs. 66, 67, *chrysalis* (see also p. 10, fig. 26) (The Common White).

Butterfly.—Allied to the foregoing species, but it may always be quickly distinguished by the pure, immaculate white color of the hind wings of the male on the under side, and by the fact that in the female the hind wings are more lightly marked along the veins by gray-green.

Winter form **vernalis**, Edwards, Plate XXXIV, Fig. 18, ♂. What has been said of the typical or summer form does not hold true of this winter form, which emerges from chrysalids which have withstood the cold from autumn until spring. The butterflies emerging from these are generally dwarfed in size, and in the males have the dark spots on the upper side of the wings almost obsolete or greatly reduced, and the dark markings along the veins on the under side well developed, as in *P. occidentalis*. The females, on the contrary, show little reduction in the size and intensity of any of the spots, but rather a deepening of color, except in occasional instances.

A dimorphic female form which is tinged with yellow on the upper and under sides was named **flava** by Edwards and renamed *flavitincta* by Comstock.

Early Stages.—The life-history of this insect has often been described. The caterpillar feeds upon cruciferous plants, like many of its congeners.

It ranges from the Atlantic to the Rocky Mountains, from Canada to the Gulf States.

(4) **Pieris sisymbrii** Boisduval. Pl. XXXIV, fig. 12, ♂ (The California White).

Butterfly.—Smaller in size than the preceding species with the veins of the fore wing black, contrasting sharply with the white ground-color. All the spots are smaller and more regular, especially those on the outer margin of the fore wing, giving the edge an evenly checkered appearance. On the under side the hind wings have the veins somewhat widely bordered with gray, interrupted about the middle of the wing by the divergence of the lines on either side of the veins in such a way as to produce the effect of a series of arrow-points with their barbs directed toward the base. The female is like the male, with the markings a little heavier. A yellow varietal form is sometimes found.

Early Stages.—The life-history is given and illustrated by Edwards in his second volume. The caterpillar, which is green, banded with black, feeds upon the *Cruciferæ*.

(5) **Pieris napi** (Linnæus). Pl. II, figs. 8, 9, *larva;* Pl. V, figs. 57, 63, 74, *chrysalis* (The Mustard White).

Butterfly.—This is a Protean species, of which there exist many forms, the result of climatic and local influences. Even the larva and chrysalis show in different regions slight microscopic differences, for the influences which affect the imago are operative also in the early stages of development. The typical form which is found in Europe is rarely found in North America, though I have specimens from the northern parts of the Pacific coast region which are absolutely indistinguishable from European specimens in color and markings. I give a few of the well-marked forms or varieties found in North America to which names have been given.

(*a*) Winter form **oleracea-hiemalis** Harris. Pl. XXXIV, fig. 16, ♂ (see also p. 4, fig. 9, and p. 10, fig. 27). The wings are white above in both sexes. Below the fore wings are tipped with pale yellow, and the entire hind wing is yellow. The veins at the apex of the fore wings and on the hind wings are margined with dusky.

(*b*) Aberrant form **virginiensis** Edwards. Pl. XXXIV, fig. 14, ♂. The wings are white above, slightly tipped at the apex of the fore wings with blackish. Below the wings are white, faintly but broadly margined with pale dusky.

(*c*) Form **pallida** Scudder. Pl. XXXIV, fig. 15, ♀. In this form the wings are white above and below, with a small black spot on the fore wing of the female above and a dark line near the inner margin, with almost no trace of dark shading along the veins on the under side.

(*d*) Alpine or arctic form **pseudobryoniæ** Verity. Plate XXXIV, fig. 17, ♀. In this form, which is found in Alaska, the veins above and below are strongly bordered with blackish, and the ground-color of the hind wings and the apex of the fore wings on the under side are distinctly bright yellow.

(*e*) Newfoundland variety **acadica** Edwards. Pl. XXXIV, fig. 19, ♀. This form is larger than the others, and in markings intermediate between *pallida* and *pseudobryoniæ*. The under side in both sexes and the upper side in the female are distinctly yellowish.

(*f*) A form, named **hulda** Edw., is shown on Pl. LXVII, figs. 24, 25.

Early Stages.—Well known, but some of the varieties need further study.

The species ranges from the Atlantic to the Pacific, and from Alaska to the northern limits of the Gulf States.

(7) **Pieris rapæ** (Linnæus). Pl. XXXV, fig. 3, ♀; Pl. II, figs. 11, 12, *larva;* Pl. V, figs. 58, 65, *chrysalis* (The Cabbage-butterfly).

Butterfly.—This common species, which is a recent importation from Europe, scarcely needs any description. It is familiar to every one. The story of its introduction and the way in which it has spread over the continent has been well told by Dr. Scudder in the second volume of "The Butterflies of New England," p. 1175. The insect reached Quebec about 1860. How it came no man knows; perhaps in a lot of cabbages imported from abroad; maybe a fertile female was brought over as a stowaway. At all events, it came. Estimates show that a single female of this species might be the progenitor in a few generations of millions. In 1863 the butterfly was already common about Quebec, and was spreading rapidly. By the year 1881 it had spread over the eastern half of the continent, the advancing line of colonization reaching from Hudson Bay to southern Texas. In 1886 it reached Denver, as in 1884 it had reached the head waters of the Missouri, and it now possesses the cabbage-fields from the Atlantic to the Pacific, to the incalculable damage of all who provide the raw material for sauer-kraut. The injury annually done by the caterpillar is estimated to amount to hundreds of thousands of dollars.

INSTINCT

Two city fathers were standing in the market-place beside a pile of cabbages. A naturalist, who was their friend, came by. As he approached, a cabbage-butterfly, fluttering about the place lit on the straw hat of one of the dignitaries. The naturalist, accosting him, said: "Friend, do you know what rests upon your head?" "No," said he. "A butterfly." "Well," said he, "that brings good luck." "Yes," replied the naturalist; "and the insect reveals to me the wonderful instinct with which nature has provided it." "How is that?" quoth the city father. "It is a cabbage-butterfly that rests upon your head."

Genus NATHALIS Boisduval

"The butterflies, gay triflers
Who in the sunlight sport."
HEINE.

Butterfly.—The butterfly is very small, yellow, margined with black. The upper radial vein in the fore wing is wanting. The subcostal has four nervules, the third and fourth rising from a common stalk emitted from the upper outer corner of the cell, the first and second from before the end of the cell. The precostal vein on the hind wing is reduced to a small swelling beyond the base. The palpi are slender; the third joint long and curved; the second joint oval; the third fine, spindle-shaped, and pointed. The antennæ are rather short, with a somewhat thick and abruptly developed club.

Early Stages.—Very little is known of these.

Three species belong to this genus, which is confined to the subtropical regions of the New World, one species only invading the region of which this volume treats.

FIG. 153.—Neuration of the genus *Nathalis*, enlarged.

(1) **Nathalis iole** Boisduval. Pl. XXXII, fig. 21, ♂; fig. 22, ♀ (The Dwarf Yellow).

Butterfly.—This little species, which cannot be mistaken, and which requires no description, as the plate conveys more information concerning it than could be given in mere words, ranges from southern Illinois and Missouri to Arizona and southern California. Its life-history has not yet been described. Expanse: 1.00–1.25 inch.

The identification of this species with *N. felicia*, Poey, which is found in Cuba, is doubtfully correct. The two species are very closely allied, but, nevertheless, distinct from each other.

Genus EUCHLOË, Hübner

(*Anthocharis* of many authors)

(The Orange-tips)

"When daffodils begin to peer,
    With, heigh! the doxy over the dale,
Why, then comes in the sweet o' the year;
    For the red blood reigns in the winter's pale."
SHAKESPEARE.

In recent years various attempts have been made to split up the species included in this group into genera and subgenera. These attempts have been founded upon differences in neuration, in genitalia, the outline of the wings, and style of markings. In the end revisionists have expressed themselves as clearly dissatisfied with their efforts. Some of the fabricators of check-lists have assigned the species *olympia* Edwards to the genus *Zegris* Rambur, founded upon the European species *eupheme* (Esper) because of certain pupal characteristics alleged by Rambur to exist, but the existence of which is now called into question, and which certainly

have not been demonstrated to occur in the American species, *olympia* Edw. I eliminate *Zegris* as a generic name from our faunal lists. The latest attempt at a division into subgenera has been made by Klots (Bull. Brooklyn Ent. Soc., Vol. XXV, 1930, pp. 80–95). It is interesting, and I partly accept his conclusions, while nevertheless feeling that his work involves unnecessary refinements.

FIG. 154.— Neuration of *Euchloë genutia.*

Butterfly.—Small; white in color; with the apical region of the fore wings either rounded or falcate; in many species, but not all, ornamented with spots of orange or crimson. On the under side the wings are more or less mottled with greenish spots or striæ.

Egg.—Spindle-shaped (see p. 4, fig. 6), laterally marked with raised vertical ridges, between which are finer cross-lines.

Caterpillar.—In its mature stage, relatively long, with the head small.

Chrysalis.—With the head relatively enormously projecting; wing-cases compressed, and uniting to form a conspicuous keel-shaped projection, the highest point of which lies at the juncture of the two ends of the silk girdle where they are attached to the supporting surface.

There are numerous species of this genus, and all are exceedingly pretty.

1. The *Ausonides*-group

(Apices of the fore wings not marked with red)

(1) **Euchloë ausonides** Boisduval. Pl. XXXII, fig. 24, ♂; fig. 25, ♀. Pl. XXXIV, fig. 3, ♂, *under side* (The Large Marble).

Butterfly.—On the under side the fore wings are greenish; the hind wings are marked with three irregular green bands, the outer one forking into six or seven branches toward the outer and inner margins. Expanse: 1.65–1.90 in.

Early Stages.—The larva and chrysalis are described by Edwards in "The Butterflies of North America," Vol. II; by Coolidge, "Entomological News," Vol. XIX, 1908, pp. 204–10; and by Comstock in his "Butterflies of California," p. 38. The caterpillar is pale whitish-green, with dark green longitudinal stripes on the side and back. It feeds on cruciferous plants.

Ausonides ranges from Arizona to Alaska, and eastward to Colorado.

A slight varietal form of this species was named **coloradensis** by Henry Edwards (synonym: *montana* Verity). It differs from specimens collected further west in being somewhat larger in size and having the dark apical black spots a trifle heavier than in the typical form. Comstock has given the names *flavidalis* and *semiflava* to two different female specimens, which on the upper side are yellowish in varying degrees.

(2) **Euchloë creusa** Doubleday and Hewitson. Pl. XXXII, fig. 23, ♂;
Pl. XXXIV, fig. 2, ♀, *under side* (The Creusa Marble).

Synonyms: *elsa* Beutenmüller; *pumilio* Strand.

Butterfly.—Similar to the preceding species, but smaller, the white more lustrous on the under side, and the green markings on the under side of the wings
heavier. Expanse: 1.20–1.40 in.

Early Stages.—We know very little of these.

The species is reported from California, Colorado, and Alberta.

(3) **Euchloë hyantis** (Edwards). Pl. LXVII, fig. 27, ♂, type (Edwards'
Marble).

Synonyms: *pseudoausonides* Verity; *orientalides* Verity.

Butterfly.—This form is closely allied to *E. creusa*, from which it is only to
be distinguished by somewhat less diffuse markings on the upper side of the
wings. It is doubtfully distinct from *E. creusa* and is merely a local race found in
Washington and British Columbia.

(4) **Euchloë lotta** Beutenmüller. Pl. LXXIII, fig. 5, ♂, paratype (The
Southern Marble).

Synonym: *belioides* Verity.

This species, or possibly varietal form of *E. creusa*, is found in southern
California and Arizona. As a rule it is distinguished from the preceding
species by the enlarged quadrangular spot at the end of the cell on the fore
wing. A large series of specimens show considerable variation and it seems
to grade into *creusa*, of which at best it is a local race. Expanse: ♂, 1.25 in.;
♀, 1.5 in.

(5) **Euchloë olympia** (Edwards). Pl. LXVII, fig. 28, ♂, type (The
Olympian Marble).

This species has by some authors been referred to the genus *Zegris* Rambur.
I do not see any good reason for separating it from *Euchloë*.

Butterfly.—♂. Upper side white, with a large gray patch at the apex of the
primaries invaded by white spots. The costal margin sprinkled with black. At
the end of the cell a black bar. The secondaries have a few black scales at the
outer angle and a small black spot on the costa toward the base. On the under
side the wings are white, mottled with patches of green scales, the secondaries being crossed by three bands of yellowish-green punctuated with small white spots
and points. Body black, clothed with gray hairs on the upper side, beneath
greenish white. Palpi whitish. Antennæ gray above, yellow below.

♀. Does not materially differ in its markings from the male. Expanse: ♂,
1.6 in.; ♀, 1.7 in.

This species ranges from the western foothills of the Appalachian Mountains
in southwestern Pennsylvania and West Virginia westward to Minnesota and
Colorado. It has also been reported from Alberta.

(6) **Euchloë rosa** (Edwards). Pl. XXXII, fig. 39, ♂, type, *under side*
(The Rosa Marble).

Butterfly.—Pure white. The transapical black band is broken in the middle, and a black bar closes the cell. The under side is well represented in the plate. Expanse: 1.35–1.40 in.

Early Stages.—Entirely unknown.

The species is found in Texas, and is allied to *E. olympia* (Edw.), but is smaller and the markings on the under side are somewhat different.

2. The *Cethura*-group

(Apices of the fore wings rounded, marked with orange or red)

(7) **Euchloë cethura** (Felder). Pl. XXXII, fig. 26, ♂; fig. 27, ♀; form **morrisoni** (Edwards). Pl. XXXIV, fig. 1, ♂. (The Cethura Orange-tip).

Synonyms: *cooperi* Behr; *angelina* Boisduval.

Butterfly.—This delicate little insect, for the identification of which the plates will abundantly serve, is regarded as having three varietal forms, one of which was named after the indefatigable collector Morrison, whose labors enriched an older generation of American entomologists. This varietal form is characterized by the heavier green markings of the under side of the wings. Expanse: 1.25–1.40 in.

A second varietal form was designated by Wright as **deserti.** It is a dwarf form, found in certain desert localities by Wright, the males having the tips of the fore wings tinted with pale orange, some of the females with the ground-color at this point white. Expanse: ♂, 1 in.; ♀, 1.25 in.

A third variety was named **caliente** by Wright from a single specimen, no doubt an aberration in which the red at the tips of the primaries is almost altogether suppressed.

(8) **Euchloë sara** (Boisduval). Pl. XXXII, fig. 28, ♂; fig. 29, ♀. (The Sara Orange-tip).

Butterfly.—The wings on the upper side in both sexes are shown in the figures above cited. On the under side the hind wings are marked with dark irregular patches of greenish-brown scales, loosely scattered over the surface, and having a "mossy appearance."

There are several forms which are regarded by recent writers as varieties and may probably be such. Of these we give the following.

(a) Variety **reakirti** (Edwards). Pl. XXXII, fig. 31, ♂; fig. 32, ♀, types (Reakirt's Orange-tip) = *flora* Wright, Pl. XXXIV, fig. 4, ♂; fig. 5, ♀. This form hardly differs at all from the form *sara*, except in being smaller, and having the margins of the hind wings marked with dark spots at the ends of the veins. It is said to be the vernal form of *sara*.

(b) Variety **stella** (Edwards). Pl. XXXII, fig. 35, ♂; fig. 36, ♀, types. (The Stella Orange-tip). The females of this form are prevalently yellowish on the upper side of the wings; otherwise they are marked exactly like the preceding variety.

(c) Variety **julia** (Edwards). Pl. XXXII, fig. 34, ♂, type; Pl. XXXIV, fig.

6, ♀, *under side*. (The Julia Orange-tip). (Synonym: *thoosa* Scudder). The only distinction in this form is the fact that the black bar dividing the red apical patch from the white on the remainder of the wing is broken, or tends to diminution at its middle.

(d) Variety **browningi** (Skinner). Pl. LXXI, fig. 14, ♂, paratype (Browning's Orange-tip).

This variety is well depicted on our plate. It was described from Utah.

Early Stages.—Unknown.

The species, in all its forms, belongs to the mountain States of the Pacific coast. *Flora* Wright was regarded by Beutenmüller, as identical with *sara*. It comes nearer the variety *reakirti* than any other form, as will be seen by an examination of the plates which give figures of the types. Expanse: 1.25–1.75 in.

(9) **Euchloë pima** (Edwards). Pl. XXXII, fig. 33, ♂, type (The Pima Orange-tip).

Butterfly.—This beautiful and well-marked species, the most brilliant of the genus, is yellow on the upper side in both sexes. The red of the upper side also appears on the lower side. The hind wings are heavily marked with solid green bands. Expanse: 1.50 in.

Early Stages.—Unknown.

The only specimens thus far known have come from Arizona, and the extreme southeastern portion of California.

3. The *Genutia*-group

Subgenus ANTHOCHARIS Boisduval

Synonym: *Falcapica* Klots

(Apices of fore wings falcate, white, or laved with red).

(10) **Euchloë genutia** (Fabricius). Pl. XXXII, fig. 37, ♂; fig. 38, ♀; Pl. II, fig. 5, *larva;* Pl. V, fig. 59, *chrysalis;* fig. 6, p. 4, *egg.* Var. **flavida** (Skinner), Pl. LXXI, fig. 15, ♂, paratype (The Falcate Orange-tip).

Synonyms: *midea* (Hübner); *lherminieri* (Godart).

Butterfly.—This species is readily recognized by the decidedly falcate tip of the fore wings. The first brood appears in early spring. It is double-brooded in the western portions of North Carolina, where I have taken it in the spring and quite abundantly late in the autumn. The variety *flavida* Skinner from Georgia has the tips of the fore wings more broadly washed with orange-red at the apex, and the marginal spots heavier. Expanse: 1.30–1.50 in.

Early Stages.—The life-history is well known. The caterpillar feeds on *Sisymbrium, Arabis, Cardamine,* and other cruciferous plants.

It ranges from New England to Texas, but is not found, so far as is known. in the regions of the Rocky Mountains and on the Pacific coast.

(11) **Euchloë lanceolata** (Boisduval). Pl. XXXII, fig. 30, ♂. (Boisduval's Marble).

Synonym: *edwardsi* (Behr).

Butterfly.—The figure gives a correct idea of the upper surface of the male. The female on the upper side is marked with light-black spots on the outer margin near the apcx. On the under side in both sexes the apex of the primaries and the entire surface of the secondaries, except a small spot on the costa, are profusely sprinkled with small brown scales. The veins of the hind wing are brown. Expanse: 1.65–1.95 in.

Early Stages.—The caterpillar, which feeds upon *Turritis*, is green, shaded on the sides with pale blue, striped laterally with white, and covered with transverse rows of minute black points, each bearing a short black bristle. A good account of the egg, caterpillar, and chrysalis is given by Comstock in his "Butterflies of California."

Genus CALLIDRYAS Boisduval

(Type *Papilio eubule* Linn.)

(The Great Sulphurs)

"A golden butterfly, upon whose wings
There must be surely character'd strange things,

. . . .

Onward it flew, . . . then high it soar'd,
And downward suddenly began to dip,
As if, athirst with so much toil, 't would sip
The crystal spout-head; so it did, with touch
Most delicate, as though afraid to smutch
Even with mealy gold the waters clear."

KEATS, Endymion.

Butterfly.—Large butterflies, brilliant lemon-yellow or orange-yellow, marked with a few darker spots and with a narrow band of brown, especially in the female sex, on the outer margin of the primaries. They are very quick and vigorous in flight, more so than is the case in any of the preceding genera.

Egg.—The eggs are spindle-shaped, flat at the base, and acutely pointed, with a few longitudinal ribs and a multitude of delicate cross-lines.

Caterpillar.—The caterpillar is relatively long, with the head small; the segments somewhat moniliform, resembling beads strung together, the surface covered with a multitude of minute papillæ ranged in transverse rows.

Chrysalis.—The chrysalis is strongly concave on the dorsal side, with the head greatly produced as a long, pointed, conical projection; the wing-cases are compressed and form a very wide, keel-shaped projection on the ventral side. This peculiar formation of the wing-cases reaches its greatest development in this genus.

The butterflies of this genus are mainly tropical. Four or five species, however, are found in the warmer parts of the United States, and one of them ranges north as far as northern New Jersey, and has been occasionally taken even in northern Illinois.

(1) **Callidryas eubule** (Linnæus). Pl. XXXIII, fig. 2, ♂; fig. 3, ♂, *under side;* Pl. II, figs. 2, 4, *larva;* Pl. V, figs. 60–62, *chrysalis* (The Cloudless Sulphur).

Synonym: *marcellina* (Cramer).

Butterfly.—The male is bright lemon-yellow on the upper side; paler below. The female is darker, in tint inclining to pale reddish yellow, with a dark mark at the end of the cell of the front wing, followed outwardly by an obscurely defined transverse bar, and with darker brown spots at the ends of the veins on the outer margin. Linnæus called the female **sennæ,** thinking it was not the same species as *eubule,* because of the difference in color and markings.

This splendid and vigorous butterfly is found from New England and Wisconsin to Patagonia, being very abundant in the tropics, where it congregates in great swarms upon moist places by the side of streams. It haunts in great numbers the orange-groves of the South, and is very fond of flowers. It is rare on the northern limits of its range, though quite common on the coast of New Jersey. Expanse: 2.50 inches. The caterpillar feeds on leguminous plants, but especially upon the different species of *Cassia.*

FIG. 155.—Neuration of the genus *Callidryas.*

(2) **Callidryas philea** (Linnæus). Plate XXXIII, Fig. 4, ♂ (The Red-barred Sulphur).

Butterfly.—This is another noble species of this fine genus, which includes some of the showiest insects of the subfamily. It may be readily recognized by the bar of deep orange crossing the cell of the primaries, and by the orange tint on the outer margin of the hind wings. Expanse: 3.00–3.50 inches.

Early Stages.—But little is as yet known of these. The larva feeds on the same kinds of plants as the larva of *C. eubule.* It occurs in Texas, and is said to have also been found in Illinois as a straggler. It is abundant in Mexico, Central America, and southward.

(3) **Callidryas agarithe** Boisduval. Pl. XXXIII, fig. 1, ♂; Pl. LXVII, fig. 19, ♀ (The Large Orange Sulphur).

Butterfly.—About the same size as *C. eubule,* but deep orange on both sides of the wings. The wings of the female are bordered somewhat heavily with brown, and are duller in color than those of the male. Expanse: 2.50–2.75 inches.

Early Stages.—The caterpillar, which resembles that of *eubule,* feeds upon various species of *Cassia.* The chrysalis is also much like that of *eubule.* We need, however, fuller information than that which we possess, drawn, for the most part, from the pages of authors who wrote in the last century.

The species occurs in the hot parts of the Gulf States, and is common throughout tropical America.

(4) **Callidryas statira** (Cramer). Pl. LXVII, fig. 22, ♂; fig. 23, ♀ (The Embossed-wing Sulphur).

Butterfly.—The male on the upper side of the wings has the outer third nearly pure white, the inner two thirds pale sulphur-yellow, the scales on the outer third being closely appressed to the surface, and the yellow tract toward the base, somewhat raised, and looser in structure. The outer area appears as if embossed. A fine black line borders the costa toward the apex, and this line extends downward for a short distance on the outer margin. The females are dimorphic. Some of them closely correspond in tint with the males, lacking the embossed appearance, which has been mentioned, and having the apical costal and outer marginal line heavier, and always with a black spot, varying in size, at the end of the cell of the fore wing. Other females tend slightly to orange yellow on their upper surface, as shown on our plate. A great many local races and varieties of this insect have been described from the Antilles, and Central and South America. The species is widely distributed in the American tropics. Expanse: ♂, 2 in.; ♀, 2.5 in.

Early Stages.—Little is as yet known of these.

Habitat.—Not uncommon in the extreme southern part of Florida.

(5) **Callidryas cipris** (Fabricius). Pl. LXXIII, fig. 30, ♂. (The Yellow Long-tailed Sulphur).

The male is well shown on our plate. The female has a large dark spot at the end of the cell of the fore wing. Expanse: 3–3.5 in.

Occasionally found in the extreme southern part of Texas; common in Mexico and Central America.

Genus GONEPTERYX Leach

Synonym: *Amynthia* Swainson

This genus includes two of the largest species of the *Pieridæ* in the New World. Only one of them is found in the fauna with which we are dealing.

(1) **Gonepteryx clorinde** (Godart). Pl. LXXI, fig. 11, ♂ (The Giant Sulphur).

Synonyms: *godarti* (Perty); *swainsonia* (Swainson).

Butterfly.—The figure on our plate will enable the student to easily recognize the species. The female is very like the male, the orange spot near the costa of the fore wing being less brilliant, and often entirely wanting in this sex. Expanse: 4–5 inches.

The species is very abundant in Mexico, but only occurs as a straggler in the extreme southwestern part of Texas.

Genus KRICOGONIA Reakirt

Butterfly.—Medium sized, bright yellow on the upper and lower sides, with some dark markings, especially in the male. The primaries in the male are generally quite strongly falcate.

Early Stages.—Nothing has, as yet, been satisfactorily ascertained in relation to these.

The genus is not large, and is confined to the tropical regions of the New World, being represented in our fauna in the vicinity of the city of Brownsville, in Texas.

(1) **Kricogonia lyside** Godart (form **terissa** Lucas). Pl. XXXIV, fig. 20, ♂; fig. 21, ♀ (Lyside).

Butterfly.—This insect, which may easily be distinguished from all its allies by its peculiar markings, is found in Florida and Texas, and is widely spread over the Antilles and tropical America. We know little of its life-history. A number of closely allied forms, reckoned as species, are known from the Antilles and Central America. They are so closely related to each other that it is believed that they are only local races. Expanse: 1.90–2.10 in.

Genus ZERENE Hübner

Synonym: *Meganostoma* Reakirt

(The Dog-face Butterflies)

"Let me smell the wild white rose,
Smell the woodbine and the may;
Mark, upon a sunny day,
Sated from their blossoms rise,
Honey-bees and butterflies."

JEAN INGELOW.

Butterfly.—Closely resembling those of the following genus *Colias*, from which they may be readily distinguished by the more acutely pointed apex of the fore wings and by the remarkable coloration of these wings in the male sex, the dark outer borders being disposed upon the lighter ground-color, so as to present the appearance of a rude outline of the head of a dog, whence these butterflies have sometimes been called the "dog-face butterflies."

Egg.—Fusiform, strongly pointed at the apex, broader at the base, the sides marked with a few delicate ridges, between which are numerous cross-lines.

Caterpillar.—Elongate, cylindrical, the head relatively small, striped on either side by a whitish lateral line, each segment having a transverse darker line. They feed upon leguminous plants.

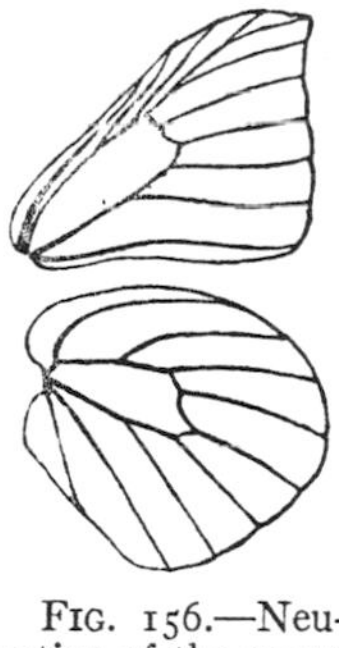

FIG. 156.—Neuration of the genus *Kricogonia.*

FIG. 157.—Neuration of the genus *Zerene.*

Chrysalis.—Pointed at the head, convex on the abdominal segments on the dorsal side, with a decided hump on the thorax. The wing-covers unite to form a moderately deep carinate, or keel-shaped, projection on the ventral side, not, however, nearly as large as in the genus *Callidryas*.

But two species of the genus are found within our fauna, one widely distributed throughout the Southern and Southwestern States, the other confined to the Pacific coast.

(1) **Zerene eurydice** (Boisduval). Pl. XXXVI, fig. 1, ♂; fig. 2, ♀ (The Californian Dog-face).

Butterfly.—The splendid purplish iridescence of the fore wings of the male is only faintly indicated in the plate. This beautiful insect is peculiar to the Pacific coast, and there is a wide difference in appearance between the sexes. Expanse: 1.80–2.00 inches.

Early Stages.—The caterpillar feeds upon *Amorpha californica*. The life-history has been accurately described, and the various stages depicted, by Edwards.

(2) **Zerene cæsonia** (Stoll). Plate XXXVI, fig. 3, ♂; fig. 4, ♀ (The Southern Dog-face).

Butterfly.—The sexes are much alike in this species, which ranges widely over the Southern States, and is found even in southern Illinois and sometimes still farther North. Expanse: 2.25 inches.

Early Stages.—These have been fully described by various authors, most carefully by Edwards.

Genus COLIAS Fabricius

Synonym: *Eurymus* Horsefield, *preoccupied*

(The Sulphurs)

"Above the arching jimson-weeds flare twos
And twos of sallow-yellow butterflies,
Like blooms of lorn primroses blowing loose,
When autumn winds arise."
JAMES WHITCOMB RILEY.

Butterfly.—Medium-sized butterflies, yellow or orange in color, with black borders upon the wings. In many species this border is heavier in the female than in the male.

Egg.—The egg is spindle-shaped, thickest at the middle, tapering at the apex and at the base, generally attached by an enlarged disk-like expansion to the point on which it is laid. The upper extremity is rounded; the sides are marked by small vertical ridges, between which are delicate cross-lines.

Caterpillar.—The caterpillars strongly resemble in appearance those of the preceding genus, from which, superficially, they cannot be distinguished by any anatomical peculiarities. They feed upon *Leguminosæ*, and especially upon clover (*Trifolium*).

Chrysalis.—The chrysalids do not generally differ in appearance from the chrysalids of the genus *Zerene*, though the wing-cases do not form as high a keel-shaped projection from the ventral side as in that genus.

This genus is very extensive, being represented throughout the temperate regions of both hemispheres, and also occurring in the cooler portions of South America, especially along the ranges of the Andes. One species is found in temperate South Africa. The brightly colored butterflies, which are sometimes found congregating in immense numbers in moist places, are familiar objects, and swarm upon the clover-fields and by the roadside in the summer months throughout the United States.

1. The *Philodice*-group

(Ground-color predominantly yellow or white)

(1) **Colias philodice** Godart. Pl. I (Frontispiece), fig. 4, ♂; fig. 5, ♀; Pl. LXVIII, fig. 13, ♂, melanic; Pl. LXXIII, fig. 29, ♀, albinic; Pl. II, fig. 10, *larva;* Pl. V, figs. 54, 55, *chrysalis* (The Common Sulphur).

FIG. 158.—Neuration of the genus *Colias.*

Butterfly.—We are all familiar with this species, the "puddle-butterfly" of our childhood, which sits in swarms in moist places by the country waysides, and makes the clover-fields gay with the flash of yellow wings in summer. There are many aberrational forms, albinos and negroes, dwarfs and giants, some of which have been given names, which clutter check-lists and catalogs, but with which I refuse to burden this page. Expanse: ♂, 1.25–1.8 in.; ♀, 1.6–2.25 in.

Early Stages.—The caterpillars feed on clover, and allied plants. The eggs when first laid are yellow, changing later to crimson. The caterpillar is slender, green, striped longitudinally with paler green. The chrysalis is pale green.

Habitat.—The species ranges from Canada to Florida and westward to the Rocky Mountains.

(2) **Colias occidentalis** Scudder. Pl. LXVIII, fig. 16, ♂; fig. 17, ♀, types (The Western Sulphur).

Butterfly.—The male is like the male of The Common Sulphur, but lacks the black spot at the end of the cell of the fore wing, and the fringes of the wings are pink; the female is different in appearance being without the heavy black borders, which are always found in *philodice*. All that remains of these borders in the Western Sulphur is a trace of grayish scaling at the outer ends of the veins on the fore wing. Expanse: ♂, 1.6–1.75 in.; ♀, 2.–2.25 in.

Early Stages.—As yet little is known of these.

Habitat.—The western provinces of Canada as far as British Columbia.

(3) **Colias chrysomelas** Henry Edwards. Pl. XXXV, fig. 12, ♂; fig. 13, ♀. (The Gold-and-black Sulphur).

Butterfly.—Larger than *C. philodice.* The male on the upper side is bright lemon-yellow, with broad black margins on both wings. The female is paler, with the black margin of the hind wing lacking or very faintly indicated, and the margin of the fore wing broken up by yellow spots. On the under side the wings of the male are dusky-orange, pale yellow on the disk of the primaries; the wings of the female on this side are pale yellow. Expanse: ♂, 2.00–2.10 in.; ♀, 2.25–2.30 in.

Early Stages.—Undescribed.

Habitat.—Ranging from northwestern Utah to the coastal ranges of California at considerable elevation.

(4) **Colias barbara** Henry Edwards. Pl. LXVIII, fig. 18, ♂; fig. 19, ♀, types (The Barbara Sulphur).

Butterfly.—This is a comparatively small species, which has been by some treated as a varietal form of *C. harfordi*, the species which follows in this list. The fore wing of the male is more rounded at the apex than in *C. harfordi*, and the black border is not as solid as in the latter species. The females of *C. barbara* and of *C. harfordi* closely resemble each other. Expanse: ♂, 1.5 in.; ♀, 1.75 in.

Early Stages.—Little is known of these.

Habitat.—Central California.

(5) **Colias harfordi** Henry Edwards. Pl. LXVIII, fig. 20, ♂; fig. 21, ♀, types (Harford's Sulphur).

Butterfly.—Very closely allied to the preceding species, as our figures of the types reveal. There is, however, a visible distinction between the two insects, the fore wing in *harfordi* being more acute at the apex, and its outer border being solidly black, especially near the costa. Expanse: ♂, 1.5 in.; ♀, 1.5 in.

Early Stages.—Described by Edwards and by Comstock.

Habitat.—The mountains of southern California.

(6) **Colias interior** Scudder. Pl. XXXV, fig. 10, ♂; fig. 11, ♀ (The Pink-edged Sulphur).

Butterfly.—The male superficially resembles *C. philodice*, but the fringes of the wings are rose-colored. The female is pale yellow above, more frequently white, with the tips of the fore wings lightly marked with blackish. On the under side the fore wings at the apex and the entire surface of the hind wings are rusty orange-yellow. The discal spot on the undersides of the hind wings is silvery, bordered with rosy-red. Expanse: ♂, 1.30–1.75 in.; ♀, 1.60–2.00 in.

Early Stages.—Little is as yet known of these.

The species was first found by Professor Louis Agassiz on the north shore of Lake Superior. It ranges through a rather narrow belt of country from Nova Scotia, through Maine, the Adirondacks, Quebec, Ontario, and westward to the Rocky Mountains north of the Valley of the St. Lawrence and the Great Lakes.

(7) **Colias alexandra** Edwards. Pl. XXXV, fig. 6, ♂; fig. 7, ♀, types (The Alexandra Sulphur).

Butterfly.—A relatively large species, the male somewhat like *C. chrysomelas*, but with much narrower outer black borders. The female is pale yellow or white, without black borders, or, at most, faint traces of them at the apex of the primaries. On the under side the wings are silvery-gray, yellow only at the base and on the inner margin of the primaries. The discal spot on the hind wings is white. Expanse: ♂, 1.85 inch; ♀, 2.10–2.30 inches.

Early Stages.—The caterpillar is uniformly yellowish-green, with a white band on each side, broken with orange-red dashes running through it. The chrysalis, which resembles that of *C. philodice* in form, is yellowish-green, darkest on the dorsal side, and adorned with three small red dots on the ventral side of the abdomen near the wing-cases. The caterpillar eats *Astragalus*, *Thermopsis*, and white clover. Expanse: ♂, 1.90–2.15 inches; ♀, 2.00–2.30 inches.

The species is found in Colorado and the mountain regions to the north and west of that State.

(8) **Colias edwardsi** Edwards. Pl. LXVIII, fig. 24, ♂; fig. 25, ♀, types (Henry Edwards' Sulphur).

Butterfly.—This species, named by W. H. Edwards in honor of his friend Henry Edwards, is closely allied to *C. alexandra*, but is decidedly smaller; the black border of the fore wing in the male is narrower and indented between the ends of the nervules, and the ground-color is laved with orange and not pure citron-yellow, as in *C. alexandra*. Expanse: ♂, 1.75 in.; ♀, 1.75 in.

Early Stages.—Little is known of these.

Habitat.—The species ranges from Nevada and Utah northward to British Columbia and Alberta.

(9) **Colias emilia** Edwards. Pl. LXVIII, fig. 22, ♂; fig. 23, ♀, types (The Emilia Sulphur).

Butterfly.—Somewhat smaller than *C. alexandra*, the dark outer border on the fore wing of the male narrower than in that species, and between the inner nerve and the first median nervule sending inwardly a quadrate, not sharply toothed, projection as in *C. alexandra*. The female is almost devoid of any dark outer border on the wings, there being only a faint trace of dark scales near the outer border of the primaries. The spot at the end of the cell of the hind wings, which does not appear upon the upper side in *C. alexandra* is conspicuous, and bright orange in *C. emklia*. Expanse: ♂, 1.65 in.; ♀, 2.1 in.

(10) **Colias scudderi** Reakirt. Pl. XXXV, fig. 8, ♂; fig. 9, ♀ (Scudder's Sulphur).

Butterfly.—The male on the upper side is colored like *C. philodice*, but the black borders are much wider. The fringes are rosy. The female is generally white—very rarely slightly yellow—with very pale dark borders, or often without any trace of black on the outer margin of the wings. On the under side the apex of the fore wings and the entire surface of the hind wings are greenish-gray. The discal spot of the secondaries is well silvered and margined with pale red. Expanse: 1.80–2.00 inches.

Early Stages.—We know but little of these, except that the caterpillar feeds on the leaves of the huckleberry and the willow.

Scudder's Sulphur is found in Colorado, Utah, Montana, and British Columbia.

(11) **Colias pelidne** Boisduval. Pl. XXXV, fig. 14, ♂; var. **labradorensis** Scudder, Pl. XXXVI, fig. 15, ♂; fig. 16, ♀ (The Labrador Sulphur).

Butterfly.—The male on the upper side is pale yellow, with a greenish tinge on the hind wings; the black borders are narrow; the fringes are pink. The female on the upper side is white, with very little or no black on the outer borders, the black marking being confined to the apex of the fore wings. On the under side the wings are much as in *C. interior*, and it is possible that the two forms are varieties of one and the same species. Expanse: 1.60–1.85 inch.

Early Stages.—Little is known of these.

Pelidne is rather abundant in Labrador at the proper season, and ranges thence westward and northward in boreal America.

The variety *labradorensis* can hardly be separated from *pelidne*, except that the female has no trace of black on the outer borders.

(12) **Colias skinneri** Barnes. Pl. LXVII, fig. 20, ♂; fig. 21, ♀, types (Skinner's Sulphur).

Butterfly.—Not distantly related to *C. pelidne*, but differing in the female sex by having the margins of the fore wings somewhat broadly margined with black. Expanse: ♂ and ♀ about 1.5 in.

Early Stages.—Entirely unknown.

Habitat.—Ranging from Wyoming northward through Idaho and Montana to Alberta.

(13) **Colias chippewa** Kirby. Pl. LXVIII, fig. 30, ♂; fig. 31, ♀ (The Chippewa Sulphur).

Butterfly.—Closely related to the preceding species, but with the black outer border of the fore wings much broader; and in the female situated on the upper margin of the secondaries and not at the middle of the margin as in the preceding species. Expanse: ♂, 1.3 in.; ♀, 1.5 in.

Early Stages.—Not studied.

Habitat.—Ranges from Labrador to Alaska.

(14) **Colias palæno** (Linnæus). Pl. LXVIII, fig. 28, ♂; fig. 29, ♀, from Lapland (The Palæno Sulphur).

Butterfly.—This species has long stood in various lists of the diurnal lepidoptera of North America, but I have never seen a specimen of undoubted American origin, which in my judgment could be correctly referred to this species. I give on the plate two European specimens as a guide to students, who may perhaps come across the species. Expanse: 1.75 in.

Early Stages.—Never studied in America.

Habitat.—Lapland, northern Siberia; alleged to occur in Labrador and Alaska.

2. The *Eurytheme*-group

(Ground-color predominantly orange)

(15) **Colias christina** Edwards. Pl. LXVIII, fig. 14, ♂; fig. 15, ♀, types (The Christina Sulphur).

Butterfly.—The male, as shown on the plate, is yellow at the base of the wings, the outer half being deep orange-red; the black outer borders in outline not unlike those of *C. occidentalis* Scudder. The female is without dark borders on the wings, very pale yellow, and some specimens almost pure white. Expanse: ♂, 1.9 in.; ♀, 2 in.

Early Stages.—Unstudied.

Habitat.—The region of Great Slave Lake, and westward. It has been reported as occurring on the mountains of Montana.

(16) **Colias astræa** Edwards. Pl. LXVIII, fig. 26, ♂; fig. 27, ♀, types (The Astræa Sulphur).

Butterfly.—In the male the ground-color is pale citron-yellow slightly laved on the disks of both wings with pale orange; the outer dark border of the fore wings in this sex is much narrower than in *C. christina*, and broken at the tips of the veins by outwardly running lines of the ground-color. The discal spot on the hind wing is pale orange. The female is nearly white, with a few fuscous scales near the apex of the fore wing. The discal spot at the end of the cell of the fore wing is prominent, but on the hind wing this spot does not appear upon the upper side. Expanse: ♂, 1.5 in.; ♀ 2 in.

Early Stages.—Unknown.

Habitat.—Wyoming and Montana.

(17) **Colias eurytheme** Boisduval. Pl. XLVIII, fig. 18, ♀, *albino;* Pl. XXXIII, fig. 5, ♂, *under side;* Pl. II, fig. 1, *larva;* Pl. V, fig. 53, *chrysalis* (The Eurytheme Sulphur).

Butterfly.—This species is strongly polymorphic. Normally the males and females are deep orange, or orange-red on the upper side of the wings, and yellow below, but albinism is common, especially in the female sex, and there are many seasonal and climatic forms, a number of which have received specific names in the past. We cite some of the more important of these, omitting a number of very slight variations with which the lists have been recently cluttered.

(a) Winter form **ariadne** Edwards, Pl. XXXVI, fig. 7, ♂; fig. 8, ♀. This form, emerging from chrysalids which have overwintered, is like the type in having the fore wings tinged with orange. Expanse: 1.75 in.

(b) Winter form **keewaydin** Edwards, Pl. XXXVI, fig. 9, ♂; fig. 10, ♀. This is a larger form, more deeply flushed with orange. Expanse: 1.85 in.

(c) Summer form **eriphyle** Edwards, Pl. XXXV, fig. 15, ♂; Pl. XLIII, fig. 3, ♂, *under side.* = *hageni* Edwards. This summer form differs from typical *C. eurytheme* in being yellow and not laved with orange. Expanse: 2.00 in.

Early Stages.—The caterpillar feeds on clover, as do most of the species of the genus.

The range of *eurytheme* is very wide. It extends from the Atlantic to the Pacific, and from Canada to the far South, though rare in the lower parts of Florida and Texas in the hot lands.

(18) **Colias meadi** Edwards. Pl. XXXVI, fig. 5, ♂; fig. 6, ♀, types (Mead's Sulphur).

Butterfly.—The wings on the upper side are orange, greenish on the under side. The discal spot on the lower side is centered with green. Expanse: 1.75 in.

Genus Colias

Early Stages.—The life-history has been written by Edwards, and may be found in the pages of the "Canadian Entomologist," Vol. XXI, p. 41. The larva feeds on clover.

The species is alpine in its habits, and is found in Colorado from nine to twelve thousand feet above sea-level.

(19) **Colias elis** Strecker. Pl. XXXVI, fig. 13, ♂; fig. 14, ♀, types (Strecker's Sulphur).

Butterfly.—This species is discriminated from the preceding principally by the narrower black margins on the wings of the male and the more abundant yellow maculation of the borders in the female. Expanse: 1.55–1.90 in.

Early Stages.—Closely resembling those of the preceding species, of which it may be a varietal form.

The habitat of the species is on the lofty peaks of the Rocky Mountains.

(20) **Colias hecla** Lefevre. Pl. LXXIII, fig. 22, ♂; fig. 23, ♀; fig. 24, ♂, *under side;* var. **pal ida** Skinner, Pl. LXXV, fig. 4, ♀, type (The Hecla Sulphur).

Butterfly.—Ground-color of fore wings rather deep orange-red with moderately wide black marginal borders in the male; in the female the borders are much wider and broken by lighter spots as shown in the figures we give upon the plates. On the under side the hind wings are more or less heavily clouded with dark green scaling, in some specimens almost blackish green. The spot at the end of the cell of the hind wings yellowish or orange-red, standing forth conspicuously. The variety **pallida** Skinner from Greenland is a lighter form, the ground-color of the upper side of the fore wings being more yellowish and not as deeply orange as in the typical form. *C. glacialis* McLachlan and *C. hela* Strecker are aberrant forms of *hecla* Lefevre, only discriminated by a slight difference in the ground-color. Expanse: ♂, 1.5 in.; ♀, 1.75 in.

Early Stages.—Nothing as yet is known of these.

Habitat.—This species has a wide distribution and locally varies. The typical form is found north of Hudson Bay ranging through the islands and peninsulas west of the waters which separate these regions from Greenland. *Pallida* is the form which occurs in Greenland. It is closely related to certain palearctic forms which occur in northern Siberia.

(21) **Colias boothi** Curtis. Pl. LXVI, fig. 30, ♂, type; Pl. LXXIII, fig. 26, ♀; fig. 27, ♀, *under side* (Booth's Sulphur).

Butterfly.—Originally described from Boothia Felix, this species ranges from Southampton Island north of Hudson's Bay through Baffinland to Boothia Felix, from which it was originally described. It is somewhat pale orange-yellow on the upper surface with light yellow submarginal spots succeeded in the male by a narrow outward marginal line on both wings. The base of the fore wing and the inner half of the hind wings are clouded with dark scales. In the female the outer margins are broadly blackish with the light submarginal markings more distinct and accentuated by the deeper color which surrounds them. On the under side the wings are more or less heavily covered with dark green scaling.

(22) **Colias chione** Curtis. Pl. LXVIII, fig. 33, ♂, type (The Chione Sulphur).

Butterfly.—This is regarded by many authors as a varietal form of *C. boothi*, from which it is distinguished principally by the absence of the dark outer marginal borders upon the upper surface of the wings and the generally lighter color of the wings on this side. There is only a faint trace of the pale yellow submarginal spots which are characteristic of typical *boothi*. On the under side the two forms *boothi* and *chione* closely resemble each other. *Chione* originally described from Boothia Felix is not uncommon in Baffinland and is quite common on Southampton Island. Expanse: 1.5–1.65 in.

3. The *Nastes*-group

(Ground-color predominantly greenish)

(23) **Colias nastes** Boisduval. Pl. XXXVI, fig. 11, ♂; fig. 12, ♀; Var. **rossi** Guenée, Pl. LXVIII, fig. 32, ♂; var. **moina** Strecker, Pl. LXXIII, fig. 28, ♀, *under side.*

Butterfly.—Recognized in both sexes by the pale greenish tint of the wings and a tendency of the outer border of the fore wings in both sexes to become divided by a band of pale spots. This is a very variable species. It ranges from Labrador northward and westward. The typical form from Labrador is well represented on our Pl. XXXVI, figs. 11, 12. There are many slight intergradations between this form and the form *rossi* Guenée, a male specimen of which is figured on our plate as above cited.

At this point it may not be improper to call attention to the suggestion which recently has been made to me by Dr. Avinoff, that *Colias boothi* and *Colias chione* may in reality be hybrids between *Colias hecla* and *Colias nastes*. In a long series, which we possess of these forms, intergradations seem to occur suggesting that *nastes* and *hecla* may interbreed. In fact the study of long series suggests that *boothi* and *chione* are very nearly related to *hecla* on one hand and to *nastes* on the other. However, nothing short of breeding experiments, which would be hard to carry on in the Arctic regions, can satisfactorily solve this problem.

(24) **Colias behri** Edwards. Pl. XXXVI, fig. 17, ♂, type (Behr's Sulphur).

Butterfly.—This little species may be easily recognized by the dark-greenish tint of the upper side of the wings and the light spot on the upper side of the hind wings. The female has the outer borders dusky like the male, the dusky shade running inward on the lines of the veins and nervules. Expanse: 1.50 in.

Early Stages.—We know little of these.

The insect has hitherto been taken only at considerable elevations among the Western Sierras, and the peaks and lofty meadows about the Yosemite Valley have been until recently the classic locality for the species.

Genus EUREMA Hübner

Synonym: *Terias* Swainson

(The Small Sulphurs)

"Hurt no living thing:
Ladybird, nor butterfly,
Nor moth with dusty wing,
Nor cricket chirping cheerily,
Nor grasshopper so light of leap,
Nor dancing gnat, nor beetle fat,
Nor harmless worms that creep."
CHRISTINA ROSSETTI.

Butterfly.—Small, bright orange or yellow, margined with black. The species are more delicate in structure and have thinner wings than most of the insects belonging to the *Pieridæ.* The outer margin of the wings is generally straight or slightly rounded, though in a few species the apex is somewhat pointed. The outer margin of the hind wings is generally rounded, though in a few species it is acuminate.

FIG. 159.—Neuration of the genus *Eurema.*

Egg.—Strongly spindle-shaped, pointed and rounded at the base and at the apex, much swollen at the middle, its sides marked by numerous broad but slightly raised vertical ridges.

Caterpillar.—Small, relatively long, cylindrical, with the head quite small, the thoracic segments somewhat larger than the others, giving the anterior portion of the body a slightly humped appearance. They feed upon leguminous plants.

Chrysalis.—Compressed laterally, with the head pointed and the wing-cases forming a deep, keel-shaped projection on the ventral side, more pronounced than in any other genus, except *Catopsilia.*

There are an immense number of species belonging to this genus scattered through the tropical and subtropical regions of both hemispheres. Many of the species are dimorphic or polymorphic, and much confusion has arisen, especially in relation to the Oriental species, on account of the great tendency to the production of seasonal varieties, many of which are strikingly different from one another.

(1) **Eurema longicauda** (Bates). Pl. XXXVII, fig. 1, ♂. (Bates' Eurema).

Butterfly.—This species is easily recognized by the orange-yellow tint of the upper side of the wings and the sharply pointed hind wings. Expanse, 1.80 inch.

Early Stages.—We know nothing of these.

The species is found in Texas, Arizona, Mexico, and Cuba.

(2) **Eurema gundlachia** (Poey). Pl. LXXIII, fig. 25, ♂. (Gundlach's Sulphur).

This species is distinguished from the preceding by the fact that the black costal margin of the primaries runs solidly from the base to the apex. In the outline of the wings it closely resembles *longicauda*, but the color is more brilliant and deeper orange-red.

Early Stages.—We know nothing of these.

The species is found in Texas, Arizona, Mexico, and Cuba.

(3) **Eurema proterpia** (Fabricius). Pl. XXXVII, fig. 2, ♂ (Proterpia).

Butterfly.—Even deeper orange than the preceding species. The hind wings are, however, less pointed; the veins and nervules are black at their ends, and the costal margin of the fore wings is evenly bordered with black, which does not run down on the outer margin as in *T. gundlachia*. Expanse: 1.50–1.75 inch.

Early Stages.—Unknown.

Proterpia is found in Texas, Arizona, and Mexico.

(4) **Eurema nicippe** (Cramer). Plate XXXVII, fig. 3, ♂; fig. 4, ♀; fig. 5 var. **flava**, ♂; fig. 6, ♀, *under side;* Plate II, fig. 6, *larva;* Plate V, figs. 51, 52, *chrysalis* (The Nicippe Sulphur).

Butterfly.—The plate gives so full a presentation of this common species as to make a lengthy description unnecessary. It is subject to considerable variation. I have specimens of many varying shades of orange and yellow, and a few albino females. The orange form depicted in Plate XXXVII, figs. 3 and 4, is typical. The form *flava* is not uncommon. Expanse: 1.50–2.00 inches.

Early Stages.—These are not as well known as they should be in view of the excessive abundance of the insect in long-settled parts of the country. The caterpillar feeds upon *Cassia* in preference to all other plants, but will eat other *Leguminosæ*.

Nicippe is very rare in New England, but is common south of latitude 40° as far as the Rocky Mountains, and ranges over Cuba, Mexico, and Guatemala, into Venezuela and even Brazil. It fairly swarms at times in the Carolinas, Tennessee, Kentucky, and southern Indiana and Illinois. I have encountered clouds of it on the wing near Jeffersonville, Indiana, and thence north along the lines of the Pennsylvania Railroad as far as Seymour. It is not common in western Pennsylvania, but in former years was taken rather frequently about Pittsburgh.

(5) **Eurema mexicana** (Boisduval). Pl. XXXVII, fig. 7, ♂; fig. 8, ♀, *under side* (The Mexican Yellow).

Butterfly.—Easily distinguished from all other species in our fauna by the pointed hind wings, margined on the outer border with black, and by the heavy black border of the fore wings, deeply excised inwardly, recalling the fore wing of the species of the genus *Meganostoma*. Expanse: ♂, 1.75 inch; ♀, 1.85 inch.

Early Stages.—We do not, as yet, know much about these.

E. mexicana is very common in Arizona, and occurs also in Texas. It is abundant in Mexico.

(6) **Eurema damaris** (Felder). Pl. XXXVII, fig. 9, ♂; fig. 10, ♂, *under side* (The Damaris Yellow).

Butterfly.—Allied to the preceding species, but readily distinguished from it by the less deeply excised outer border of the fore wing, by the fact that the black outer margin of the secondaries extends inwardly beyond the angulated point of the wing, and by the different color and style of the markings of the lower side. Expanse: 1.35–1.65 inch.

Early Stages.—Unknown.

Damaris occurs in Arizona, and thence ranges south into Venezuela.

(7) **Eurema westwoodi** (Boisduval). Pl. XXXVII, fig. 11, ♂ (Westwood's Yellow).

Butterfly.—Pale yellow or orange-yellow, with a narrow black border on the fore wings, beginning on the costa beyond the middle, and not quite reaching the inner angle. On the under side the wings are pale yellow, immaculate, or at the apex of the fore wing and the outer angle of the hind wing broadly marked with very pale reddish-brown. Expanse: 1.75–2.00 inches.

Early Stages.—Unknown.

Westwood's Yellow occurs in Texas and Arizona, but is not common. It is abundant farther south.

(8) **Eurema lisa** (Boisduval and Leconte). Pl. XXXVII, fig. 13, ♂; Pl. II, fig. 3, *larva;* Pl. V, fig. 56, *chrysalis* (The Little Sulphur).

Butterfly.—Allied to the three following species, from which it may at once be distinguished by the absence of the black bar on the inner margin of the fore wings and by the profusely mottled surface of the under side of the hind wings. It is subject to considerable variation, albino females and melanic males being sometimes found, as well as dwarfed specimens of very small size. Expanse: 1.25–1.60 inch.

Early Stages.—These have not been thoroughly studied and described, in spite of the fact that the insect is very common in many easily accessible localities. The caterpillar feeds on *Cassia* and on clover.

E. lisa ranges from New England south and west as far as the foothills of the Rocky Mountains, and into Mexico and Honduras. It is found in the Antilles and Bermuda. An interesting account of the appearance of a vast swarm of these butterflies in the Bermudas is given by Jones in "Psyche," vol. i, p. 121:

"Early in the morning of the first day of October last year (1874), several persons living on the north side of the main island perceived, as they thought, a cloud coming over from the northwest, which drew nearer and nearer to the shore, on reaching which it divided into two parts, one of which went eastward, and the other westward, gradually falling upon the land. They were not long in ascertaining that what they had taken for a cloud was an immense concourse of small yellow butterflies (*Terias lisa* Boisduval), which flitted about all the open grassy patches and cultivated grounds in a lazy manner, as if fatigued after their long voyage over the deep. Fishermen out near the reefs, some few miles to the north of the island, very early that morning, stated that numbers of these insects fell upon their boats, literally covering them. They did not stay long upon the islands, however, only a few days, but during that time thousands must have fallen victims to the vigorous appetite of the bluebird (*Sialia sialis*, Baird) and blackbird (*Mimus carolinensis*, Gray), which were continually preying upon them."

As the nearest point of land is Cape Hatteras, about six hundred miles distant, it is seen that, weak and feeble as this little creature appears, it must possess, when aided by favoring winds, great power of sustained flight.

(9) **Eurema elathea** (Cramer). Pl. XXXVII, fig. 12, ♂ (The Elathea Sulphur).

Butterfly.—Distinguished from its near ally, *T. delia*, by the fact that the ground-color of the hind wings is white. The female in this, as in the allied species, is without the black bar on the inner margin of the primaries. Expanse: 1.25–1.40 inch.

Early Stages.—Unknown.

Elathea is found in Florida, Mexico, and the Antilles.

(10) **Eurema delia** (Cramer). Pl. XXXVII, fig. 14, ♂ (Delia).

Butterfly.—Almost exactly like the preceding species, but having the upper side of the hind wings yellow. On the under side the fore wing at the tip and the entire hind wing are red. Expanse: 1.25–1.50 inch.

Early Stages.—But little is known of them. The caterpillar feeds on *Cassia*.

Delia occurs commonly in the Gulf States.

(11) **Eurema jucunda** (Boisduval and Leconte). Pl. XXXVII, fig. 15, ♂; fig. 16, ♂, *under side* (The Fairy Yellow).

Butterfly.—Distinguished from the preceding species by the dark marginal band surrounding the hind wing and the pale under surface. Expanse: 1.60–1.75 inch.

Early Stages.—Unknown.

This little species is found in the Gulf States.

AN ASTRONOMER'S IDEA OF AN ENTOMOLOGIST.
(This was my place-card at a dinner given by Dr. John A. Brashear in 1896, to a party of scientific friends).

THE FIRST PICTURE OF AN AMERICAN BUTTERFLY*

On Plate LXXVII we give a photographic reproduction of the very first draw-ing of an American butterfly made by the hands of man. It fortunately still exists in the library of the British Museum in Bloomsbury, London. To the Trustees of that library I am indebted through the kind intervention of my friend, Captain N. D. Riley, of the Natural History Museum in South Kensington, for the privi-lege of being able to reproduce it.

While the picture itself possesses great interest, the inscriptions on the right side of the plate are even more interesting. These have never before been pub-lished. The lower inscription is as follows:

Hanc ê Virginia Americana Candidus ad me Pictor detulit, 1587.

Literally translated it is, "Candidus, the Painter, brought this to me from Ameri-can Virginia, 1587." The demonstrative pronoun "hanc" being feminine, the ellipsis must be that of a feminine noun. This might be "rem" = *thing*, or "pic-turam" = *picture*. If the writer had used the masculine "hunc," it might mean "papilionem" = *butterfly*; if he had used the neuter "hoc" it might mean "speci-men." The use of the feminine, taken in conjunction with the use of the word "*Pictor*," leaves no doubt that the writer of the inscription meant to designate the very *picture*, or identical *thing*, upon which he was writing, as having been brought to him from "American Virginia" in 1587.

The word "Candidus," given as the name of the donor, is good Latin for *White*. The inscription thus rendered reads: "White, the painter, brought this picture to me from American Virginia, 1587." Thereby hangs a tale.

The inscription recalls the story of the first attempt made by Englishmen to establish a colony in the New World.

Sir Walter Raleigh, having received from Queen Elizabeth a patent for colonization, sent out Philip Amidas and Arthur Barlowe in 1584 to seek a suit-able place at which to locate a colony. They soon returned with a glowing ac-count of what is now the coast of North Carolina. At that time the whole Atlantic coast of North America north of Florida was called Virginia in honor of "The Virgin Queen." In fact, some of the early writers speak of "the continent Vir-ginia." On June 9, 1585, one hundred and eight colonists under Ralph Lane sailed from Plymouth in seven small vessels. The commander of the fleet was Sir Richard Grenville. The colony was landed at the north end of Roanoke Island on August 17. A week later Grenville sailed on his return to England. In the follow-ing year, on June 19, the colony, half starved and in fear of their lives from hostile Indians, sailed for England in the fleet of Sir Francis Drake, which had appeared at Roanoke. Only a few days after these first colonists had set sail on their return Sir Richard Grenville again arrived at the spot with provisions and more colon-

*Reprinted from *The Scientific Monthly*, Vol. XXIX, pp. 45–48.

ists. Only fifteen of those whom Grenville brought out on this second expedition consented to remain. Grenville again returned to England. Raleigh resolved to send a third body of colonists. John Fiske in his "Old Virginia and Her Neighbors," relating the story of this adventure, says: "John White, a man deft with water-colours, who had been the artist of Lane's expedition, was their governor." With White went his daughter and her husband, Ananias Dare, who helped in the care of the party. They arrived at Roanoke Island on July 22, 1587, and were forced to remain there, for the sailors refused to go to the Chesapeake, whither they had intended to remove the colony. Not a trace of the fifteen colonists who had been left the year before could be found. On August 18 White's daughter Eleanor, Mrs. Dare, presented her husband with a baby daughter, the first child of English parentage born in the New World. On August 20 the child was baptized Virginia Dare. White not long after returned to England for supplies for the colony, but when he came back the next year the company of over one hundred persons whom he had left behind had vanished, and all that could be discovered was the word "CROATAN" carved on a tree. From this it was inferred that they had gone away with Indians of that name, among whom in later years were found people of apparently mixed blood, bearing English names, who were thought to be descendants of the "lost colony."

Among those "lost" in the piney woods about Hatteras were White's daughter, Eleanor, her husband, Ananias, and their baby daughter, Virginia Dare. It must have been with a heavy heart that White, bereft of daughter and grandchild, again set sail to return to England.

There seems to be no doubt that the picture was painted by John White, the commander of Sir Walter Raleigh's third expedition to "Virginia" in the year 1587. It represents (in impressionistic style) the male Tiger Swallowtail, one of the common butterflies of the Carolinas, *Papilio turnus* Linn., the dimorphic female of which is *Papilio glaucus* Linn.

But there is another inscription on the original drawing in a different hand from that which we have been considering, and written with different ink. It is "*Mamank anois*." What does it mean? I think it is the Indian name of the insect.* We can fancy White, "deft in the use of water-colors," receiving the butterfly from the hands of an Indian lad, seating himself with a scrap of paper, rapidly painting the picture and interrogating the boy for its name, which White scribbled upon the margin of his sketch.

But now another question arises. Who was the man who wrote the words: "*Hanc è Virginia Americana Candidus ad me Pictor detulit, 1587*"? Who was "me"?

A wood-cut of the original painting first appeared in that curious and now very rare old book: "Insectorum sive Minimorum Animalium Theatrum." The

---

*Since the writing of the above, Mr. M. W. Sterling, chief of the American Bureau of Ethnology, has kindly called my attention to the fact that in the Vocabulary contained in Strachey's "Historie of Travaile into Virginia Britannia, etc., 2," the expression "manaanggwas" is given as the Indian equivalent of the word *butterfly*. My suspicion is thus confirmed.

authorship of this book is exceedingly composite and a long time elapsed between its inception and its final publication. The subtitle of the book is as follows:

Olim ab
EDOARDO WOTTONO.
CONRADO GESNERO.
THOMAQUE PENNIO.
inchoatum:
Tandem
THO. MOVFETI *Londinati opera sumptibusq.*
maximis concinnatum,
auctum, perfectum;
Et ad vivum expressis Iconibus supra
quingentis illustratum.*

Below this comes the famous picture of the beehive, the trade-mark of the printer, Thomas Cotes, familiar to all Shakespearean students, for Thomas Cotes about this time was printing the second folio of Shakespeare, which has on its title-page the same beehive shown on the title-page of the work of which we are speaking, but not surrounded, as in the "Insectorum Theatrum," by figures of bugs, butterflies, spiders and millipedes. At the foot of the title-page are the words:

Londini ex Officina typographica
Thom. Cotes.
Et venales extant apud
Benjamin Allen
in diverticulo, quod Anglice dicitur,
Popes-head Alley,
1634.†

Sir Edward Wotton stood high in the English diplomatic service. In 1586 he was sent to France to explain to Henri IV the intrigues of Mary, Queen of Scots, against Queen Elizabeth; and afterwards in 1610 he was ambassador extraordinary to France. He held many offices and died in 1626. He was deeply interested in entomology. Conrad Gesner died in December, 1565. He was for his day a great naturalist and the author of some of the earliest writings on natural history published in western Europe. He was a close friend of Dr. Thomas Penny. Penny was with Gesner on the continent when he died, and after his death helped to arrange Gesner's collections.

Penny was a physician of great repute and so was his friend Thomas Moffett, Mouffet or Muffet. Both had graduated at Cambridge; both had studied medicine on the continent; both were court physicians; both were botanists and entomologists. They collaborated for years. The interesting old book, concerning which I am

---

**Translation:* Begun long ago by Edward Wotton, Conrad Gesner and Thomas Penny; finally prepared, enlarged and perfected by the labor and very great expense of Thomas Moufet, born in London, and illustrated by over five hundred figures drawn to life.

†*Translation:* From the printing office in London of Thom. Cotes, for sale by Benjamin Allen in the lane which in English is called Popes Head Alley, 1634.

writing, was begun by Penny and Gesner working together in Germany. Sir Edward Wotton lent a helping hand. When Dr. Penny died his friend and colleague, Moffett, took up the unfinished work, which he arranged and completed. In 1590 he dedicated it by royal permission to Queen Elizabeth and received official sanction to print it at The Hague. But delays followed. When James I of England came to the throne in 1603, Dr. Moffett changed the dedication to the king. At Moffett's death in 1604 the manuscript with its illustrations, pasted in where they were to appear, came into the hands of Darnell, Moffett's apothecary. Darnell sold the manuscript to Sir Theodore Turquat de Mayerne, Baron Albone, court physician in the time of Charles I. Baron Albone published the book at his own expense in 1634, dedicating it to Sir William Paddy, and in his dedication speaks of Moffett as "an eminent ornament of the Society of Physicians, a man of the more polite and solid learning, and renowned in most branches of science."

This in brief is the story of the book in which our picture first appeared on page 98, as a wood-cut, faithfully reproducing the original drawing. But who was the man who received the drawing from John White, and recorded the fact on its margin? It can not have been Gesner. He had died, as already stated, in 1565. I doubt that Dr. Moffett wrote the inscription upon the original drawing, for the handwriting is distinctly different from that of the body of the manuscript written by Moffett's pen. This leaves only two others of the joint authors to be considered. Dr. Penny died in 1589. Sir Edward Wotton stood high at the English court. He was the friend of Sir Francis Drake and of Sir Walter Raleigh. He was very likely to have been brought into contact with John White, when the latter returned to report to Raleigh what he had done. I am not able to decide the question, but I am strongly inclined to think that the author of the inscription was Sir Edward Wotton, who gave it to Dr. Moffett, who pasted it into the manuscript where it to-day remains. Some student of chirography delving among the old papers in the British Museum may be able to settle the question. The original manuscript is preserved in the British Museum in the Sloane Collection (No. 4014). It carries both the dedication to Queen Elizabeth and to James I.

What is clear is that the first picture of an American butterfly was painted by John White, the leader of Sir Walter Raleigh's third expedition to Roanoke, in the year 1587, less than one hundred years after Columbus had made his first landfall in the New World, twenty years before Captain John Smith and his associates reached Virginia and thirty-three years before the Pilgrim Fathers disembarked at Plymouth. The artist was the grandfather of the first white child of English parentage born on the continent of North America, Virginia Dare.

FAMILY VI

PAPILIONIDÆ (THE PARNASSIANS AND SWALLOWTAILS)

Butterfly.—From medium-sized to large, or very large; often (except in the Parnassians) with the hind wings adorned with tail-like projections. One of the structural features of the group is the absence of the internal vein on the hind wings, the submedian vein taking the place of the internal, and functioning for both veins.

Larva.—The larvæ back of the head have osmateria, or organs, which emit an offensive odor; and which are instinctively protruded when they are disturbed or alarmed.

The family is subdivided into two subfamilies: the *Parnassiinæ*, in which pupation takes place upon the ground, among loosely scattered leaves, which are interwoven with a few strands of silk, forming a loose cocoon-like structure; and the *Papilioninæ*, the chrysalids of which are formed in sheltered places attached at the anal extremity by a button of silk, and supported around the middle by a girdle of silk, in which respect they are like the *Pieridæ*.

SUBFAMILY PARNASSIINÆ (THE PARNASSIANS)

"Some to the sun their insect wings unfold,
Waft on the breeze, or sink in clouds of gold;
Transparent forms, too fine for mortal sight,
Their fluid bodies half dissolv'd in light."

POPE

Genus PARNASSIUS Latreille

Butterfly.—Of medium size, with more or less diaphanous wings, generally white or yellow in color, marked with black spots and round pink or yellow spots margined with black. The head is relatively small, thickly clothed with hairs. The antennæ are short and straight, having a gradually thickened club. The palpi are very thin, straight, and clothed with long hairs. The forewings are generally translucent on the margin, with a rounded apex. The upper radial is lacking. The subcostal is five-branched, the third, fourth, and fifth nervules being emitted from a common stalk which springs from the upper outer angle of the cell. The first subcostal nervule rises well before the end of the cell; the second from the same point from which the stalk which bears the other three nervules springs. The cell of the hind wing is evenly rounded at its outer extremity. The inner margin of the hind wing is more or less excavated.

308

Early Stages.—The egg is turban-shaped, flattened, profusely covered with small elevations, giving it a shagreened appearance. The caterpillars have very small heads. They are flattened, having a somewhat leech-like appearance; they are black or dark brown in color, marked with numerous light spots. The chrysalis is short, rounded at the head, and pupation takes place on the surface of the ground, among leaves and litter, a few loose threads of silk being spun about the spot in which transformation occurs.

A remarkable phenomenon in this genus is the fact that in all its known species, with the alleged exception of *P. simo* (an oriental species) there is at the time of copulation a structure formed attached to the abdomen of the female, which is known as the "pouch." It never is found in the case of virgin females. It is produced by the secretion of a waxy substance emitted by the male, and effectually precludes the repetition of impregnation by another male. This curious appendage was first described by J. C. Schäffer of Regensburg in 1754. Much

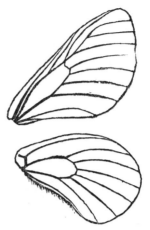

Fig. 160.—Neuration of the genus *Parnassius*.

has been written about it since his day. It occurs in some other genera of the *Parnassiinæ*. Some writers have used it as a character having value in showing the relationship of species, inasmuch as it presents a measure of uniformity in certain groups, while in others it differs.

The genus *Parnassius* has been a favorite with collectors, especially in Europe. As there is much individual variability, a multitude of so-called varieties and aberrations have been described and named. In the case of the well-known European species, *P. apollo* Linnæus, the number of such named varieties has risen in recent years to an astonishing extent. The situation reminds of nothing more than the celebrated "Tulip-craze," which once took possession of Holland. This form of nomenclatorial insanity has thus far not deeply infected lepidopterists on this side of the Atlantic, though there are symptoms of the disorder in some quarters. It is unreasonable to burden the literature of science by describing as "new species" or "new varieties" butterflies which happen to have a few more red scales at a point where others have fewer, or a couple of black scales, where usually there are none. The only persons who profit by such capers are the "dealers," who are in the habit of exacting huge prices for "rarities," from those who are so foolish as to buy them. In one case, which has come under my observation, it has been discovered that a "rarity" put upon the market had been artificially produced by the use of India ink!

(1) **Parnassius delius** Esper, var. **golovinus** Holland. Pl. LXIX, fig. 3, ♂, *upper side;* fig. 4, ♂, *under side;* fig. 5, ♀, *upper side;* fig. 6, ♀, *under side.* (The Golovin Parnassius.)

The form which I figure, which is not distantly related to the variety *corybas* Fischer de Waldheim occurring on the Asiatic mainland, is sufficiently distinct to deserve a subspecific name. The types from Golovin Bay are figured upon the plate. It is less robust than the following variety, on the upper side of the fore wing lacking the large dark discal spot, which in *apricatus* is always prominent between the lower vein and the first median nervule.

(2) **Parnassius delius** var. **apricatus** Stichel. Pl. LXXVI, fig. 19, ♂, type (The Kodiak Parnassius).

This form, originally in error described as a variety of *P. smintheus*, is a more robust insect than var. *golovinus*, and has a largish black spot on the fore wing below the first median nervule, somewhat beyond its origin. Our figure is a reproduction of the type of this insect, which was taken on Kodiak Island.

(3) **Parnassius clodius** Ménétries. Pl. XXXIX, fig. 9, ♂, fig. 10, ♀. Var. **baldur** Edwards, Pl. XXXIX, fig. 7, ♂, fig. 8, ♀. Var. **claudianus** Stichel, Pl. LXIX, fig. 7, ♂, fig. 8, ♀. Var. **menetriesi** Henry Edwards, Pl. LXIX, fig. 9, ♂, fig. 10, ♀. Ab. **immaculata** Skinner, Pl. LXXV, fig. 3, ♂. Ab. **altaurus** Dyar, Pl. LXIX, fig. 11, ♂.

Superficially this species may be distinguished from others by the more broadly translucent outer margins of the fore wings in the male sex. Many subspecies and varieties have been named and described. The more important of these are given upon our plates.

The metropolis of *P. clodius* seems to be British Columbia, and its varieties occur here and there, north and south, east and west, wherever they turn up.

The typical form has an expanse of wing as follows: ♂, 2.5–2.75 in.; ♀, 2.5–3.0 in.

The larva feeds upon *Sedum* and *Saxifraga*, as do other species of the genus.

(4) **Parnassius smintheus** Doubleday and Hewitson. Pl. XXXIX, fig. 3, ♂, fig. 4, ♀; var. **behri** Edwards, fig. 1, ♂, fig. 2, ♀; var. **hermodur** Henry Edwards, Pl. XXXIX, fig. 5, ♂, fig. 6, ♀; var. **nanus** Neumœgen, Pl. LXIX, fig. 15, ♂; var. **minusculus** Bryk, Pl. LXIX, fig. 14, ♂; var. **sayi** Edwards, Pl. LXIX, fig. 12, ♂, fig. 13, ♀.

This species was the first of the genus to be described from North America, and the type was a rather diminutive specimen from Canada. *P. smintheus* may always be distinguished by the opaque white fore wings of the male, which have a very narrow translucent outer border (often none); the relatively narrow translucent border of the fore wings of the female; and the fact that invariably in both sexes the veins have minute dark triangles at their tips. The species varies greatly in size.

The insect called *P. magnus* Wright is simply a large specimen from Montana, scores of which I have seen. The variety *sayi* Edwards is the common form on the mountains of Colorado. *P. nanus* is a dwarf from the high altitudes, and represents under-feeding and extreme cold. Most of the varietal names given to specimens of this species, and there are a score of them, are purely nomenclatorial rubbish. I do not dignify them by giving them place on these pages. Any lively boy, collecting on a ten-acre lot in Montana, when *P. smintheus* is on the wing, can turn up almost all of the so-called subspecies and "forms," which now burden our lists, and no doubt many others, which the microscopic eyes of dealers in insects would be glad to "put upon the market."

(5) **Parnassius eversmanni** Ménétries. Pl. LXIX, fig. 1, ♂; fig. 2, ♀ (Eversmann's Parnassius).

Synonym: *thor* Henry Edwards, ♀.

Many specimens of this species have passed through my hands, coming principally from the valley of the Kuskokwim River, though I have had them from numerous other points in western Alaska. They do not differ materially from typical specimens of the same species coming from eastern and northeastern Siberia. The female of the species was named *thor* by Wm. H. Edwards. It differs in color from the male, as our plate shows, the male being yellowish, the female being prevalently whitish in the ground-color. Expanse: 2–2.25 in.

(6) **Parnassius nomion** Fisher de Waldheim.

This large and very conspicuous species was attributed to the fauna of Alaska by Boisduval. It occurs in northeastern Siberia, but since Boisduval's day no specimen of this species has been captured on American soil.

(7) **Parnassius nominulus** Staudinger.

This species or variety, as you please, was originally described from eastern Siberia. Dr. William Barnes kindly has informed me that it was included in his last published Check-list on the strength of a specimen, which had been compared with the type by Bang-Haas, to which specimen Herman Strecker had affixed the label "Alaska." Collectors, as well as other good men, sometimes make mistakes. At all events nobody since the days of Strecker has found this insect in Alaska, and its occurrence there needs verification.

SUBFAMILY PAPILIONINÆ (THE SWALLOWTAILS)

"The butterfly the ancient Grecians made
The soul's fair emblem, and its only name—
But of the soul, escaped the slavish trade
Of mortal life! For in this earthly frame
Ours is the reptile's lot—much toil, much blame,—
Manifold motions making little speed,
And to deform and kill the things whereon we feed."
COLERIDGE.

The general characteristics of this subfamily have already been pointed out (See p.308).

Genus PAPILIO Linnæus

Butterfly.—Generally large, frequently with the hind wings tailed. A figure of the neuration characteristic of this genus is given on p. 16, Fig. 38. From this it may be seen that the internal vein of the hind wing is lacking, the submedian vein occupying the space which is commonly occupied by the internal vein. The median vein of the fore wing is connected with the submedian by a short vein, from the point of union of which with the submedian there proceeds a short internal vein in this wing. There is great diversity of form in the wings of this genus, some species even mimicking the species of the *Danainæ* and *Heliconiinæ* very closely, and being entirely without tails. In all cases, however, in spite of obvious diversities in color and in form, there is substantial anatomical agreement in the structure of the wings; and the caterpillars and chrysalids reveal very strongly marked affinities throughout the whole vast assemblage of about five hundred distinct species, and numerous named varieties.

Early Stages.—The eggs are somewhat globular, flattened at the base, and smooth. The caterpillars are cylindrical, smooth, fleshy, thicker in the anterior portion of the body than in the posterior portion, and are always provided with osmateria, or protrusive scent-organs, which, when the larva is alarmed, are thrust forth, and emit a musky odor, evidently intended to deter other creatures from attacking them. The chrysalids are always attached by a button of silk at the anal extremity, and held in place by a girdle of silk about the middle. The chrysalids are, however, never closely appressed to the surface upon which pupation takes place.

There are about thirty species found within the limits of boreal America. Our fauna is therefore much richer in these butterflies than that of Europe, in which but three species of *Papilio* are known. The genus is wonderfully developed in the tropics both of the New and the Old World, and has always been a favorite with collectors, containing many of the largest as well as the handsomest insects of the order.

Polydamus-group

(1) **Papilio polydamus** Linnæus. Pl. XLI, fig. 4, ♂ (The Polydamas Butterfly.)

Allied in color and general style of maculation, as well as in its larval form and habits, to *P. philenor*, but without having tailed hind wings. The caterpillar feeds upon *Aristolochia*. The insect occurs in Florida and Texas, and has a broad range southward through the Antilles and the tropical regions of Central and South America. Expanse: 3–3.5 in.

(2) **Papilio philenor** Linnæus. Pl. XLII, fig. 2, ♂; Pl. II, figs. 13, 20, 21, *larva;* Pl. VI, figs. 14, 17, 20, *chrysalis* (The Pipe-vine Swallowtail).

Butterfly.—The figures on the plates obviate the necessity for describing this familiar but beautiful insect, the glossy blue-green of which flashes all summer long in the sunlight about the verandas over which the *Aristolochia* spreads the shade of its great cordate leaves. Expanse: 3.75–4.25 in.

Early Stages.—The caterpillar feeds upon the leaves of *Aristolochia sipho* (the Dutchman's-pipe) and *Aristolochia serpentaria*, which abound in the forest lands of the Appalachian region.

Philenor is always abundant during the summer months in the Middle Atlantic States, and ranges from Massachusetts to Arizona, into southern California and southward into Mexico. It is double-brooded in western Pennsylvania.

and the writer has found females ovipositing as late as October. The caterpillars are familiar objects about houses on which the *Aristolochia* is grown as an ornamental vine.

An insignificant variety, in which the pale spots on the upper sides of the wings tend to become partly or wholly obsolete, was named var. **obsoleta** by Ehrman. In the process of evolution a form has been developed on the Pacific Coast, in which the scales of the thorax and abdomen have become lengthened, giving to these parts a shaggy or woolly appearance. To this variety Dr. Henry Skinner gave the name **hirsuta**. A figure of his type specimen is shown on Pl. LXXV, fig. 5. A very striking aberration, in which the light marginal lunules are extended inwardly and fuse with the submarginal spots, so that both wings are bordered by light quadrate marginal markings, has been named var. **wasmuthi** Weeks, after the gentleman who happened to collect the specimen.

(3) **Papilio acauda** Oberthür. Pl. LXXVI, fig. 18 (The Acauda Swallowtail).

Synonyms: *nezahualcoyotl* Strecker; *corbis* (Salv. & Godm.; *orsua* Salv. & Godm.

This appears to be a dwarfed form of *P. philenor*, in which the tail is greatly abbreviated. It has been captured in Arizona, and turns up not infrequently in Mexico.

(4) **Papilio devilliersi** Godart. Pl. LXX, fig. 1, ♂, *under side* (De Villiers' Swallowtail).

The lower sides of the wings of this species are most characteristic, and are shown on the plate. On the upper side it rather closely resembles *P. philenor*. It is common in Cuba, but also occurs sparingly in Florida. The Academy of Natural Sciences in Philadelphia has a couple of specimens, which were captured in southern Florida.

Machaon-Group

The butterflies of this large group, judging from their present range of distribution, undoubtedly had their origin in the New World. In this respect they are like the horse and the camel. During the long geologic period in which North America was connected with the Eurasian continent by the "land-bridge," which at that time spanned the area today covered by Behring's Sea, migrations of animals took place both eastward and westward. From the originally migrant forms various subspecies were in the lapse of time evolved under varying conditions of environment. The most western form of this group, which is found as far west as Great Britain, was named *Papilio machaon* by Linnæus, and, though it is the type of the genus, is a distant straggler from the ancestral home of the group to which it belongs. On the continent of Asia there are found a number of species or subspecies of the *Machaon*-Group, which, the nearer we approach Alaska, become more like the Alaskan form; and going eastward and southward from Alaska on the American continent, we find many divergent forms, ranging as far east as Newfoundland and as far south as northern South America. A comprehensive study of the various forms tends to show that the evolutionary process is still going on.

(5) **Papilio aliaska** Scudder. Pl. XLI, fig. 1, ♂ type (The Alaskan Swallowtail).

Synonyms: *joannisi* Verity; *orientis* Verity (not *aliaska* Verity, which is *kamtchadalus* Alpheraky).

This species, one of the "types" of which, determined by Scudder, is shown upon the plate, has a very wide range in subarctic America. The specimen on our plate was taken at Rupert's House on Hudson Bay. I have another "type" from Scudder's original material labelled as from "Alaska," which exactly agrees with Verity's figure of *joannisi*. The Carnegie Museum has a specimen taken on the Peninsula of Labrador, on the eastern shore of Hudson Bay, which is the same. Besides these we have long series of specimens from all parts of Alaska, which are unmistakably the same thing. These specimens have been carefully compared with specimens from northeastern Siberia, labelled *orientis* by Verity, and they are indistinguishable from the latter. In the long suite of specimens which we have critically examined, the only difference is an almost inappreciable variation in the width of the black outer margin of the fore wings, which is only individual, and reveals itself both in American and Asiatic specimens. The insect, as our figure shows, resembles *P. machaon* of Europe, but with the yellow areas of the wings not as wide as in the latter.

(6) **Papilio polyxenes** Fabricius, var. **asterius** Cramer. Pl. XL., fig. 1, ♂; Pl. II, figs. 17, 24, 27, *larvæ;* Pl. VI, figs. 13, 18, 19, *chrysalis* (The Common American Swallowtail).

Synonyms: *asterias* Fabr. and others; *ajax* Clerck (1763) and Barnes & Benjamin (1927).

The name *polyxenes* was originally given by Fabricius to the Antillean race which does not have the yellow spots of the wings as well developed as in the continental form, *asterius*. Otherwise there is no marked difference.

Butterfly.—A normal male of this commonest of all American Swallowtails is shown on our plate. The larva feeds on domesticated umbelliferous plants, such as carrots, parsnips, fennel, parsley, and the numerous species of wild *Umbelliferæ* (*Daucus*, etc.) which grow in all parts of America.

The species is very variable, and a number of so-called varietal forms have been described in recent years. A notable aberration, the type of the female of which is shown upon Pl. XLI, fig. 6, is *P. calverleyi* Grote. Another form is **P. curvifascia** Skinner, a male paratype of which is shown on Pl. LXX, fig. 12; it was originally described from Rincon, New Mexico. The female of this form was figured by Strecker and erroneously named *P. asterioides* Reakirt. Another mutation is **P. ampliata** Ménétries, originally described from Mexico, in which the yellow discal and submarginal spots of the fore and hind wings tend to disappear, or are only faintly developed. This form is found not only in Mexico, but often in the north. In the var. *alunata* Skinner and Aaron the marginal spots of the hind wing are obsolescent. In var. *ehrmanni* Ehrman the submarginal spots of the fore wing are lost. Var. *semialba* Ehrman has the yellow spots a trifle more whitish than in the general run of specimens.

(7) **Papilio americus** Kollar. Pl. LXX, fig. 8, ♂ (Kollar's Swallowtail). Synonym: *sadalus* Lucas.

This species is reported as having been taken in Arizona, and the specimen I figure from the Edwards Collection is labelled as from "Arizona, Wheeler Expedition." Barnes and McDunnough have figured a female (Cont. Nat. Hist. Lep. N. A., Vol. III, No. 2, 1916 p. 53, pl. IV, fig. 1) which emerged from a chrysalis found in Arizona. This may be the female of this species, but differs from Central American specimens in the great breadth of the yellow discal band of the hind wings. The insect is not common in collections made on our side of the Mexican border-line.

(8) **Papilio brevicauda** Saunders. Pl. XL, fig. 5, ♀ (The Newfoundland Swallowtail).

Butterfly.—There are two varieties of this species: one with bright-yellow spots; one with the spots more or less deeply marked with orange-yellow on the upper sides of the wing. The latter variety is represented on the plate. The form with the yellow spots is common on the island of Anticosti and elsewhere, the other occurs quite abundantly in Newfoundland. Expanse: 2.75–3.00 in.

Early Stages.—Both the caterpillar and the chrysalis show a very strong likeness to those of *P. asterius.* The larva feeds on umbelliferous plants.

The range of the species is confined to the northeastern part of our faunal territory.

(9) **Papilio bairdi** Edwards. Pl. XL, fig. 2, ♂, type (Baird's Swallowtail).

Butterfly.—This insect, the male of which is represented on the plate, in general is characterized by being larger than *P. asterius,* and having the postmedian band of yellow spots broader. The female is prevalently darker and larger than that sex in *P. asterius.* Expanse: 3.25–3.50 in.

Early Stages.—Not unlike those of *P. asterius.* The caterpillar feeds upon *Umbelliferæ.*

The metropolis of this species is Arizona, whence it ranges northward and eastward.

(10) **Papilio brucei** Edwards. Pl. XL, fig. 4, ♂, type (Bruce's Swallowtail).

Butterfly.—This species is found in Colorado. The bands of the wings are broader than in *P. bairdi* and narrower than in *P. oregonia.* It was named in honor of Mr. David Bruce of Lockport, New York, in his day an ardent collector in the field. Expanse: 3.25–3.60 in.

Early Stages.—These have been fully described by Edwards. They are much like those of *P. asterius,* and it feeds on the same food-plants.

Bruce's Swallowtail is commonly found in Colorado on the mountains and is also reported from California.

(11) **Papilio hollandi** Edwards. Pl. XL, fig. 3, ♂, type (Holland's Butterfly).

Butterfly.—This species has the yellow spots on the upper side of the wings intermediate in breadth between those of *P. bairdi* and *P. zelicaon*. It is characterized by the fact that the abdomen is always laterally striped with yellow, or is wholly yellow. Expanse: 3.25–3.50 in.

Early Stages.—We as yet know nothing of these.

(12) **Papilio oregonia** Edwards. Pl. LXX, fig. 5, ♂, paratype (The Oregon Swallowtail).

Synonym: *hippocrates* var. *oregonia* Edw.

This species was originally described by W. H. Edwards as a variety of *P. hippocrates*, an Asiatic species, which it somewhat closely resembles, but from which it is quite distinct. As may be seen from the plate, it is characterized by the great breadth of the yellow discal transverse bands. In the female the inner margin of the hind wings is blacker than in the male, but otherwise there is superficially very little difference between the sexes. The specimen figured on our plate is one of those collected by H. K. Morrison near Olympia in Washington Territory in 1879. The insect is not far removed in many respects from *P. machaon* of Europe. Expanse: ♂, 3.5–4 in.; ♀, 4–4.15 in.

The species ranges from the southern parts of British Columbia through Oregon and as far east as western Colorado.

(13) **Papilio zelicaon** Lucas. Pl. XXXVIII, fig. 1, ♂ (The Zelicaon Swallowtail).

Synonym: *zolicaon* Boisduval.

Butterfly.—Somewhat nearly related to the preceding, but at once distinguished from it by the broader black borders of the wings, the deeper black on the upper side, and the longer tails of the secondaries. The figure given on the plate is only two-thirds of the natural size.

Early Stages.—These have been fully described by Edwards and others, and are shown to be much like those of *P. asterius*. The caterpillar feeds upon the *Umbelliferæ*.

Zelicaon ranges southward from Vancouver Island to Arizona, and eastward to Colorado. It is more abundant in the valleys and foothills than on the sierras.

A form in which the light bands of the wings are not yellow, but inclined to orange, as in the form of *Papilio turnus* named *australis* (q. v.), was named **P. coloro** by Wright. It occurs in California. A number of minor variations of no special significance have had varietal names given them.

(14) **Papilio nitra** Edwards. Pl. XLI, fig. 2, ♂, type (The Nitra Swallowtail).

Butterfly.—This insect, which has never thus far been taken in large numbers, occurs in Montana and to the north. Its life-history is as yet undescribed.

(15) **Papilio indra** Reakirt. Pl. XLI, fig. 3, ♀ (The Indra Swallowtail).

Butterfly.—Easily distinguished by the short tails of the secondaries and the narrow bands of yellow spots closely resembling those on the wings of the male of *P. asterius*. The early stages are still unknown. It occurs on the higher sierras of eastern California and on the mountains of Nevada and Colorado.

(16) **Papilio pergamus** Henry Edwards. Pl. LXX, fig. 9, ♂, type (The Pergamus Swallowtail).

This species may be described as a long-tailed *P. indra*, the latter species having the hind wing with only a short tip, while *pergamus* has a longer tail. The early stages are unknown. It occurs not uncommonly in southern California and the adjacent states. The specimen shown on our plate has the yellow band on the hind wing straight, and not crossing the end of the cell. Many specimens have this band extending across the outer end of the cell; others have the lower end of the band above the tail broken into spots. There is no use in giving names to such trifling mutations.

Thoas-Group

This is a large group of butterflies, nearly related to each other in form and color, which are found in the Antilles and tropical America. Only four species of the group occur within our faunal limits. One of these, *P. thoas*, in one or more of its varietal forms, is occasional in the subtropical parts of Florida and Texas; the second, *P. ornythion*, is a straggler into Texas; the third *P. cresphontes*, has an extensive range, but is commoner in the Southern than in the Northern States; the fourth, *P. ponceanus* Schaus is restricted to Florida.

(17) **Papilio thoas** Linnæus, var. **autocles** Rothschild and Jordan. Pl. XLII, fig. 4, ♂ (The Thoas Butterfly).

Since the first edition of this book appeared my learned friends, Lord Rothschild and Dr. Karl Jordan, have brought out in the "Novitates Zoologicæ," Vol. XIII, pp. 411-752, their great monographic work upon the American Papilios. In this they have applied the above subspecific name to the insect figured upon the plate. They claim that the form is restricted to Brazil, but it occurs as far north as Texas, as shown by specimens coming from that state.

The caterpillar feeds upon *Ptelea*, *Xanthoxylon*, and the various species of the genus *Citrus*, which have been introduced into America. The early stages have not yet been completely described.

(18) **Papilio ornythion** Boisduval. Pl. LXXI, fig. 8, ♂ (The Ornythion Swallowtail).

The figure given will enable the student to identify this species. It is very common in Mexico in the region between Laredo and Monterey, and occurs as a straggler in our territory on the southeastern borders of Mexico.

(19) **Papilio cresphontes** Cramer. Pl. XLII, fig. 3, ♂; Pl. II, fig. 16, *larva*; Pl. VI, figs. 8-10, *chrysalis* (The Giant Swallowtail).

In *P. thoas* and its many subspecies the transverse discal band runs from near the apex of the fore wing, where it is broken into spots, directly across the inner half of the hind wing to the inner margin, gradually widening inwardly. In *P. cresphontes* this band, which on the fore wing is narrower and more or less broken into separate spots, runs to the inner margin of the fore wing, and is not continued directly to the inner margin of the hind wing, but is continued as a broad band which turns inwardly almost at right angles to the axis of the abdomen. Between this band of light yellow on the costal margin of the hind wing and the series of large yellow submarginal spots there is left a large dark triangular spot at the lower angle of which are found the lunules of the anal angle. The differences between *P. thoas* and *P. cresphontes* in the disposition of the markings are well shown on Pl. XLII.

The larva feeds upon *Ptelea*, *Xanthoxylon*, and *Citrus*. In Florida the orchardists call the caterpillar the "Orange puppy." It has a wide range northward as far as Ontario. The plate shows a small male. I have female specimens six inches in expanse of wing.

(20) **Papilio ponceanus** Schaus. Pl. LXX, fig. 10, ♂.

This represents in Florida the species known as *P. aristodemus* Esper, which is found in Cuba and Haiti. The last mentioned species has the yellow bands in the upper side of the wings composed of large yellow spots arranged somewhat as in *P. cresphontes*; in *P. ponceanus* the spots are much reduced in size and whitish. The underside of *P. aristodemus* is prevalently yellow with narrow bands, the submedian band of the hind wing being composed of light green metallic lunules. In *P. ponceanus* the bands on both wings are much broader and darker, and the series of metallic lunules on the hind wing are followed inwardly by a broad band of rich dark maroon. The insect occurs about Miami, Florida. It is a valid species.

Turnus-Group

This group contains half a score of species and subspecies, of which some are among the most lovely butterflies in our fauna. The first American butterfly drawn by the hands of man was one of the species of this group. (See p. 304.) They are characterized by having the ground-color some shade of yellow or yellowish white, banded with black, and are often called "Tiger Swallowtails."

(21) **Papilio turnus** Linnæus. Pl. XLIII, fig. 1, ♂; fig. 2, dimorphic ♀, **glaucus** Linnæus, *under side;* Pl. II, figs. 15, 26, 28, *larva;* Pl. VI, figs. 1-4, *chrysalis*. Var. **canadensis** R. & J., Pl. LXX, fig. 6, ♂; fig. 7, ♀ (The Tiger Swallowtail.)

Synonyms: *ajax* Linnæus (in part); *autilochus* Linnæus; *alcidamas* Cramer.

Linnæus gave the name *glaucus* to the dimorphic female of *turnus*, thinking he was dealing with a different species. Writers have generally elected to call the insect *P. turnus*, and to restrict the name *glaucus* to the dimorphic female.

Butterfly.—The "Lordly Turnus" is one of the most beautiful insects of the Carolinian fauna. The species is dimorphic in the female sex only in the southern portions of its range. In Canada and northward and westward in northern latitudes the dark dimorphic female does not occur. Expanse: ♂, 3.00–4.00 in.; ♀, 3.50–5.00 in.

A small dwarfed form of this species, which is found from Newfoundland to British Columbia ranging as far north as the region of Great Slave Lake, has been called var. *canadensis* R. & J. Such dwarfs also are common in the early spring in Pennsylvania and West Virginia. They reflect the effects of wintry cold upon the chrysalids. They must not be confounded with the arctic variety of the next species. Pl. LXX, fig. 6, shows a male of the variety *canadensis* from Longue Lac near Nipigon in Ontario, and fig. 7, a female from Great Slave Lake, much farther north.

A variety which occasionally turns up in the Southern States was named var. **australis** by Maynard. It is shown on Pl. LXX, fig. 4. The ground-color is not clear yellow, but ochreous.

(22) **Papilio rutulus** Lucas. Pl. XLV, fig. 1, ♂; var. **arizonensis** Edwards, Pl. LXX, fig. 2, ♂ type; var. **arcticus** Skinner, Pl. LXXV, fig. 6, ♂, type, *under side;* Pl. LXX, fig. 3, ♀, *upper side.*

Butterfly.—This insect closely resembles the preceding species in color and markings, but the female is never dimorphic as in *P. turnus,* and the marginal spots on the under side of the fore wings run together, forming a continuous band, as in *eurymedon,* and are not separate as in *P. turnus.* By these marks it may always be distinguished. Expanse: ♂, 3.50–4.00 in.; ♀, 3.75–4.25 in.

Early Stages.—These have been described with accuracy by W. H. Edwards in the second volume of his great work. The caterpillar differs from that of *P. turnus* in many minute particulars. It feeds on alder and willow. It is the representative on the Pacific coast of its Eastern congener, the common Tiger Swallowtail.

In Alaska it is represented by a small dwarfed form named *arcticus* by Skinner, which is shown on our plates, and which should not be confounded with the small variety of *turnus,* called *canadensis.*

There is a variety now and then found in the arid lands of southeastern California, in which the bright yellow is replaced by ochreous yellow, as in the variety *australis* of *P. turnus.* This form is known as var. *ammoni* Behrens. The variety *arizonensis* Edwards is found in Arizona and northern Mexico, and may be distinguished by the shorter and slightly incurved tails and other minor differences.

(23) **Papilio daunus** Boisduval. Pl. XXXVIII, fig. 2, ♂ (The Daunus Swallowtail).

Synonym: *multicaudata* Peale (*ined.*); Barnes and Benjamin (*errore*).

Butterfly.—This magnificent species, which is even larger than *turnus* (the figures in the plate are greatly reduced), resembles the preceding species in color and markings, but may at once be distinguished by the two tails on the hind wing and the projection of the lobe at the anal angle of this wing. It is found among the eastern valleys of the Rocky Mountain ranges, and descends into Mexico, where it is very common, and flies all the year round. In Arizona it is quite common. Expanse: 4.00–5.25 in.

Early Stages.—The mature caterpillar and the chrysalis have been well described by Comstock in his "Butterflies of California," p. 23. The caterpillar feeds upon cherry, ash, willow, and different *Rosaceæ.*

(24) **Papilio pilumnus** Boisduval. Pl. XXXVIII, fig. 3, ♂ (The Pilumnus Swallowtail).

Butterfly.—Resembles the preceding species, but is smaller, and has the bands and black margins of the wings decidedly broader, and the lobe of the anal angle of the hind wing so much lengthened as to give the wing the appearance of being furnished with three tails. Expanse: 3.8–4.3 inches.

Early Stages.—These are only known thus far by the account given by Schaus in "Papilio," Vol. IV, p. 100. Dr. Schaus says that "the larva feeds on laurel." The insect ranges from Arizona, where it is not very common, through Mexico to Guatemala.

(25) **Papilio eurymedon** Boisduval. Pl. XLIV. Fig. 5, ♂ (The Pale Swallowtail).

Butterfly.—This beautiful insect in the style of the markings recalls *P. turnus*, but the ground-color is always pale whitish-yellow or white, the tails of the hind wings are slenderer and the white marginal spots on the under side of the fore wings are fused together, forming a continuous band. There are other differences, but these, with the help of the plate, will suffice for the ready identification of the species. Expanse: 3.50–4.00 inches.

Early Stages.—The caterpillar resembles that of *P. turnus*, but may be distinguished by its paler color and the much smaller spots composing the longitudinal series on the back and sides, and by the different color of the head. It feeds upon a variety of plants, and is especially partial to *Rhamnus californica*.

The species ranges from northern Mexico to British Columbia, and eastward as far as Colorado. It is very abundant in the valleys of the Coast Range, and I have found it very common in the cañon of the Fraser River, in British Columbia, in the month of June.

A small aberrant form is *P. albanus* Felder, which has the fore wing more pointed, the ground-color paler, and the black bands wider. It is figured by Comstock, "Butterflies of California," Pl. 1, fig. 2. It occurs on the high sierras of California. A melanic aberration, wholly black on the upper side was named var. *cocklei* by Gunder. It is figured by Comstock *l. c.*, Pl. 1, fig. 1.

Troilus-Group

This is a small group including but two species: *Papilio troilus* Linnæus and *Papilio palamedes* Drury, both of which occur in our fauna.

(26) **Papilio troilus** Linnæus, Pl. XLI, fig. 5, ♂; Pl. II, figs. 18, 19, 22, *larva;* Pl. VI, figs. 5-7, *chrysalis* (The Spice-bush Swallowtail).

Synonyms: *ilioneus* Smith and Abbot; *texanus* Ehrman.

Butterfly.—The upper side of the male is accurately depicted in the plate. The female has less bluish-green on the upper side of the hind wings. Expanse: 3.75–4.25 in.

Early Stages.—The caterpillar lives upon the leaves of the common spice-bush and sassafras, and draws the edges of a leaf together, thus forming a nest in which it lies hidden.

The insect is found throughout the Atlantic States and in the Mississippi

Valley. The southern form, depicted by Smith and Abbot as *ilioneus*, does not differ from the main race except in having the submarginal spots of both wings larger. It was redescribed as *P. texanus* by Ehrman.

(27) **Papilio palamedes** Drury. Pl. XLII, fig. 1, ♀ (The Palamedes Swallowtail).

Synonyms: *chalcas* Fabricius, *et al.*; *chalcus* Fabr.; *flavo-maculatus* Gœze.

Butterfly.—The upper side of the wings is accurately depicted on the plate. On the under side the predominant tint is bright yellow. Expanse: 3.50–4.25 in.

Early Stages.—These are described by Scudder in the third volume of his work "The Butterflies of New England." The food-plant is *Magnolia* and the *Lauraceæ*.

The insect ranges from southern Virginia to Key West, to southern Missouri and Texas, thence south into Mexico, where aberrant forms have developed.

Ajax-Group

(28) **Papilio ajax** Linnæus. Pl. II, fig. 14, *larva;* figs. 11, 12, *chrysalis*. Pl. XLIV, fig. 1, form **carolinianus** George Edwards, described, in 3rd Edit. of Catesby (1771) = *marcellus* Cramer (1777) ♂; fig. 2, form **floridensis** Holland, ♂; fig. 3, the insect figured by George Edwards in his "Natural History of Uncommon Birds," Pl. 34 (1743) and cited by Linnæus = var. *lecontei* Rothschild & Jordan; fig. 4, var. **walshi** W. H. Edwards (The Papaw Butterfly).

This species is polymorphic. There are several forms of the spring brood, emerging from chrysalids which have over-wintered. The commonest of these is the var. *carolinianus* Geo. Edwards = *marcellus* Cramer. The spring form in Florida is very dark and is shown on Pl. XLIV, fig. 2. Another form larger than those just mentioned was figured by George Edwards in his "Natural History of Uncommon Birds," Pl. 34, which figure is cited by Linnæus in his original description, and may be therefore accepted as typical. To this form (misidentified by Boisduval and Leconte as *marcellus* Cram.) Messrs. Rothschild and Jordan gave the name *lecontei*, which I think falls as a synonym for *ajax*.

There has been a great deal of dispute about the names which should be borne by the different forms of this beautiful insect, but the writer is inclined to the belief that the best solution of the vexing problems of the nomenclature is given in what immediately precedes.

The caterpillar feeds on the leaves of the Papaw (*Asimina triloba*) and wherever this plant grows, from Florida to Canada and westward. the insect is found, often very abundantly.

(29) **Papilio celadon** Lucas. Pl. LXX, fig. 11, ♂ (The Celadon Swallowtail).

Synonym: *sinon* Cramer (not Poda) and others. *P. sinon* Poda is a synonym of the European *P. podalirius* L.

This beautiful little Papilio, which is common in Cuba, also occurs in southern Florida.

P. **mylotes** Bates apparently was credited to our fauna in an article published by Dr. W. J. Showalter in the "National Geographic Magazine," Vol. LII, Pl. VI, figs. 1 and 6. This species is very common in Central and South America, but I can discover no record of its occurrence north of the Rio Grande. Its presence in our fauna suggested by Dr. Showalter is extremely doubtful.

A single stray specimen of **Papilio idæus** Fabricius=**pandion** Felder, is in the possession of Mr. R. A. Gottholt, of Marfa, Texas, which is seventy miles north of the Mexican border. On the strength of this unique specimen we may regard this species as a straggler in our southern territory. The winds now and then may blow other Mexican species across the border, but the occasional advent of such specimens hardly entitles them to be listed as species of the boreal fauna.

In the foregoing few pages I have endeavored within narrow compass to sketch what is definitely known of the various species belonging to the genus *Papilio* within the territory covered by this book. The nomenclature of the species *ajax* involves the most difficulty. Messrs. Rothschild and Jordan in their Revision of the American Papilios simply dropped the specific name *ajax* Linn., holding that it had been so vaguely and variously applied by the immortal Swede that its use according to a strict application of "the law of priority" is impossible. They substitute the name *marcellus* for *ajax*. But the name *carolinianus* George H. Edwards has priority over *marcellus* Cramer. In Gmelin's edition of the "Systema Naturæ" published in 1788 *marcellus* is definitely cited as a synonym of *ajax* Linnæus.

Dr. Aurivillius of Stockholm maintained that the specific name *ajax* must apply to the Papaw Swallowtail and its various varieties. I concur with Aurivillius rather than with my friends Rothschild and Jordan. I cannot bring myself to drop the specific name *ajax* from our terminology. For one hundred and seventy-five years the name *ajax* has been applied to our Papaw Swallowtail, with but few exceptions. Under this name the butterfly appears not only in the technical literature of entomology, but in encyclopædias, dictionaries, and a vast body of popular literature. It has been used thousands of times in print, and is on the tongue of every American schoolboy and schoolgirl, who studies butterflies. I cannot think that anything is gained by designating this specific name as unusable. I am in accord with the former Secretary of the Royal Academy of Sciences in Stockholm, Dr. Aurivillius, the most critical and exact student of the writings of Linnæus, since "The Father of Natural History" died.

THE CATERPILLAR AND THE ANT

"A pensy Ant, right trig and clean,
Came ae day whidding o'er the green,
Where, to advance her pride, she saw
A Caterpillar, moving slaw.
'Good ev'n t' ye, Mistress Ant,' said he;
'How 's a' at hame? I'm blyth to s' ye.'

The saucy Ant view'd him wi' scorn,
Nor wad civilities return;
But gecking up her head, quoth she,
'Poor animal! I pity thee;
Wha scarce can claim to be a creature,
But some experiment o' Nature,
Whase silly shape displeased her eye,
And thus unfinish'd was flung bye.
For me, I'm made wi' better grace,
Wi' active limbs and lively face;
And cleverly can move wi' ease
Frae place to place where'er I please;
Can foot a minuet or jig,
And snoov't like ony whirly-gig;
Which gars my jo aft grip my hand,
Till his heart pitty-pattys, and—
But laigh my qualities I bring,
To stand up clashing wi' a thing,
A creeping thing the like o' thee,
Not worthy o' a farewell t' ye.'
The airy Ant syne turned awa,
And left him wi' a proud gaffa.
The Caterpillar was struck dumb,
And never answered her a mum:
The humble reptile fand some pain,
Thus to be banter'd wi' disdain.
    But tent neist time the Ant came by,
The worm was grown a Butterfly;
Transparent were his wings and fair,
Which bare him flight'ring through the air.
Upon a flower he stapt his flight,
And thinking on his former slight,
Thus to the Ant himself addrest:
'Pray, Madam, will ye please to rest?
And notice what I now advise:
Inferiors ne'er too much despise,
For fortune may gie sic a turn,
To raise aboon ye what ye scorn:
For instance, now I spread my wing
In air, while you're a creeping thing.'"

ALLAN RAMSAY.

FAMILY VII

HESPERIIDÆ (THE SKIPPERS)

"Bedouins of the pathless air."—H. H.

This family is not very well represented in the Palearctic Region, but finds its greatest development in the Nearctic and Neotropical Regions. It is also well developed in the Indo-malayan and Ethiopian Regions. There are at the present time more than two thousand named species belonging to this group of lepidoptera.

Many recent writers have classified these insects under the superfamily name *Hesperioidea;* a few have even gone so far as to regard them as constituting a separate order, to which they have applied the name *Grypocera* Reuter, or *Netrocera* Spuler. This usage is not in vogue, except among a few German authors.

Egg.—The eggs, so far as we are acquainted with them, may be said to be almost without exception, more or less hemispherical, with the flat section of the hemisphere serving as the base. They are sometimes smooth, but not infrequently ornamented with raised ridges parallel to the base and cross-lines at right angles. The ornamentation in some cases is very beautiful and curious.

Caterpillar.—The caterpillars of the *Pyrrhopyginæ, Hesperiinæ,* and *Pamphilinæ* are cylindrical, smooth, tapering forward and backward from the middle, and having large globular or pyramidal heads. The larvæ of the *Megathyminæ,* which burrow in the stems of various species of *Yucca,* and allied plants, do not greatly agree in outline with those of the first three subfamilies, and are modified to adapt them to their different mode of life.

Chrysalis.—The chrysalids of the first three subfamilies are generally formed between two or more leaves of the food-plant, which are drawn together by strands of silk, forming an exceedingly loose cocoon-like structure, within which the chrysalis is suspended by its cremaster attached to a small button of silk. There is considerable variety in the form of the chrysalids. In the *Hesperiinæ* the sheaths enclosing the tongue are about as long as the wing-sheaths; in the *Pamphilinæ* they are longer, and in some genera greatly exceed the length of the wing-sheaths. The chrysalids of the *Megathyminæ* are formed at the end of the tunnel cut by the larva in a funnel-shaped opening lined with silk.

Butterfly.—The butterflies of this great group are almost without exception characterized by having relatively robust bodies and comparatively small wings.

They are exceedingly quick and powerful in flight, darting from point to point, and rarely remaining long at one place, when the skies are bright. When on the wing, most of the species are so rapid in their movements as almost to elude the eye. But their movements are generally only for short distances. From this habit of darting from one point to another the insects have in familiar English parlance been called "Skippers."

In the following pages an attempt has been made to simplify the classification of the forms found within our faunal limits by avoiding the use of some generic names founded upon minor and often microscopic distinctions. As has been well said by one of my learned correspondents, himself a recognized authority upon this group, "We have too many genera in the *Hesperiidæ*." A genus is merely a classificational device, intended to facilitate study by bringing nearly allied forms into one category. In recent years there has arisen a tendency to split up genera and multiply them, so that if the process is continued, we shall have a generic name for each species. There is no good reason for such a course.

I may further add at this point the remark that in the naming of the larger categories, such as subfamilies, I have held to what is now recognized as good usage, according priority to long established and accepted names, when such groups contain representatives of the genera originally included in them, even if later critical researches may suggest that a species originally included in a genus as its supposed type, belongs elsewhere. It is only by adhering to this method that we avoid wholesale mutations in nomenclature, based upon the more or less fluctuating opinions of individual authors.

SUBFAMILY PYRRHOPYGINÆ

"Seeing only what is fair,
Sipping only what is sweet."
EMERSON.

This subfamily is composed of closely related genera, which are found only in the New World. They may be easily recognized by the large blunt club of the antennæ. The cell of the fore wing is always very long, being two thirds the length of the costa; the lower radial vein usually rises from the end of the cell, nearer the third median nervule than the upper radial. They are said, when at rest, to extend all their wings horizontally.

But one genus belonging to this subfamily is represented within the limits of the United States.

Genus PYRRHOPYGE Hübner

Butterfly.—The neuration is as represented in Fig. 162 and need not, therefore, be described at length. The club of the antennæ is thickened, usually bluntly pointed and bent.

(1) **Pyrrhopyge araxes** Hewitson, subsp. **arizonæ** Godm. & Salv. Pl. XLV, fig. 9, ♂ (The Araxes Skipper).

FIG. 161.—Head and antenna of *Pyrrhopyge*, magnified 2 diameters.

FIG. 162.—Neuration of the genus *Pyrrhopyge*.

Butterfly.—Easily recognized from the figure on the plate. The hind wings are prevalently yellow on the under side. It is wholly unlike any other species found within our faunal limits. The wings expand about two inches. We have no knowledge of the life-history of the insect. It occasionally occurs in southern Texas, but is quite common in Arizona and northern Mexico. True *P. araxes*, found farther south, is much darker upon the upper side.

SUBFAMILY HESPERIINÆ (THE HESPERIDS)

"Twine ye in an airy round,
Brush the dew and print the lea;
Skip and gambol, hop and bound."
DRAKE, *The Culprit Fay*

Butterfly.—The cell of the fore wing is always long, often more than two thirds the length of the costa; the lower radial vein is generally nearer the upper radial than the third median nervule; the upper radial is emitted near the upper angle of the cell. The hind wing is frequently produced at the inner angle into a tooth-like projection; sometimes into a long tail. Thorax and abdomen stout, the latter not projecting beyond the hind margin of the posterior wing. The fore wing is usually furnished in the male sex with a costal fold, but is never marked with a discal stigma, or bunch of raised scales. The antennæ always terminate in a fine point and are usually bent into a hook. The butterflies when at rest, for the most part, hold their wings erect, though some of them hold them extended horizontally, or half expanded.

Egg.—Subconical, or hemispherical, vertically ribbed, these ribs connected by less elevated cross-ribs.

Caterpillar.—Head viewed from in front more or less bilobed, rounded, or quadrangular; body tapering fore and aft from the middle, relatively plump.

Chrysalis.—The sheath of the tongue not extending beyond the wing-sheaths.

Genus PHOCIDES Hübner

This genus, containing about thirty species and named varieties, is well developed in Central and South America. Only on the extreme southern borders of the United States is it represented by straggling species, one of which, *P. batabano* Lucas, is not uncommon in southern Florida. Fig. 163 on page 327 shows the neuration of this species. The cell of the fore wing is very greatly lengthened; the lower margin of the hind wing is produced, but not tailed. The antennæ have the anterior part of the spindle-shaped club recurved, though not as much as in some of the allied genera. The second joint of the palpi is well developed, very hairy, quadrate in form, and closely appressed to the front, the third joint minute and concealed in the hairy vestiture of the second joint. The figures given on our plate will enable the student easily to name the species which occur within our faunal limits.

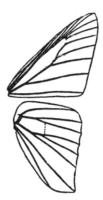

FIG. 163.—Neuration of *Phocides batabano.*

(1) **P. batabano** (Lucas). Pl. XLIX, fig. 1 (The Batabano Skipper).

Synonyms: *mancinus* (Herrich-Schæffer); *okeechobee* (Worthington).

Butterfly.—The prevailing color of the insect is dark blackish brown, somewhat paler on the underside than on the upper; the interior of the costal fold is pale yellow. Hind wings marked both on the upper and lower side beyond the end of the cell by one or two incomplete bands of metallic blue-green, more conspicuous on the upper than on the lower side. Expanse: 2 in.

This insect, common in Cuba, also occurs in southern Florida, ranging as far north as Indian River.

(2) **Phocides lilea** (Reakirt). Pl. XLIX, fig. 2, ♂ (The Bloody Spot).

Synonyms: *albicilla* (H.-S.); *sanguinea* (Scudder); *cruentus* (Scudder).

Butterfly.—Readily distinguished by the red spot on the fore wing near the middle of the costa. It occurs as a straggler in southern Texas and Arizona. It is common in Mexico and southward.

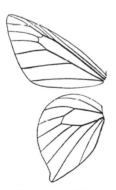

FIG. 164.—Neuration of *Nascus euribates.* ♂

(3) **Phocides urania** (Westwood and Hewitson). Pl. XLIX, fig. 3, ♀ (The Urania Skipper).

Synonym: *texana* (Scudder).

The figure on the plate will enable the student to recognize the species, which has many allied forms in the American tropics. It occurs as a straggler in Texas, and is common farther south.

Genus NASCUS Watson

The antennæ are half as long as the costa, rather slender, the club with a very long, sharp, slender tip, which bends abruptly downward at nearly a right angle to the body of the club. The palpi are appressed to the front, the first and second joints densely scaled, the third joint minute, concealed in the vestiture of the second joint. The outer margin of the fore wing is longer than the hind margin; apex produced; a fold on the costa of the male; the cell is narrow, more than two thirds the length of the costa; discocellulars very oblique; third median emitted near the end of the cell, the first median relatively near the base of the cell, rather close to the origin of the submedian. The hind wing is narrow, outwardly evenly rounded and produced at the end of the submedian vein, rounded at the anal angle. The females have broader and more rounded wings.

(1) **Nascus euribates** (Cramer). Pl. XLIX, fig. 4, ♂ (The Euribates Skipper).

Synonym: *hesus* of many authors, not *hesus* (Westwood and Hewitson).

The correct specific name is *euribates*. We have specimens from Texas, Guatemala, Honduras, Brazil, and Bolivia. Our females, which sex Cramer made the type of the species, agree with his figure (*Pap. Exot.*, Pl. 393, fig. D). The specimen shown on our plate was collected in Texas and is contained in the collection of Theodore L. Mead, which I own. It lacks the two small dark brown spots at the base of the fore wing shown in Hewitson's figure of *N. hesus*. Expanse: ♂, 2.5; ♀, 2.75–3 in.

Genus POLYGONUS Hübner

Synonyms: *Acolastus* Scudder; *Nennius* Kirby.

Antennæ slender, about half as long as the costa of the fore wing, terminating in a spindle-shaped club, the slender tip of which is strongly retrorse; palpi

hairy, appressed, third joint minute; eyes large, prominent; thorax robust; abdomen relatively short. Fore wings somewhat truncate at apex, without costal fold; hind wings with the outer margin evenly rounded, produced at the extremity of the submedian vein, as in the two preceding genera, to which the genus is structurally closely related.

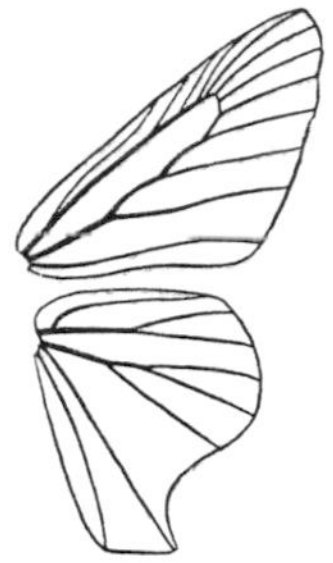

(1) **Polygonus amyntas** (Fabricius). Pl. XLIX, fig. 5 (The Amyntas Skipper).

Synonyms: *lividus* Hübner; *savigny* Latreille.

Butterfly.—The only species in the genus may easily be recognized from the figure given on our plate. It is widely distributed throughout the tropical regions of the New World and occurs in Florida, Texas, and Arizona. The typical form has the wings quite dark on both sides. A variety, which occurs in Arizona, is a trifle paler above and below; and has received the varietal name *arizonensis* Skinner. Expanse: 1.75 inches.

Fig. 165. — Neuration of *Polygonus amyntas*, ♂.

Genus PROTEIDES Hübner

Synonym: *Dicranaspes* Mabille

Antennæ slender, not half as long as the costa of the fore wing. The spindle-shaped club is strongly retrorse at the tip. The first and second joints of palpi very hairy; appressed; the third joint minute, concealed; thorax and abdomen very robust; fore wing elongated, without costal fold, greatly produced toward the apex, which is truncate, the outer margin somewhat excavated; hind wing externally evenly rounded, with a tooth-like projection at the extremity of the submedian nervule. This genus includes a number of species found in the American tropics, only one of which occurs within our faunal limits.

FIG. 166.—Neuration of *Proteides idas*, ♀.

(1) **Proteides idas** (Cramer). Pl. XLIX, fig. 6, ♂; fig. 7, ♀, *under side* (The Idas Skipper).

Synonym: *mercurius* Fabricius.

This species, which is the only representative of its genus attributed to our fauna, may easily be recognized by the figures on our plate. Widely distributed throughout the American tropics, many insular varieties and local races have been named and described. Expanse: ♂, 2.25 in.; ♀, 2.5–2.75 in.

The larval stages are only partially known. The caterpillar feeds upon leguminous plants.

Genus EPARGYREUS Hübner

Butterfly.—The antennæ have the club stout, gradually thickened, tapering to a fine point, and abruptly bent into a hook. The palpi are profusely covered with thick scales, in which the third joint is almost entirely concealed. The fore wing of the male is furnished with a costal fold; the hind wing is prominently produced at the end of the submedian vein.

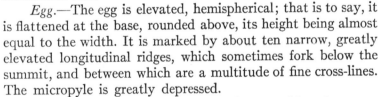

FIG. 167.—Neuration of the genus *Epargyreus.*

Egg.—The egg is elevated, hemispherical; that is to say, it is flattened at the base, rounded above, its height being almost equal to the width. It is marked by about ten narrow, greatly elevated longitudinal ridges, which sometimes fork below the summit, and between which are a multitude of fine cross-lines. The micropyle is greatly depressed.

Caterpillar.—The caterpillar closely resembles the caterpillar of the genus *Eudamus*, but the head is not as strongly bilobed.

Chrysalis.—The chrysalis likewise resembles the chrysalis of the genus *Eudamus*; the cremaster, however, is not as strongly hooked as in that genus.

(1) **Epargyreus tityrus** Fabricius. Pl. XLIII, fig. 5, ♂; Pl. II, figs. 30, 31, 33, *larva*; Pl. VI, figs. 22, 25, 26, *chrysalis* (The Silver-spotted Skipper).

Synonym: *clarus* (Cramer).

Butterfly.—This very common and beautiful insect may easily be recognized from the figure on the plate. The broad, irregular silvery spot on the under side of the hind wings distinguishes it at a glance from all other related species in our fauna. Expanse: 1.75–2.00 inches.

A specimen, in which the broad honey-yellow band on the upper side of the fore wing is reduced to three small dots and the silvery spot on the under side of the hind wing is greatly enlarged, was baptized var. *obliteratus* by Scudder. It is a freak.

Early Stages.—These have been accurately described by several authors, and a very full account of them is contained in "The Butterflies of New England." The caterpillar feeds upon leguminous plants, and is especially common upon the *Wistaria*, which is grown about verandas, and on the common locust (*Robinia pseudacacia*). The caterpillar makes a nest for itself in the same manner as *Eudamus proteus*. Pupation generally takes place among fallen leaves or rubbish at the foot of the trees upon which the caterpillar has fed.

This butterfly has a wide range, extending to the Gulf, south of a line passing from Quebec to Vancouver, and ranging still farther south as far as the Isthmus of Panama. It is single-brooded in the North, and double- or triple-brooded in the South.

(2) **Epargyreus exadeus** (Cramer). Pl. XLIX, fig. 8, ♂; fig. 9, ♀, *under side* (The Exadeus Skipper).

Synonym: *socus* Hübner.

Our figures will enable the student to easily distinguish the species. It is common in the American tropics, and occurs as a straggler in southern California, New Mexico, and Arizona. Expanse: ♂, 2 in.; ♀, 2.25 in. The early stages have been briefly and unsatisfactorily described in Seitz, Vol. V, p. 680.

(3) **Epargyreus zestos** (Geyer). Pl. XLIX, fig. 10, ♂ (The Zestos Skipper). Synonym: *oberon* Worthington.

Occurring in Florida and the Antilles, and easily distinguished from its congeners by the total absence on the under side of the hind wing of all silvery markings. Expanse: ♂, 2.25 in.; ♀, 2.5 in.

The early stages thus far have not been described.

Genus EUDAMUS Swainson

The generic name *Goniurus* Hübner (undescribed) having been by Scudder and other authors restricted to certain species with *cœlus* (Cramer) as the type, the generic name *Eudamus* Swainson, with *proteus* (Linnæus) as the type, must stand, although *Goniurus* antedates the name *Eudamus*.

The Long-tailed Skippers of the American tropics in recent years have been split up into a number of so-called genera, founded for the most part upon little more than specific and microscopic differences. These subdivisions in this book are disregarded, as they are by most systematists.

Butterfly.—The antennæ terminate in a fine point bent into a hook at the thickest part of the club. The cell of the fore wing is very long. The discocellulars are inwardly oblique and on the same straight line, the upper discocellular being often reduced to a mere point. The lower radial is equidistant between the upper radial and the third median nervule. The hind wing is always produced into a long tail.

Egg.—The egg is more nearly globular than is true in most of the genera, but is strongly flattened at the base and is marked with a number of longitudinal ridges, somewhat widely separated, between which are finer latitudinal cross-lines. The micropyle at the summit is deeply depressed.

Caterpillar.—The caterpillar is cylindrical, tapering rapidly from the middle forward and backward. The head is much larger than the neck and is distinctly bilobed.

Chrysalis.—The chrysalis is provided with a somewhat hooked cremaster, is rounded at the head, humped over the thorax, and marked on the dorsal side of the abdominal segments with a few small conical projections. The chrysalis is formed between leaves loosely drawn together with a few strands of silk.

This genus is confined to the tropics of the New World, and is represented in the southern portions of the United States by a number of species figured on our plates.

(1) **Eudamus proteus** (Linnæus). Pl. XLV, fig. 6, ♀ ; Pl. II, fig. 34, *larva*; Pl. VI, fig. 23, *chrysalis* (The Long-tailed Skipper).

Butterfly.—The upper side of the wings is brown, glossed with green at the base of both wings. The spots on the primaries of both sexes are alike, and are well represented in the plate. On the under side the wings are pale brown; the primaries are marked as on the upper side; the secondaries have the anal portion and the tail dark brown; in addition they are crossed by a short dark band at the end of the cell, and another similar but longer postmedian band, which does not quite reach the costa and loses itself below in the dark shade which covers the anal portion of the wing. About the middle of the costa of the hind wings are two small subquadrate black spots. Expanse: 1.60–1.75 inch.

Fig. 168.—Neuration of the genus *Eudamus*.

Early Stages.—The plates give us representations based upon Abbot's drawings of the mature caterpillar and the chrysalis. The student who desires to know more may consult the pages of Scudder's "Butterflies of New England." The caterpillar feeds upon leguminous plants, especially upon the *Wistaria* and various species of *Clitoria* (Butterfly-pea). It makes a rude nest by drawing two of the leaves together with strands of silk.

The species is tropical and is found all over the warmer regions of the New World, but ranging northward, and on the Atlantic seacoast, has been occasionally found as far north as New York City, where it has been taken in Central Park.

(2) **Eudamus dorantes** (Stoll). Pl. XLIX, fig. 11, ♂, *under side;* fig. 12, var. **rauterbergi** Skinner, ♂, *under side*, paratype (The Dorantes Skipper).

Synonyms: *amisus* Hewitson; *protillus* H.-S.

This species, which is common in Mexico and southward is found as a straggler in southern Texas. The variety *rauterbergi*, which is smaller and darker on the under side, with the translucent spots of the fore wing reduced in size, is found in Arizona and northwestern Mexico, and has also been reported from southern California.

(3) **Eudamus simplicius** (Stoll). Pl. XLIX, fig. 13, ♂ (The Simplicius Skipper).

Prevalently dull olive-brown on the upper side of the wings. On the under side the ground-color is a trifle darker and the outer borders incline to blackish, while the hind wings are crossed by two parallel transverse dark bands about the middle, the inner of which is short, surmounted by two black spots near the costa. Occasionally specimens occur, in which the fore wings show a transverse subapical translucent narrow band somewhat like that in *E. eurycles*, but quite indistinct.

(4) **Eudamus eurycles** (Latreille). Pl. XLIX, fig. 14, ♂ (The Eurycles Skipper).

Resembling *E. simplicius*. The fore wings always have a short narrow line on the costa behind the apex, and a much longer light line running from about the middle of the costa across the cell toward the inner angle, which it does not quite reach. The fringes are light in color. On the under side the hind wings are crossed by two parallel dark bands like those in *E. simplicius*, but broader. The two spots surmounting the shorter inner band are larger and more conspicuous than in *simplicius*. Expanse: 1.66 in.

The butterfly occurs as a straggler in southern Texas, and is common in Mexico and Central America.

(5) **Eudamus albofasciatus** (Hewitson). Pl. XLIX, fig. 16, ♂, *under side* (The White-banded Skipper).

Easily distinguished from other species in our fauna by the straight white band across the middle of the hind wing on the under side.

It rarely occurs in southern Texas and in Arizona, but is common in Mexico.

(6) **Eudamus zilpa** Butler. Pl. XLIX, fig. 18, ♂, *under side* (The Zilpa Skipper).

Readily distinguished by the peculiar markings on the under side of the wings. It has been taken in Texas and in Arizona.

(7) **Eudamus alcæus** (Hewitson). Pl. XLIX, fig. 16, ♀, *under side* (The Alcæus Skipper).

This insect has been by Lindsey transferred to his genus *Codatractus*, but it is a true *Eudamus*, not distantly related to *E. dorantes*, from which it is principally distinguished by the broad white linear spot above the origin of the tail on the hind wing, and by the narrower, more pointed tail. It is a rare straggler into our territory from Mexico, where it is common.

Genus CODATRACTUS Lindsey

Synonym: *Heteropia* Mabille, preoccupied

This generic name has recently been proposed by Lindsey (*Cf.* University of Iowa Studies in Natural History, Vol. IX, No. 4, 1918, p. 26) because the name *Heteropia* Mabille has been discovered by Lindsey to have been already used to designate a genus of sponges, and therefore according to the rules of nomenclature cannot be employed.

There are about half a dozen species, which have been by writers referred to *Heteropia* Mabille = *Codatractus* Lindsey. They are all Mexican or Central American, and bear a very close general resemblance to each other in the outline and maculation of the wings.

The only species belonging to the genus in our region is a varietal form of the Mexican insect named *Heteropia melon* by Godman and Salvin, to which the late Dr. Henry Skinner applied the subspecific name *arizonensis*.

(1) **Codatractus melon** var. **arizonensis** (Skinner). Plate XLIX, fig. 15, ♂ (The Melon Skipper).

The only notable difference between *C. melon* (G. & S.) and the form found in Arizona is the fact that the latter has the outer margin of the hind wing on the under side near its lower angle blotched with white, while in true *C. melon* there is little or no white at this point.

Genus TELEGONUS Hübner

This is a moderately large genus of the American tropics, only one species of which has been alleged to occur within our borders.

(1) **Telegonus hahneli** Staudinger. Pl. XLIX, fig. 19, ♂ (Hahnel's Skipper).

The specimen figured on the plate was received by the writer from the late Dr. Otto Staudinger of Dresden shortly after he had published his description of the species. It may therefore be regarded as paratypical as well as topotypical, for it came from Merida, Venezuela, whence the type described by Dr. Staudinger was derived. It does not differ from the illustration on Plate 98 of Staudinger's *Exotische Schmetterlinge*, which the good Doctor in the text tells us was by a blunder of an assistant wrongly named *cassander*, which species he had intended to figure upon the plate, but *hahneli* was substituted. The specimen also agrees very well, even better, with the fig. of *hahneli* given by Salvin and Godman (Biol. Cent.-Amer., Rhopalocera, Pl. 77, figs. 13, 14). *T. cassander* (Fabr.) has the hind wing on the under side near the anal angle suffused with pale fulvous, which is not the case in *T. hahneli*. There is a similar, but quite distinct, Jamaican species, of which I possess a long series of specimens, which has been confounded with *hahneli*.

Hahnel's Skipper has been attributed to our fauna by Dr. Skinner, who cites it as occurring in Arizona. It must be a rare straggler into our territory. Its metropolis is Venezuela; which is a long way from the United States. It is not a pretty insect, being mostly brownish black on both sides of the wings, with an obscure dark transverse band of even darker color crossing the hind wing beyond its middle on the under side. By giving a figure of a typical specimen it may be that some future butterfly-hunter in Arizona may be able to identify it, if it turns up.

Genus ZESTUSA Lindsey

Synonym: *Plestia* Mabille, preoccupied

The generic name *Plestia* was employed by Stål in the *Hemiptera* long before Mabille used it for a genus of butterflies. So we must accept the new name *Zestusa* suggested by Lindsey.

Butterfly.—The club of the antennæ is flattened, sickle-shaped, terminating in a fine point. The male has a costal fold upon the fore wing. The lower radial is nearer to the upper radial than to the third median nervule. The hind wing is produced into a short tail. The fifth vein is wanting.

Early Stages.—Unknown.

This genus is peculiar to Mexico and Central America. But one species is found within our limits, and is confined to Arizona.

(1) **Zestusa dorus** (Edwards). Pl. XLV, fig. 11, ♂ (The Short-tailed Arizona Skipper).

Butterfly.—The upper side is accurately depicted on the plate. On the under side the wings are hoary. The spots of the upper side reappear, the lower spots of the primaries being partially lost in the broad honey-yellow tint which covers the inner margin of that wing. The secondaries are crossed by obscure dark-brown basal, median, and postmedian bands, portions of which are annular, or composed of ring-like spots. The anal angle is clouded with dark brown. Expanse: 1.50–1.60 inch.

Early Stages.—Unknown.

The species has been taken in considerable numbers in Arizona, and ranges thence southward into Mexico.

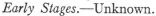

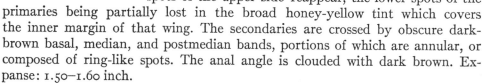

FIG. 169.—Genus *Zestusa*. Antenna, magnified 2 diameters. Neuration.

Genus THORYBES Scudder

Synonyms: *Lintneria* Butler; *Cocceius* G. & S.

(The Dusky-wings)

Butterfly.—The club of the antennæ is not very heavy, hooked, the hooked portion about as long as the rest of the club. The palpi are directed forward, with the second joint heavily scaled, and the third joint very small. The fore wing may be with, or without, the costal fold in the male sex. Fig. 170 gives a correct idea of the neuration. The hind wing is evenly rounded on the outer margin, sometimes slightly angled at the extremity of the submedian vein.

Egg.—The egg is subglobular, somewhat flattened at the base and on top, marked with numerous fine and not much elevated longitudinal ridges. The micropyle covers the upper surface of the egg and is not depressed.

Caterpillar.—The caterpillar somewhat resembles that of the genus *Epargyreus*, but is relatively shorter, the head proportionately larger and more globular. The neck is greatly strangulated.

Chrysalis.—The chrysalis is somewhat curved in outline, with a strongly hooked cremaster and a prominent projection on the back of the thoracic region.

(1) **Thorybes pylades** (Scudder). Pl. XLVIII, fig. 6, ♀ ; Pl. II, figs. 25, 29, *larva;* Pl. VI, fig. 28, *chrysalis* (The Northern Dusky-wing).

Butterfly.—The upper side is represented correctly on Pl. XLVIII. On the under side the wings are dark brown, shading into hoary-gray on the outer margins. The hind wings are crossed by irregular basal, median, and postmedian brown bands of darker spots, shaded with deeper brown internally. The translucent spots of the upper side reappear on the lower side of the fore wings. Expanse: 1.60 inch.

Early Stages.—These are elaborately described in the pages of Dr. Scudder's great work. The caterpillar feeds on clover, *Lespedeza*, and *Desmodium*.

FIG. 170.—Neuration of the genus *Thorybes*.

This insect is found throughout the United States and Canada, but is not as yet reported from the central masses of the Rocky Mountain region. It probably, however, occurs there also in suitable locations. It is very common in New England. An aberrant form, lacking the translucent spots of the fore wings, has been named *immaculata* by the late Dr. Henry Skinner.

(2) **Thorybes bathyllus** (Smith & Abbot). Pl. XLVIII, fig. 5, ♀ ; Pl. II, fig. 32, *larva;* Pl. VI, fig. 24, *chrysalis* (The Southern Dusky-wing).

Synonym: *daunus* Barnes and McDunnough (not Cramer).

Butterfly.—Easily distinguished from the preceding species by the much larger size of the translucent spots on the fore wings. Expanse: 1.40–1.50 in.

Early Stages.—The habits of the larva are very similar to those of the preceding species, and the caterpillar feeds on herbaceous *Leguminosæ.*

It ranges from the Connecticut Valley, where it is rare, southward along the coast and through the Mississippi Valley as far south and west as Texas.

(3) **Thorybes confusus** Bell. Pl. L, fig. 1, ♂ ; fig. 2, ♀ paratypes (Bell's Dusky-wing).

Synonym: *confusis* Bell (err. typogr.)

At first sight presenting a general resemblance to *T. bathyllus*, this species may easily be discriminated from the latter by the great reduction in size of the light spots on the fore wings of the males, which, with the exception of those near the apex, are frequently almost obsolete, or mere points, while on the under side in both sexes the color of the hind wings is more or less hoary outwardly, the outer border including the fringes being dark brown at the ends of the nervules, a feature which does not occur in *T. bathyllus*, where the fringes on the lower side of the wings are concolorous, and not checkered as in *T. confusus*. There are other differences of an anatomical character, such as the form of the genitalia, and so forth, which have been pointed out. Expanse: ♂, 1.31–1.45 in.; ♀, 1.4–1.6 in.

The insect appears to be abundant on the southwestern side of the peninsula of Florida about Tampa, and is said to range westward as far as Arkansas.

(4) **Thorybes nevada** Scudder. Pl. L, fig. 3, ♀ (The Nevada Dusky-wing).

This species is not distantly related to *T. pylades*, but is smaller, and uniformly dark on the upper side of the wings, except for the minute pre-apical spots on the fore wing. Some writers have regarded it as identical with *T. mexicanus*, with which opinion I cannot concur in the light of material before me. It was originally described from high elevations in Nevada, and is reputed to be found at similar elevations in eastern California. Expanse: ♂, 1.2 in.; ♀, 1.25 in.

(5) **Thorybes drusius** (Edwards). Pl. L, fig. 4, ♂, type (The Drusius Skipper).

The species occurs in Mexico and Arizona. It is as yet not common in collections, and nothing is known as to its preliminary stages.

(6) **Thorybes mexicanus** (Herrich-Schæffer). Pl. L, fig. 5, ♂; fig. 6, ♀, *under side* (The Mexican Dusky-wing).

This is a relatively small species, which may readily be distinguished by the markings of the lower side, which are distinctive. It ranges from Mexico into southern California and Arizona. It is doubtfully recorded from southern Colorado. Expanse: 1.2 in.

Thorbyes æmilia Skinner. Pl. XLVI, fig. 39, ♂, type (Mrs. Owen's Dusky-wing).

Butterfly.—This little species, which may readily be identified by the figure of the type given on the plate, is as yet quite rare in collections. We know nothing of the early stages. The types were taken at Fort Klamath, in Oregon. Dr. Skinner named it in honor of the estimable wife of Professor Owen of the University of Wisconsin, the discoverer of the species. Expanse: 1.20 inch.

Genus ACHALARUS Scudder

Butterfly.—The antennæ and palpi are as in the preceding genus. The neuration is represented in the cut. The hind wing is slightly lobed at the anal angle; the fore wing may or may not be provided with a costal fold.

FIG. 171.—Neuration of the genus *Achalarus.*

(1) **Achalarus lycidas** (Smith and Abbot). Pl. XLV., fig. 10, ♀, *under side;* Pl. II, fig. 23, *larva;* Pl. VI, fig. 21, *chrysalis* (The Hoary-edge).

Synonym: *lyciades* (Geyer).

Butterfly.—The general appearance of the upper side of the wings strongly recalls *E. tityrus*, but the hoary edge of the secondaries and the absence of the broad median silvery spot found in *tityrus* at once serve to discriminate the two forms. Expanse: 1.65–1.95 inch.

Early Stages.—What is known of them may be ascertained by consulting the pages of "The Butterflies of New England." The caterpillar is found on the leaves of *Desmodium* (Beggar's-lice).

The insect is rare in southern New England, and ranges thence southward and westward to Texas, being scarce in the Mississippi Valley north of Kentucky, and apparently not ranging west of Missouri.

(2) **Achalarus epigona** (H.-S.). Pl. XLVIII, fig. 13, ♂ (Butler's Dusky-wing).

Synonyms: *epigena* (Butler); *orestes* (Edwards).

Butterfly.—Readily distinguished by its large size, the conspicuous white fringes of the hind wings on the upper side, and the broad white marginal band of these wings on the under side. Expanse: 2.00 inches.

Early Stages.—Unknown.

This insect is common in Arizona and Mexico.

Genus MURGARIA Watson

This genus was erected by Watson for the reception of the species originally named *Telegonus albociliatus* Mabille, which ranges from Mexico to Colombia. The neuration of the wings is much as in the genus *Rhabdoides*, but the secondaries are much more produced at the anal angle, though not tailed. There are also minor differences in the palpi and the antennæ.

(1) **Murgaria coyote** (Skinner). Pl. LXXIV, fig. 7, ♂, type; fig. 7a, *under side*, type (Skinner's Dusky-wing).

A number of recent writers have suggested that this insect is identical with *M. albociliatus* Mabille. In this view the writer does not concur. I am indebted to the authorities of the Academy of Natural Sciences in Philadelphia for the privilege of giving a figure of this, as well as of a number of other types of the species described by Dr. Skinner, which are in their custody. The type is unique. It came from Texas; I have a ragged specimen from Arizona. The insect is still rare in collections.

Genus RHABDOIDES Scudder

This genus was erected by Scudder for the reception of the species named *cellus* Boisd. & Lec. There is found in it a commingling of features which occur both in the genus *Achalarus* and *Thorybes*. It is not synonymous with *Cecrops* Hübner (preoccupied) = *Cecropterus* H.-S., the type of which is the species *zarex* Hübner. The species *cellus* has nothing whatever to do with *zarex*, which is diminutive, totally differing anatomically and superficially from *cellus*. The genus *Cecropterus* H.-S., to which *cellus* has been assigned by some recent compilers of lists, does not occur in our faunal limits. I accept Dr. Scudder's generic name, but with the feeling that it is an almost unnecessary refinement to separate *cellus* from the genus *Achalarus*, in which I placed it in the first edition of this book.

(1) **Rhabdoides cellus** (Boisd. & Lec.). Pl. XLV, fig. 12, ♂ (The Golden-banded Skipper).

Butterfly.—The figure on the plate will enable the instant identification of this beautiful species, which, on the under side, has the hind wings banded much as in *E. proteus*. Expanse: 2.00 inches.

Mexican specimens are larger and the light band is narrower.

Early Stages.—What little we know of these is based mainly upon the observations of Abbot. The habits of the larva apparently are not greatly different from those of allied species.

A. cellus is found in the Virginias, and thence southward and westward to Arizona and Mexico. It is common in the Carolinas.

(2) **Rhabdoides pseudocellus** (Coolidge & Clemence). Pl. L, fig. 9, ♂. (Coolidge's Skipper).

This species is, like the preceding, referred to the genus *Rhabdoides*, although it, like that species, is very near to *Achalarus*. It is much smaller than *cellus* and is characterized invariably by having the antennæ pale yellow at the base of the club by which character the species can always be distinguished. Expanse: 1.6 in.

It is common in Arizona and in the state of Chihuahua, Mexico.

Genus CABARES Godman and Salvin

(1) **Cabares potrillo** (Lucas). Pl. L, fig. 10, ♂ (The Potrillo Skipper).

The only species of the genus *Cabares* in our fauna is the insect figured upon our plate and it may be at once distinguished from all others closely related to it by the tooth-like projection on the outer border of the hind wing.

Habitat.—Mexico, Cuba, and Texas.

Genus COGIA Butler

Palpi projecting, the second joint hairy, the third very small, but not concealed by the vestiture of the second. Antennæ half the length of costa, the club spindle-shaped, the tip short, retrorse at a right angle. The wings in outline like those of *Thorybes;* with the costa straight; no costal fold; the cell two thirds the length of the costa, the lower median vein equidistant between the third median and the upper radial. The hind wings of the males have a tuft of androconia on the inner fold on the submedian vein near the base of the wing.

(1) **Cogia hippalus** (Edwards). Pl. L, fig. 8, ♂; fig. 7, ♀, type, *under side* (The Hippalus Skipper).

Synonym: *gila* (Ploetz).

The insect may easily be identified by the figures. The fringes are white. It is the largest species of the genus in our fauna. Expanse: 1.6 in.

Common in New Mexico, Arizona, and northern Mexico.

(2) **Cogia outis** (Skinner). Pl. L, fig. 11, ♂, paratype (The Outis Skipper). Much smaller than *C. hippalus*. Fringes light fuscous. The light spots on the

fore wings vary and often are greatly reduced in size, thus causing the insect to resemble the following species, from which it can, however, be distinguished by its smaller size and paler color. Expanse: 1.2 in.

Habitat.—Texas.

(3) **Cogia calchas** (Herrich-Schæffer). Pl. L, fig. 12. ♂. (The Calchas Skipper).

Synonym: *terranea* (Butler).

The butterfly is darker brown on the upper side than either of the other species, and wholly without light spots, except the small preapical spot on the fore wing. Fringes pale fuscous, darker at ends of veins. Expanse: 1.33 in.

The species occurs in Texas. It is not uncommon in Mexico and the Antilles.

Genus PHŒDINUS Godman and Salvin

This genus can scarcely be distinguished from the preceding, and is only separated from it by the absence of the sexual tuft near the inner margin of the hind wing of the male, and the more prominent palpi, which are porrect, with the third joint not concealed by the hairs of the second.

(1) **Phœdinus caicus** (Herr.-Schaeff.). Pl. L, fig. 13, ♂ (type of *moschus* Edw.) fig. 14, ♂, *under side* (Schaeffer's Skipper).

Synonyms: *schæfferi* Ploetz; *moschus* Edwards.

The figures on our plate represent the upper and under sides of the type and a paratype of *Eudamus moschus* Edwards, which is apparently a synonym of *caicus* H.-S., specimens of which I have in some numbers from different parts of the American tropics. The insect varies somewhat in size, and the specimens we figure are under, rather than over, the size of the general run of specimens. The insect somewhat closely resembles *Cogia hippalus*, from which it can at once be discriminated by the less pronounced dark banding of the lower sides of the wings and the lighter color of the costa of the fore wing on the under side, which is always narrowly edged with yellowish.

Nothing so far is known of the early stages. The insect occurs in Arizona, Mexico, and southward, and also is found in the Antilles.

(2) **Phœdinus mysie** (Dyar). Pl. LXXIV, figs, 8, 8a, type (Dyar's Skipper).

The habitat of this insect is Arizona, from which its was originally described. Little is known about it, except what is contained in the original description, which is to be found in the Journal of the New York Entomological Society, Vol. XII, 1904, p. 40.

Genus HESPERIA Fabricius

(Type *Papilio malvæ* Linnæus)

This genus, the type of which was beyond question fixed by Cuvier as *Papilio malvæ* Linnæus, has been cut up in past years into a number of subgenera, or minor subdivisions, founded upon minute distinctions.

Butterfly.—The antennæ are relatively short; the club is stout and blunt at the tip. The palpi are bent upward, with the third joint buried in the scales covering the second joint. The hind wing is usually evenly rounded. In all the American species the male is provided with a costal fold. The neuration is represented in Fig. 172.

Egg.—Hemispherical, ribbed.

Caterpillar.—The caterpillar is much like those which have been previously described, but is relatively much smaller.

Chrysalis.—The chrysalis has a somewhat blunt and not very distinctly developed cremaster.

Fig. 172.—Genus *Hesperia.* Neuration. Antenna, magnified 3 diameters.

Section 1. Subgenus PYRGUS Hübner

Wings prevalently dark on the upper side, checkered with light spots; for the most part inhabiting temperate regions, high mountains, and subarctic or arctic localities.

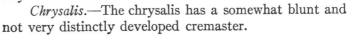

(1) **Hesperia centaureæ** (Rambur). Pl. XLVII, fig. 13, ♂ (The Grizzled Skipper).

Synonym: *wyandot* (Edwards).

Butterfly.—The upper side may easily be recognized by the help of the figure on the plate. On the under side the wings are dark, the lighter spots of the primaries, however, reappear, the submarginal curved row of spots coalescing to form a narrow white band; the white spot at the end of the cell flowing around the dark spot, which it only partly incloses on the upper side, forms an eye-like spot. The hind wings are brown, scaled with green, and crossed by basal, median, and marginal bands of quadrate spots. The fringes are whitish, checkered with gray. Expanse: 1.15 in.

Early Stages.—These await description.

This species, which originally was believed to be confined to Scandinavia and Lapland in Europe, and to eastern Labrador in this country, is now known to have a wide range in North America, extending from Labrador to the Carolinas on the Appalachian ranges, and occurring on the Rocky Mountains from British Columbia to southern Colorado.

A subspecies, said to occur in Labrador, has recently been named *freija* by Warren. It is based upon genitalic distinctions. Its validity is open to question. Dr. Lindsey informs me that microscopic examinations made by him have revealed that the specific distinctions relied upon by Warren are found, now on one side of the body, now on the other, in specimens of *centaureæ*, which he has investigated.

(2) **Hesperia ruralis** (Boisduval). Pl. XLVII, fig. 14, ♀. (The Two-banded Skipper).

Synonyms: *cæspitalis* (Boisd.); *ricara* (Edw.); *petreius* (Edw.).

Butterfly.—On the upper side strongly resembling the preceding species, but the inner row of white spots on the hind wings is more complete. On the under side the fore wings are black, crossed by a double row of white spots, as on the upper side, these spots standing out conspicuously on the dark ground. The hind wings on the under side are more or less ferruginous, with the white spots more or less conspicuous. The fringes are checkered white and gray. Expanse: 1.00 in.

Early Stages.—But little is known concerning these.

The species occurs in California, Oregon, and Nevada.

(3) **Hesperia xanthus** (Edwards). Pl. XLVII, fig. 15, ♂ (The Xanthus Skipper).

Synonym: *mcdunnoughi* (Oberthür).

Butterfly.—Resembling the preceding species, but easily distinguished by the larger size of all the spots on the upper side of the wing and the paler under side, the secondaries being marked somewhat as in *H. communis*. Expanse: 1.00 in.

Early Stages.—Hitherto undescribed.

The species has thus far been received only from southern Colorado, but undoubtedly will be found elsewhere in that portion of the land.

(4) **Hesperia scriptura** (Boisduval). Pl. XLVII, fig. 12, ♀ (The Small Checkered Skipper).

Butterfly.—Quite small. The hind wings on the upper side are almost entirely dark gray, the only white mark being a spot or two at the end of the cell. The fore wings are marked on this side as in the two foregoing species. On the under side the fore wings are blackish toward the base, with the costa, the apex, and the outer margin narrowly whitish. The hind wings below are pale, with an incomplete median band of white spots and broad white fringes, which are not checkered with darker color as in the preceding species. Expanse: .85 in.

Early Stages.—Unknown.

Inhabits southern Colorado, New Mexico, and Arizona.

(5) **Hesperia syrichtus** (Fabricius). Pl. L, fig. 16, ♀, *upper side;* fig. 17, ♂, *under side* (The Blue-gray Skipper).

This species is easily distinguished from its not remote congener, *H. communis* Grote, by the grayish blue hairs, or elongated scales, which clothe the basal areas of both wings on their upper surface in the case of the males, and by the presence of three dark spots, arranged in a horizontal series along the costa on the under side of the secondaries. The species is closely related to **H. orcus** (Cramer) (Pl. L, fig. 15, ♂) which doubtfully occurs within our limits, but is very common in the American tropics. In the latter species there is but one small dark spot near the costa at the base of the hind wing on the lower side. The female of *H. syrichtus* is darker than the male, as is shown upon our plate, and lacks the grayish blue squamation near the base of the wings on the upper side. Expanse: 1.2–1.3 inches.

The early stages await study. The insect is not uncommon in tropical America, and has been collected in Texas and Florida.

(6) **Hesperia montivaga** (Reakirt) Pl. L, fig. 18, ♂, *under side* (Reakirt's Skipper).

Synonym: *fumosus* Reverdin.

This species, or varietal form of *H. syrichtus* closely resembles it in all respects, save for the fact that the hind wings on the under side are heavily clouded with smoky brown, or reddish, giving the wings quite a different appearance on this side from those of *H. syrichtus*. The insect has the same range in our territory as the latter species, and appears to be the dominant form in Jamaica, from which island I have received it in numbers.

(7) **Hesperia communis** (Grote). Pl. L, fig. 19, ♂; fig. 20, ♀; fig. 21, ♂, *under side;* fig. 22, melanic female; Pl. VI, fig. 35, *chrysalis* (The Common Checker-spot).

Synonyms: *tessellata* Scud., preoccupied by *H. tessellata* Hew., an Asiatic species; *montivaga* Scud., not *montivaga* Reakirt.

Butterfly.—Both sides are correctly figured on our plates. The under side of the fore wings is much paler than the upper side, but with all the spots and markings of that side reproduced. The hind wings are creamy white, crossed by basal, median, postmedian, and marginal bands of pale ochreous, somewhat annular spots. There is usually a small black spot at the angle of the secondaries on the lower side. Expanse: 1.15–1.25 in.

The early stages have been in part described by Scudder. The caterpillar feeds on malvaceous plants. The insect has a wide range from the Atlantic westward, and from the Gulf to Canada.

There has been a good deal of discussion in recent years as to the name which should be given to this widely distributed species. It has generally been named *tessellata* Scudder, but it seems that the name *communis* (Grote) has priority. It is a somewhat variable insect, and those who are given to making small and microscopic distinctions, might find room for setting up a number of varieties when having before them, as I have, hundreds of specimens from all parts of the land. Such hair-splitting, however, has little charm for the present writer, and he is content to admit but one of the varietal forms, which has been named *occidentalis* by the late Dr. Skinner. (See No. 8).

(8) **Hesperia communis**, var. **occidentalis** Skinner. Plate XLVII, fig. 18, ♂; Pl. L, fig. 23, ♂, *under side* (The Western Checkered Skipper).

This form, which ranges from Kansas southward and westward to the Pacific, is the prevalent form in the arid regions of Arizona and southern California. It is characterized by the lighter upper surface of the wings and the much paler under surface of both the fore and hind wings, with an obsolescence of the darker transverse markings of the under side, specimens from Arizona being almost devoid of these.

The early stages are described and beautifully illustrated by Comstock ("Butterflies of California," p. 208). The larva feeds upon the *Malvaceæ*.

(9) **Hesperia philetas** (Edwards). Plate L, fig. 24, ♂ type (The Philetas Skipper).

This small but distinctly marked species has hitherto only been reported from Arizona. It is rare in collections. Nothing is known of its life-history.

Section 2. Subgenus HELIOPETES Billberg

Wings prevalently white on the upper side, with the neuration on the under side often black; the lower sides of the wings in some species marked with dark brown spots; mainly confined to sub-tropical and tropical localities.

(10) **Hesperia domicella** (Erichson) Plate XLVII, fig. 19, ♂ (Erichson's Skipper).

Synonym: *nearchus* Edwards.

Allied both to the preceding and the following species, between which it seems to form a connecting link, though much more closely related to those which follow than to those which precede. It is easily recognized by the broad, solid white bands on both the fore and the hind wings. Expanse: 1.25 in.

The early stages are unknown. It is found in Arizona and thence southward.

(11) **Hesperia ericetorum** (Boisduval) Plate L, fig. 27, ♂; fig. 28, ♀. (The Large White Skipper).

Synonym: *alba* Edwards.

The species occurs in southern California, Arizona, and Mexico. Its life-history is given by Comstock ("Butterflies of California," p. 209).

(12) **Hesperia macaira** (Reakirt). Pl. L, fig. 30, ♂; fig. 31, ♂, *under side* (The Macaira Skipper).

Synonym: *locutia* Hewitson.

This is a common species in Mexico and southward, and occasionally occurs as a straggler in the extreme southern part of Texas. It may be easily identified from our figures.

(13) **Hesperia laviana** (Hewitson). Pl. L, fig. 25, ♂; fig. 26, ♀ (The Laviana Skipper).

Synonym: *oceanus* Edwards.

The female has the outer margins of the fore and hind wings much more broadly marked with black than the male. The type of *oceanus* (Edw.), which is before me, is a female of this species, and not of *macaira*, as has been erroneously stated by numerous authors. It is quite differently marked below.

The species is rare in Texas, but common farther south.

(14) **Hesperia nivella** Mabille. Pl. L, fig. 29, ♂, *under side* (The Snowy Skipper).

Synonym: *nivea* Scudder (not *nivea* (Cramer) = *arsalte* (Linn.)).

The figure of the under side of the insect will enable it to be quickly identified. It has nothing to do with *H. macaira*, with which it has been by some authors erroneously confounded.

It occurs as a rare straggler in the extreme southern part of Texas; common in Mexico.

Genus CELOTES Godman & Salvin

This is a genus hitherto only represented by a single species, which has very properly been set off by Godman and Salvin from all others. The insect is not

Genus Pholisora

included in *Pholisora*, where Edwards located it; nor in *Hesperia*, where, with others, I placed it in the first edition of this book, nor in *Antigonus* Hübner.

(1) **Celotes nessus** (Edwards). Pl. XLVII, fig. 17, ♂ (The Nessus Skipper). Synonym: *notabilis* (Strecker).

This singularly marked little species can be easily identified from the figure given on the plate. Expanse: .80 in.

Its early stages are unknown. It is not uncommon in Texas and Arizona.

Genus SYSTASEA Butler

Butterfly.—The palpi are porrect, the third joint projecting forward, the second joint densely scaled below. The antennæ are slender, the club moderately stout, somewhat bluntly pointed, bent, not hooked. The hind wings are somewhat crenulate, and deeply excised opposite the end of the cell. In the fore wing the lower radial arises from a point nearer the upper radial than the third median nervule. The fore wings are crossed about the middle by translucent spots or bands.

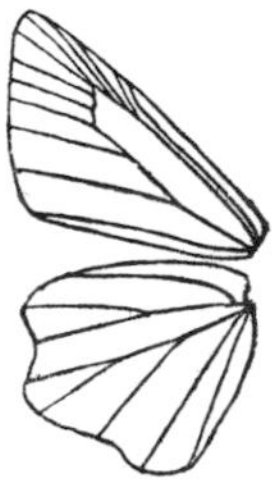

Early Stages.—Unknown.

(1) **Systasea pulverulenta** (Felder). Pl. XLVI, fig. 1, ♂, type of *zampa* Edw. (The Powdered Skipper).

Synonym: *zampa* Edwards.

Butterfly.—The wings on the upper side are ochreous, mottled and clouded with dark brown. The primaries are marked about the middle and before the apex by translucent transverse linear spots. In addition there are a number of pale opaque spots on the primaries. The secondaries are traversed by a pale sub-marginal whitish line. The under side of the wings is pale, with the light markings of the upper side indistinctly separated. Expanse: 1.10–1.25 inch.

FIG. 173.—Neuration of the genus *Systasea*.

Early Stages.—Unknown.

This interesting little species occurs in Arizona and northern Mexico. It has been erroneously referred in recent times to the genus *Antigonus*.

Genus PHOLISORA Scudder

Butterfly.—The palpi are porrect, the second joint loosely scaled, the third joint slender and conspicuous. The antennæ have the club gradually thickened, the tip blunt. The fore wing is relatively narrow, provided with a costal fold in the case of the male. The cut gives a correct idea of the neuration.

Egg.—The egg is curiously formed, much flattened at the base, marked on the side with longitudinal ridges and cross-lines, these ridges developing alternately at their apical extremities into thickened, more or less rugose elevations, the ridges pointing inwardly and surrounding the deeply depressed micropyle.

Caterpillar.—Slender, with the head broad, rounded; the body stout, thickest in the middle, tapering toward either end, and somewhat flattened below.

344

Chrysalis.—The chrysalis is slender, very slightly convex on the ventral side, somewhat concave on the dorsal side behind the thorax. The wing-cases are relatively smaller than in the preceding genera.

(1) **Pholisora catullus** (Fabricius). Pl. XLV, fig. 4, ♂; Pl. VI, figs. 29, 36, 41, *chrysalis* (The Sooty-wing).

Butterfly.—Black on both sides of the wings, with a faint marginal series and a conspicuous submarginal series of light spots on the primaries in the male sex on the upper side, and, in addition to these, in the female sex, a faint marginal series on the secondaries. On the under side only the upper spots of the submarginal series of the primaries reappear. Expanse: .80–1.15 inch.

Fig. 174. —Neuration of the genus *Pholisora.*

Early Stages.—The caterpillar feeds on "lamb's-quarter" (*Chenopodium album*) and the *Amarantaceæ*. It forms a case for itself by folding the leaf along the midrib and stitching the edges together with a few threads of silk. It lies concealed during the day and feeds at night. A minute account of all its peculiarities is given by Scudder in "The Butterflies of New England," vol. ii, p. 1519.

The insect ranges over the whole of temperate North America.

(2) **Pholisora mejicanus** (Reakirt). Pl. L; fig. 32, ♂ (The Mexican Sooty-wing).

Synonym: *catullus* ♀ Holland, Butt. Guide, Pl. CXXXIV, fig. 1.

Somewhat resembling *P. catullus*, from which it may be discriminated by the fact that the fore wings are marked with an irregular curved submedian line of white dots running from the costa to the inner margin, whereas in *catullus*, the white spots do not extend downwardly beyond the third median nervule, and by the bluish hoary tint of the underside of the wings. Expanse: 1.2 in.

As the name implies, this is a southern form, and so far as is known, only occasionally occurs along our southern borders, though not uncommon in Mexico.

(3) **Pholisora libya** Scudder. Pl. XLVIII, fig. 14, ♂ (The Mohave Sooty-wing).

Butterfly.—Easily distinguished from the two preceding species by the white fringes of the wings and by the markings of the under side. The primaries on the lower side are dark, tipped at the apex with light gray, and in the female having the costa and the outer margin broadly edged with light gray. The hind wings are pale gray of varying shades, marked with a number of large circular white spots on the disk and a marginal series of small white spots. Expanse, ♂, .80–1.25 in.; ♀, 1.15–1.40 in.

Early Stages.—These await full description.

This species is found from Nevada to Arizona, and is apparently very common in the Mohave Desert.

(4) **Pholisora lena** (Edwards). Pl. L, fig. 36, ♂, *under side*, type (The Montana Sooty-wing).

Very like *libya*. Wings on the under side paler than in typical *libya*; the hind wings marked with but one light spot in the center of the wing at the end of the cell, whereas in typical *libya* the light spots on the under side are numerous. Expanse: 1.25–1.40 in.

This species occurs in Montana, and may be the northern representative of *P. libya*.

(5) **Pholisora alpheus** Edwards. Pl. XLV, fig. 2, ♂ (The Alpheus Sootywing).

Synonym: *oricus* Edw.

Butterfly.—This little species is nearer *P. hayhursti* than any of the others we have described, but may at once be recognized and discriminated by the checkered margins and white tip of the fore wing and the linear shape of the spots composing the submarginal and median bands on the upper side of this wing. The hind wings on the under side are marked with a number of light spots arranged in marginal and median bands.

Early Stages.—Unknown.

Alpheus occurs in Nevada, Arizona, and New Mexico.

(6) **Pholisora hayhursti** Edwards. Pl. XLVIII, fig. 16, ♀ (Hayhurst's Skipper).

Butterfly.—Easily distinguished from the preceding species by the somewhat crenulate shape of the outer margin of the hind wings, the white color of the under side of the abdomen, and the different arrangement of the white spots on the fore wings, as well as by the dark bands which cross both the fore and the hind wings on the upper side. Expanse: .90–1.15 in.

Early Stages.—Our information as to these is incomplete.

The species ranges from the latitude of southern Pennsylvania westward and southward to the Gulf, as far as the Rocky Mountains.

(7) **Pholisora ascalaphus** (Staudinger). Pl. L, fig. 33, ♂; fig. 34, ♀, paratypes (The Ascalaphus Skipper).

The figures which we give of this species are those of specimens received from the author, and therefore may be accepted as representing his conception thereof. Like the preceding species, the outer margins of the hind wings are somewhat crenulate. Expanse: 1.20 in.

The early stages have not been studied. The insect is common in Mexico and occurs not infrequently in southern Texas.

(8) **Pholisora ceos** Edwards. Pl. L, fig. 35, ♂, type (The Ceos Skipper).

On the upper side this very black little butterfly has no light markings, except a few pale reddish scales on the upper side of the head and palpi. On the under side the palpi and breast are snow-white, and there are two very minute paired white spots just before the apex of the fore wing. Expanse: 1 in.

Habitat.—Arizona and northern Mexico.

Genus EANTIS Boisduval

This genus, which must not be confounded with the genus *Achlyodes* Hübner, the type of which has become by elimination the species *fridericus* Hübner, contains seven or eight species peculiar to the American tropics. In all of them the fore wing is strongly falcate, or sickle-shaped at the apex, with the external margin broadly rounded. The hind wings are relatively broad, and evenly rounded. The palpi are porrect, the two first joints heavily scaled, the third joint short and conical. The butterflies are of medium size, though one or two species are among the largest of the *Hesperiidæ*, having wings three inches in expanse, or even more. The males are generally dark in color, of some shade of brown or black, in several of the species shot with blue or violet reflections. The females are always lighter in color. A number of the species are adorned on the lower side by large yellowish or pale brown markings. Only one species, the type of the genus, *E. thraso* Hübner, occurs within our limits.

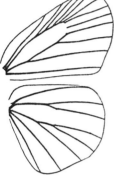

FIG. 175.—Neuration of *Eantis thraso*, enlarged.

(1) **Eantis thraso** (Hübner). Plate L, fig. 39, ♂. (The Sickle-winged Skipper).

Synonym: *tamenund* (Edwards).

This butterfly, which is common from Mexico to Paraguay, is now and then taken in Texas. Expanse: 1.5–1.7 in.

Genus XENOPHANES Godman and Salvin

The palpi are much as in the genus *Pholisora*, the first and second joints being heavily clothed, the third produced, conical. The club of the antenna is slender, strongly retrorse, or backwardly curved. The only species in the genus is widely distributed from the southern boundaries of the United States to southern Brazil and Paraguay, and with the exception of a small insular variety, scarcely worthy of being named, is the same throughout the immense area in which the insect occurs.

(1) **Xenophanes tryxus** (Cramer). Pl. L, fig. 38, ♂. (The Glassy-winged Skipper).

The butterfly, which may easily be known from the figure we give, has now and then been taken in southern Texas. Its early stages have not as yet been carefully studied and little is known of them. Expanse: 1.3 in.

Genus MELANTHES Mabille

(Not *Ephyriades* Hübner, the type of which is *Papilio otreus* Cramer, which is not congeneric, nor identical with *zephodes* H.-S. *Cf.* Draudt, in Seitz, Gross-Schmett. d. Erde, Vol. V, p. 918).

In the Annals of the Carnegie Museum, Vol. X, 1916, p. 504, *et seq.*, I discussed at some length the status of the genus *Melanthes* Mabille, and the species referred to it. Since then additional studies and correspondence with European lepidopterists have led me to revise the opinions then provisionally expressed. I am now of the decided opinion that *P. otreus* Cramer is not identical with *zephodes* Hübner, and that the species named *brunnea* by Herrich-Schæffer is not a variety of the former. I accept the genus *Melanthes* Mabille with *brunnea* H.-S. as its type, as Mabille intended, believing that *brunnea* H.-S. is a valid species, and quite distinct from *zephodes* Hübner.

(1) **Melanthes brunnea** (Herrich-Schæffer). Plate L, fig. 40, ♂; fig. 41, ♀. (The Brown Skipper).

The insect, which is common in Cuba, has been reported from the Keys of southern Florida.

(2) **Melanthes zephodes** (Hübner). Pl. LI, fig. 5, ♂; fig. 6, ♀ (The Zephodes Skipper).

Synonym: *Eudamus electra* Lintner.

Differentiated from *M. brunnea* by the form of the wings, the shape and arrangement of the vitreous markings on them, and the color of the underside. The only specimen of this species known to have been taken in our territory was captured at Hamilton, Ontario. Coming into the possession of Prof. Lintner he named it *Eudamus electra*. I have long owned the type, and many years ago pointed out to Dr. Henry Skinner its identity with *zephodes*. Skinner subsequently published an article upon the subject (*Cf.* Trans. Am. Ent. Soc., XXXVIII, 1911, p. 208). The specimen no doubt reached Hamilton as a chrysalis hidden in a bunch of bananas imported from some island of the West Indies.

Genus CHIOMARA Godman and Salvin

This genus, which was set up by its authors with *mithrax* Mœschler as its type, is of somewhat doubtful validity. The species *gesta* (H.-S.) originally included in it, is undoubtedly a true *Thanaos*. The third species is *asychis* (Cram.)

(1) **Chiomara asychis** (Cramer). Pl. L., fig. 37, ♂ (The Asychis Skipper).

This striking little butterfly ranges from Texas to Argentina. On the under side the wings, except on their margins, are creamy white. The outer margins, the costa, and the bases of the wings are laved with fuscous. Expanse: 1.5 in.

Early Stages.—Unknown.

Genus THANAOS Boisduval

(Type *Papilio tages* Linnæus)

Synonym: *Erynnis* Rambur (not Schrank)

(The Dusky-wings)

Butterfly.—The antennæ have a moderately large club, curved, bluntly pointed. The palpi are porrect, the third joint almost concealed in the dense hairy vestiture of the second joint. The neuration of the wings is represented in the cut. The fore wing in the case of the male always has a costal fold. The butterflies comprised in this genus are all, without exception, dark in color, in a few species having bright spots upon the hind wings.

The genus reaches its largest development in North America. The discrimination of the various species is difficult.

Egg.—The egg is somewhat like the egg in the genus *Achalarus*, but the micropyle at the upper end of the egg is relatively larger and not as deeply depressed below the surface. The sides are ornamented, as in *Achalarus*, by raised vertical ridges, between which are numerous cross-ridges; in a few cases the vertical ridges are beaded, or marked by a series of minute globose prominences, upon the edge.

FIG. 176.— Neuration of the genus *Thanaos*.

Caterpillar.—The caterpillars are cylindrical, tapering from the middle forward and backward, marked with lateral and dorsal stripes, with the neck less strangulated than in the preceding genera.

Chrysalis.—Not greatly differing in outline from the chrysalis of the preceding genera, in most species having the outline of the dorsum straight on the abdominal segments, with the thoracic segments forming a slight hump or elevation; convex on the ventral side, the cremaster being usually well developed.

(1) **Thanaos gesta** Herrich-Schæffer. Pl. LI, fig. 1, ♂; fig. 2, ♀ (The Antillean Dusky-wing).

Synonyms: *invisus* Butler & Druce; *llano* Dodge.

Found in southern Texas and Arizona, ranging thence southward to Colombia; abundant in the greater Antilles. On the upper side, as shown by our figure, the wings are warm shining brown, crossed by darker bands; the fringes only slightly paler. On the under side the wings are lighter than above, without any distinctive markings. Expanse: 1.25–1.35 in.

The early stages have not been studied, so far as the writer recalls.

The next three species, *T. brizo* Bdv., *T. burgessi* Skinner, and *T. lacustra* Wright, are exceedingly closely related to each other. They can only be separated by the microscopic examination of the male genitalia. Even so, I find it practically impossible to distinguish *burgessi* Skinner and *lacustra* Wright from each other.

Superficially the three forms are quite alike, having on the fore wings two bands of raised black scales parallel to the outer margin from the costa to the first median nervule, then bending outwardly. Between these dark narrow bands the squamation is lighter, especially toward the costa.

(2) **Thanaos brizo** Boisd. & Lec., Pl. XLV, fig. 7, ♀ ; Pl. VI, fig. 38, *chrysalis* (The Sleepy Dusky-wing).

Butterfly.—The band of postmedian spots on the fore wing composed of dark markings, is regular, crosses the wing from the costa to the hind margin, and is reproduced on the under side as a series of pale-yellowish spots more or less distinct. The hind wings have a double series of faint yellow spots; these as well as the marginal spots of the primaries are very distinct on the under side. Expanse: 1.25–1.60 in.

Early Stages.—The caterpillar feeds on oaks, *Galactia*, and possibly *Baptisia*. The life-history has been only partially ascertained, in spite of the fact that the insect has a wide range and is not uncommon.

Brizo occurs from the Atlantic to the Pacific, ranging from the latitude of New England to that of Arizona.

(3) **Thanaos burgessi** Skinner. Pl. LI, fig. 7, ♂, paratype (Burgess' Dusky-wing).

The insect was described from Arizona. I have a number of specimens taken at the same time and place by the same collector. Superficially the type to my eye **is** indistinguishable from *T. brizo*.

(4) **Thanaos lacustra** (Wright). Pl. LI, fig. 8, ♂ (Wright's Dusky-wing).

I have an excellently clear photograph of the type of Wright's *lacustra*, for which I am indebted to Mr. J. D. Gunder. It brings out the maculation of the fore wing, far more distinctly than it is shown on Wright's plate in his "Butterflies of the West Coast." I also have a specimen received from Wright, which I figure on the plate. At the time Wright sent me the specimen he had affixed no name to it, and submitted it to me for determination. My recollection is that I told him it was a specimen of *T. brizo*. This specimen agrees absolutely with the photograph of his type of *lacustra*.

Williams (Trans. Am. Ent. Soc., Vol. L, p. 196) has maintained that the name *lacustra* is a synonym of *callidus* Grinnell, the latter having priority. Comstock in his "Butterflies of California," p. 212, informs us that in figuring *lacustra* Wright he used the "female type" of *callidus* Grinnell, it having been discovered to be in fact a male and not a female. Comstock's figure unfortunately is so dark and devoid of detail, that it is hard to recognize its identity with *lacustra*. For my part, as already stated, it seems impossible to separate the three species, *brizo*, *burgessi*, and *lacustra* = *callidus* (*fide* Williams) unless it be by minor genitalic differences which may be individual, not specific.

(5) **Thanaos icelus** (Scudder & Burgess). Pl. XLVIII, fig. 17, ♂; Pl. VI, fig. 27, *chrysalis* (The Dreamy Dusky-wing).

Butterfly.—Prevalently smaller in size than the three preceding species. The under side of the wings is paler than the upper side, and the outer third of both the primaries and secondaries is marked with a profusion of small indistinct yellow spots, which do not form well-defined bands as in the preceding species. On the upper side of the fore wing the median area is generally marked by a broad band of pale gray, but this is not invariably the case. Expanse: 1.00–1.20 inch.

Early Stages.—These have been described by Scudder. The caterpillar feeds on a variety of plants, as the aspen, oaks, and witch-hazel.

Icelus ranges across the continent from Nova Scotia to Oregon, and south to Florida and Arizona.

(6) **Thanaos somnus** (Lintner). Pl. XLVIII, fig, 2, ♂; Pl. LI, fig. 3, ♂, fig. 4, ♀, Lintner's types (The Dark Dusky-wing).

Butterfly.—A little larger than the preceding species, especially in the female sex. The male is generally quite dark, the banding of the fore wing on the upper side obscured. The hind wings have a row of light marginal and submarginal spots, more distinct on the under side than on the upper. The female generally is light gray on the upper side of the wings, with broad median and submarginal bands of dark brown, tending to fuse or coalesce at a point near the origin of the first median nervule. Expanse: ♂, 1.25 inch; ♀, 1.50 inch.

Early Stages.—But little is known of these.

All of the specimens I have ever seen came from southern Florida.

Some writers have contended that this is a form of *T. brizo*, but, with the types before me, I am unable to agree with this opinion. It is much nearer *T. icelus.*

(7) **Thanaos lucilius** (Scudder & Burgess). Pl. XLVIII, fig. 10, ♂; Pl. VI, figs. 30-32, *chrysalis* (Lucilius' Dusky-wing).

Butterfly.—This species is difficult to distinguish from *T. persius*. As a rule both sexes are darker than in *T. persius*, and the females show less clearly defined maculation. The two species are very close to each other and they may only be local races, as has been suggested by Lindsey. Expanse: 1.20–1.40 in.

Early Stages.—Dr. Scudder has fully described these. The caterpillar feeds on the columbine (*Aquilegia canadensis*).

Lucilius ranges from New England to Georgia, is common in western Pennsylvania and West Virginia, and extends westward at least as far as the Rocky Mountains. Williams contends that *lucilius* is the same as *T. persius*.

(8) **Thanaos persius** (Scudder). Pl. XLVIII, fig. 1, ♂; Pl. VI, fig. 34, *chrysalis* (Persius' Dusky-wing).

Butterfly.—This is a variable species, some specimens being light and others dark in color. It is superficially very close to *T. lucilius*. There is scarcely any positive clue to the specific identity of the insect, except that which is derived from the study of the genital armature of the male, which is a microscopic research capable of being performed only by an expert in such matters. Expanse: 1.20–1.45 in.

Early Stages.—The caterpillar feeds on willows. Scudder has with patient care described its life-history.

The insect ranges from New England southward, and inland across the continent to the Pacific.

A small black form, regarded as a variety of *T. persius*, hitherto only known from the region of Mt. Tamalpais near San Francisco, has been named **pernigra** by Grinnell. (*Cf.* Comstock, "Butterflies of California," p. 213, Pl. 59, figs. 5-6). (Grinnell's Dusky-wing).

(9) **Thanaos afranius** (Lintner). Pl. XLV, fig. 5, ♂ (Afranius' Dusky-wing).

Butterfly.—Closely related to *T. persius*. The hind wings on the upper side in the male sex are almost solid black, the fringes paler. On the under side there is a double row of light spots along the margin of the hind wing in both sexes. The female is generally paler in color on the upper side than the male. The specimen we figure is labelled by Edwards "*Afranius* ♂, Lintner, ms.," and was no doubt sent to Edwards by Lintner, before the latter had published his description.

Early Stages.—Unknown.

It ranges from Colorado to California and Arizona, where the thing is apparently not rare.

(10) **Thanaos avinoffi** sp. nov. Pl. LI, fig. 28, ♂; fig. 29, ♀. (Avinoff's Dusky-wing).

Butterfly.—*Male:* The wings on the upper side almost uniformly dark brownish black; the fringes a trifle lighter than the rest of the wings; the fore wings have a thin, sharply defined marginal, black line, followed by a series of slightly lighter intraneural marginal markings, succeeded by deep black minute sagittate markings, which in turn are succeeded by a slightly lighter narrow submarginal band obscurely defined inwardly, and running from the costa to the inner margin. There are three very minute preapical translucent spots on the costa, and in some specimens a similar minute translucent spot above the second median nervule at its origin; the remainder of the wing toward the base is deep black. The hind wings above are deep brownish black, without apparent markings, except the fine black marginal line. On the under side both wings are a trifle paler than on the upper side, lightest at the inner angle of the primaries; the translucent pale spots on the fore wings more distinct on this side than above. Close scrutiny reveals a very faint and obscure post-median band of lighter markings on the hind wing, but these are not always present. *Female:* Somewhat lighter in color than the male on both sides of the wings, with the paler markings more distinct. Some of the females have a minute translucent spot at the end of the cell of the fore wing, and most specimens have two spots, one above, the other below the second median nervule at the point where it is emitted on the fore wing. Expanse: 1.12 in.

Described from a series of over forty specimens coming from the Yukon Valley, White Horse Pass, the Valley of the Kuskokwim, and other points in Alaska. The great uniformity in size and in the markings of this obscure little species, which is the prevalent form of the genus throughout Alaska, leads me to regard it as worthy of a specific name. It is the insect, which I designated as *T. persius* in the Ent. News, Vol. XI, 1900, p. 420, basing my record at that time upon a single specimen from Fort Selkirk sent me by the late S. Hall Young. I name it in honor of Dr. A. Avinoff, whose grandfather, the Admiral, explored the coast of Alaska for the Russian Government, and whose name is borne by one of its capes.

(11) **Thanaos martialis** (Scudder). Pl. XLVIII, fig. 4, ♂; Pl. VI, fig. 37, *chrysalis* (Martial's Dusky-wing).

Butterfly.—The upper side of the wings is paler than in most species, and has a distinctly purplish-gray cast. The fore wings are crossed by irregular bands of dark spots. The hind wings on the outer half are profusely mottled with small pale spots. All the light spots are repeated on the under side of both wings, and are more distinct on this side than on the upper. Expanse: 1.25–1.40 inch.

Early Stages.—These are partly known. The caterpillar feeds on *Indigofera* and *Amarantus*.

The species ranges from Massachusetts to Georgia, and westward to Missouri and New Mexico.

An aberrant dark form, without the translucent hyaline spots, was named *ausonius* (Scudder).

(12) **Thanaos juvenalis** (Fabricius). Pl. XLVIII, fig. 11, ♀ ; Pl. VI, fig. 33, *chrysalis* (Juvenal's Dusky-wing).

Synonyms: *juvenis* (Hbn.); *costalis* (Westw. & Hew.); *nævius* (Scud. & Burg.).

Butterfly.—Larger than the preceding species. The wings have a number of translucent spots arranged as a transverse series beyond the middle of the wing. They are far more distinct and larger in the female than in the male. The under side of the wings is paler than the upper side, and profusely but indistinctly marked with light spots. Expanse: 1.35–1.60 inch.

Early Stages.—For a full knowledge of these the reader may consult the pages of "The Butterflies of New England." The caterpillar feeds on oaks and leguminous plants of various species.

This insect ranges from Quebec to Florida, and westward as far as Arizona and California.

(13) **Thanaos propertius** (Scudder & Burgess). Pl. LI, fig. 12, ♂ (Propertius' Dusky-wing).

Synonym: *tibullus* (Scudder & Burgess).

This insect ranges, so far as is known, from Texas to California, and northward into the western part of the Dominion of Canada. Fresh specimens, such as shown on our Plate, are distinguished by the presence of a somewhat hoary vestiture of scales on the uppersides of the wings, but when the insects have flown for some time, this light scaling is lost and the butterflies become very black in appearance. Expanse: 1.5 in.

What has been alleged to be a dwarfed dark race of this species from the Mackenzie region was named var. *borealis* by Cary. The type was unique. We have specimens from the same region, which appear to be the insect described by Cary. They cannot be confounded with *T. avinoffi*.

(14) **Thanaos horatius** (Scudder & Burgess). Pl. XLVIII, fig. 7, ♀ ; fig. 15, ♀ ; Pl. LI, fig. 11, ♂ (Horace's Dusky-wing).

Butterfly.—Allied in size to the preceding species, but the translucent spots of the transverse band are not, as in that species, continued toward the inner margin, but terminate at the first median nervule. The outer third of the primaries is pale, the inner two thirds dark. The under side of the wings of the male is uniformly dusky, slightly, if at all, marked with lighter spots. The under side of the wings of the female is less distinctly marked with light spots than is the case in allied species. Expanse: 1.50–1.75 inch.

Early Stages.—Unknown.

This species ranges from New England to Florida and westward.

(15) **Thanaos terentius** (Scudder & Burgess). Pl. XLVIII, Fig. 3, ♀ (Terence's Dusky-wing).

Synonyms: *ovidius* (Scud. & Burgess); *nœvius* (Lintner).

Butterfly.—This insect is closely allied to *T. horatius*, but the translucent spots on the fore wing are smaller, and there is generally a light spot near the costa before the three subapical translucent spots.

Early Stages.—Unknown.

This species ranges from Florida as far north as eastern Pennsylvania and New Jersey.

Williams, whose opinions I hold in high respect, maintains that this species is "practically the same" as the species found in Cuba and named *zarucco* by Lucas. The latter name according to Williams should replace *terentius*.

(16) **Thanaos callidus** Grinnell (The Artful Dusky-wing).

As stated under No. 4 (*T. lacustra*), Williams maintains that *T. callidus* is the same as *lacustra* Wright, and that the latter name should be dropped as a synonym. Comstock in the "Butterflies of California" figures *callidus*, and maintains that it is distinct from *lacustra*. Williams maintains that *T. lilius* Dyar is one of the insects described by Grinnell under the name *callidus*, for Grinnell "got things mixed," and it is alleged that he described two or three species under *callidus*. It is a perplexing tangle. From Comstock's figures I can make nothing out of the case, because they "all look alike to me." I believe I have a specimen of the insect in my collection from the State of Washington, but nothing except a study of the genitalia could determine, and, being at this writing in the eighty-third year of my age, I am not inclined to devote myself, as I once did, to genitalic studies. I merely list the name.

(17) **Thanaos lilius** Dyar. This case is analogous to that of the preceding species. "The Doctors disagree; who can decide?" The genitalia of *T. lilius* = *callidus* Grinnell are said to be like those of *pacuvius*, though Dyar claimed they were like those of *tibullus* = *propertius*. I merely list the name. According to Benjamin, *T. lilius* Dyar is a synonym of *T. callidus* Grinnell.

(18) **Thanaos pacuvius** (Lintner). Pl. XLVIII, fig. 9, ♀. (Pacuvius' Dusky-Wing).

Butterfly.—Small, with the fore wings on the upper side rather regularly banded with dark brown upon a lighter ground. The hind wings are almost solid black above, with the fringes toward the anal angle pure white. Expanse: 1.15–1.30 in.

Early Stages.—Unknown.

This species occurs in Colorado, Mexico, Arizona, and California.

(19) **Thanaos scudderi** Skinner. Pl. LI, fig. 9, ♂, paratype (Scudder's Dusky-wing).

This insect is much like *T. pacuvius*. The fringes of the hind wings appear to be whiter throughout, and the outline of the wings is slightly different from what is seen in *pacuvius*. The specimen we figure is a paratype, which has been compared with the type, and thoroughly agrees with it. The butterfly has been recorded from Texas and Arizona. Expanse: 1.25 in.

(20) **Thanaos clitus** Edwards. Pl. XLV, fig. 8, ♂, type (The Clitus Dusky-wing).

Butterfly.—Larger than the preceding species. The hind wings are solidly deep black, fringed broadly with pure white. The fore wings of the male are dark, of the female lighter. Expanse: 1.60–1.75 in.

Early Stages.—Unknown.

The habitat of this species is Arizona and New Mexico.

(21) **Thanaos tristis** Boisduval. Pl. LI, fig. 10, ♂ (The Sad Dusky-wing).

Very closely related to the preceding species; white fringes of the hind wings longer than in *clitus* and the under side generally lighter than in that species. Expanse: 1.25–1.35 in.

Occurs in Arizona, California, and Mexico.

(22) **Thanaos tatius** Edwards. Pl. LXXV, fig. 15, ♂; fig. 16, do., *under side*, enlarged photograph of type (Tatius' Dusky-wing).

This insect is preserved in the Museum of the Brooklyn Institute, and I am indebted to Dr. Engelhardt for the privilege of figuring the unique specimen. It has been treated by some compilers of lists as a varietal form of *T. tristis.*

As it is a unique specimen, its genitalia have not yet, for a wonder, been re moved and dissected.

(23) **Thanaos funeralis** (Scud. & Burg.). Pl. XLVIII, fig. 12, ♂ (The Funereal Dusky-wing).

The insect, of which we know but little thus far, ranges from western Texas to Arizona. It differs from the species preceding it in our list by the relatively narrower fore wings and the broad and somewhat rounded hind wings. Expanse: 1.35 in.

The early stages are not known.

The student will observe from the study of the foregoing list that the butterflies of this somber group are difficult in many cases to specifically differentiate. Great reliance has been placed by those, who have devoted themselves to their study, to slight differences in the genitalia. Whether dependence can be placed upon a few dissections of these organs for specific determinations is an open question, though such researches may lead in many cases to correct results. There is, however, reason to believe that these organs themselves vary considerably, and, as the preparation of microscopic slides may be accompanied at times with more or less distortion, too great reliance cannot be placed upon a few examinations made in this way.

Upon the whole this group of butterflies is one of the most difficult in our fauna, but all the more interesting on that account. The young student is apt to say in their presence "All coons look alike to me!" Their study by the dissecting brotherhood has reminded me of the saying of a celebrated pomologist, who used to remark "The only way to really tell what variety of apple is before you, is to eat it." The only way to tell what species of *Thanaos* you have in many cases is to dissect it. But what then becomes of your specimen? As it is, the abdomens of a lot of mine have mysteriously disappeared. Where did they go? I cannot tell. Curators should be watchful!

Genus TIMOCHARES Godman and Salvin

The second joint of palpi heavily clothed with hairs, the third joint conical; antennæ relatively short, not half as long as the costa of the primaries; fore wing of the male with a fold, the apex truncate, the outer margin rounded. The secondaries subtriangular, not produced at anal angle.

(1) **Timochares ruptifasciatus** (Ploetz). Pl. LI, fig. 14, ♂ (The Broken-banded Dusky-wing).

Butterfly.—The general color of the upper side of the wings is reddish fawn, with dark brown transverse bands and markings. Expanse: 1.50–1.60 in.

It may easily be recognized from our plate.

It is not uncommon in Mexico and southward. It occurs as a straggler in Texas.

Genus GRAIS Godman and Salvin

(1) **Grais stigmaticus** (Mabille). Pl. LI, fig. 13, ♂ (Stigmatic Dusky-wing).

This insect may readily be recognized from the figure we give. It is a large brownish species, which, like the preceding, straggles into our territory from Mexico, where it is not rare. Expanse: 1.75–1.85 in.

COLLECTIONS AND COLLECTORS

In almost every community there is to be found some one who is interested in insects, and who has formed a "*collection.*" The commonest form of a collection is exceedingly primitive and unscientific, in which a few local species are pinned together in a glass-covered box or receptacle, which is then framed and hung upon the wall. Formerly every village bar-room contained such monstrous assemblages of insects, skewered on pins, in more or less frightful attitudes. As evidencing an innate interest in the beauties of natural objects, these things are interesting, but show a want of information, which, as has been already pointed out, is largely due to a lack of literature relating to the subject in this country. In many of the schools of the land small collections, arranged more scientifically, have been made, and some of the collections contained in the high schools of our larger towns and cities are creditable to the zeal of teachers and of pupils. There is no reason why every school of importance should not, in the lapse of time, secure large and accurately named collections, not only of the insects, but of the other animals, as well as the plants and minerals of the region in which it is located. Every high school should have a room set apart for the use of those students who are interested in the study of natural history, and they ought to be encouraged to bring together collections, which should be properly arranged and preserved. The expense is not great, and the practical value of the training, which such studies impart to the minds of young people, is inestimable.

The great systematic collections in entomology in the United States are for the most part in the hands of the museums and universities of the country. The entomological collections of the United States National Museum at Washington are large and rich in interesting material. The collections possessed by Harvard College and the Boston Society of Natural History are extensive; so are also the collections of the American Museum of Natural History, the Academy of Natural Sciences in Philadelphia, and those of the Carnegie Museum in Pittsburgh. The collection in the latter institution is altogether the largest and most perfect collection of the butterflies of North America in existence, and largely covers the butterflies of the world, there being about eighteen thousand species of butterflies represented, including all known genera.

The formation of great collections has always had a charm for those who have possessed the knowledge, the time, and the means to form them; and the ranks of those who are engaged in the study of butterflies include many of the most famous naturalists, among them not a few of noble rank. One of the most enthusiastic collectors in Europe used to be the Grand Duke Nicholas Michailovitch of Russia. The Nestor among German collectors in the past was Dr. Staudinger of Dresden, whose collection is now in the National Museum in Berlin. In France M. Charles Oberthür of Rennes was the possessor of the largest and most perfect collection on French soil; it has since his death been sold and scattered. In England there is the great collection contained in the British Natural History Museum, which has absorbed the great collections of Hewitson, Lord Walsingham, Mr. F. D. Godman, H. J. Elwes, and others. The largest private collection in England belongs to Lord Rothschild and is lodged in his museum at Tring.

There are many men who make the collecting of natural-history specimens a business. Some have been among the most intrepid and indefatigable explorers of modern times. The late Henry W. Bates and Mr. Alfred Russel Wallace were in early life leaders in this work, and we are indebted to their researches for a knowledge of thousands of species. Two of the most successful collectors who followed in their footsteps were Mr. Herbert H. Smith and Mr. William Doherty, both of them Americans, both long employed by the writer. Mr. Smith was one of the most enthusiastic and successful explorers in South and Central America; Mr. Doherty the most diligent explorer of the Indo-Malayan Region. The stories of the travels and adventures of these two men were tales full of romantic interest which, alas! were by neither of them committed to writing.

SUBFAMILY PAMPHILINÆ

"Into the sunshine,
Full of light,
Leaping and flashing
From morn till night."
RUSSELL.

The *Pamphilinæ* found in our fauna fall into two groups.

Group A.—The antennæ are not greatly hooked and generally sharply pointed; the palpi have the third joint short and inconspicuous, sometimes porrect; the cell of the fore wing is always less than two thirds the length of the costa; the lower radial is somewhat nearer to the third median nervule than to the upper radial. The hind wing is often lobed. The lower radial in the hind wing is generally lacking. The male never has a costal fold on the fore wings, and is without a discal stigma.

The genera belonging to this section of this subfamily found in our fauna are *Pamphila Oarisma, Dalla,* and *Amblyscirtes.*

Group B.—The antennæ are sometimes curved, but never hooked, the palpi having the third joint minute, sometimes horizontally porrect. The cell of the fore wing is less than two thirds the length of the costa. The lower radial arises much nearer to the third median nervule than to the upper radial. The hind wing may be elongated, but never tailed. The male is never provided on the fore wing with a costal fold, but in most genera is furnished with a discal stigma on the fore wing. When in a state of rest the majority of the species elevate their fore wings and depress their hind wings, an attitude which is peculiar to the insects of this group.

Genus PAMPHILA Fabricius

(Type *Papilio palæmon* Pallas)

Synonyms: *Carterocephalus* Lederer; *Pamphilidia* Lindsey.

Butterfly.—The antennæ are very short, less than half the length of the costa. The club is stout, elongate, and blunt at its extremity; the palpi are porrect, densely clothed with scales, concealing the third joint, which is minute, slender, and bluntly conical. The body is long, slender, and somewhat produced beyond the hind margin of the secondaries. The neuration of the wings is represented in fig. 177.

Egg.—Hemispherical, vertically ribbed, the interspaces uniformly marked with little pitted depressions.

Caterpillar.—The body is cylindrical, slender, tapering forward and backward; the neck less strangulated than in many of the genera. The body is somewhat hairy; the spiracles on the sides open from minute subconical elevations.

Chrysalis.—Not materially differing in outline and structure from the chrysalids of other genera which have already been described.

But few species belonging to the genus are found in North America. There are several in Europe.

(1) **Pamphila mandan** Edwards. Pl. XLVII, fig. 1, ♂ (The Arctic Skipper).

Synonym: *mesapano* (Scud.).

FIG. 177.—Neuration of the genus *Pamphila*.

Butterfly.—No description of this interesting little insect is necessary, as the figure on the plate will enable the student at once to distinguish it. It is not identical with *P. palæmon* Pallas, though very closely related. Expanse: 1.10 in.

Early Stages.—These have been described by Dr. Scudder and Mr. Fletcher. The caterpillar feeds on grasses.

The insect ranges from southern Labrador as far south as the Pocono Mountains in Pennsylvania, thence westward, following a line curving north of the Great Lakes to Vancouver Island. It ranges southward along the summits of the Western Cordilleras as far as northern California.

(2) **Pamphila skada** (Edwards). Pl. LI, fig. 18, ♂ (The Skada Skipper).

This insect, which may be recognized by our figure, differs strikingly from *P. mandan*, the form which prevails in the eastern and more southern parts of the range of the genus. It is a lighter insect than *mandan* and the maculation is different. We have received it in some numbers from northern and western Alaska. It seems to be intermediate between *mandan* and *palæmon* of Europe.

Genus OARISMA Scudder

Butterfly.—Closely related to the preceding genus. The antennæ are very short; the club is long, cylindrical, bluntly rounded at the apex, not curved. The palpi are stout, the apical joint very slender, elongated, and porrect. The head is broad; the body is long and slender, projecting somewhat beyond the posterior margin of the secondaries. The neuration of the wings is represented in the cut.

Early Stages.—So far as known to me the life-history of no butterfly of this genus has yet been ascertained.

(1) **Oarisma garita** (Reakirt). Pl. LI, fig. 16, ♂; fig. 17, ♂, *under side* (The Garita Skipperling).

Synonym: *hylax* (Edwards).

Butterfly.—This obscure little insect is dark on the upper side; on the under side the fore wings are bright fulvous on the costa, with the inner margin laved with dark gray. The hind wings are paler fulvous, inclining to gray, with a dark ray near the inner margin. Expanse: .65–.80 in.

Early Stages.—We know little of these. The species is found in Arizona and Mexico.

(2) **Oarisma edwardsi** Barnes. Pl. XLVII, fig. 3, ♂ (Edwards Skipperling).

This is the insect, which in the first edition of this book was figured as *O. garita* Reakirt, but is different from that species, a figure of the true *garita* being cited above. The insect has been named *edwardsi* by Barnes since The Butterfly Book first appeared. It is intermediate between the true *garita*, which is a smaller insect, and *O. powesheik* Parker, which is a larger and darker form. Expanse: 1.0–1.2 in.

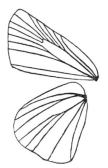

FIG. 178.—Neuration of the genus *Oarisma*. Enlarged.

It is found in Arizona.

(3) **Oarisma powesheik** Parker. Pl. XLVII, fig. 4, ♂ (The Powesheik Skipperling).

Butterfly.—This species may be distinguished from its ally *edwardsi* by its larger size, the darker color of the upper side of the wings, and the red markings on the costa of the fore wings. On the under side the fore wings are black, edged on the costa and outer margin for a short distance below the apex with light fulvous. The hind wings are dusky, with the veins and nervules white, standing forth conspicuously upon the darker ground-color. Expanse: 1.00–1.25 inch.

Early Stages.—Unknown.

Powesheik occurs in Wisconsin, and ranges thence westward to Nebraska, northward to Dakota, and southward as far as Colorado.

Genus DALLA Mabille

This genus was erected for the reception of species not congeneric with those belonging to the genus *Butleria* Kirby, which genus is at present restricted to a small group, mainly found in Chile, characterized by the brilliant coloring of the under side of the wings, as well as by certain structural details. The type of *Butleria* Kirby is *valdivianus* Philippi = *exornatus* Felder.

The species included by the writer in the genus *Dalla* Mabille are mostly small, dark colored, with the costa of the fore wing not as distinctly bowed, or rounded in front, as in *Butleria*.

(1) **Dalla pirus** (Edwards). Pl. LI, fig. 15, ♂ type (The Pirus Skipperling).

Butterfly.—*Male:* dark brown on the upper side with a very minute white spot at the end of the cell of the fore wing; three small preapical spots near its costa, the upper and lower oval, the middle spot of the series small and circular; two minute spots, one at the origin of the first submedian, the second at the origin of the second submedian. The hind wings have no markings whatever; the fringes of both wings are very slightly paler than the ground color on the upper side. On

360

the under side the fore wings are dark fulvous with the spots more distinct than on the upper side. The hind wings on the lower side are fulvous or dark brick-red. The palpi and front on the under side are white. *Female:* marked like the male both on the upper and under side, but with the wings somewhat broader. Expanse: ♂, .8; ♀, 1 in.

This species occurs in southern Colorado, Utah, and Arizona.

(2) **Dalla polingi** (Barnes). Pl. LI fig. 19, ♂; fig. 20, ♂, *under side*, paratype (Poling's Skipper).

This species may easily be distinguished from the preceding by the more distinct and numerous light spots on the upper side of the fore wing as well as by the presence of two light spots on the disk of the hind wing, and by the entire difference in the appearance of the under side of the wings, the secondaries having a moderately large light spot in the middle of the cell, beyond which is a median band of three light spots, of which the one nearest the costa is the largest, sub-triangular in outline. The species may be easily recognized from our plate. Expanse: 1 in.

It has only hitherto been reported from Arizona, where it appears to be not uncommon.

(3) **Dalla microsticta** Godman and Salvin.

This little species, which is congeneric with the preceding, occurs in northern Mexico, and is reported as having been taken in Arizona near the Mexican border. It may be distinguished from the other species, which we have listed, by the white fringes of the wings and by the more numerous light spots on the secondaries as well as by the fact that the hind wings on the lower side are grayish and not reddish, as in the other two species. It is figured by Godman and Salvin "Biol. Centr. Am., Rhop., Vol. III, Pl. 92, figs. 1-3." Expanse: .8 inch.

FIG. 179.—Neuration of the genus *Amblyscirtes*, enlarged.

Genus AMBLYSCIRTES Scudder

Butterfly.—The antennæ are short, with a moderately thick club, crooked at the end; the third joint of the palpi is bluntly conical, short, and erect. The costa of the fore wing is straight, slightly rounded before the apex. None of the species has a true stigma on the fore wing, although in several of the species there are a few androconia located below the cell near the origin of the second median nervule, which, being visible under the microscope, suggest a rudimentary stigma. The neuration is shown in Fig. 179.

Egg.—Hemispherical.

Caterpillar.—Not differing materially in its characteristics from the caterpillars of other Hesperid genera.

Chrysalis.—Somewhat slender, with the dorsal and ventral outlines straighter than in any of the preceding genera, and the dorsum very slightly elevated in the region of the thoracic segments.

Genus Amblyscirtes

(1) **Amblyscirtes vialis** (Edwards). Pl. XLVII, fig. 5, ♂; Pl. VI, fig. 40, *chrysalis* (The Roadside Skipper).

Butterfly.—This little species, an exceptionally bright example of which is represented in the plate, may be known by the dark color of the upper surface, almost uniformly brown, with a few subapical light spots at the costa. In the specimen that is figured these light spots are continued across the wing as a curved band, but this is not usual. The wings on the under side in both sexes are very much as on the upper side, save that both wings on the outer third are lightly laved with gray. Expanse: 1.00 inch.

Early Stages.—These have been described with minute accuracy by Dr. Scudder.

The Roadside Skipper ranges from Montreal to Florida, and westward as far as Texas and Nevada. It is not a common species in the valley of the Mississippi; it seems to be far more common in southern New England and in Colorado. At all events, I have obtained more specimens from these localities than from any others.

(2) **Amblyscirtes samoset** (Scudder). Pl. XLVII, fig. 6, ♂; Pl. VI, fig. 45, *chrysalis* (Pepper-and-Salt Skipper).

Synonyms: *hegon* (Scud.); *nemoris* (Edw.).

Butterfly.—This little species on the upper side has the ground-color as in the preceding species; the fringes on both wings are pale gray. There are three small subapical spots on the fore wing, three somewhat larger spots, one on either side of the second median nervule and the third near the inner margin, and two very minute spots at the end of the cell. On the under side the wings are pale gray, the white spots of the upper side of the fore wing reappearing. The hind wing is in addition marked by a semicircular median band of white spots, a small spot at the end of the cell, and another conspicuous white spot about the middle of the costa. Expanse: 1.00–1.10 inch.

Early Stages.—The caterpillar apparently feeds upon grasses. We know as yet very little of the life-history of the insect.

It is found in Maine, New Hampshire, along the summits of the Appalachian mountain-ranges as far south as West Virginia, and is reported to be common in Wisconsin and Michigan.

(3) **Amblyscirtes nereus** (Edwards). Pl. LI, fig. 42, ♂, type (The Nereus Skipper).

Closely allied to the preceding species, from which it may be distinguished by its larger size, darker color on the upper side, the total absence of the two small light dots at the end of the cell of the forewing, and the invariable presence of a dark band or ray near the inner margin of the hind wing on the under side. Expanse: ♂, 1.2; ♀, 1.3 in.

Its habitat is Arizona, where it is not rare.

(4) **Amblyscirtes carolina** (Skinner). Pl. XLVI, fig. 36, ♂, type (The Carolina Skipper).

362

Butterfly.—On the upper side the butterfly is as represented on the plate. The spots are repeated on the under side of the fore wing, but less distinctly defined. The costa is edged with brownish-yellow. The hind wings on the under side are yellow, spotted with small dark-brown dots. Expanse: ♂, 1.00 inch. The female is unknown.

Early Stages.—Wholly unknown.

This species has thus far been found only in North Carolina.

What appears to be a variety of this insect, in which the small dark dots, which are characteristic of the under side of the hind wings in true *A. carolina*, are replaced by light spots, has been described and figured by Jones as **A. reversa** (See Entom. News, XXXVII, p. 197, pl. IX, figs. 3, 4). It is from southern Virginia and the Carolinas.

(5) **Amblyscirtes textor** (Hübner). Pl. XLVII, fig. 16, ♂, *under side* (The Woven-winged Skipper).

Synonyms: *oneko* (Scud.); *wakulla* (Edw.).

Butterfly.—This little species, the under side of which is accurately delineated on the plate, needs no description to characterize it, as its peculiar markings serve at once to distinguish it from all other species, except the following. Expanse· 1.25–1.45 inch.

Early Stages.—Unknown.

The insect ranges from North Carolina southward to Florida, Louisiana, and Texas.

(6) **Amblyscirtes cassus** Edwards. Plate LI, fig. 31, ♂, type (The Cassus Skipper).

This insect in the general disposition of the markings somewhat resembles the preceding species, but may be at once distinguished by its somewhat light reddish color on both sides of the wings; *textor* being dark blackish above and cold gray below; while *cassus* is reddish above, with its light spots bright fulvous, not whitish as in *textor*, and on the underside the costal and dorsal area of the forewing in *cassus* is bright pale fulvous. Though near to each other the two insects are distinct. Expanse: ♂, 1 in.; ♀, 1.2 in.

The species is found in Arizona.

(7) **Amblyscirtes ænus** Edwards, Pl. XLVII, fig, 7, ♀ (The Bronze Skipper).

Butterfly.—This obscure species has the upper side of the wings somewhat tawny, the markings are not white, but yellowish. The wings on the under side are almost uniformly dark purplish gray, the fringes being paler. The spots of the upper side of the fore wing are repeated below, but very indistinctly. Close scrutiny reveals in the hind wing a very small light spot at the end of the cell, and a few beyond it, which in some specimens tend to form a postmedian transverse band, though exceedingly obscure.

In this species some specimens of the male sex have a few black androconia near the origin of the second median, but they do not form a distinct stigma. Expanse: ♂, 1.00; ♀, 1.20 in.

Early Stages.—These are unknown.

The species occurs in western Texas and Arizona.

(8) **Amblyscirtes nanno** Edwards. Pl. LI, fig. 35, ♂; fig. 36, ♀, types (The Nanno Skipper).

The species is the largest of the genus found in our fauna. It may at once be distinguished from the two preceding species, which it somewhat resembles, by the absence of all tawny coloration, the wings being blackish above, the minute size of the light spots on the upper side, the hoary gray coloration of the lower side of both wings, and the maculation of the under side of the secondaries, which have two small light spots near the costa and a median series of similar small spots parallel with the curve of the outer margin. Expanse, ♂, 1.10 in.; ♀, 1.2–1.3 in.

We have a long series of specimens from Arizona.

(9) **Amblyscirtes celia** Skinner. Pl. LI, fig. 30, ♂, paratype (The Celia Skipper).

Wings darker (blackish) on the upper side than in the preceding species, hoary on the under side, the fringes light, tipped with dark gray at the ends of the nervules. On the upper side the fore wings have three minute white preapical spots, and three small white spots on the disk, disposed at right angles to the preapical series. The hind wings above are without spots. On the under side the light spots of the fore wing are repeated, but are sharper and more distinct; the hind wings on this side have a small circular white spot before the base near the costa, and two parallel rows of small indistinct white spots, one crossing the wing near its middle, the other nearer the outer margin, to the curvature of which both are conformed. Expanse, ♂, .9–1. in.; ♀, 1–1.15 in.

Originally described from Texas.

(10) **Amblyscirtes nysa** Edwards. Pl. LI, fig. 24, ♂; fig. 25, ♀, *under side*, types (The Nysa Skipper).

The species may be distinguished from all others by the markings of the under side of the hind wings, composed of relatively large dark sub-triangular spots on a lighter ground. Expanse: ♂, .9 in.; ♀, 1.10 in.

The species ranges from Texas to Arizona.

(11) **Amblyscirtes eos** (Edwards). Pl. LI, fig. 26, ♂; fig. 27, ♀ (types of *comus*) (The Eos Skipper).

Synonym: *comus* Edwards.

Very dark, almost black on the upper side; on the under side the color of the wings is lighter, but darkening toward the base. Upon the lower side of the hind wings there are two somewhat parallel transverse series of light spots, which are sharply and distinctly defined, far more in number than on the upperside, where in most specimens there are few such spots, except those of the preapical series of the fore wing. Expanse: ♂, 1 in.; ♀, 1.2 in.

The species occurs in Texas and Arizona.

(12) **Amblyscirtes phylace** (Edwards). Pl. LI, fig. 32, ♂ type (The Phylace Skipper).

The wings on the upper side are without spots, and very dark, the fringes whitish. The top of the head and the collar are bright orange. The palpi on the lower side are creamy white. Expanse: 1.–1.2 in.

Phylace ranges from Colorado through New Mexico into Arizona.

(13) **Amblyscirtes bellus** (Edwards). Pl. LI, fig. 38 ♂ (The Bellus Skipper).

Uniformly deep brown, almost black, upon the upper side; paler, inclining to bluish gray on the under side. No light spots. The fringes on both sides uniformly orange, by which feature the species can easily be identified, Expanse: 1.–1.3 in.

Common in Arizona.

(14) **Amblyscirtes alternata** (Grote and Robinson) Pl. LI, fig. 34, ♂; fig. 33, ♀. (The Least Floridan Skipper).

Synonym: *meridionalis* Dyar.

This very small skipper may be distinguished from *A. eos*, with which it has been confused, by the different outline of the wings, the different color of the pectus, and the different color and markings of the hind wings on the under side. The fore wings in *alternata* are somewhat more rounded on the outer margin; in *alternata* the pectus is dark gray, in *eos* it is white; in *alternata* the hind wings have few or no light spots, in *eos* there are two parallel bands of sharply defined and distinct white spots. Besides, the expanse of wing is smaller in *alternata* than in *eos*. Expanse: .75 in.

The species was originally described from Georgia; it is also found in Florida.

(15) **Amblyscirtes oslari** (Skinner). Pl. LI, fig. 39, ♂, paratype (Oslar's Skipper).

The wings are light fuscous, with a few darker androconia upon the fore wing. On the under side of the male the fore wing is blackish with a still darker black dash corresponding in location to the androconia on the upper side, above which there is a slight yellowing of the wing. The hind wings below are powdered with white scales and there are faint indications of a pale post-median semi-circular band of lighter spots. The fringes of both wings are light. This obscure species is placed by me in the genus *Amblyscirtes*, and in the form of its wings is not unlike *bellus*. It was originally described from Colorado.

EXCHANGES

One of the best ways of adding to a collection is by the method known as exchanging. A collector in one part of the country may find species which are rare, or altogether unknown, in another part of the country. By a system of exchanges with other collectors he is able to supply the gaps which may exist in his collection. No one, however, cares to effect exchanges with collectors who are careless or slovenly in the preparation of their specimens, or inaccurate in naming them. A collector who contemplates making an exchange should, as the first step, prepare double lists, in one of which he gives the names and the number of specimens of either sex of the butterflies which he is able to offer in exchange; in the other he sets forth the things which he desires to obtain. The first list is said to be a list of "offerta"; the second is a list of "desiderata." As an illustration of the manner in which such lists may be conveniently arranged, I give the following:

OFFERTA

Papilio turnus,	♂ 3; ♀ 4.
Dimorphic var. glaucus,	♀ 6.
Colias alexandra,	♂ 4; ♀ 6.

DESIDERATA

Papilio nitra,	♀ .
Papilio brevicauda, orange-spotted var.	

The collector who receives these lists of offerta and desiderata will be able to decide what his correspondent has which he desires, and what there may be in his own collection which the correspondent wishes that he can offer in exchange; and the process of exchange is thus immediately facilitated.

Persons who exchange insects with others should always be extremely careful as to the manner of packing the specimens, and the directions given in the introductory portion of this book should be very carefully followed. Too much care cannot be taken in preventing damage to specimens in transit.

GROUP B

Most of the genera with the male bearing a distinct stigma on the fore wing.

Genus ADOPÆA Billberg

This is an European genus, which is only represented by one species, which has been introduced from Europe and seems to have become domiciled in the Province of Ontario, whence it has spread to Michigan and northwestern Ohio. Its home is continental Europe. It has only recently turned up in England.

(1) **Adopæa lineola** (Ochsenheimer). Pl. LI, fig. 37, ♂ (The New English Skipper).

The insect may be recognized from the figure which we give on our plate.

Genus ANCYLOXYPHA Felder

Butterfly.—Quite small, the antennæ very short, the club straight, bluntly pointed. The palpi have the third joint long, slender, and suberect. The neuration of the wings is shown in Fig. 180. The abdomen is slender, extending far beyond the hind margin of the secondaries. The fore wings are without a discal stigma.

Egg.—Hemispherical, marked with lozenge-shaped cells; yellow when laid, later marked with orange-red patches.

Caterpillar.—The entire life-history has not yet been ascertained. The caterpillars live upon marsh grasses; they construct for themselves a nest by drawing together the edges of a blade of grass with bands of silk. In form they do not differ from other Hesperid larvæ.

Chrysalis.—Not as yet accurately known.

(1) **Ancyloxypha numitor** Fabricius. Pl. XLVII, fig. 2, ♂ (The Numitor Skipperling).

Butterfly.—The upper side is correctly delineated in the plate. On the under side the fore wings are black, margined on the costa and on the outer margin with reddish-fulvous. The hind wings are pale fulvous. Expanse: .75–.95 inch.

Early Stages.—What has been said in reference to these in connection with the description of the genus must suffice for the species.

This pretty little insect is widely distributed, and abounds among grasses about watercourses. It ranges from the Province of Quebec to eastern Florida, thence westward across the Mississippi Valley as far as the Rocky Mountains.

Specimens, which now and then turn up, having the fore wings solidly black, belong to the variety named *longleyi* by French.

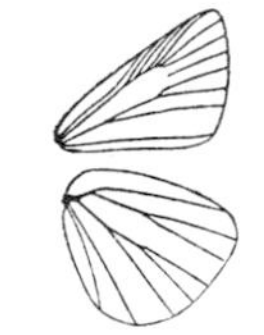

(2) **Ancyloxypha arene** (Edwards). Pl. LXXIII, fig. 15, ♂; fig. 16, ♀, *under side* (The Arene Skipperling).

There has been much confusion as to this inconspicuous little species. It is distinguished from all other forms, with which it has been confounded, by the fact that the under side of the wings both of the male and of the female are solidly and uniformly pale reddish fuscous, without any silvery rays. The type was taken in Arizona and is a male. We have numerous specimens from Mexico. It must not be confounded with *myrtis* Edwards, as has been done.

FIG. 180.—Neuration of the genus *Ancyloxypha.*

(3) **Ancyloxypha myrtis** (Edwards). Pl. XLVII, fig. 11, ♂, type (The Myrtis Skipperling).

This species, which is a true *Ancyloxypha* and not a *Copæodes*, as is shown by the structure of the body and the outline of the wings, resembles *Copæodes minima* by having the under side of the wings marked much as in the latter species with a silvery ray, which traverses the hind wings longitudinally. It is on the upper side darker and more reddish in color than *A. arene*, and is easily discriminated from that species by the presence of the silvery ray on the secondaries, which, as has been said, is lacking in *A. arene*. Expanse: .75 in.

Genus COPÆODES Edwards

Butterfly.—This genus is close to the preceding, but differs by having the fore wings more triangular, pointed, not rounded at the apex, and in the male with a narrow linear stigma below the cell. The antennæ are very short, the club thick, rounded at the tip. The palpi are as in the preceding genus. The neuration is shown in Fig. 181. The abdomen of the male is slender, projecting beyond the hind margin of the secondaries, but not nearly as far as in *Ancyloxypha*.

Early Stages.—Not as yet described.

(1) **Copæodes aurantiaca** (Hewitson). Pl. LI, fig. 21, ♂ (The Orange Skipperling).

I only know this species from Mexican specimens, one of which, determined by Godman, and compared with the type in the British Museum, is figured on our plate. The species is not identical with *waco* Edw. = *procris* Edw., as has been maintained by some, who have held that *aurantiaca* occurs within our limits, founded upon their misidentification of this species with *waco* (*procris* Edw.)

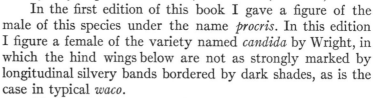
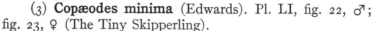
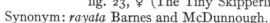

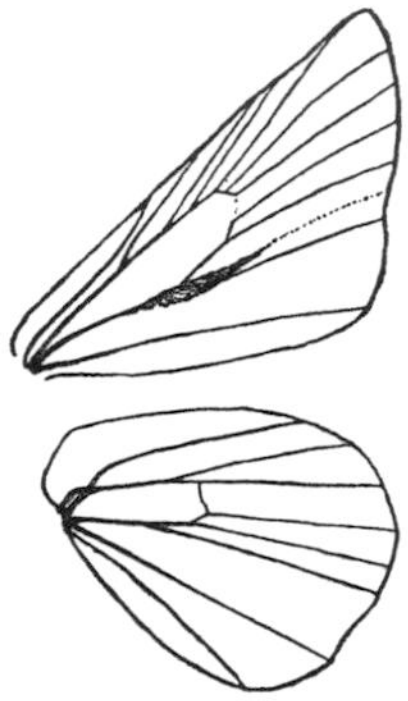

(2) **Copæodes waco** Edwards. Pl. XLVII, fig. 9, ♂; Pl. LI, fig. 40, ♀, var. *candida* Wright, *under side* (The Waco Skipper).

Synonym: *procris* Edwards; *aurantiaca* (*auctorum*).

In the first edition of this book I gave a figure of the male of this species under the name *procris*. In this edition I figure a female of the variety named *candida* by Wright, in which the hind wings below are not as strongly marked by longitudinal silvery bands bordered by dark shades, as is the case in typical *waco*.

FIG. 181.—Neuration of the genus *Copæodes*, enlarged.

(3) **Copæodes minima** (Edwards). Pl. LI, fig. 22, ♂; fig. 23, ♀ (The Tiny Skipperling).

Synonym: *rayata* Barnes and McDunnough.

This minute species, the male of which on the upper side somewhat resembles *aurantiaca* (Hew.) but is at once distinguished by the fact that on the under side of the secondaries there are one or two longitudinal silvery white rays on the darker background, more conspicuous in the female than in the male. The female on the upper side of the primaries has a dark line below the cell. Expanse: ♂, .6 in.; ♀, .75 in.

The species ranges from Florida to Arizona and southward.

Genus PSEUDOCOPÆODES Skinner and Williams

(Type: *Copæodes wrighti* Edw., misidentified as *C. eunus* Edw.)

(1) **Pseudocopæodes eunus** (Edwards). Pl. LXXIII, fig. 6, ♂, *under side*, type (The Eunus Skipper).

Synonym: *Adopæodes bistriata* ♀, Godman and Salvin.

The type of this insect has long been unique in the Edwards Collection, and it is now figured for the first tine. The label in Edwards' handwriting states that it is from "Washington Ty."; the published description states that it was taken on "Mount Hood." In his "Revised Catalogue of The Butterflies of North America" (Trans. Amer. Ent. Soc., Vol. XI, p. 308), Edwards says: "Hab.— Kern River, Cala." This change made in his list was never made upon the original label. *Eunus* has been consistently and invariably confused by recent students with *wrighti* Edwards, which is congeneric, but is a different species, which may at once be distinguished from *eunus* by the much paler tint of both the upper and under sides. Both species have two silvery longitudinal stripes on the under side of the hind wings, but in *wrighti* the ground-color is very pale and the white longitudinal stripes are therefore faintly defined, whereas in *eunus* the ground color is very dark. The figure given of *bistriata* ♀ by Godman and Salvin is an excellent representation of the under side of *eunus*, save that between the two light bands the figure given by Godman and Salvin lacks the minute marginal markings, which are found in *eunus* at this point, However, these minute maculations might well be overlooked by an artist, who was not exceedingly attentive to minor details. I am convinced that the Mexican form described and figured by Godman and Salvin from an unique female is identical with *eunus*, and that *eunus* is quite distinct from *wrighti*, although on the upper surface at first glance there is a close resemblance. The stigmata of both species correspond in form; the two species are manifestly congeneric, and agree in the matter of size.

The species may be a straggler from Mexico.

(2) **Pseudocopæodes wrighti** (Edwards). Pl. XLVII, fig. 10, ♂, type (Wright's Skipper). (Not "*C. eunus*" of most authors, who have almost without exception confused the two species).

This species may be easily distinguished from the preceding, as has already been pointed out, by the lighter color both of the upper and under sides.

Early Stages.—Unknown.

We have a large series collected by Wright in the Mojave Desert, including the types.

Genus CHÆROPHON Godman and Salvin

Only three species belonging to this genus occur within our borders. They may be quickly identified by their markings, which are characteristic, especially those of the under side of the wings.

(1) **Chærophon rhesus** (Edwards). Plate LI, fig. 45, ♂; fig. 46, ♀, *under side*, types (The Rhesus Skipper).

We trust the figures we give will suffice for the identification of the species, which ranges from Colorado into northern Mexico. Expanse: ♂, 1 in.; ♀, 1.35 in.

(2) **Chærophon carus** (Edwards). Plate LI, fig. 43, ♂; fig. 44, ♀, types (The Carus Skipper).

This species may easily be separated from the preceding by the fact that the hind wings on the upper side have a series of postmedian light spots, which do not occur in *rhesus*, the hind wings of which are solidly black and by the different and less distinctly defined markings of the under side of the wings. Expanse: ♂, 1 in.; ♀, 1.3 in.

(3) **Chærophon simius** (Edwards), Pl. XLVII, fig. 8, ♂, type (The Simius Skipper).

The upper side of the male is correctly figured on the plate. The wings on the under side are quite pale. The spots of the fore wing reappear on the under side, and the fore wing is blackish at the base; the hind wing has the angle at the base

369

broadly white, with a broad white blotch at the end of the cell. A semicircular curved band of obscure spots traverses the middle of the wing. Expanse: ♂, .90 in.; ♀, 1.20 in.

The early stages are unknown. The species was originally described from Colorado.

Genus CHORANTHUS Scudder

(1) **Choranthus radians** (Lucas). Pl. LI, fig. 47, ♂, *under side* (Lucas' Skipper).

We only show the under side on the plate; on the upper side the insect closely resembles the next species. Expanse: 1.15 in.

Reported from the Keys of Florida.

(2) **Choranthus haitensis** Skinner. Pl. LI, fig. 41, ♂, paratype (The Haiti Skipper).

This species, which closely resembles the preceding on the upper side, is totally different on the under side, the ground-color of the fore wing being brilliant tawny red, the fore wings narrowly edged with black, at the base and along the lower border deep black. On this side the hind wings are uniformly bright tawny red, without any lines or markings whatever. Expanse: 1.2 in.

Said to occur as a straggler at the southern end of Florida.

Genus ERYNNIS Schrank

(Type *Papilio comma* Linnæus)

Synonyms: *Pamphila* of many authors (not Fabricius); *Hesperia* of many authors (not Fabricius).

Butterfly.—The antennæ are short, less than half the length of the costa; the club is robust, with a very minute terminal crook; the palpi have the third joint minute, suberect, and bluntly conical. There is a discal stigma on the fore wing of the male.

Egg.—Somewhat spherical.

Caterpillar.—Feeds upon grasses, and is stouter in form than most hesperid larvæ, and sluggish in proportion to its stoutness. It does not make a nest, but conceals itself between the leaves of grass at the point where they unite with the stem, and is not very difficult to discover.

Chrysalis.—The chrysalis is elongated, cylindrical. Our knowledge of this stage is not very accurate as yet.

FIG. 182.—Neuration of the genus *Erynnis*, enlarged.

The following five species have been by some writers classified as varieties of the European species, *E. comma* (L.). While more or less closely related to that form, we see no reason for sinking them as varieties of it, though they, as well as it, no doubt in past ages had a common ancestry.

(1) **Erynnis manitoba** Scudder. Pl. XLVI, fig. 2, ♂; fig. 3, ♀ (The Canadian Skipper).

Butterfly, ♂.—The upper side of the wings is shown on the plate by a specimen, which is darker than the type, which is paler, but otherwise the same. On the under side the wings are lighter, the fore wings fulvous on the cell, pale gray at the apex and on the outer margin. There is a black shade at the base of the primaries, and a black streak, corresponding in location to the discal stigma on the upper side. The hind wings are pale ferruginous, except a broad streak along the inner margin, which is whitish. All the light spots of the upper side of both wings reappear on the under side, but are more distinctly defined, and are pearly-white in color.

♀.—The female, on the under side of the fore wing, has the black discal streak replaced by a broad ferruginous shade. The hind wings are darker, and the light spots stand forth more conspicuously upon the darker ground. Expanse: ♂, 1.25 in.; ♀, 1.30 in.

Early Stages.—These remain to be ascertained.

The Canadian Skipper is found across the entire continent north of a line roughly approximating the boundary between the United States and the Dominion of Canada. Along the Western Cordilleras it descends into the United States, as far south as Colorado and northern California.

A form, common in Quebec and Labrador, was named *laurentina* by Lyman. On Pl. LI, figs. 48, 49, I show a typical pair of this variety, which genitalically is close to *manitoba*. It is hard to distinguish *laurentina* Lyman from the European *catena* Staud. (1860), of which I have a series from Lapland, received from Dr. Staudinger himself.

(2) **Erynnis colorado** (Scudder). Pl. LII, fig. 1, ♂; fig. 2, ♀, *under side* types (The Colorado Skipper).

Like the preceding species, this form varies in color from specimens which are pale above to those which are dark. The darker specimens come from high altitudes, the paler specimens from lower levels.

The insect ranges from Colorado westward to the Pacific coast, but is generally found on the mountains, or higher plateaus, and does not seem to occur at sea-level.

(3) **Erynnis idaho** (Edwards). Pl. LII, fig. 3, ♂, type (The Idaho Skipper).

This is apparently only a lighter form of *E. colorado* which was described from "Oregon, Washington, and California." The specimen we figure is labelled as from "Eastern California." In recent years it has been reported from Utah and Idaho.

(4) **Erynnis assiniboia** (Lyman). Pl. LII, fig. 4, ♂, *under side* (The Assiniboian Skipper).

This form is very close to the preceding, but may be distinguished by the very pale greenish gray of the under side, and the more or less obsolescent state of the light markings.

The type locality is Regina.

(5) **Erynnis oregonia** (Edwards). Pl. LII, fig. 5, ♂; fig. 6, ♀, types (The Oregon Skipper).

We take pleasure in figuring two of the types, male and female, of this species, which were collected in northern California by O. T. Baron, and form a part of the series before Edwards, when he wrote his description.

(6) **Erynnis juba** (Scudder). Pl. LII, fig. 7, ♂; fig. 8, ♀; fig. 9, ab. **ogdenensis,** ♀. ab. nov. (The Juba Skipper).

Readily distinguished from the species, which go before, by the fact that "the fuscous borders of the primaries above end abruptly against the fulvous ground," instead of gradually dissolving into the fulvous.

Fig. 9 on Pl. LII, represents a highly aberrant female, which is light yellow on the upper side, on the lower side whitish, with the dark markings strongly accentuated. It was taken at Ogden, Utah, whence the name.

E. juba ranges from Colorado to California and Washington.

(7) **Erynnis viridis** (Edwards). Plate LII, fig. 10, ♂, *under side* (The Green Skipper).

Fresh specimens are quite green on the lower side of the wings. Some students have claimed that the form is a mere variety of the preceding species; others have maintained its entire distinctness on the ground of differences in the genitalia, and the different disposition of the markings on the under side, which are shown by our figure.

The butterfly has been reported from Texas, Colorado, and Arizona.

(8) **Erynnis woodgatei** (Williams). Pl. LII, fig. 11, ♂, *under side;* paratype (Woodgate's Skipper).

Very much like the preceding species, but characterized by the reduction of the light spots on the lower side of the hind wings to mere points and the grayish color of the anal area of the wings on the same side.

The insect occurs in New Mexico and Arizona.

(9) **Erynnis nevada** (Scudder). Pl. LII, fig. 12, ♂; fig. 13, ♀; fig. 14, ♀, *under side,* types (The Nevada Skipper).

The specimens figured are part of the catch made in Colorado by Mead and submitted by him to Dr. Scudder, who named the species. The male was sent me by Dr. Scudder with the label *"nevada"* upon the pin in his own handwriting, and designated as "Type." The females are from the Mead collection also labelled *"nevada"* in Scudder's well known hand. There can be no doubt that the specimens accurately represent the species.

Originally described from Colorado, the insect has been found to range southward and westward to Arizona and California, and northward to Saskatchewan.

(10) **Erynnis morrisoni** (Edwards). Pl. XLVI, fig. 26, ♂; fig. 27, ♀; Pl. LII, fig. 15, ♂, *under side,* types (Morrison's Skipper).

Butterfly.—The upper and under sides of the wings are sufficiently well depicted upon the plates to obviate the necessity of a detailed description. Expanse: ♂, 1.2 in.; ♀, 1.2–1.35 in.

Early Stages.—Unknown.

The species ranges from southern Colorado to Arizona.

(11) **Erynnis columbia** (Scudder). Pl. XLVII, fig. 44, ♂; Pl. LII, fig. 16, ♂, *under side* (The Columbia Skipper).

Synonyms: *sylvanoides* (Scudder, not Boisd.); *california* Wright; *erynnioides* (Dyar).

Butterfly.—The upper and under sides of the male are well shown upon the plates. The female on the upper side is less fulvous, being prevalently fuscous, the red color reduced to a spot at the end of the cell of the primaries and a median band of spots on the secondaries. On the under side in both sexes the wings are much paler than on the upper side, with the costa near the base and the cell deeper reddish. The primaries at the base and along the inner margin are black. The light spots on the under side of the secondaries in the female are less distinctly defined than in the male. Expanse: 1.25–1.35 in.

Early Stages.—Unknown.

Ranges along the Pacific coast from British Columbia to California and eastward to Colorado.

(12) **Erynnis cabelus** (Edwards). Pl. LII, fig. 17, ♂; fig. 18, ♂, *under side,* types (The Cabelus Skipper).

The types of this species, which are depicted on the plate, will enable it to be identified. They are from Idaho. Little is as yet known about this species, which is characterized by the obsolescence of the markings on the lower side of the wings, which are uniformly pale reddish, without any light spots.

(13) **Erynnis harpalus** (Edwards). Pl. LII, fig. 19, ♂; fig. 20, ♀, types (The Harpalus Skipper).

This species is near the preceding, but differs in having the wings faintly spotted on the under side. The butterfly is thus far only known from Nevada. In the style of its markings it resembles in a general way *E. sassacus*, and it has been suggested that it may be a "desert form" of the latter.

(14) **Erynnis sassacus** (Harris). Pl. XLVI, fig. 13, ♂; Pl. LII, fig. 23, ♀ (The Sassacus Skipper).

Butterfly.—The upper sides of the male and the female are as shown on the plates. The female is larger, the fulvous ground-color paler, the outer marginal shades darker, and the discal stigma is replaced by a dark-brown shade. On the under side in both sexes the wings are pale fulvous, with the spots of the upper side feebly reproduced as faint lighter spots. The fore wings in both sexes are black at the base. Expanse: ♂, 1.10–1.25 in.; ♀, 1.25–1.35 in.

Early Stages.—The caterpillar, which is plumper than most hesperid larvæ, feeds on grasses.

The insect ranges from New England to Georgia, and westward to Colorado.

A varietal form, found in the region of Lake Nipigon, Ontario, is figured on Pl. LII, fig. 21, ♀, and has been named *E. manitoboides* by Fletcher. It differs by having the discal spots of the hind wing below well marked and distinct.

Genus Erynnis

(15) **Erynnis dakotæ** (Skinner). Pl. LII, fig. 22, ♂, paratype (Skinner's Dakota Skipper).

Williams says that the male "may be distinguished from *sassacus* by the fact that the fuscous border dissolves gradually into the fulvous basic color, the spot beyond the stigma, so prominent in *sassacus*, is obsolescent or obsolete in *dacotæ*, and in general the upper side has a washed-out appearance." The females are almost entirely fuscous on the upper side.

The range of the species, so far as at present known, is from South Dakota to Winnipeg.

(16) **Erynnis attalus** (Edwards). Pl. XLVII, fig. 23, ♂; Pl. LII, fig. 24, ♀, type, *under side* (The Attalus Skipper).

Butterfly.—The male is fairly well depicted in the plate, but the light spots are too red. The female is larger and darker. On the under side the wings are quite pale, with the light spots reproduced in faint gray. Expanse: ♂, 1.25 in.; ♀, 1.45 in.

Early Stages.—Unknown.

The species occurs very rarely in New England, is found from New Jersey to Florida and Texas, and ranges westward to Wisconsin and Iowa.

(17) **Erynnis seminole** (Scudder). Pl. LII, fig. 25, ♂; fig. 26, ♀; fig. 27, ♂, *under side* (The Seminole Skipper).

This form is a trifle brighter than *attalus* and the spots on the upper side of the wings are reduced in size. On the under side *seminole* and *attalus* are somewhat alike, but the tints in *seminole* are much darker than in *attalus*.

The specimens of *seminole* in my possession come from North Carolina to Florida. It has been recorded from New Jersey.

(18) **Erynnis licinus** (Edwards). Pl. LII, fig. 28, ♂, type (The Licinus Skipper).

The type, which is the only specimen of this species thus far known, is figured on the plate. It was taken at Waco, Texas. On the under side the hind wings are dark gray with the minute postmedian white spots arranged in the form of a triangle with its apex pointing to the outer margin. On the upper side the fore wings show the preapical light spots very faintly. The stigma is narrower than in *seminole*, of which it may be an aberrant form.

(19) **Erynnis ottoë** (Edwards). Pl. XLVI, fig. 11, ♂; fig. 12, ♀, types (The Ottoë Skipper).

Butterfly.—The wings in both sexes are very pale yellowish fulvous. The male has the outer borders narrowly margined with black, and the discal stigma is black and prominent. The female has the outer borders more broadly, but more faintly margined with dusky. Both sexes have the under side of the wings uniformly pale buff, marked with blackish at the base of the fore wings. Expanse: ♂, 1.35 in.; ♀, 1.45–1.50 in.

Early Stages.—Unknown.

Thus far only recorded from Kansas and Nebraska.

(20) **Erynnis pawnee** (Dodge). Pl. LII, fig. 30, ♂, paratype; fig. 31, ♀ (The Pawnee Skipper).

Related to, but distinct from, the preceding species. The male figured on the plate is from Nebraska, the type-locality, and was sent to W. H. Edwards by Dodge, the author of the species. The female figured is from Montana, and used because the specimen is in better condition than the female sent by Dodge, with which it absolutely agrees.

The known range is from Nebraska northward and westward to Idaho.

(21) **Erynnis ogallala** (Leussler). Pl. LXXIII, fig. 20, ♂; fig. 21, ♂, *under side*; paratypes (The Ogallala Skipper).

This has been regarded by some students as a varietal form of *E. pawnee*, to which it is certainly closely related. It occurs in Nebraska. I am indebted to the author of the species for the specimens figured on the plate. Expanse: ♂, 1.4; ♀, 1.5 in.

(22) **Erynnis montana** (Skinner). Pl. LII, fig. 29, ♂, paratype (The Mountain Skipper).

This insect by some has been regarded as a small form of *pawnee*. It occurs in Colorado and Montana, and has also been attributed to California. The figure on the plate agrees with the type, with which it has been compared. Genitalically the form is said to agree with *pawnee*. Expanse: 1.10 in.

(23) **Erynnis uncas** (Edwards). Pl. XLVII, fig. 27, ♂; fig. 28, ♀ (The Uncas Skipper).

Butterfly.—The upper side of the wings of both sexes is well represented on the plate. On the under side in both sexes the wings are beautifully marked with conspicuous pearly-white spots on a greenish gray ground. The spots are defined inwardly and outwardly by dark olive shades. Expanse: ♂, 1.3 in.; ♀, 1.5 in.

Early Stages.—Unknown.

The insect ranges from Pennsylvania to Saskatchewan and New Mexico.

(24) **Erynnis lasus** (Edwards). Pl. LXXII, fig. 15, ♂; fig. 16, ♀; fig. 17, ♀, *under side* (The Lasus Skipper).

The type of this species, which for many years was unique, and was found in the Neumoegen Collection in Brooklyn, now deposited in the U. S. National Museum, has been attentively studied, and I have photographs of its upper and under sides, which I had intended to reproduce in this book. But I have preferred to give colored figures from the really fine series of the species collected in Utah, and forming a part of the Lindsey Collection, now in the possession of the Carnegie Museum. Expanse: ♂, 1.3; ♀, 1.5 in.

The insect turns out not to be uncommon in the valley of the Great Salt Lake, Utah.

(25) **Erynnis metea** (Scudder). Pl. XLVII, fig. 33, ♂; fig. 34, ♀ (The Cobweb Skipper).

Butterfly.—The upper side of the wings is fairly well represented in the plate, the male being a little too red, and the wings at the base and the discal stigma not being dark enough. On the under side the wings are brown, darker than on the upper side. The pale markings of the upper side are all repeated below as distinct pearly-white spots, and in addition on the hind wings near the base there is a curved band of similar white spots. Expanse: ♂, 1.20 inch; ♀, 1.25–1.30 inch.

Early Stages.—We know as yet but little of these.

The species occurs in New England, New York, and westward to Wisconsin and Missouri, thence southward to Florida.

(26) **Erynnis meskei** (Edwards). Pl. LII, fig. 32, ♂; fig. 33, ♀, type; fig. 34, ♂, type of *straton* Edwards, *under side* (Meske's Skipper).

Synonym: *straton* Edwards.

The female we show on the plate (fig. 33) is the type of *meskei* from Bastrop, Texas. It is the only Texan specimen in the Edwards Collection, but thoroughly agrees with numerous males and females labelled as from "Indian River, Fla." in the same collection. The under side of the male (fig. 34) is that of the type of *straton* Edwards, which thoroughly agrees with other males labelled *meskei* by Edwards. The insect ranges from Texas to Florida.

(27) **Erynnis leonardus** (Harris). Pl. XLVII, fig. 35, ♂; fig. 36, ♀ (Leonard's Skipper).

Butterfly.—Stouter and larger than the preceding species, and notably darker in coloring. The upper side of the wings is shown on the plate. On the under side the wings are dark brick-red. The primaries are blackish on the outer half, interrupted by the spots of the median series, which on the under side are large, distinct, and shade from pale fulvous to white toward the inner margin. The secondaries have a round pale spot at the end of the cell, and a curved median band of similar spots, corresponding in location to those on the upper side. Expanse: ♂, 1.25 inch; ♀, 1.35 inch.

Early Stages.—These are only imperfectly known. The caterpillar feeds on grasses.

The butterfly, which haunts flowers and may easily be captured upon them, ranges from New England and Ontario southward to Florida, and westward to Iowa and Kansas.

(28) **Erynnis horus** (Edwards). Pl. LXXV, fig. 13, ♀; fig. 14, ♀, *under side*, type (The Horus Skipper).

This species, which was described as being from Texas, is thus far only known by the unique type, which is preserved in the Museum of Comparative Zoölogy at Cambridge, Mass. It possibly is an aberrant form of some other species, and may even belong to another genus. In fact I am suspiciously inclined to regard it as being an aberration of *Atrytone logan* Edw., but content myself for the present in listing it in the order, in which most writers have placed it. Expanse: 1.5 in.

(29) **Erynnis lindseyi** Holland. Pl. LXXIII, fig. 10, ♂; fig. 11, ♀, types (Lindsey's Skipper).

Synonym: *ruricola* of many authors, not Boisduval.

This insect, which long has been passed by American authors as *ruricola* Boisd., is now definitely known not to be that species. The true *ruricola* is the malc of the species, the female of which was named *vestris* by Boisduval. The species *ruricola* Boisd. belongs to the genus *Atrytone*. Specialists may refer in this connection to the paper published by the writer in the Ent. News, Vol. XL, 1929, p. 326.

Genus HYLEPHILA Billberg

Butterfly.—The antennæ are very short, scarcely one third the length of the costa of the fore wing; the club is robust and short, with a very minute crook at the end; the palpi are as in the two preceding genera. The neuration of the wings is represented in Fig. 183.

Early Stages.—As yet but partially known.

The larva feeds on grasses, and the mature form has been figured by Abbot, a copy of whose drawing is given by Dr. Scudder in Plate 77 of "The Butterflies of New England."

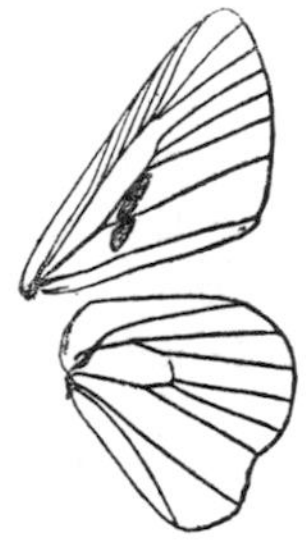

Hylephila phylæus (Drury). Pl. XLVI, fig. 18, ♂; fig. 19, ♀; Pl. XLVII, fig. 40, ♂; Pl. VI, fig. 39, *chrysalis* (The Fiery Skipper).

Butterfly.—The upper side is correctly shown on the plates. On the under side the wings are pale yellow, with a few small, round spots on the margin and disk of the hind wings, a black patch at the base, large black marginal spots, and a central, interrupted, longitudinal black streak on the disk of the primaries. Expanse, 1.15–1.25 inch.

Fig. 183.—Neuration of the genus *Hylephila*, enlarged.

The insect ranges from Connecticut to Patagonia, over all the habitable parts of the New World, south of the fortieth parallel of latitude.

Genus AUGIADES Hübner

(Type *Papilio sylvanus* Esper)

This genus, as constituted, is a sort of "catch-all" for a number of species, which are probably not all strictly congeneric. They are superficially characterized by the broad, velvety-black stigma of the males, and the generally light color of the upper side of the wings. The type of the genus, *P. sylvanus* Esper, is a palearctic insect, which is very variable, its forms occurring in central and eastern Asia being quite different from the typical form, which is found in Europe. In fact some of the Siberian varieties are almost undistinguishable from forms found in America.

(1) **Augiades sylvanus** (Esper) (The Sylvan Skipper).

I have in my possession a male of this European species taken at Richmond, Virginia. Its chrysalis may have been brought over in hay, or packing material, and the butterfly emerged on this side of the Atlantic. It differs in no respect from specimens from Germany, of which I have many. The case is analogous to that of *Melanthes zephodes* and *Adopæa lineola*, the latter of which has become established in Ontario. It is a stray immigrant.

Genus Augiades

(2) **Augiades sylvanoides** (Boisduval). Pl. LII, fig. 35, ♂; fig. 36, ♀ (The Woodland Skipper).

Synonyms: *pratincola* ♀ (Boisd.); *agricola* Plœtz (not Boisduval); *francisca* Plœtz.

I figure a male from Washington and a female from Oregon, selected from a score or more of specimens which have been sedulously compared with the figures of Boisduval's types given by Oberthür, with which they agree.

The insect ranges from California to British Columbia.

(3) **Augiades nemorum** (Boisduval). Pl. LII, fig. 39, ♂; fig. 40, ♀ (The Forest Skipper).

I give on the plate a figure of a male, which has been closely compared with the figure of the type of the species given by Oberthür (Lép. Comp., Vol. IX, pl. CCXL, fig. 2085) with which it agrees. The female figured is undoubtedly that sex of the species. The insects had been misidentified by Edwards as *agricola* and so labelled.

The insect is not uncommon in California.

(4) **Augiades verus** (Edwards). Pl. LII, fig. 42, ♂; fig. 43, ♀, types (The Verus Skipper).

For purposes of identification and comparison I give figures of the specimens upon which Edwards founded his species *verus*. The insect has been regarded by some recent writers as being identical with *A. nemorum*, and another has stated that in his opinion it represents a race of *agricola*. I am quite sure of the incorrectness of the latter view; and disagree with the former. As our plate shows, the insects are smaller than *nemorum*; the stigma is shorter, and broader basad; the fuscous outer margins of the wings are in some respects different from those of *nemorum*; and the spots in the stigmatic area in the female are different in form and arrangement from those of the last mentioned species. That *nemorum* and *verus* are very closely related is to be admitted, but they do not appear to me to be identical.

The types are from Havilah, Kern County, California.

(5) **Augiades milo** (Edwards). Pl. LII, fig. 44, ♂, type (The Milo Skipper).

For the purpose of making the record complete I give a figure of the type of *milo* Edwards. It differs from *nemorum* and *verus* in that the stigma is quite short, not so much produced toward the apex, and relatively a trifle broader; and the fuscous margin of the fore wing is not as broad as in *verus*. On the under side this specimen does not show any appreciable difference from *verus*. The insect has nothing whatever to do with *A. agricola* (Boisd.) of which some authors have made it a synonym.

The type, which is unique, was taken by Morrison in "Washington Territory."

(6) **Augiades pratincola** (Boisduval). Pl. LII, fig. 41, ♂ (The Meadow Skipper).

The type of *pratincola*, ♂, is figured by Oberthür (Lép. Comp., Vol. IX, Pl. CCXL, fig. 2088) and Comstock in his "Butterflies of California" has reproduced

378

that figure. I have never encountered any specimen, which exactly shows all the features of the insect represented by Oberthür. On the plate, as cited above, I give a figure of a specimen, which is nearer that delineated by Oberthür than any other with which I am acquainted. On the under side it is exactly like Oberthür's figure. It is a trifle larger than Oberthür's specimen; the stigma is a little broader; and the general color is a shade darker. I figure the insect, because it is the only specimen known to me, which seems nearly to meet the figure and description of what Boisduval designated as *pratincola*. I regard it as very probably the same, remembering that minor variations in tint and markings are very common among specimens. The example was collected in Nevada by Morrison. It was labelled "*agricola*" by Edwards, which it most assuredly is not.

(7) **Augiades agricola** (Boisduval). Pl. LII, fig. 45, ♂; fig. 46, ♀ (The Field Skipper).

Synonym: *yreka* Edwards.

This is a well marked species, of which both sexes are shown upon the plate. The narrow, light, almost white lines above and below the outer end of the stigma in the male furnish an unmistakable clue to the identity of the insect. *Yreka* (Edw.) the type of which is before me, as I write, is merely a slightly smaller and more brightly colored specimen of *agricola*, in which the light lines along the stigma are more distinct and whiter than in the usual run of specimens. Edwards when he wrote his description of *yreka* had not clearly defined in his mind what the species named *agricola* by Boisduval actually was. He did not differ in this respect from others. It is only in recent years, since the publication by Oberthür of exact figures of the types of Boisduval, that we have arrived at clear conceptions of these species. And we are not yet quite sure of some things in this connection.

The insect is not uncommon in California.

(8) **Augiades yuma** (Edwards). Pl. LIII, fig. 1, ♂ (The Yuma Skipper).

Unfortunately the type of the species, which was unique, has mysteriously disappeared. So far as I can recall it was not contained in the Edwards Collection when I received it. Comstock in "The Butterflies of California" figures the male and the female of what he regards as *yuma* (Edw.), but his specimens are slightly different in appearance from the insect, which I figure, which has long stood in my collection as *yuma*, although not the *type*. The type was from Arizona; the insect I figure is from Utah.

(9) **Augiades scudderi** (Skinner). Pl. LIII, fig. 2, ♂ paratype (Sendder's Yuma Skipper).

Generally, and probably quite correctly, regarded as identical with *yuma*. Dr. Skinner obtained his type from from the valley of the White River in western Colorado. We have it from the valley of the Green River near its confluence with White River in Utah.

(10) **Augiades snowi** (Edwards). Pl. XLVII, fig. 29, ♂; fig. 30, ♀ (Snow's Skipper).

Butterfly.—The upper side of the wings of both sexes is well represented on the plate. On the under side the wings are uniformly reddish-brown, with the primaries black at the base, and the median spots enlarged near the inner margin and whitish. The light spots of the upper side reappear below as pale spots, which are well defined on the dark ground-color. Expanse: 1.25–1.40 inch.

Early Stages.—Unknown.

The species ranges from southern Colorado to Arizona.

Genus POLITES Scudder

Butterfly.—The antennæ and the palpi are as in the preceding genus; the neuration of the wings is also very much the same. The genus was founded by Dr. Scudder upon the shape of the discal stigma in the wing of the male. His description of this feature is as follows: "Discal stigma of male consisting of an interrupted, gently arcuate or sinuate streak of dead-black retrorse scales or rods, edged below, especially in the middle, by a border of similar, but dust-colored, erect rods, and followed beneath by an inconspicuous large area of loosely compacted, erect, dusky scales."

FIG. 184.—Neuration of the genus *Polites*, enlarged.

Egg.—Approximately hemispherical, elevated, reticulated, the lines forming hexagonal figures upon the surface.

Caterpillar, etc.—Of the stages beyond the egg we know as yet comparatively little. The caterpillar feeds on grasses.

(1) **Polites verna** (Edwards). Pl. XLVI, fig. 32, ♂ (The Little Glass-wing).

Synonym: *pottowattomie* (Worthington).

Butterfly.—The upper side of the male is correctly delineated on the plate. On the under side the wings are paler, inclining to purplish-red. The spots of the upper side are repeated, but in addition about the middle of the hind wings there is a semicircle of pale spots. Expanse: ♂, 1.15 inch; ♀, 1.35 inch.

Early Stages.—We do not know much of these; what little we do know may be found recorded in the pages of "The Butterflies of New England." The caterpillar feeds on grasses.

It ranges from southern New England to Virginia, westward to Colorado, and northward to the province of Alberta. It is quite common in Ohio, Indiana, and Illinois.

(2) **Polites manataaqua** (Scudder). Pl. XLVI, fig. 30, ♀ ; Pl. LIII, figs. 3 and 31, ♂ ♂; fig. 32, ♀ (The Cross-line Skipper).

Butterfly.—The male on the upper side is dusky-olive, with a black discal streak below the cell, which is slightly touched with reddish, becoming deeper and clearer red on the costa at the base. The wings on the under side are more or less pale gray, with a transverse series of pale spots on the primaries, and a very faint curved discal series of similar spots on the secondaries. The female, the upper side of which is well shown on the plate, is marked below much like the male. The males and female shown on the plates were taken at Coalburg, W. Va..

by W. H. Edwards, and agree with specimens in the Edwards Collection labelled by Scudder in his own handwriting, which he sent to Edwards. Expanse: 1.25 in.

Early Stages.—These have been described by Scudder.

Occurs in New England and Canada, ranging westward to Nebraska and North Dakota.

(3) **Polites rhena** (Edwards). Pl. LIII, fig. 4, ♂, type (The Rhena Skipper).

This insect recently has been treated as a western race of the preceding. As our figure shows it is very different in appearance from *manataaqua*. Williams, however, says that the genitalia of the two are the same in structure.

It occurs in Colorado and New Mexico.

(4) **Polites alcina** (Skinner). Pl. LIII, fig. 5, ♂, paratype (The Alcina Skipper).

Much paler and brighter on the upper and under sides than the two foregoing forms. The specimen figured agrees with Skinner's type. It may represent a variety of *manataaqua*, but I do not attempt to decide.

Its range is the same as that of *rhena*.

(5) **Polites taumas** (Fabricius). Pl. XLVII, fig. 20, ♂; Pl. LIII, figs. 6 and 7, dimorphic ♀ ♀ ; Pl. VI, fig. 44, *chrysalis* (The Tawny-edged Skipper).

Synonyms: *cernes* (Boisd. & Lec.); *ahaton* (Harris).

Butterfly.—The upper side of a typical male is shown on Pl. XLVII. On Pl. LIII two forms of the female are represented. In one of these the red color, which appears on the costa of the male, perdures; the other is more or less melanic. Expanse: ♂, 1 in.; ♀ , 1.2 in.

Early Stages.—Well described by Scudder in "The Butterflies of New England."

The insect ranges from Canada to the Gulf, and westward to the Dakotas, Utah, and New Mexico.

(6) **Polites mardon** Edwards. Pl. XLVII, fig. 26, ♂; Pl. LIII, fig. 12, ♀ , types (The Little Oregon Skipper).

Butterfly.—On the under side the wings are pale gray, with the light spots of the primaries, and a curved median band of spots on the secondaries whitish. Expanse: ♂, 1.10 inch; ♀ , 1.20 inch.

Early Stages.—Unknown.

The only specimens I have, including the types, were taken in Oregon and Washington.

(7) **Polites baracoa** (Lucas). Pl. LIII, fig. 21, ♂; fig. 22, ♀ (The Baracoa Skipper).

Synonyms: *amadis* (H.-S.); *myus* (French).

This small species is common in the Antilles and occurs in Florida about Key West. Expanse: .9 in.

(8) **Polites sonora** (Scudder). Pl. LIII, fig. 10, ♂, paratype; fig. 11, ♀ , *under side* (The Sonora Skipper).

This insect, which is closely related to the two following species, like them may easily be distinguished by the markings of the lower side of the hind wings.

In *sonora* they are simple and consist of a slightly curved longitudinal light bar parallel with the upper edge of the cell and a curved series of light spots more or less discrete, parallel to the outer border. In typical *sonora* the ground-color of the under side is grayish, with the light markings not very sharply contrasting.

The insect ranges from southern California to British Columbia and eastward to Colorado, and usually occurs at considerable elevations.

(9) **Polites siris** (Edwards). Pl. LIII, fig. 9, ♂, type (The Siris Skipper).

This is darker and more sharply marked than the preceding. The types (there are six in the Edwards Collection) are all labelled "Mt. Hood." There are four specimens in the Mead Collection, which are also labelled "Mt. Hood." In Edwards' "Revised Catalogue," 1884, he gives the habitat as "Puget Sound, W. Terr." This was probably due to a lapse of memory, or a slip of the pen. At all events he did not change the labels on his type specimens, and they agree with his published description. Since he wrote, this form has been found in Washington Territory near Puget Sound and also upon the flanks of Mt. Shasta in California and elsewhere at considerable elevations in that general region. It is a northern or alticoline form and may be distinguished from the preceding by the fact that it is darker on the upper side, and the ground-color of the lower side of the wings is rich dark ferruginous, upon which the light spots stand out sharply and clearly defined.

(10) **Polites utahensis** (Skinner). Pl. LIII, fig. 13, ♂, *under side*, paratype (Skinner's Utah Skipper).

The specimen figured is a paratype, which agrees absolutely with the type in the Skinner Collection. It may represent a very light form of *sonora*, in which the ground-color of the under side of the hind wings is pale greenish gray, against which the light spots contrast but feebly.

Originally described from Utah, it has been found to occur on Pike's Peak in Colorado, in Wyoming, Idaho, and also New Mexico.

(11) **Polites peckius** (Kirby). Pl. XLVII, fig. 24, ♂; fig. 25, ♀; Pl. LIII, fig. 14, ♀, *under side* (Peck's Skipper).

Synonym: *wamsutta* Harris.

Butterfly.—This little species, the upper side of which in both sexes is correctly shown on the plates, has the under side of the wings dark brown, with the light spots of the upper side greatly enlarged, especially upon the disks of the wings, fused, and pale yellow, thus contrasting strongly with the rest of the wings. Expanse: ♂, 1.00 inch; ♀, 1.25 inch.

Early Stages.—These are not thoroughly known as yet. The larva feeds on grasses.

Peck's Skipper ranges from Canada southward as far as Central America, and west to Wyoming.

(12) **Polites draco** (Edwards). Pl. LIII, fig. 15, ♂; fig. 16, ♀, *under side*, types. (The Draco Skipper).

Easily distinguished by the outwardly projecting toothlike spot about the middle of the series of light spots which form a curved band beyond the middle of the underside of the hind wing. The only other species, which has such a projecting spot at this point is the preceding, but in *peckius* this projection is fused and lost in the broad expansion of all the spots into a wide band covering the middle of the wing. In *draco*, while the outer row of spots often merge into a narrow line of yellow, this one spot is always prominent, and projects outwardly.

The species is evidently nearly related to *peckius*, and seems to replace it at considerable elevations in the western and northwestern parts of the continent. Originally described from the high mountains of Colorado, it has since then been taken on mountain-peaks in New Mexico and Utah. I have several specimens captured on White Horse Pass in the Yukon Territory.

(13) **Polites sabuleti** (Boisd.), Pl. XLVII, fig. 42, ♂; Fig. 43, ♀ (The Sand-hill Skipper).

Butterfly.—Small, the male on the upper side looking like a diminutive and darkly bordered *phylæus*. On the under side the wings are paler than on the upper side; the still paler spots of the discal areas are defined outwardly and inwardly by elongated dark spots. Expanse: 1.00–1.10 inch.

Early Stages.—Unknown.

The habitat of this species is California.

(14) **Polites tecumseh** (Grinnell). Pl. LIII, fig. 17, ♂ (The Tecumseh Skipper).

Synonym: *chispa* Wright.

Students seem to agree that this is a small, dark, alticoline variety of *P. sabuleti*. It occurs at high elevations in the mountains of California and Oregon. *Chispa* (Wright) was apparently based upon a small, somewhat dwarfed specimen. Expanse: .9 in.

(15) **Polites chuska** (Edwards). Pl. LIII, fig. 18, ♂, type; fig. 19, ♀ (The Chuska Skipper).

Synonym: *sabuleti* var. *comstocki* Gunder, ♂.

For the information of students I figure the male holotype of this species. Williams states that in his opinion *chuska* is the same as *sabuleti*, basing his remark upon a "much rubbed" example, which he says is the "type." I am confident that he alludes to the example in the American Museum of Natural History, erroneously labelled "type" by somebody, which is a rubbed female. The true type is the male figured on our plate. The American Museum specimen is an old and battered female specimen, which, however, agrees with the female we figure. The species is not identical with *sabuleti*, being immaculate on the under side, and much lighter in color both above and below.

Habitat.—Arizona.

(16) **Polites mystic** (Scudder). Pl. XLVI, fig. 22, ♂; fig. 23, ♀; Pl. LIII, fig. 20, ♀, *under side* (The Long-dash).

The figures on the plates convey a good idea of both the upper and under sides. Expanse: ♂, 1.10 in.; ♀, 1.25 in.

383

Genus Polites

Early Stages.—These have been elaborately described by Scudder. The caterpillar feeds on grasses, making a tubular nest for itself among the leaves.

The insect ranges through southern Canada and New England to Pennsylvania, and westward to Iowa.

A melanic aberration of *mystic* was named *weetamoo* by Scudder. Another aberration with the dark areas suffused with yellowish was called *nubs* by the same author.

Lindsey maintains that *pallida* (Skinner), which he regards as identical with *dacotah* (Edw.) is a western race of *mystic*. Williams says that the genitalia of *pallida* are the same as those of *mystic*.

(17) **Polites napa** (Edwards). Pl. LII, fig. 37, ♂, type; fig. 38, ♀, allotype; Pl. LIII, fig. 23, ♂, type of *dacotah* Edw. (The Napa Skipper).

Synonym: *dacotah* Edw.

This insect, which is a trifle larger and brighter in color than the preceding species, has been regarded by some authors as a Coloradan form of *mystic*. Lindsey assigned *napa* to the genus *Augiades*, but it is from my point of view a true *Polites*. Edwards sank the species *dacotah*, which he had described, as a synonym of *napa*. For my part I can see no difference of specific or generic rank between the types of the two things, which I figure upon the plates. There is an apparent determination on the part of some to keep the specific name *dacotah* alive, al though sunk as a synonym by Edwards, the author of both species. I can see no difference of moment between *napa* and *dacotah*. I am also sceptical as to the view that *dacotah* = *napa* (*fide* Edwards) represents a western race of *mystic*. A comparison of the under side of *mystic* (See Pl. LIII, fig. 20) with the under sides of *napa*, which are pale and immaculate, does not lend itself to this opinion. To the best of my knowledge and belief *mystic* is not found farther west than Iowa and Manitoba. *P. napa* and *P. mystic* are congeneric, but distinct.

(18) **Polites brettus** (Boisd. & Lec.). Pl. XLVII, fig. 41, ♀ ; Pl. LIII, fig. 24, ♂; fig. 25, ♂, *under side* (The Whirlabout).

Synonyms: *wingina* (Scudder); *unna* Plœtz.

Butterfly.—The figures we give of both sexes and of the lower side of the male are sufficient to distinguish the species.

Early Stages.—Still only partially known. The caterpillar feeds on grasses.

The insect is rare as a straggler in the northern parts of the United States. but is common in the Gulf States.

(19) **Polites brettoides** (Edwards). Pl. LIII, fig. 26, ♂, type.

This is a slight variety of *brettus*, according to my opinion, in which the marginal borders of the wings above are narrower, and the spots below a little smaller than in *brettus*. Wright in error figures *phylœus* as *brettoides* in his "Butterflies of California."

(20) **Polites vibex** (Geyer). Pl. LIII, fig. 27, ♂ (Geyer's Skipper).

This is a form, closely related to *brettus*, which is found in the hotter parts of Central and South America, and occasionally in Texas. It is characterized by the darker color of the secondaries on the upper side, some specimens being almost entirely without fulvous markings, and by the more diffuse maculation on the under side of the wings.

(21) **Polites stigma** (Skinner). Pl. LIII, fig. 28, ♂, paratype.

Closely allied to *vibex*, but with the upper side of the wings more broadly and brightly pale fulvous, and with the stigma standing out boldly on the lighter background. It is found in Texas and New Mexico.

Genus ATALOPEDES Scudder

Butterfly.—Antennæ short, less than half the length of the costa; club short, stout, crooked just at the end; the palpi as in the preceding genus. The cut shows the neuration. The only mark of distinction between this genus and the two genera that follow is found in the shape of the discal stigma on the wing of the male, which is described as follows by Dr. Scudder: "Discal stigma in male consisting of, first, a longitudinal streak at base of middle median interspace of shining black, recurved rods; second, of a semilunar field of dead-black erect rods in the lowest median interspace, overhung above by long, curving scales; followed below by a short, small striga of shining black scales, and outside by a large field of erect, loosely compacted scales."

Fig. 185.—Neuration of the genus *Atalopedes*, enlarged.

Egg.—Hemispherical, covered with a network of delicate raised lines describing small polygons over the surface; minutely punctate.

Caterpillar.—Cylindrical, tapering backward and forward; head large; the neck less constricted than in the genus *Eudamus* or in the genus *Thanaos*; dark in color.

Chrysalis.—The chrysalis is slender, cylindrical, a little humped upon the thorax, with the tongue-sheath free and projecting to the end of the fifth abdominal segment.

(1) **Atalopedes campestris** (Boisd.) Pl. XLVI, fig. 4, ♂; fig. 5, ♀; Pl. VI, figs. 43, 47, *chrysalis* (The Sachem).

Synonym: *huron* (Edwards).

Butterfly.—The upper side of the wings in both sexes is well represented in the plate. On the under side the wings are paler, with the light spots of the upper side faintly repeated. Expanse: ♂, 1.15 inch; ♀, 1.35 inch.

Early Stages.—These are described in full with painstaking accuracy by Scudder in "The Butterflies of New England." The caterpillar feeds on grasses.

The species ranges from southern New York to Florida, thence westward and southward into Mexico.

Genus CATIA Godman and Salvin

This genus has been separated from others because of the fact that the bent tip of the antennæ when examined under a microscope is a trifle longer than in

Genus Problema

Polites and particularly because the stigmata on the fore wing of the male are composed of two small round tufts of scales located one above the other at the origin of the first median nervule. The distinction is recognizable, for which the student should be grateful.

(1) **Catia otho** (Smith and Abbot). Pl. XLVI, fig. 28, ♂; fig. 29, ♀, var. **egeremet** (Scudder); Pl. LIII, fig. 29, ♀, *under side;* Pl. VI, fig. 42, *chrysalis* (Otho's Skipper).

Synonyms: *ætna* Scudder (not Boisd.), Holland 1st Ed. Butt. Book; *druryi* (Latreille); *pustula* (Geyer).

Two forms of this species have been recognized, the southern, typical *otho,* which is red on the under side of the hind wings; and a northern form, in which the under side of the wings is blackish. The latter is known as var. *egeremet* (Scudder).

The species ranges from southern Canada to the Bahamas and westward to the Rocky Mountains.

Genus PROBLEMA Skinner and Williams

This genus is founded upon certain anomalies in the genital armature. (See Trans. Am. Ent. Soc., Vol. L, p. 64).

(1) **Problema byssus** (Edwards). Pl. XLVI, fig. 20, ♀; Pl. LIII, fig. 38, ♂, types (The Byssus Skipper).

Butterfly.—The discal stigma appears to be wanting in the male, or at best consists of a few raised scales below the cell. Our figures show the male and the female of the species. On the under side the primaries are bright orange, paler than the secondaries, tinged towards the costa and base with red. On this side the light median spots of the upper side are very faintly indicated in the male, but are more pronounced in the female. The secondaries below are deep red. Expanse, ♂, 1.45 in.; ♀, 1.65 in.

Early Stages.—We know nothing of these.

(2) **Problema kumskaka** (Scudder). Pl. LIII, fig. 39, ♂, paratype (The Kumskaka Skipper).

This species occurs in the northwestern states, and is widely separated in its distribution from *byssus,* the metropolis of which is Florida. It may easily be distinguished from the latter species by its much lighter coloration. I figure a paratype received by W. H. Edwards from Dr. Scudder.

(3) **Problema bulenta** (Boisd. & Lec.). Pl. LXXV, figs. 17, 17a, ♂; figs. 18, 18a, ♀ (The Bulenta Skipper).

The species named *bulenta* was lost to sight for nearly a century, and only known from the illustrations given by Boisduval and Leconte. In July, 1925, Mr. Frank Morton Jones of Wilmington, Delaware, rediscovered the insect in the vicinity of Wilmington, North Carolina. He published in "The Entomological News," Vol. XXXVII, pp. 193-196, a full account of his capture of this interesting species, which probably may be found in suitable localities along the coast of the Carolinas and Georgia, from which latter state it was originally described. It is congeneric with *P. byssus*.

Genus ATRYTONE Scudder

The genus consists of a number of mostly rather large species, which are characterized by the relatively great length of the antennal club and the absence of spines on the mid tibiæ. The primaries of the males in some of the species have stigmata; in other species these are lacking.

(1) **Atrytone arogos** (Boisduval and Leconte). Pl. XLVI, fig. 6, ♂ (The Iowa Skipper).

Synonyms: *vitellius* (Smith & Abbot) (not Fabr.); *iowa* (Scud.); *mutius* (Ploetz).

FIG. 186.—Neuration of the genus *Atrytone*, enlarged.

Butterfly.—The male on the upper side is as shown in the plate. The female on the upper side has the hind wings almost entirely fuscous, very slightly yellowish about the middle of the disk. The fore wings have the inner and outer margins more broadly bordered with fuscous than the male, and through the middle of the cell there runs a dark ray. On the under side the wings are bright pale yellow, with the inner margin of the primaries clouded with brown. Expanse: ♂, 1.25 inch; ♀, 1.45 inch.

Early Stages.—Very little is known of these.

The species ranges through the Gulf States, and northward in the valley of the Mississippi as far as Nebraska and Iowa. It seems to be quite common in Nebraska, and probably has a wider distribution than is reported.

(2) **Atrytone logan** (Edwards). Pl. XLVI, fig. 24, ♂; fig. 25, ♀ (The Delaware Skipper).

Synonym: *delaware* Edwards.

Butterfly.—The plate well shows the upper side of the wings. On the under side the wings are bright orange-red, clouded with black at the base and on the inner angle of the fore wings. Expanse: ♂, 1.25–1.35 in.; ♀, 1.35–1.50 in.

Early Stages.—Very little is known of these.

The butterfly is found from southern New England and northern New York as far south as Florida and Texas, ranging as far west as Wyoming and Montana.

(3) **Atrytone lagus** (Edwards). Pl. LIII, fig. 30, ♂, type (The Lagus Skipper).

This is a western variety of *A. logan* in which the fuscous border of the wings is greatly reduced. The type is from Texas. It has been taken from Texas northward to Colorado and is as yet rare in collections.

(4) **Atrytone arpa** (Boisd. & Lec.). Pl. LIII, fig. 33, ♂; fig. 34, ♀, *under side* (The Arpa Skipper).

This and the species of the genus which hereafter follow, have a stigma on the fore wing of the male.

The specimens representing the two sexes of *arpa* are from Florida.

(5) **Atrytone palatka** (Edwards). Pl. XLVI, fig. 21, ♂; Pl. LIII, fig. 35, ♀, *under side*, typical specimens (The Palatka Skipper).

This is the largest species of the genus. The figures we give render a lengthy verbal description unnecessary. It is not uncommon in Florida and has been recorded from southern Alabama.

Expanse: ♂, 1.5–1.65 in.; ♀, 1.9–2. in. Its life-history is unknown.

(6) **Atrytone dukesi** Lindsey. Pl. LIV, fig. 26, ♂, type.

The figure on the plate will enable the identification of the species. It occurs in southern Alabama and probably elsewhere along the Gulf.

(7) **Atrytone dion** (Edwards). Pl. LIII, fig. 36, ♂, type; fig. 37, ♀, *under side* (The Dion Skipper).

Easily distinguished by the light longitudinal streak on the upper side of the hind wings. Professor Lindsey has given the varietal name *alabamœ* to a dark form taken at Mobile. Expanse: ♂, 1.3 in.; ♀, 1.65 in.

It occurs near lakes and rivers; we have it in beautiful examples from Pymatuning Swamp in northwestern Pennsylvania. I suspect that the larva feeds upon the foliage of some aquatic plant or marsh-grass. The species has a wide range from New York to Nebraska and southward.

(8) **Atrytone pontiac** (Edwards). Pl. XLVI, fig. 16, ♂; fig. 17, ♀ (Pontiac's Skipper).

Synonyms: ♀, *inconspicua* (Edwards); *orono* (Scudder).

The wings on the under side are pale red, clouded with fuscous, the spots of the upper side indistinctly repeated on this side. Expanse: ♂, 1.15 in.; ♀, 1.25 in.

Little is known of the early stages. It ranges from Massachusetts to Nebraska.

(9) **Atrytone bimacula** (Grote & Robinson). (The Two-spotted Skipper).
Synonyms: *acanootus* (Scudder); *illinois* (Dodge).

I am unfortunate in having neglected to figure this species upon one of the plates, as I had intended to do. At the eleventh hour I have endeavored to atone

FIG. 187.—*Atrytone bimacula*, ♂, enlarged.

for the omission by making a cut, which is here presented, and which may enable the student to recognize the insect, when he captures it.

A. bimacula is nowhere common, though it has a wide range, having been reported from Ontario through New York and Pennsylvania to Nebraska. Expanse: ♂, 1.10 in.; ♀, 1.25 in.

(10) **Atrytone ruricola** (Boisduval). Pl. LXXIII, fig. 12, ♂, paratype from the Guenée Collection, through the kindness of M. Réné Oberthür, *under side;* Pl. LIII, fig. 8, ♀, *vestris* (Boisd.); Var. **metacomet** (Harris) Pl. XLVI, fig. 31, ♂ (The Dun Skipper).

Synonyms: ♀, *vestris* (Boisd.); *metacomet* (Harris); *rurea* (Edwards); *kiowa* (Reakirt); *osyka* (Edwards); *californica* (Mabille).

Butterfly.—The male is dark in color on the upper side, with the stigma losing itself in the ground-color in specimens from the eastern part of the continent; in specimens from California the ground-color is appreciably lighter, with the stigma more distinctly defined, faintly margined below with a lighter shade. On the under side the wings are much paler than on the upper side. The female has some faint traces of translucent apical spots near the costa and two minute translucent spots on either side of the second median nervule near its origin. On the under side the spots reappear. There is a faint trace of a semicircle of pale spots about the middle of the hind wing. Female specimens vary on the underside from pale brown to purplish brown. Expanse: ♂, 1.15 in.; ♀, 1.30 in.

Early Stages.—Next to nothing is known of these.

The range of the species is from Quebec to Florida and westward to the Pacific coast.

Recent investigation has established the fact that the species was first named *ruricola* by Boisduval, this being the name published by him, although the specimen he described bore on the label the name "rubicola," which he failed to change. The insect he described is the male of the insect, which in the same paper he named *vestris*, the type of the latter being a solitary female in his possession. The name "ruricola" has page-priority over "vestris," and takes its place. The insect named *californica* by Mabille is a male identical with *ruricola* of Boisduval. All of the specimens were collected by Lorquin.

(11) **Atrytone osceola** (Lintner). Pl. LIII, fig. 40, ♂; fig. 41, ♀, paratypes (The Osceola Skipper).

This has been treated by some compilers of check-lists as a synonym of the preceding species. I cannot agree with this opinion. The insect is distinctly larger, the squamation of the upper side of the wings is heavier, having in fresh specimens an almost woolly appearance, the palpi on the under side are distinctly yellow, not grayish white, as in *ruricola*. The facies of the species shows that it is not the same as, though closely related to, *ruricola*. Expanse: ♂ 1.35 in.; ♀, 1.75 in.

The specimens figured are from Florida and were determined by Lintner, the author of the species.

Genus POANES Scudder

This genus as arranged by Lindsey is an aggregation of forms, which, while related, show great differences. The species *massasoit* is made the type. Its neuration is given in our cut, Fig. 188.

Butterfly.—The antennæ are short; the club is stout, bent, acuminate at the tip. The third joint of the palpi is slender, cylindrical, short.

(1) **Poanes massasoit** Scudder. Pl. XLVII, fig. 21, ♂; fig. 22, ♀ (The Mulberry-wing).

Butterfly.—The upper side of the wings in both sexes is correctly shown in the plate. On the under side the fore wings are black, with the costa and the outer margin bordered with reddish, with three small subapical light spots and two or three median spots. On the under side the hind wings are bright yellow, bordered on the costa and on the outer margin for part of their distance with reddish-brown. The female on the under side is more obscurely marked than the male, and the hind wings are more or less gray in many specimens, lacking the bright yellow which appears upon the wings of the male. There is considerable variation on the under side of the wings. Expanse: ♂, 1.15 in.; ♀, 1.20 in.

A slight variety, which has the under side of the hind wings powdered with rusty scales was named *suffusa* by Laurent.

Early Stages.—Only partially known.

Ranges from Massachusetts to Nebraska and southward.

(2) **Poanes hobomok** (Harris). Pl. XLVII, fig. 37, ♂; fig. 38, ♀; Pl. LIII, fig. 42, ♂, *under side;* fig. 43, dimorphic ♀, **pocohontas** (Scudder); fig. 44, dim. ♀, **quadaquina** (Scudder) paratype; fig. 45, **alfaratta** Holland, ♀, type (The Hobomok Skipper).

Fig. 188.— Neuration of *Poanes massasoit,* enlarged.

This species, which in error I named *zabulon* in the first edition of this book, has polymorphic females. To one of these I give the name *alfaratta.* The upper side is correctly shown on the plate; on the under side it is like typical *hobomok.* The variety named *friedlei* by Watson is much like *quadaquina* (Scudder). The variety *pallida* Watson is a male form, which is very pale on both sides of the wings, having a "washed-out" appearance.

The early stages have been only partly ascertained. The insect ranges from southern Canada and New England southward to the Carolinas and westward to Nebraska.

(3) **Poanes zabulon** (Boisd. & Lec.) Pl. LIII, fig. 46, ♂; fig. 47, ♂, *under side;* Pl. XLVII, fig. 39, ♀ (The Zabulon Skipper).

In the first edition of this book I gave the name *pocohontas* to the female of this species. I am glad to correct the error at this point.

The early stages are described by Scudder. The species ranges from Connecticut to Illinois and southward.

(4) **Poanes taxiles** (Edwards). Pl. XLVII, fig. 31, ♂; fig. 32, ♀, types (The Taxiles Skipper).

Butterfly.—The fore wings on the under side of the male are bright yellow, black at the base, slightly clouded on the outer margin with pale brown. The hind wings on the under side in this sex are still paler yellow, margined externally with pale brown, and crossed near the base and on the disk by irregular bands of pale brown. In the female sex the fore wings on the under side are fulvous, marked much as in the male, but darker, especially toward the apex, where the subapical spots and two small pale spots beyond the end of the cell near the outer margin interrupt the brown color. The hind wings on the under side are pale ferruginous, crossed by bands of lighter spots, and mottled with darker brown. Expanse: ♂, 1.45 inch; ♀, 1.50 inch.

Early Stages.—Unknown.

The range of this species is from western Nebraska through Colorado to Arizona.

(5) **Poanes melane** (Edwards). Pl. XLVI, fig. 7, ♂; fig. 8, ♀, types (The Umber Skipper).

Butterfly.—The male on the upper side somewhat resembles *A. zabulon*, var. *pocahontas;* the female likewise closely resembles specimens of this variety. The wings on the under side are ferruginous, clouded with blackish toward the base and on the inner angle, the light spots of the upper side being repeated. The hind wings on the under side are reddish, with a broad irregular curved median band of pale yellow spots. In the female the band of spots is far more obscure. Expanse: ♂, 1.3 in.; ♀, 1.5 in.

Early Stages.—Little is known of these.

The species is not uncommon in southern California and ranges as far north as San Francisco.

(6) **Poanes aaroni** (Skinner). Pl. XLVI, fig. 37, paratype (Aaron's Skipper).

Butterfly.—This small species, the male of which is figured in the plate, may be easily recognized from the figure there given. On the under side the fore wings are black at the base; the middle area of the wing is tawny, paler than on the upper side, and bordered as above, but the border below is cinnamon-brown and not fuscous. The hind wings on the under side are uniformly light cinnamon-brown, without any spots. The female is like the male, but larger, the colors somewhat lighter and the markings not so well defined. Expanse: ♂, 1.00 in.; ♀, 1.25 in.

Early Stages.—Unknown.

The specimens thus far contained in collections have all been taken about Cape May, in New Jersey, in the salt-marshes.

(7) **Poanes howardi** (Skinner). Pl. XLVI, fig. 14, ♂; fig. 38, ♂, type; Pl. LIV, fig. 1, ♀, paratype (Howard's Skipper).

Butterfly.—The figures on the plates give the upper sides of both sexes. In the male the discal streak is composed of light-colored scales of the same tint as the rest of the wing, in this respect resembling *P. aaroni.* The under side of the wings is described by Dr. Skinner as follows: "Superiors with tawny central area and border same as upper side. There is a large triangular spot extending into the wing from the base. The tawny color above this spot is of a darker hue than that below and outside of it. Inferiors very light brown, generally with four or five very faint tawny spots in the central area." Expanse: ♂, 1.5 in.; ♀, 1.6 in.

Early Stages.—Unknown.

The home of this species is Florida. It is suggested by Williams that it may be a large form of *P. aaroni,* inasmuch as the genitalia are similar. All of the specimens I possess show a pale longitudinal streak on the lower side of the hind wing, which does not occur in *P. aaroni.*

(8) **Poanes yehl** (Skinner). Pl. XLVI, fig. 40, ♂, type (Skinner's Skipper).

Butterfly.—The upper side of the male is shown in the plate. On the under side the wings are lighter, the secondaries uniformly pale cinnamon-brown, marked with a semicircle of four yellowish round spots, with a small spot on the cell toward the base. Expanse, 1.25–1.35 inch.

Early Stages.—Unknown.

The species has been taken in Florida, and is as yet not common in collections.

Genus PHYCANASSA Scudder

Butterfly.—Antennæ short; club straight, with a long tapering point at the end. The palpi are as in the preceding genus, but a trifle longer. The neuration is shown (Fig. 189), and is very much like that of the preceding genus.

Early Stages.—These are wholly unknown.

(1) **Phycanassa viator** (Edwards). Pl. XLVI, fig. 15, ♀ ; Pl. LIV, fig. 2, ♂, types (The Broad-winged Skipper).

FIG. 189.—Neuration of *Phycanassa.* Enlarged.

Butterfly.—Accurately delineated on the plates. On the under side the wings are as on the upper side, but paler; the light spots of the upper side appear indistinctly on the under side. Expanse: ♂, 1.45 in.; ♀, 1.6 in.

Early Stages.—Unknown.

It is not uncommon in the Gulf States, and has been found as far north as New Jersey, northern Illinois, and Wisconsin.

Genus PHEMIADES Hübner

This is a genus the species of which are tropical American. Only one occurs as a straggler at the extreme southern end of the peninsula of Florida. I am indebted to my friend, Dr. Schaus, for the privilege of showing the upper and under sides of the type of this species.

(1) **Phemiades jamaicensis** (Schaus). Pl. LXXV, fig. 9, ♂ ; fig. 9a, *under side*, type (Schaus' Jamaican Skipper).

The contrasting light and dark maculation of this species is striking, and any collector who may be so fortunate as to capture the insect, will have no trouble in identifying it with the help of the figure on our plate. Expanse: 2 in.

Genus ATRYTONOPSIS Godman and Salvin

(Type *Hesperia deva* Edwards)

Palpi rather heavy; second joint heavily scaled in front, the third small, protruding obliquely from the vestiture of the second. Antennæ not quite half as long as the costa of the primaries, the club terminating in a small point at right angles to the axis. The abdomen projects, but not greatly, beyond the hind wings. The middle tibiæ are spined. The fore wings are triangular, produced at the apex, the costa straight, or nearly so, the outer margins slightly rounded.

The hind wings are elongated triangular, the inner margin longer than the costal, the outer margin rounded. The neuration is given in Fig. 190. The absence of all yellow or reddish coloration, the prevalently gray tints of the lower sides of the wings, and the rather sharply pointed fore wings of the males are distinctive features.

The life-history of few of the species has as yet been ascertained. All of them, with the exception of *A. hianna* and *A. loammi* have their habitat in the southwestern states. The genus is well represented in Mexico.

FIG. 190.—Neuration of *Atrytonopsis deva*, ♂. Enlarged.

(1) **Atrytonopsis deva** (Edwards). Pl. LIV, fig. 13, ♂; fig. 14, ♀, typical (The Deva Skipper).

The species has the fringes white on the middle border of the hind wing. I figure a male, which absolutely agrees with the type, which is an old and faded specimen, and also a fresh female. Expanse: ♂, 1.25 in.; ♀, 1.75 in.

Originally described from Arizona, the insect has also been reported from Utah and southern Colorado.

(2) **Atrytonopsis vierecki** (Skinner). Pl. LIV, fig. 3, ♂, paratype (Viereck's Skipper).

This species is smaller and grayer than *A. deva*, and may be distinguished from the latter by the presence at the outer end of the cell of the fore wing of two, often confluent, white spots and a spot near the inner border of the same wing below the two discal spots, which form the discal series in *A. deva*. Expanse: 1.4 in.

Hitherto only reported from New Mexico.

(3) **Atrytonopsis lunus** (Edwards). Pl. LIV, fig. 15, ♂; fig. 16, ♀, *under side*, types (The Lunus Skipper).

Considerably larger than *deva* and differing in having a spot at the end of the cell of the fore wing like *vierecki*, which spot, however, differs in form from that in the latter species. The spot has the shape of the letter U laid horizontally, with the two arms pointing outwardly. It can readily be discriminated from the two preceding species by the dark under side of the secondaries, dusted externally with gray and marked by a dark black transverse bar beyond the end of the cell. Expanse: 1.8–1.9 in.

Habitat.—Arizona.

(4) **Atrytonopsis pittacus** (Edwards). Pl. LIV, fig. 11, ♂, type (The Pittacus Skipper).

Smaller than *A. vierecki*. The fore wings are narrow, but have the same maculation as *vierecki*. The species is readily separated from all others by the straight band of white spots on the hind wings beyond and below the cell. Expanse: 1.25 in.

Habitat.—Arizona.

(5) **A. python** (Edwards). Pl. LIV, fig. 4, ♂; fig. 5, ♀, *under side*, types (The Python Skipper).

The Python skipper is readily distinguished by the pale honey-yellow **color** of the translucent spots, the small light spot on the secondaries near the outer angle, the checkered fringes, and the different pattern of maculation on the under side. Expanse: ♂, 1.38 in.; ♀, 1.5 in.

A varietal form of this species is **A. margarita** (Skinner). One of Skinner's specimens agreeing with his type is shown on Pl. LIV, fig. 12. It is a dwarfed form. Expanse: 1.15 in.

Habitat.—A. python and its variety, *A. margarita*, are found in Arizona.

(6) **Atrytonopsis cestus** (Edwards). Pl. LXXV, figs. 12 and 12a, type, ♂ (The Cestus Skipper).

This species, only known thus far by the unique type, preserved in the Collection of the Brooklyn Entomological Society, has, like *A. pittacus*, a band of white spots below the cell of the secondaries, which band is not straight as in *pittacus*, but angulated; and in addition there is a white spot at the end of the cell of the secondaries, which is not seen in *pittacus*. On the under side the wings are very different from *pittacus*, as shown in our figure. It is a distinct and well marked species. I am indebted to Dr. Engelhardt, the Curator of Entomology in the Brooklyn Museum for enabling me to illustrate this hitherto unfigured species. Expanse: 1.5 in. (Fig. 12a is enlarged).

Habitat.—Southern Arizona.

(7) **Atrytonopsis edwardsi** Barnes & McDunnough. Pl. LXXI, fig. 16, ♂ (Edwards' Atrytonopsis).

Synonym: *Pamphila cestus* Wright (not Edwards).

Readily distinguished by the relatively large quadrate spots on the fore wing and the curved discal series of spots on the hind wing and the spot in the cell. Expanse: 1.–1.5 in.

Habitat.—Arizona.

(8) **Atrytonopsis hianna** Scudder. Pl. XLVI, fig. 9, ♂; fig. 10, ♀. (The Dusted Skipper).

Butterfly.—The upper side is accurately represented in the plate. The wings on the lower side are as on the upper side, a trifle paler and somewhat grayer on the outer margin. Expanse: ♂, 1.15 inch; ♀, 1.25 inch.

Early Stages.—Unknown.

It ranges through southern New England, westward to Nebraska, and south to Oklahoma and Texas.

(9) **Atrytonopsis loammi** (Whitney). Pl. LIV, fig. 6, ♂; fig. 7, ♀, *under side*; fig. 8, ♀ (The Loammi Skipper).

Synonym: *Pamphila regulus* Edwards.

The figures we give will enable the student to readily identify the species. It is known to range from the Carolinas to Florida, and is not uncommon in the latter state. Like *A. hianna*, it is a species existing far removed from the metropolis of the genus, which is in the southwestern states and Mexico. Expanse: ♂, 1.25 in.; ♀, 1.35 in. (The ♀ figured on the plate is dwarfed).

The type of *P. regulus* in my possession is a small and much worn specimen of *A. loammi.*

Genus THESPIEUS Godman and Salvin

This is a genus of Central and South American distribution, founded by its authors for the reception of a number of species, only one of which occurs within our borders. As this insect is well represented on the plate a lengthy generic description may be foregone.

(1) **Thespieus macareus** (Herrich-Schæffer). Pl. LIV, fig. 9, ♂; fig. 10, ♂, *under side* (The Macareus Skipper).

Genus MEGISTIAS Godman and Salvin

This genus was proposed by its authors for a number of small and obscure Central American species, having moderately long and slender antennæ, slender bodies, and fore wings not as acutely pointed at the apex as is the case in the genus *Cobalus*, with which comparison was made. Godman and Salvin state that *Hesperia fusca* Grote & Robinson belongs to this genus.

(1) **Megistias lherminieri** (Latreille). Pl. LIV, fig. 18, ♂; fig. 19, ♀ (The Fuscous Skipper.)

Synonym: *Hesperia fusca* Grote and Robinson.

This species, which we represent by typical male and female specimens, is immaculate above; the under side of the secondaries of the male is brownish, of the female paler and whitish; fringes dark. Expanse: .75–1. in.

Common in the Gulf States, it occurs as a straggler as far north as Pennsylvania, according to Dr. Skinner.

(2) **Megistias neamathla** (Skinner and Williams). Pl. LIV, fig. 17, ♂, paratype (The Neamathla Skipper).

Much like the preceding species, but paler slaty-gray on the upper side, with the fringes, especially of the hind wings, somewhat broadly white, more so at the anal angle. On the under side the hind wings are ashen gray, paler than the fore wings. Expanse: 1 in.

Habitat.—Florida.

Genus LEREMA Scudder

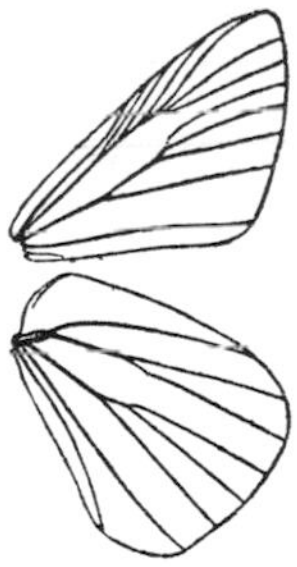

Butterfly.—Antennæ relatively short, slender, with a short club. Third joint of palpi erect, short, conical. The neuration is shown on Fig. 191. The male has a linear glandular streak on the upper side of the fore wing.

Egg.—Hemispherical, covered with more or less pentagonal cells.

FIG. 191.—Neuration of the genus *Lerema*, enlarged.

Caterpillar.—Feeds upon grasses; body slender, tapering from middle forward and backward; head small.

Chrysalis.—Slender, smooth, with a tapering conical projection at the head, and the tongue-case long and free, reaching almost to the end of the abdomen.

395

(1) **Lerema accius** (Smith and Abbot). Pl. XLVIII, fig. 8, ♂; Pl. VI, fig. 46, *chrysalis* (The Accius Skipper).

Butterfly.—The male on the upper side is dark blackish-brown, with three small subapical spots and one small spot below these, near the origin of the third median nervule. The female is exactly like the male, except that it has two spots, the larger one being placed below the small spot corresponding to the one on the fore wing of the male. The wings on the under side are dark fuscous, somewhat clouded with darker brown, the spots of the upper side reappearing on the under side. Expanse: ♂, 1.4 in.; ♀, 1.5 in.

Early Stages.—Very little has been written about these.

The butterfly ranges from southern Connecticut to Florida, thence westward to Texas, and along the Gulf coast in Mexico.

Genus LERODEA Scudder

Butterfly.—The antennæ are about half as long as the costa; the club is robust, slightly elongated, with a distinct crook at the extremity; the palpi have the third joint erect, minute, and bluntly conical. The neuration is represented in Fig. 192.

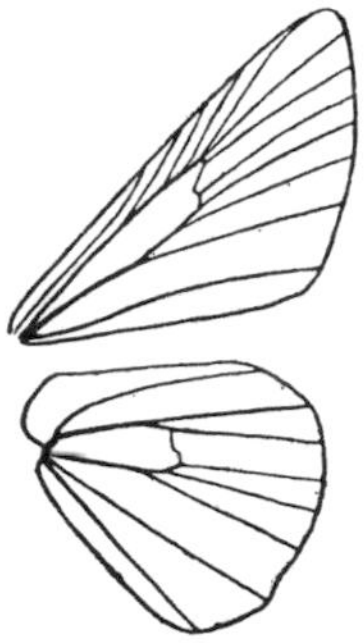

Early Stages.—These are not known.

(1) **Lerodea eufala** Edwards. Pl. XLVI, fig. 33, ♀ (The Eufala Skipper).

Butterfly.—The plate shows the upper side of the female. The male is not different, except that the fore wings are a little more pointed at the apex. The under side is like the upper side, but a shade paler. The lower side of the abdomen is whitish. When seen on the wing the creature looks like a small *Prenes ocola.* Expanse: 1.10–1.20 inch.

Early Stages.—Unknown.

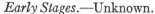

FIG. 192.—Neuration of the genus *Lerodea*, enlarged.

This butterfly is found in the Gulf States.

(2) **Lerodea arabus** (Edwards). (The Arabus Skipper).
Synonym: *dysaules* Godman and Salvin.

Originally described by Edwards from a single female specimen from Arizona. The type has disappeared from the Edwards Collection, and I cannot figure it. It, however, undoubtedly is the insect described and figured by Godman and Salvin under the specific name *dysaules.*

Genus OLIGORIA Scudder

Butterfly.—The antennæ are as in the preceding genus; the palpi have the third joint minute and almost entirely concealed in the thick vestiture of the second joint. The neuration is represented in Fig. 193.

(1) **Oligoria maculata** (Edwards). Pl. XLVI, fig. 35, ♂ (The Twin-spot).
Synonym: *norus* Ploetz.

The species has nothing to do with *maculala* Brem. & Gray, an Asiatic species, which belongs to another genus, and is therefore not a synonym of this.

Butterfly.—The upper side of the male is as shown in the plate. The female closely resembles the male, but the spots on the fore wing are larger. On the under side the wings are brown, almost as dark as on the upper side. The primaries are whitish near the outer angle. The spots of the upper side of the primaries are reproduced on the lower side. The hind wings have three conspicuous pearly-white spots about the middle, two located one on either side of the second median nervule, and one removed from these, located between the upper radial and the subcostal nervule. Expanse: ♂, 1.40 inch; ♀, 1.50 inch.

FIG. 193.—Neuration of the genus *Oligoria*, enlarged.

Early Stages.—But little is known of these.

This is a Southern species, found abundantly in Florida, and ranging northward into Georgia and the Carolinas. A specimen is reported to have been taken near Albany, New York, and diligent collecting may show that it has a far more northern range than has heretofore been supposed.

Genus PRENES Scudder

Butterfly.—The antennæ are short, not half the length of the costa. The head is broad, and the antennæ are inserted widely apart. The club is moderate, terminating in a fine point which is bent back at right angles, forming a distinct crook. The abdomen is long and slender, but does not project beyond the hind margin of the secondaries. The fore wings are pointed at the apex and are relatively longer and narrower than in the preceding genus. The neuration is illustrated in Fig. 194.

FIG. 194.—Neuration of the genus *Prenes*, enlarged.

Early Stages.—These have not yet been closely studied.

(1) **Prenes nero** (Fabricius). Pl. LIV, fig. 25, ♂ (Nero's Skipper).

Synonyms: *corrupta* (Herr.-Schæf.); *sylvicola* Scudder; *fusina* (Hew.); *fufidia* (Hew.). I follow in part the synonymy given by Godman and Salvin, which in the main I believe to be correct. *Nyctelius* (Latreille) according to N. D. Riley is not the same as *nero*.

Butterfly.—This common species is found all through the Antilles, Central and South America. The synonymy, which has been created is based upon variations in the band of white spots on the under side of the hind wings, which sometimes is broad, sometimes is narrow, sometimes is faint, or even wanting. There is considerable variation throughout the wide range of the species in this respect.

It occasionally occurs in southern Florida in the form, which is common in Cuba.

(2) **Prenes panoquin** (Scudder). Pl. LIV, fig. 20, ♂; fig. 21, ♀, *under side* (The Panoquin Skipper).

Synonym: *ophis* (Edwards).

Easily recognized by the elongated white markings on the under side of the hind wings. It is a comparatively small species, and is not uncommon in Florida, ranging northward in marshy places upon the Atlantic coast as far as New Jersey.

(3) **Prenes panoquinoides** (Skinner). Pl. LIV, fig. 23, ♂, paratype (The Panoquinoides Skipper).

This obscure insect, which resembles *panoquin* on the upper side, differs in the absence of the elongated white markings on the under side of the secondaries. It is found in Florida.

(4) **Prenes errans** (Skinner). Pl. LIV, fig. 24, ♂, paratype (The Wandering Skipper).

This species is considerably smaller than *P. ocola*, which it resembles on the upper side. It differs on the under side by having the hind wings broadly powdered with gray scales and traversed beyond the middle by a narrow band of pale yellowish white spots, which are altogether absent in *ocola*, the hind wings of which are uniformly dark brownish gray.

(5) **Prenes ocola** (Edwards). Pl. XLVI, fig. 34, ♂; Pl. LIV, fig. 22, ♀ (The Ocola Skipper).

Butterfly.—Accurately depicted on the plates.

The under is like the upper side, but a shade paler. The under side of the abdomen is whitish. Expanse: 1.4–1.6 in.

Early Stages.—Unknown.

This is a Southern species, found commonly in the Gulf States, and ranging northward to Pennsylvania, southern Ohio, and Indiana.

FIG. 195.—Neuration of the genus *Calpodes*, enlarged.

Genus CALPODES Hübner

Butterfly.—Rather large, stout; head broad; antennæ as in the preceding genus, but stouter. The neuration, considerably enlarged, is accurately delineated in Fig. 195.

Egg.—Hemispherical, ornamented with irregular, more or less pentagonal cells.

Caterpillar.—Cylindrical, slender, tapering forward and backward from the ninth segment, rapidly diminishing in size posteriorly; the head relatively small, the neck not much strangulated; spiracles surrounded by radiating blackish bristles.

Chrysalis.—The chrysalis is relatively slender, gently convex both on the ventral and dorsal aspects, with a curved delicate frontal tubercle. The tongue-case is long and projects for a considerable distance beyond the somewhat short cremaster.

(1) **Calpodes ethlius** (Cramer). Pl. XLV, fig. 3, ♀ ; Pl. VI, fig. 48, *chrysalis* (The Brazilian Skipper).

Butterfly.—There can be no mistaking this robust and thick-bodied species. The wings on the under side are dull olive, blackish at the base of the primaries, with all the spots of the upper side repeated. Expanse, 2.–2.15 in.

Early Stages.—The caterpillar feeds on the leaves of the canna.

It is common in the Gulf States, and ranges north to South Carolina. A stray specimen was once taken at West Farms, New York. Southward it ranges everywhere through the Antilles to Argentina, in South America.

SUBFAMILY MEGATHYMINÆ (THE GIANT SKIPPERS)

Medium to very large in size for Hesperids, having an expanse of wing ranging from one and one quarter of an inch to three and one-half inches. So far as known the eggs are more or less flattened hemispherical, the micropyle depressed, and the sides of the eggs pitted like a thimble. The larvæ feed at first upon the outer tissues of the fleshy leaves of various species of *Yucca* and *Agave*, concealed in the crevices between the leaves, but presently burrow into the stems and the roots of these plants. They pupate at the end of the burrow at the surface of the stem weaving for themselves silk-lined tunnels, in which they remain until they emerge from the chrysalis.

In the neuration of the wings, the structure of the antennæ, and the other organs, they reveal close affinity to the other subfamilies of the *Hesperiidæ*, and they must be included in the *Hesperioidea*, having only a superficial resemblance to the large day-flying moths, known as the *Castniidæ*, with which some authors have erroneously sought to associate them. The antennæ are relatively long, rigid, with a stout club, slightly recurved at the tip. The primaries have the cell about two thirds the length of the costa; the first submedian vein originates a little beyond the middle of the cell, the second and third arise near the end of the cell; the lower radial arises near the origin of the third median, and is widely separated from the upper radial. The secondaries have the second and third submedian nervules well toward the end of the cell. The body is robust. The tip of the abdomen in most species does not greatly extend beyond the outer margin of the hind wings, though in the males of some species it strongly protrudes. The palpi are relatively small, the third joint minute, and more or less covered by the scales of the second joint. The tibiæ of the second and third pair of legs are spined.

Most of the species thus far known occur in the semi-arid regions of the southwestern States and in Mexico. Two species are found in Georgia and Florida, thence ranging westward, wherever their food-plant is found, at least as far as Texas and Colorado.

Mating in the case of some species is said to occur late in the afternoon, or even in the dusk of the evening, though the males are said to be on the wing in the bright morning sunshine.

Genus MEGATHYMUS Scudder

The genus comprises butterflies with very stout bodies, broad wings, long and stoutly clubbed antennæ, and relatively minute palpi. What has been said of the family applies to the genus. The caterpillars at first live between the bases of the leaves, and in later stages burrow in the pith and root-stalks of various species of *Yucca* and allied plants.

FIG. 196.—*Megathymus yuccæ*, ♀.

FIG. 197.—Chrysalis of *Megathymus yuccæ*.

(1) **Megathymus yuccæ** (Boisduval and Leconte). (The Yucca Skipper).

The female of the species is shown in Fig. 196, which is reproduced from the excellent account prepared by the late Dr. C. V. Riley and published by him in his now classic "Eighth Annual Report of the State Entomologist of Missouri,"

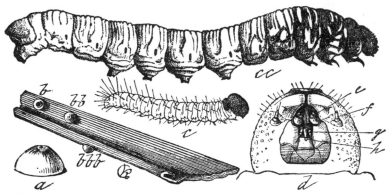

FIG. 198.—*Megathymus yuccæ: a*, egg, magnified; *b*, egg from which larva has escaped; *bb, bbb*, unhatched eggs, natural size; *c*, newly hatched larva, magnified; *cc*, larva, natural size; *d*, head, enlarged to show the mouth-parts; *e*, maxillary palpi; *f*, antenna; *g*, labial palpi; *h*, spinneret.

p. 169. Further details as to the life-history of the insect are set forth in Fig. 198, in which the eggs, a magnified illustration of the young larva just out of the egg, and a representation of the mature larva of natural size are given. Fig. 197 provides an excellent representation of the chrysalis. All of these figures were drawn by Dr. Riley.

The first figure of *M. yuccæ* appeared in the work published upon the Lepidoptera of North America by Boisduval and Leconte without any text. It is to C. V. Riley that we are really indebted for our best information in regard to the species. Originally described from Georgia, it is found in the Gulf States, ranging westward to Texas and Colorado. Expanse: ♂, 1.75–2.25 in.; ♀, 2.75–3.15 in.

(2) **Megathymus yuccæ** var. **coloradensis** Riley. Pl. LIV, fig. 27, ♂; fig. 28, ♂, *under side* (The Colorado Giant Skipper).

This subspecies is, as its name implies, found in Colorado, and the states west and south of Colorado. The wings are narrower than in *M. yuccæ yuccæ* (Bdv. & Lec.) and the secondaries near the costa are more widely marked with silvery spots, there being but one such spot in typical *yuccæ*, while in the variety *coloradensis* there are two, or even three, tending to coalesce to form a silvery longitudinal costal band.

(3) **Megathymus ursus** Poling. Pl. LXXII, fig. 1, ♀, type (Poling's Giant Skipper).

This is the largest species of the genus. On the plate we give a reproduction of the figure of the type published in the Entomological News, Vol. XIII, 1902, p. 97, Pl. IV. The type, which is a female, has an expanse of 3.5 in. The insect is so far only known from Arizona.

(4) **Megathymus cofaqui** Strecker. Pl. LIV, fig. 35, ♂; fig. 34, ♀ (The Cofaqui Skipper).

This is one of the smaller species of the genus. Strecker confused it with another, but larger, insect, which is now named *M. streckeri* (see below). The expanse of wing ranges in the male from 1.25 to 2 in.; in the female to 2.25 inches. Thus far it is only known from Georgia and Florida. The male figured on the plate was captured at Lutz, Florida, not far from Tampa, and is a small specimen.

(5) **Megathymus streckeri** Skinner. Pl. LIV, fig. 30, ♂, *under side* (Strecker's Giant Skipper).

The species is much larger than *M. cofaqui* and quite differently marked. The male has the upper side of the hind wings profusely covered with long hair-like black scales, which stand up like a brush, and present a very odd appearance when the wing is looked at from the side. There are traces of such an arrangement in *M. cofaqui*, but not comparable in size and extent to what is seen in the present species. The two species are quite differently marked on the under side of the wings, *cofaqui* being dark brown with a few little white spots; *streckeri* being prevalently gray, with numerous light spots surrounded by blackish scales, as shown on the plate. This species is found in the arid and semi-arid regions of Texas, New Mexico, and Arizona. Expanse: ♂, 2.75–3 in.; ♀, 3–3.25 in.

A smaller form of this species has received the varietal name *texana* Barnes and Mc Dunnough.

(6) **Megathymus leussleri** Holland. Pl. LXXII, fig. 10, ♂; fig. 11, ♂, *under side;* fig. 12, ♀, types (Leussler's Giant Skipper).

The larva of this species feeds upon *Yucca glauca*, which is common on the sandhills of Nebraska. It is distantly related to *M. streckeri*, and some males on the under side of the hind wings have many silvery white spots and streaks, as is the case in the latter species, the under side of a male of which is shown on Pl. LIV, fig. 13.

M. leussleri is, however, well differentiated from *M. streckeri* by the uniformly black color of the abdomen above and below, the presence on the under side of the fore wings of the submarginal band of light spots, which does not appear in *M. streckeri* except subapically, the reduced area covered by androconial scales on the upper surface of the secondaries, and the prevalently larger size of the insect. These are all features which separate this form from typical *M. streckeri*. Expanse: ♂, 2.5 in.; ♀, 2.75 in.

(7) **Megathymus albocincta** Holland. Pl. LXXI, fig. 17, ♂; fig. 18, ♂, *under side*, types (The White-rimmed Giant Skipper).

This species is a close ally of the preceding, but much smaller in size, and the marginal light spots of the primaries differ in being much elongated inwardly. There is an almost total obliteration of light markings on the disk of the secondaries on the under side, which are however girdled with pale gray, as in *M. leussleri*, but the girdle is not interrupted at the ends of the veins with dark spots as in the latter species. Expanse: ♂, 1.75–2. in.; ♀, 2–2.10 in.

Habitat.—Southwestern Texas.

(8) **Megathymus smithi** Druce.

This is a small dark form, which is said to occur in the extreme southern part of Texas, and is still very rare in collections. It is figured by Druce in the Biologia Centrali-Americana, Heterocera, Vol. II, Pl. XX, fig. 5.

(9) **Megathymus mariæ** Barnes & Benjamin (Cont. Nat. Hist. Lep. N. A., Vol. V, No. 3, 1924, p. 100) (Mary's Giant Skipper).

This species, so-called, is discriminated from *M. neumoegeni* and *M. polingi* by having the lower spot in the submarginal series of the fore wing longer than those above it, whereas, in the other two species mentioned this spot is shorter. The genitalia are also said to be different. Expanse: ♂, about 1.75 in.; ♀, 1.75–2.10 in.

Habitat.—El Paso, Texas, and vicinity.

(10) **Megathymus polingi** Skinner. Pl. LIV, fig. 31, ♂; fig. 32, ♀, paratypes, Skinner *det.* (Poling's Giant Skipper).

This species is readily distinguished from its congeners by the greater expanse on the primaries of the light yellow spots on the upper side of the fore wings. There is some variation in this respect, occasional specimens having broader and more coalescent spots than others. Expanse: ♂, 1.5 in.; ♀, 2 in.

The habitat of the species is Arizona.

(11) **Megathymus neumœgeni** Edwards. Pl. LIV, fig. 29, ♂ (Neumoegen's Giant Skipper).

Closely allied to *M. aryxna* Dyar, with which it is often confused in collections. But aside from slight variations in the genital armature, this species can always be distinguished from the following by the smaller size of the submarginal spots on both the fore and the hind wings. Expanse about 2 in. It occurs rather commonly in Arizona between the Catalina and Rincon Mountains.

(12) **Megathymus aryxna** Dyar. Pl. LIV, fig. 33, ♂ (Dyar's Giant Skipper).

Close to the foregoing species, but greater in expanse of wing, with the submarginal spots on the upper side wider, and with a nearly complete semicircular band of small and indistinct submarginal spots on the lower side of the hind wing, the two spots near the costa being, though small, distinct and somewhat sharply defined. Expanse: 2.25 in.

The insect is found in Arizona and northern Mexico.

(13) **Megathymus stephensi** Skinner. Pl. LXXII, fig. 13, ♂; fig. 14, ♀, *under side* (Stephen's Giant Skipper).

This insect is depicted in Wright's "Butterflies of the West Coast," Pl. XXXII, fig. 463. It is said by Barnes and Benjamin to be identical with the insect, the lower side of which is figured by Barnes and McDunnough in their Cont. Nat. Hist. Lep. N. A., Vol. I, No. 3, Pl. II, fig. 7. Wright's figure looks like a small rubbed specimen of *M. neumœgeni*, but Barnes and Benjamin find it to be genitalically distinct. (See Skinner, Ent. News, XXIII, 1912, p. 126; Do., *l.c.* XXVIII, p. 232; Barnes and Benjamin, *l.c.*, XXXIV, p. 318. Wright gives the habitat of the species as southeastern California.

THE END

The writer in laying down his pen at the end of what has been to him a pleasurable task, expresses the hope that what he has written may tend to stimulate a deeper and more intelligent interest in the wonders of Creative Wisdom, and takes occasion to remind the reader that it is true, as was said by Fabricius, that nature is most to be admired in those works which are least—"*Natura maxime miranda in minimis.*"

INDEX

INDEX

(Synonyms in italics)

Index

Index

Index

Index

Index

Index

Index

Index

Index

PLATES

(II–LXXVII)*

*Plate I is frontispiece

Explanation of Plate II

Reproduced, with the kind permission of Dr. S. H. Scudder, from "The Butterflies of New England," Vol. III, Plate 76.

CATERPILLARS OF PAPILIONIDÆ AND HESPERIIDÆ

1. *Colias eurytheme.*
2. *Callidryas eubule.*
3. *Eurema lisa.*
4. *Callidryas eubule.*
5. *Euchloë genutia.*
6. *Eurema nicippe.*
7. *Pieris protodice.*
8. *Pieris napi*, var. *oleracea.*
9. *Pieris napi*, var. *oleracea.*
10. *Colias philodice.*
11. *Pieris rapæ.*
12. *Pieris rapæ.*
13. *Papilio philenor.*
14. *Papilio ajax.*
15. *Papilio turnus.* Just before pupation.
16. *Papilio cresphontes.*
17. *Papilio asterius.* In second stage.

18. *Papilio troilus.*
19. *Papilio troilus.* In third stage; plain.
20. *Papilio philenor.*
21. *Papilio philenor.* In third stage; dorsal view.
22. *Papilio troilus.* In third stage; dorsal view.
23. *Achalarus lycidas.* Dorsal view.
24. *Papilio asterius.* In fourth stage; dorsal view.
25. *Thorybes pylades.*
26. *Papilio turnus.* Dorsal view.
27. *Papilio asterius.*
28. *Papilio turnus.*
29. *Thorybes pylades.*
30. *Epargyreus tityrus.*
31. *Epargyreus tityrus.*
32. *Thorybes bathyllus.*
33. *Epargyreus tityrus.*
34. *Eudamus proteus.*

35. *Epargyreus tityrus.* In third stage.

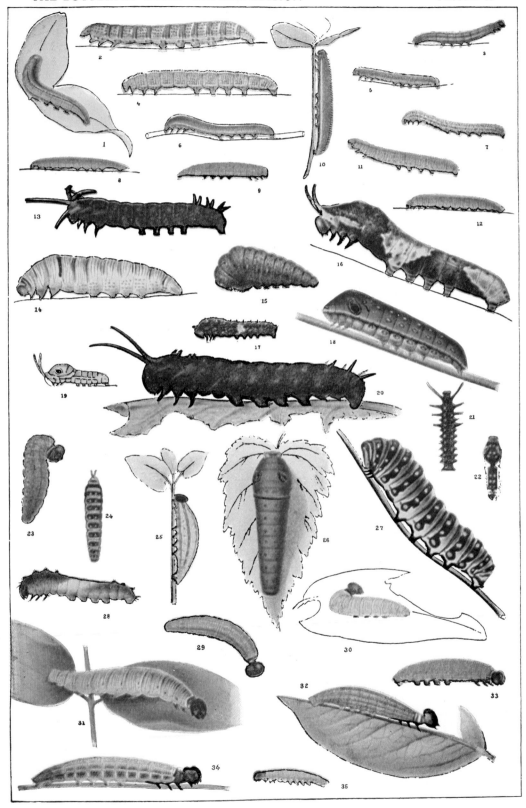

Explanation of Plate III

Reproduced, with the kind permission of Dr. S. H. Scudder, from "The Butterflies of New England," Vol. III, Plate 74.

1. *Œneis semidea.* Penultimate stage.
2. *Œneis semidea.*
3. *Euptychia euryta.*
4. *Œneis semidea.*
5. *Danais plexippus.*
6. *Euptychia euryta.*
7. *Œneis semidea.* Just hatched.
8. *Euptychia phocion.*
9. *Satyrodes eurydice.*
10. *Euptychia euryta.*
11. *Œneis jutta.* Just hatched.
12. *Euptychia phocion.*
13. *Euptychia euryta.* Penultimate stage.
14. *Euptychia euryta.* Plain and enlarged.
15. *Œneis semidea.*
16. *Enodia portlandia.*
17. *Basilarchia astyanax.*
18. *Cercyonis alope.*
19. *Basilarchia archippus.*
20. *Asterocampa clyton.*
21. *Basilarchia astyanax.*
22. *Basilarchia archippus.* Plain outline to show the attitude sometimes assumed.
23. *Polygonia interrogationis.*
24. *Basilarchia archippus.*
25. *Basilarchia astyanax.* Plain.
26. *Basilarchia arthemis.*
27. *Polygonia interrogationis.*
28. *Aglais antiopa.*
29. *Junonia cœnia.*
30. *Junonia cœnia.*
31. *Polygonia progne.*
32. *Polygonia faunus.*
33. *Polygonia satyrus.*
34. *Vanessa virginiensis.*
35. *Vanessa atalanta.*
36. *Aglais milberti.*
37. *Vanessa cardui.*
38. *Polygonia comma.*

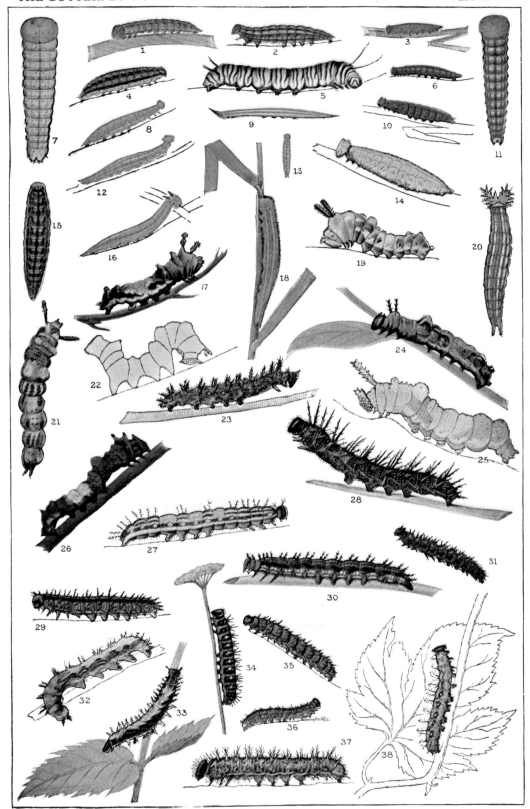

Explanation of Plate IV

Reproduced, with the kind permission of Dr. S. H. Scudder, from "The Butterflies of New England," Vol. III, Plate 83.

CHRYSALIDS IN COLOR AND IN OUTLINE—NYMPHALIDÆ

1. *Danais plexippus*. Side view.
2. *Danais plexippus*. In outline.
3. *Danais plexippus*. Dorsal view.
4. *Œneis semidea*.
5. *Œneis semidea*. Dorsal view.
6. *Enodia portlandia*.
7. *Cercyonis nephele*.
8. *Cercyonis nephele*. Dorsal view.
9. *Satyrodes eurydice*. Side view.
10. *Euptychia phocion*. Side view.
11. *Euptychia phocion*. Side view.
12. *Basilarchia astyanax*. Side view.
13. *Basilarchia astyanax*. Side view.
14. *Basilarchia arthemis*. Side view.
15. *Asterocampa clyton*. Side view.
16. *Asterocampa clyton*. Side view.
17. *Asterocampa clyton*. Dorsal view.
18. *Basilarchia archippus*. Ventral view.
19. *Basilarchia archippus*. Side view.
20. *Basilarchia archippus*. Side view.
21. *Polygonia interrogationis*. Dorsal view.
22. *Polygonia interrogationis*. Side view.
23. *Basilarchia arthemis*. Dorsal view.
24. *Polygonia interrogationis*. Outline of meso-thoracic tubercle from the side.
25. *Polygonia interrogationis*.
26. *Polygonia interrogationis*. Outline of head from in front.
27. *Polygonia comma*. Outline of head from in front; enlarged.
28. *Euptychia euryta*. Side view.
29. *Polygonia comma*. Outline of mesothoracic tubercle from the side.
30. *Polygonia comma*. The same from another specimen.
31. *Polygonia faunus*. Outline of head from in front.
32. *Polygonia progne*. Outline of head from in front.
33. *Polygonia faunus*. Side view.
34. *Polygonia faunus*. Side view in outline.
35. *Polygonia faunus*. Ventral view in outline.
36. *Aglais j-album*. Outline of mesothoracic tubercle from the side.
37. *Polygonia progne*. Side view.
38. *Polygonia progne*. Side view.
39. *Polygonia comma*. Side view.
40. *Polygonia interrogationis*. Side view.
41. *Polygonia satyrus*. Side view.
42. *Polygonia satyrus*. Ventral view.
43. *Aglais milberti*. Side view.
44. *Aglais j-album*. Side view.
45. *Aglais j-album*. Ventral view.
46. *Polygonia comma*. Side view.
47. *Polygonia comma*. Side view.
48. *Polygonia comma*. Dorsal view.
49. *Aglais milberti*. Side view.
50. *Aglais milberti*. Dorsal view.
51. *Aglais antiopa*. Side view.
52. *Vanessa atalanta*. Side view.
53. *Vanessa atalanta*. Dorsal view.
54. *Vanessa virginiensis*. Side view.
55. *Vanessa atalanta*. Side view.
56. *Junonia cœnia*. Side view.
57. *Junonia cœnia*. Dorsal view.
58. *Aglais antiopa*. Side view.
59. *Aglais antiopa*. Dorsal view.
60. *Vanessa cardui*. Side view.
61. *Vanessa cardui*. Side view.
62. *Vanessa cardui*. Dorsal view.
63. *Vanessa virginiensis*. Dorsal view.
64. *Vanessa virginiensis*. Side view with nest woven before pupation.
65. *Junonia cœnia*. Side view.
66. *Junonia cœnia*. Side view.
67. *Junonia cœnia*. Side view.

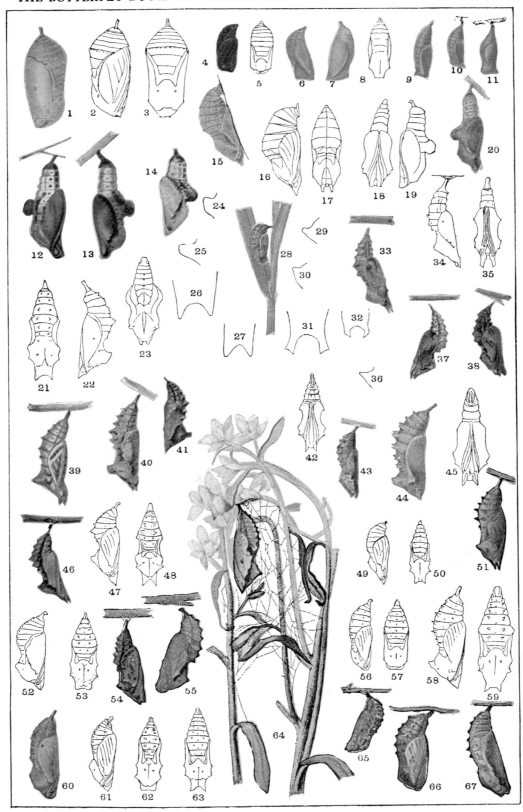

Explanation of Plate V

Reproduced, with the kind permission of Dr. S. H. Scudder, from "The Butterflies of New England," Vol. III, Plate 84.

CHRYSALIDS IN COLOR AND IN OUTLINE—NYMPHALIDÆ, LYCÆNIDÆ, PIERIDÆ

1. *Argynnis cybele.* Side view.
2. *Argynnis cybele.* Dorsal view.
3. *Argynnis cybele.* Side view.
4. *Argynnis idalia.* Side view.
5. *Argynnis aphrodite.* Side view.
6. *Argynnis atlantis.* Side view.
7. *Melitæa phaëtona.* Side view.
8. *Euptoieta claudia.* Side view.
9. *Euptoieta claudia.* Side view.
10. *Brenthis bellona.* Side view
11. *Brenthis bellona.* Side view.
12. *Brenthis myrina.* Side view.
13. *Brenthis myrina.* Side view.
14. *Brenthis myrina.* Dorsal view.
15. *Melitæa phaëtona.* Side view.
16. *Melitæa phaëtona.* Dorsal view.
17. *Melitæa harrisi.* Side view.
18. *Melitæa harrisi.* Dorsal view.
19. *Phyciodes nycteis.* Side view.
20. *Phyciodes tharos.* Dorsal view.
21. *Phyciodes tharos.* Side view.
22. *Phyciodes tharos.* Side view.
23. *Libythea bachmanni.* Side view.
24. *Libythea bachmanni.* Side view.
25. *Thecla calanus.* Side view.
26. *Thecla irus.* Side view, enlarged.
27. *Thecla calanus.* Side view.
28. *Thecla liparops.* Side view.
29. *Thecla edwardsi.* Side view.
30. *Thecla gryneus.* Side view.
31. *Thecla gryneus.* Side view, enlarged.
32. *Thecla irus.* Dorsal view.
33. *Thecla irus.* Side view.
34. *Thecla irus.* Side view.
35. *Thecla acadica.* Side view.
36. *Lycæna pseudargiolus.* Side view.
37. *Thecla titus.* Side view.
38. *Thecla niphon.* Side view.
39. *Thecla melinus.* Side view. Copied from Abbot's drawing in the British Museum.
40. *Thecla niphon.* Side view. Copied from Abbot's drawing in Dr. Boisduval's library.
41. *Lycæna scudderi.* Side view, enlarged.
42. *Lycæna comyntas.* Side view. Copied from Abbot's drawing in Dr. Boisduval's library.
43. *Lycæna pseudargiolus.* Side view, enlarged. Copied from Abbot's drawing in Dr. Boisduval's library.
44. *Lycæna pseudargiolus.* Side view.
45. *Feniseca tarquinius.* Side view.
46. *Feniseca tarquinius.* Side view. Copied from Abbot's drawing in the British Museum.
47. *Lycæna comyntas.* Side view, enlarged.
48. *Lycæna comyntas.* Side view.
49. *Chrysophanus hypophlæas.* Side view.
50. *Chrysophanus thoë.* Side view.
51. *Eurema nicippe.* Side view.
52. *Eurema nicippe.* Dorsal view.
53. *Colias eurytheme.* Side view.
54. *Colias philodice.* Dorsal view.
55. *Colias philodice.* Side view.
56. *Eurema lisa.* Side view.
57. *Pieris napi,* var. *oleracea.* Side view.
58. *Pieris rapæ.* Side view.
59. *Euchloë genutia.* Side view.
60. *Callidryas eubule.* Side view.
61. *Callidryas eubule.* Side view.
62. *Callidryas eubule.* Dorsal view.
63. *Pieris napi,* var. *oleracea.* Side view.
64. *Pieris napi,* var. *oleracea.* Dorsal view.
65. *Pieris rapæ.* Dorsal view.
66. *Pieris protodice.* Dorsal view.

67. *Pieris protodice.* Side view.

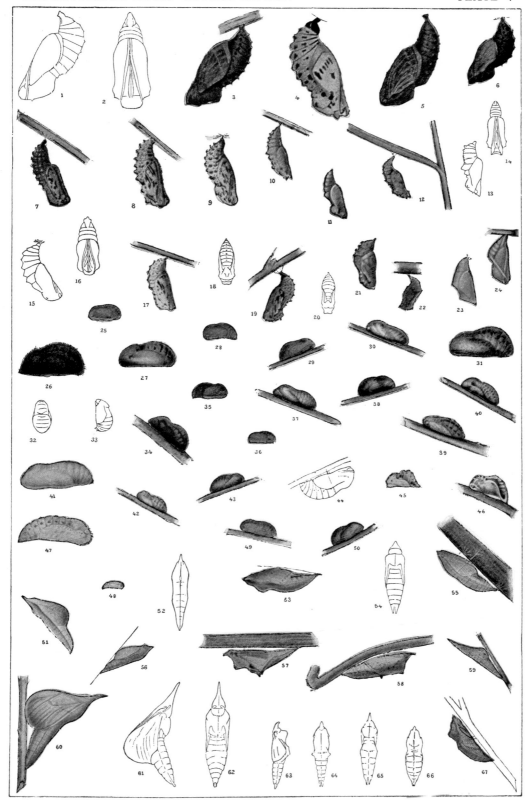

Explanation of Plate VI

Reproduced with the kind permission of Dr. S. H. Scudder, from "The Butterflies of New England," Vol. III, Plate 85.

CHRYSALIDS IN COLOR AND IN OUTLINE—PAPILIONIDÆ AND HESPERIIDÆ

1. *Papilio turnus.*
2. *Papilio turnus.* Dorsal view.
3. *Papilio turnus.*
4. *Papilio turnus.*
5. *Papilio troilus.* Dorsal view.
6. *Papilio troilus.*
7. *Papilio troilus.*
8. *Papilio cresphontes.*
9. *Papilio cresphontes.* Dorsal view.
10. *Papilio cresphontes.*
11. *Papilio ajax.*
12. *Papilio ajax.* Dorsal view.
13. *Papilio asterius.*
14. *Papilio philenor.* Dorsal view.
15. *Papilio philenor.* Dorsal view.
16. *Papilio philenor.*
17. *Papilio philenor.*
18. *Papilio asterius.* Dorsal view.
19. *Papilio asterius.*
20. *Papilio philenor.*
21. *Achalarus lycidas.*
22. *Epargyreus tityrus.*
23. *Eudamus proteus.* From the original by Abbot in the British Museum.
24. *Thorybes bathyllus.* From the original by Abbot in the British Museum.
25. *Epargyreus tityrus.*
26. *Epargyreus tityrus.*
27. *Thanaos icelus.*

28. *Thorybes pylades.*
29. *Pholisora catullus.* From the original by Abbot in the British Museum.
30. *Thanaos lucilius.*
31. *Thanaos lucilius.* Dorsal view.
32. *Thanaos lucilius.*
33. *Thanaos juvenalis.*
34. *Thanaos persius.*
35. *Hesperia montivaga.* From the original by Abbot in the British Museum.
36. *Pholisora catullus.*
37. *Thanaos martialis.* From the original by Abbot in the British Museum.
38. *Thanaos brizo.* From the original by Abbot in Dr. Boisduval's library.
39. *Hylephila phylæus.* From the original by Abbot in Dr. Boisduval's library.
40. *Amblyscirtes vialis.*
41. *Pholisora catullus.*
42. *Catia otho.* According to Scudder = *Thymelicus ætna.* From the original by Abbot in Dr. Boisduval's library.
43. *Atalopedes campestris.*
44. *Polites taumas.*
45. *Amblyscirtes samoset.* After the original by Abbot in the British Museum.
46. *Lerema accius.* After the original by Abbot in Boston Society of Natural History.
47. *Atalopedes campestris.*

48. *Calpodes ethlius.*

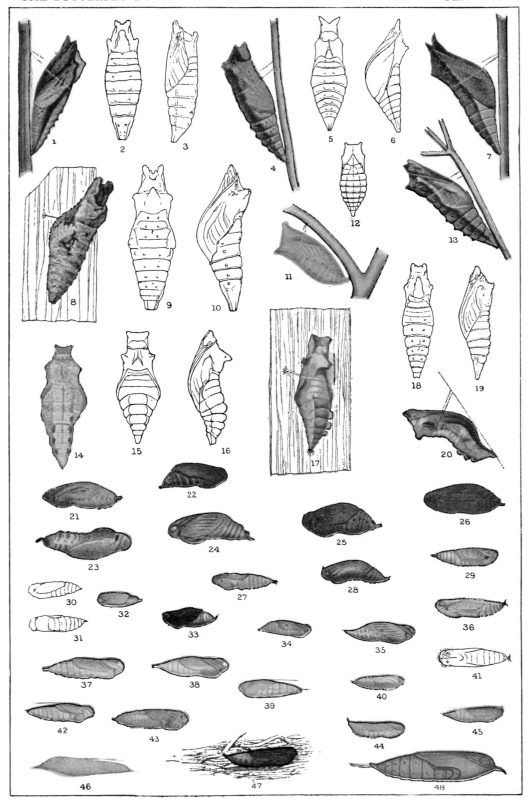

EXPLANATION OF PLATE VII

EXPLANATION OF PLATE VIII

1. *Dircenna klugi* (Geyer), ♂.
2. *Mechanitis lycidice* Bates, var. *californica* Reakirt, ♂.
3. *Ithomia anaphissa* H.-S., ♂.
4. *Colænis delila* (Fabricius), ♂.
5. *Heliconius charithonius* (Linn.), ♂.
6. *Colænis julia* (Fabricius), ♂.
7. *Dione vanillæ* (Linn.), ♂.
8. *Euptoieta hegesia* (Cramer), ♂.
9. *Euptoieta claudia* (Cramer), ♂.

Explanation of Plate IX

1. *Argynnis diana* (Cramer), ♂.
2. *Argynnis diana* (Cramer), ♀.
3. *Argynnis cybele* (Fabricius), ♂.
4. *Argynnis cybele* (Fabricius), ♀.
5. *Argynnis leto* Behr, ♂.
6. *Argynnis leto* Behr, ♀.

Explanation of Plate X

1. *Argynnis nokomis* Edwards, ♂.
2. *Argynnis nokomis* Edwards, ♀.
3. *Argynnis idalia* (Drury), ♀.
4. *Argynnis nevadensis* Edwards, ♂, *under side.*

5. *Argynnis montivaga* Behr, ♂, *under side.*
6. *Argynnis alcestis* Edwards, ♂.
7. *Argynnis bremneri* Edwards, ♂.
8. *Argynnis electa* Edwards, ♂.

9. *Argynnis atlantis* Edwards, ♂.

EXPLANATION OF PLATE XI

1. *Argynnis callippe* Boisduval, ♂.
2. *Argynnis callippe* Boisduval, ♀.
3. *Argynnis callippe* Boisduval, ♀, *under side.*
4. *Argynnis edwardsi* Reakirt, ♂.
5. *Argynnis edwardsi* Reakirt, ♀.

6. *Argynnis rhodope* Edwards, ♀, *under side.*
7. *Argynnis bischoffi* Edwards, ♂.
8. *Argynnis cornelia* Edwards, ♂.
9. *Argynnis nausicaä* Edwards, ♂.
10. *Argynnis coronis* Edwards, ♂.

11. *Argynnis coronis* Edwards, ♀.

Explanation of Plate XII

1. *Argynnis hesperis* Edwards, ♂.
2. *Argynnis hesperis* Edwards, ♀, *under side.*
3. *Argynnis cypris* Edwards, ♂.
4. *Argynnis cypris* Edwards, ♀.
5. *Argynnis oweni* Edwards, ♂.
6. *Argynnis oweni* Edwards, ♂, *under side.*

7. *Argynnis eurynome* Edwards, ♂.
8. *Argynnis rupestris* Behr, ♂.
9. *Argynnis rupestris* Behr, ♂, *under side.*
10. *Argynnis hippolyta* Edwards, ♂.
11. *Argynnis laura* Edwards, ♂.
12. *Argynnis laura* Edwards, ♀.

13. *Argynnis artonis* Edwards, ♂, *under side.*

Explanation of Plate XIII

1. *Argynnis cybele* (Fabricius), ♀, *under side.*
2. *Argynnis semiramis* Edwards, ♂, *under side.*
3. *Argynnis semiramis* Edwards, ♀.
4. *Argynnis nitocris* Edwards, ♂, *under side.*
5. *Argynnis halcyone* Edwards, ♂.
6. *Argynnis halcyone* Edwards, ♀, *under side.*
7. *Argynnis monticola* Behr, ♂, *under side.*

8. *Argynnis monticola* Behr, ♂.
9. *Argynnis macaria* Edwards, ♂.
10. *Argynnis inornata* Edwards, ♀, *under side.*
11. *Argynnis liliana* Henry Edwards, ♂.
12. *Argynnis atossa* Edwards, ♂.
13. *Argynnis egleis* Boisduval, ♂.
14. *Argynnis egleis* Boisduval, ♂, *under side.*

15. *Argynnis egleis* Boisduval, ♀.

Explanation of Plate XIV

1. *Argynnis meadi* Edwards, ♂.
2. *Argynnis meadi* Edwards, ♂, *under side.*
3. *Argynnis columbia* Henry Edwards, ♂.
4. *Argynnis adiaste* Behr, ♀.
5. *Argynnis clio* Edwards, ♂.
6. *Argynnis clio* Edwards, ♀.
7. *Argynnis clio* Edwards, ♂, *under side.*
8. *Argynnis opis* Edwards, ♂, *under side.*

9. *Argynnis zerene* Boisduval, ♂, *under side.*
10. *Argynnis behrensi* Edwards, ♂, *under side.*
11. *Argynnis aphrodite* (Fabricius), ♀, *under side.*
12. *Argynnis lais* Edwards, ♂.
13. *Argynnis lais* Edwards, ♀.
14. *Argynnis eurynome* Edwards, ♀.
15. *Argynnis eurynome* Edwards, ♂, *under side.*
16. *Argynnis chitone* Edwards, ♀.

17. *Argynnis monticola* Behr, ♀.

EXPLANATION OF PLATE XV

1. *Brenthis myrina* (Cramer) ♂.
2. *Brenthis myrina* (Cramer) ♂, *under side.*
3. *Brenthis triclaris*, var. *alticola* B. & McD., ♂.
4. *Brenthis chariclea* (Schneider) ♂.
5. *Brenthis boisduvali* (Duponchel) ♂.
6. *Brenthis boisduvali* (Duponchel) ♀, *under side.*
7. *Brenthis montinus* Scudder, ♂.
8. *Brenthis montinus* Scudder, ♀, *under side.*
9. *Brenthis freija* (Thunberg) ♂.
10. *Brenthis freija* (Thunberg) ♀, *under side.*
11. *Brenthis freija* (*Thunberg*) ♂.
12. *Brenthis freija* (Thunberg) ♂, *under side.* Figs. 11 & 12 dark form from Labrador.
13. *Brenthis frigga* (Thunberg), var. *saga* Staudinger, ♂.
14. *Brenthis frigga* (Thunberg), var. *saga* Staudinger, ♀, *under side.*
15. *Brenthis alberta* (Edwards) ♂.
16. *Brenthis bellona* (Fabricius) ♂.
17. *Brenthis epithore* (Edwards), ♂.
18. *Brenthis epithore* (Edwards), ♂, *under side.*

Explanation of Plate XVI

1. *Melitæa phaëtona* (Drury) ♂.
2. *Melitæa chalcedona* Doubl. & Hew., ♂.
3. *Melitæa macglashani* Rivers, ♂.
4. *Melitæa augusta* Edwards, ♂.
5. *Melitæa colon* Edwards, ♂.
6. *Melitæa nubigena* Behr, ♂, from Colorado.
7. *Melitæa baroni* Henry Edwards, ♂.
8. *Melitæa editha* Boisduval, ♂.
9. *Melitæa nubigena* Behr, ♂, from Colorado.
10. *Melitæa rubicunda* Henry Edwards, ♂.
11. *Melitæa acasta* Edwards, ♂.
12. *Melitæa acasta* Edwards, ♂, *under side*.
13. *Melitæa palla* Boisduval, ♂.
14. *Melitæa palla* Boisduval, ♂, *under side*.
15. *Melitæa gabbi* Behr, ♂.
16. *Melitæa taylori* Edwards, ♂.
17. *Melitæa fulvia* Edwards, ♂.
18. *Melitæa dymas* Edwards, ♂.
19. *Melitæa perse* Edwards, ♂.
20. *Melitæa leanira* Boisduval, ♂.
21. *Melitæa nympha* Edwards, ♂.
22. *Melitæa minuta* Edwards, ♀, *pale aberrant form*.

Explanation of Plate XVII

1. *Melitæa alma* Strecker, ♂, *dwarf*.
2. *Melitæa ulrica* Edwards, ♂.
3. *Melitæa chara* Edwards, ♂.
4. *Melitæa chara* Edwards, ♂, *under side*.
5. *Melitæa harrisi* Scudder, ♂.
6. *Melitæa harrisi* Scudder, ♀, *under side*.
7. *Melitæa whitneyi* Behr, ♂.
8. *Melitæa whitneyi* Behr, ♂, *under side*.
9. *Melitæa wrighti* Edwards, ♂.
10. *Melitæa wrighti* Edwards, ♀, *under side*.
11. *Melitæa arachne* Edwards, ♂, *under side*.
12. *Melitæa arachne* Edwards, ♂.
13. *Melitæa hoffmanni* Behr, ♂.
14. *Melitæa hoffmanni* Behr, ♀, ab. *hollandæ* Gunder.
15. *Melitæa thekla* Edwards, ♂, *under side*.
16. *Melitæa thekla* Edwards, ♂.
17. *Phyciodes vesta* (Edwards) ♂.
18. *Phyciodes vesta* (Edwards) ♀.
19. *Phyciodes vesta* (Edwards) ♀, *under side*.
20. *Phyciodes picta* (Edwards) ♀, *under side*.
21. *Phyciodes picta* (Edwards) ♂.
22. *Phyciodes phaon* (Edwards) ♂.
23. *Phyciodes phaon* (Edwards) ♀, *under side*.
24. *Phyciodes gorgone* Hübner, ♂.
25. *Phyciodes gorgone* Hübner, ♂, *under side*.
26. *Phyciodes montana* Behr, ♀, *under side*.
27. *Phyciodes montana* Behr, ♂.
28. *Phyciodes nycteis* Doubl. & Hew., ♂, *under side*.
29. *Phyciodes nycteis* Doubl. & Hew., ♂.
30. *Phyciodes nycteis* Doubl. & Hew., ♀.
31. *Phyciodes orseis* Edwards, ♂.
32. *Phyciodes camillus* Edwards, ♂.
33. *Phyciodes camillus* Edwards, ♀.
34. *Phyciodes camillus* Edwards, ♂, *under side*.
35. *Phyciodes batesi* Reakirt, ♂.
36. *Phyciodes batesi* Reakirt, ♂, *under side*.
37. *Phyciodes campestris* (Behr) ♂.
38. *Phyciodes campestris* (Behr) ♀, *under side*.
39. *Anthanassa tulcis* (Bates) ♂.
40. *Phyciodes mylitta* Edwards, ♂, *under side*.
41. *Phyciodes mylitta* Edwards, ♂.
42. *Anthanassa frisia* (Poey) ♂.

EXPLANATION OF PLATE XVIII

1. *Phyciodes tharos* (Drury) ♂.
2. *Phyciodes tharos* (Drury) ♀.
3. *Phyciodes tharos*, var. *marcia* Edwards, ♂.
4. *Phyciodes tharos*, var. *marcia* Edwards, ♀.
5. *Phyciodes barnesi* Skinner, ♂.
6. *Argynnis snyderi* Skinner, ♂.
7. *Argynnis platina* Skinner, ♂.
8. *Anthanassa texana* (Edwards) ♂.
9. *Anthanassa texana* (Edwards) ♂, *under side*.
10. *Chlosyne janais* (Drury) ♂.
11. *Chlosyne lacinia*, var. *adjutrix* Scud., ♂.
12. *Anthanassa ianthe* (Fabr.) ♂.
13. *Melitæa beani* Skinner, ♂.
14. *Brenthis astarte* (Doubl. & Hew.) ♂.
15. *Brenthis astarte* (Doubl. & Hew.) ♂, *under side*.
16. *Brenthis helena* Edwards, ♂, *under side*.
17. *Brenthis helena* Edwards, ♂.
18. *Enodia creola* (Skinner) ♂.
19. *Enodia creola* (Skinner) ♀.
20. *Enodia portlandia* (Fabr.) ♂.
21. *Gyrocheilus tritonia* Edwards, ♂.

Explanation of Plate XIX

1. *Polygonia interrogationis* (Fabr.) var. *fabricii* (Edwards) ♂.
2. *Polygonia interrogationis* (Fabr.) var. *umbrosa* (Lintner) ♀.
3. *Polygonia comma* (Harris) var. *dryas* (Edwards) ♂.
4. *Polygonia comma* (Harris) var. *harrisi* (Edwards) ♂.
5. *Polygonia silenus* (Edwards) ♂.
6. *Polygonia silenus* (Edwards) ♂, *under side.*
7. *Polygonia hylas* (Edwards) ♂.
8. *Polygonia hylas* (Edwards) ♂, *under side.*
9. *Aglais j-album* (Boisd. & Lec.) ♀.
10. *Polygonia gracilis* (Gr. & Rob.) ♂.
11. *Polygonia gracilis* (Gr. & Rob.) ♀, *under side.*
12. *Polygonia faunus* (Edwards) ♂.
13. *Polygonia faunus* (Edwards) ♂, *under side.*
14. *Polygonia satyrus* (Edwards) var. *marsyas* (Edwards) ♂.
15. *Polygonia satyrus* (Edwards) var. *marsyas* (Edwards) ♂, *under side.*

Explanation of Plate XX

1. *Polygonia satyrus* (Edwards) ♀.
2. *Polygonia satyrus* (Edwards) ♀, *under side.*
3. *Polygonia progne* (Cramer) ♂.
4. *Polygonia progne* (Cramer) ♂, *under side.*
5. *Polygonia zephyrus* (Edwards) ♂.
6. *Polygonia zephyrus* (Edwards) ♂, *under side.*

7. *Junonia cœnia* (Hübner) ♀.
8. *Junonia lavinia* (Cramer) ♂.
9. *Junonia genoveva* (Cramer) ♂.
10. *Aglais milberti* (Godart) ♂.
11. *Aglais californica* (Boisduval) ♂.
12. *Vanessa carye* (Hübner) ♂.

13. *Anartia jatrophæ* (Linnæus) ♂.

PLATE XX

Explanation of Plate XXI

1. *Athena coresia* (Godart) ♂.
2. *Athena coresia* (Godart) ♂, *under side*.
3. *Athena petreus* (Cramer) ♂.
4. *Athena chiron* (Fabricius) ♂.
5. *Diæthria clymena* (Cramer) ♂.

6. *Diæthria clymena* (Cramer) ♂, *under side*.
7. *Eunica monima* (Cramer) ♂.
8. *Eunica monima* (Cramer) ♀.
9. *Hypolimnas misippus* (Linnæus) ♂.
10. *Hypolimnas misippus* (Linnæus) ♀.

Explanation of Plate XXII

1. *Basilarchia astyanax* (Fabricius) ♂.
2. *Heterochroa californica* Butler, ♀.
3. *Basilarchia lorquini* (Boisduval) ♂.

4. *Basilarchia arthemis* (Drury) ♂.
5. *Basilarchia arthemis* (Drury) var. *proserpina* (Edwards) ♂.

6. *Basilarchia weidemeyeri* (Edwards) ♂.

Explanation of Plate XXIII

1. *Asterocampa flora* (Edwards) ♂.
2. *Asterocampa flora* (Edwards) ♀.
3. *Asterocampa celtis* (Boisd. & Lec.) ♂.
4. *Asterocampa celtis* (Boisd. & Lec.) ♀.
5. *Asterocampa clyton* (Boisd. & Lec.) ♂.
6. *Asterocampa clyton* (Boisd. & Lec.) ♀.
7. *Asterocampa montis* (Edwards) ♂

8. *Asterocampa montis* (Edwards) ♀.
9. *Asterocampa alicia* (Edwards) ♂.
10. *Asterocampa alicia* (Edwards) ♀.
11. *Asterocampa leilia* (Edwards) ♂.
12. *Asterocampa antonia* (Edwards) ♂.
13. *Asterocampa celtis* (Boisd. & Lec.) ♂, *under side.*

EXPLANATION OF PLATE XXIV

1. *Anæa andria* Scudder, ♀.
2. *Anæa morrisoni* (Holland) ♀.
3. *Anæa portia* (Fabricius) ♂.
4. *Ageronia feronia* (Linnæus) ♂.
5. *Ageronia fornax* Hübner, ♂, *under side.*

6. *Victorina steneles* (Linnæus) ♂.
7. *Mestra amymone* (Ménétries) ♂.
8. *Chlosyne crocale* (Edwards) ♂, *under side.*
9. *Chlosyne crocale* (Edwards) ♂.
10. *Hypanartia lethe* (Fabricius) ♂.

Explanation of Plate XXV

1. *Satyrodes eurydice* (L. & Johans.) ♂.
2. *Euptychia gemma* Hübner, ♂, *under side.*
3. *Euptychia rubricata* Edwards, ♂.
4. *Euptychia euryta* (Fabricius) ♂.
5. *Euptychia sosybia* (Fabricius) ♂, *under side.*
6. *Euptychia mitchelli* (French) ♂, *under side.*
7. *Euptychia phocion* (Fabricius) ♂, *under side.*
8. *Euptychia henshawi* (Edwards) ♂.
9. *Cœnonympha california* Dbl. & Hew., var. *galactinus* Boisduval, ♂.
10. *Cœnonympha california*, Dbl. & Hew., var. *eryngii* Henry Edwards, ♂.
11. *Cœnonympha ochracea* Edwards, ♂.
12. *Cœnonympha ochracea* Edwards, ♂, *under side.*
13. *Cœnonympha inornata* Edwards, ♂, *under side.*
14. *Cœnonympha california* Dbl. & Hew., ♀.
15. *Neominois ridingsi* Edwards, ♂.
16. *Neominois dionysius* Scudder, ♂.
17. *Erebia magdalena* Strecker, ♂.
18. *Erebia sofia* Strecker, = *ethela* Edwards, ♀.
19. *Erebia discoidalis* (Kirby) ♂.
20. *Erebia callias* Edwards, ♂.
21. *Cœnonympha ampelos* Edwards, ♂, *under side.* = *insulana* McD., from Vancouver Island.
22. *Cœnonympha kodiak* Edwards, ♀.
23. *Erebia disa*, var. *mancinus* Dbl. & Hew., ♂.
24. *Cœnonympha haydeni* Edwards, ♂.
25. *Cœnonympha elko* Edwards, ♀, *under side.*
26. *Cœnonympha elko* Edwards, ♂.
27. *Cœnonympha brenda* Edwards, ♀.
28. *Erebia epipsodea* Butler, ♂.
29. *Cœnonympha inornata* Edwards, ♂.
30. *Cœnonympha ampelos* Edwards, ♂, from Vancouver Island.
31. *Cœnonympha brenda* Edwards, ♂.

Explanation of Plate XXVI

1. *Cercyonis alope* (Fabricius) ♂.
2. *Cercyonis alope* (Fabricius) ♀.
3. *Cercyonis nephele* (Kirby) ♂.
4. *Cercyonis nephele* (Kirby) ♀, *under side.*
5. *Cercyonis ariane* (Boisduval) ♂.
6. *Cercyonis ariane* (Boisduval) ♀, *under side.*
7. *Cercyonis æta* (Boisduval) ♂.
8. *Cercyonis æta* (Boisduval) ♂, *under side.*
9. *Cercyonis olympa* (Edwards) ♂.
10. *Cercyonis olympa* (Edwards) ♀, *under side.*
11. *Cercyonis charon* (Edwards) ♂.
12. *Cercyonis charon* (Edwards) ♀.
13. *Cercyonis meadi* (Edwards) ♀.
14. *Cercyonis meadi* (Edwards) ♂, *under side.*
15. *Cercyonis baroni* (Edwards) ♂.
16. *Cercyonis baroni* (Edwards) ♂, *under side.*
17. *Cercyonis gabbi* (Edwards) ♀, *under side.*
18. *Cercyonis pegala* (Fabricius) ♀. *under side.*
19. *Cercyonis paula* (Edwards) ○, *under side.*
20. *Cercyonis sthenele* (Boisduval) ♂, *under side*

EXPLANATION OF PLATE XXVII

1. *Œneis gigas* Butler, ♂.
2. *Œneis gigas* Butler, ♀.
3. *Œneis macouni* (Edwards) ♂.
4. *Œneis iduna* (Edwards) ♂.
5. *Œneis iutta* Hübner, ♀.
6. *Œneis taygete* Hübner, ♂.

7. *Œneis brucei* (Edwards) ♂.
8. *Œneis varuna* (Edwards) ♂.
9. *Œneis ivallda* (Mead) ♂.
10. *Œneis caryxus* (Dbl. & Hew.) ♂.
11. *Œneis semidea* (Say) ♂.
12. *Œneis uhleri* (Reakirt) ♂.

EXPLANATION OF PLATE XXVIII

1. *Libythea bachmanni* Kirtland, ♂.
2. *Libythea bachmanni* Kirtland, ♂, *under side.*
3. *Libythea carinenta* (Cramer) ♂.
4. *Apodemia cythera* (Edwards) ♀, *under side.*
5. *Apodemia cythera* (Edwards) ♂.
6. *Apodemia virgulti* (Behr) ♂.
7. *Apodemia mormo* (Felder) ♂, *under side.*
8. *Polystigma nais* (Edwards) ♂.
9. *Polystigma nais* (Edwards) ♀.
10. *Apodemia duryi* (Edwards) ♀.
11. *Apodemia palmeri* (Edwards) ♂.
12. *Calephelis borealis* Gr. & Rob., ♂, *under side.*
13. *Calephelis borealis* Gr. & Rob., ♂.
14. *Calephelis australis* Edwards, ♂.
15. *Calephelis nemesis* Edwards, ♂.
16. *Calephelis virginiensis* (Gray) ♂.
17. *Emesis ares* (Edwards) ♂.
18. *Emesis ares* (Edwards) ♀.
19. *Emesis cleis* (Edwards) ♂.
20. *Emesis cleis* (Edwards) ♀.
21. *Feniseca tarquinius* (Fabr.) ♂.
22. *Eumæus atala* Poey, ♂, *under side.*
23. *Chrysophanus virginiensis* Edwards, ♂.
24. *Chrysophanus virginiensis* Edwards, ♀.
25. *Chrysophanus hypophlæas* Boisduval, ♂.
26. *Chrysophanus editha* Mead, ♂.
27. *Chrysophanus editha* Mead, ♀.
28. *Chrysophanus amicetus* Scudder, ♂.
29. *Chrysophanus xanthoides* Boisduval, ♂.
30. *Chrysophanus xanthoides* Boisduval, ♀.
31. *Chrysophanus thoë* Boisduval, ♂.
32. *Chrysophanus thoë* Boisduval, ♀.
33. *Chrysophanus helloides* Boisduval, ♂.
34. *Chrysophanus helloides* Boisduval, ♀.
35. *Chrysophanus gorgon* Boisduval, ♂.
36. *Chrysophanus gorgon* Boisduval, ♀.
37. *Chrysophanus mariposa* Reakirt, ♂.
38. *Chrysophanus mariposa* Reakirt, ♀.

PLATE XXVIII

EXPLANATION OF PLATE XXIX

1. *Chrysophanus arota* Boisd., ♂.
2. *Chrysophanus arota* Boisd., ♀.
3. *Chrysophanus sirius* Edwards, ♂.
4. *Chrysophanus sirius* Edwards, ♀.
5. *Chrysophanus rubidus* Behr, ♂.
6. *Chrysophanus rubidus* Behr, ♀.
7. *Chrysophanus snowi* Edwards, ♂.
8. *Chrysophanus snowi* Edwards, ♀.
9. *Thecla halesus* (Cramer) ♂.
10. *Thecla m-album* Boisd. & Lec., ♂.
11. *Thecla crysalus* Edwards, ♂.
12. *Thecla grunus* Boisd., ♂.
13. *Thecla autolycus* Edwards, ♀.
14. *Thecla alcestis* Edwards, ♀.
15. *Thecla acadica* Edwards, ♂.
16. *Thecla acadica* Edwards, ♀, *under side*.
17. *Thecla itys* Edwards, ♀.
18. *Thecla cecrops* Hübner, ♀, *under side*.
19. *Thecla wittfeldi* Edwards, ♀.
20. *Thecla wittfeldi* Edwards, ♂, *under side*.

21. *Thecla spinetorum* Boisd., ♀.
22. *Thecla favonius* Sm. & Abbot, ♂.
23. *Thecla læta* Edwards, ♂.
24. *Thecla læta* Edwards, ♂, *under side*.
25. *Thecla adenostomatis* Henry Edwards, ♂.
26. *Thecla calanus* Hübner, ♂.
27. *Thecla edwardsi* Saunders, ♀, *under side*.
28. *Thecla liparops* Boisd. & Lec., ♀, *under side*.
29. *Thecla gryneus* Hübner, var. *discoidalis* Skinner, ♂.
30. *Thecla tacita* Henry Edwards, ♂.
31. *Thecla melinus* Hübner, = *humuli* Harris, ♂
32. *Thecla gryneus* Hübner, var. *castalis* Edwards, ♂, *under side*.
33. *Thecla sæpium* Boisd., ♂.
34. *Thecla sæpium* Boisd., ♂, *under side*.
35. *Thecla ines* Edwards, ♂.
36. *Thecla chalcis* Behr, ♂.
37. *Thecla chalcis* Behr, ♀, *under side*.
38. *Thecla acis* (Drury) ♂, *under side*.

39. *Thecla simæthis* (Drury) ♂, *under side*.

EXPLANATION OF PLATE XXX

1. *Thecla dumetorum* Boisd., ♂.
2. *Thecla dumetorum* Boisd., ♂, *under side.*
3. *Thecla affinis* Edwards, ♀, *under side.*
4. *Thecla behri* Edwards, ♂.
5. *Thecla behri* Edwards, ♂, *under side.*
6. *Thecla clytie* Edwards, ♀.
7. *Thecla cecrops* Hübner, ♂.
8. *Thecla nelsoni* Boisd., ♀, *under side.*
9. *Thecla siva* Edwards, ♂, *under side.*
10. *Thecla titus* (Fabricius) ♂.
11. *Thecla niphon* Hübner, ♀.
12. *Thecla irus* Godart, ♂.
13. *Thecla nelsoni* Boisd., ♀.
14. *Thecla titus* (Fabricius) ♂, *under side.*
15. *Thecla augustinus* Westwood, ♀.
16. *Satyrium fuliginosum* (Edwards) ♂, *under side.*
17. *Thecla eryphon* Boisd., ♀, *under side.*
18. *Thecla martialis* Herr.-Schæff., ♀, *under side.*
19. *Lycæna pseudargiolus* Bvd. & Lec., var. *marginata* Edw., ♂, *under side.*
20. *Ditto* var. *lucia* Kirby, ♂, *under side.*
21. *Thecla henrici* Grote & Robinson, ♀.
22. *Thecla niphon* Hübner, ♀, *under side.*
23. *Lycæna couperi* Grote, ♂.
24. *Lycæna fulla* Edwards, ♂.
25. *Lycæna fulla* Edwards, ♀.
26. *Chrysophanus clara* (Henry Edwards) ♀.
27. *Lycæna marina* Reakirt, ♀, *under side.*
28. *L. sæpiolus* dim. form *dædalus* Behr, ♀, *under side.*
29. *Lycæna icarioides* Boisd., ♂, *under side.*
30. *Lycæna enoptes* Boisd., ♀, *under side.*
31. *Lycæna glaucon* Edwards, ♀, *under side.*
32. *Lycæna pseudargiolus* Boisd. & Lec., ♂, *under side.*
33. *Lycæna isola* Reakirt, ♂, *under side.* (The specimen figured is the type of *L. alce*, Edwards.)
34. *Lycæna couperi* Grote, ♂, *under side.*
35. *Lycæna antiacis* Boisd., ♂, *under side.*
36. *Lycæna antiacis* Boisd., ♂.
37. *Lycæna pheres* Boisd., ♂.
38. *Lycæna isola* Reakirt, ♀.
39. *Lycæna glaucon* Edwards, ♂.
40. *Lycæna aster* Edwards, ♂.
41. *Lycæna antiacis* Boisd., ♀.
42. *Lycæna pheres* Boisd., ♀, *under side.*
43. *Lycæna xerces* Boisd., ♂, *under side.*
44. *Lycæna piasus* Boisd., ♀, *under side.*
45. *Lycæna catilina* (Fabricius) ♀, *under side.*
46. *Lycæna aster* Edwards, ♀.
47. *Lycæna aster* Edwards, ♂, *under side.*
48. *Lycæna scudderi* Edwards, ♂.
49. *Lycæna scudderi* Edwards, ♀.
50. *Lycæna lygdamus* Doubleday, ♀, *under side.*
51. *Lycæna enoptes* Boisd., ♂.

EXPLANATION OF PLATE XXXI

1. *Lycæna pseudargiolus* Boisd. & Lec., var. *lucia* Kirby, ♂.
2. *Lycæna pseudargiolus* Boisd. & Lec., var. *marginata* Edwards, ♂.
3. *Lycæna pseudargiolus* Boisd. & Lec., var. *marginata* Edwards, ♀.
4. *Lycæna pseudargiolus* Boisd. & Lec., var. *nigra* Edwards, ♂.
5. *Lycæna pseudargiolus* Boisd. & Lec., var. *violacea* Edwards, ♂.
6. *Lycæna pseudargiolus* Boisd. & Lec., ♂.
7. *Lycæna pseudargiolus* Boisd. & Lec., ♀.
8. *Lycæna pseudargiolus* Boisd. & Lec., var. *neglecta* Edwards, ♂.
9. *Lycæna pseudargiolus* Boisd. & Lec., ar. *neglecta* Edwards, ♀.
10. *Lycæna pseudargiolus* Boisd. & Lec., var. *arizonensis* Edwards, ♂.
11. *Lycæna sæpiolus*, dim. form, *dædalus* Behr, ♂.
12. *Lycæna sæpiolus*, dim. form, *dædalus* Behr, ♀.
13. *Chrysophanus heteronea* Boisd., ♂.
14. *Chrysophanus heteronea* Boisd., ♀.
15. *Lycæna sæpiolus* Boisd., ♂.
16. *Lycæna sæpiolus* Boisd., ♀.
17. *Lycæna lygdamus* Doubleday, ♂.
18. *Lycæna lygdamus* Doubleday, ♀.
19. *Lycæna piasus* Boisd., ♂.
20. *Lycæna piasus* Boisd., ♀.
21. *Lycæna sonorensis* Felder, ♂.
22. *Lycæna sonorensis* Felder, ♀.
23. *Lycæna shasta* Edwards, ♂.
24. *Lycæna shasta* Edwards, ♀.
25. *Lycæna melissa* Edwards, ♂.
26. *Lycæna melissa* Edwards, ♀.
27. *Lycæna acmon* Dbl. & Hew., ♂.
28. *Lycæna acmon* Dbl. & Hew., ♀.
29. *Lycæna comyntas* Godart, ♂.
30. *Lycæna comyntas* Godart, ♀.
31. *Lycæna catilina* (Fabricius) ♀.
32. *Lycæna marina* Reakirt, ♀.

Explanation of Plate XXXII

EXPLANATION OF PLATE XXXIII

1. *Callidryas agarithe* (Boisduval) ♂.
2. *Callidryas eubule* (Linnæus) ♂.
3. *Callidryas eubule* (Linnæus) ♂, *under side*.

4. *Callidryas philea* (Linnæus) ♂.
5. *Colias eurytheme* Boisduval, ♂, *under side*.
6. *Vanessa virginiensis* (Drury), ♂, *under side*.

Explanation of Plate XXXIV

1. *Euchloë cethura* (Felder) var. *morrisoni* (Edwards) ♂.
2. *Euchloë creusa* (Dbl.-Hew.) ♀, *under side.*
3. *Euchloë ausonides* (Boisduval) ♂, *under side.*
4. *Euchloë sara* (Boisduval) var. *flora* (Wright) ♂.
5. *Euchloë sara* (Boisduval) var. *flora* (Wright) ♀.
6. *Euchloë sara* (Boisduval) var. *julia* (Edwards) ♀, *under side.*
7. *Neophasia menapia* (Felder) ♂.
8. *Pieris beckeri* Edwards, ♂, *type.*
9. *Pieris beckeri* Edwards, ♀, *type.*
10. *Pieris protodice* Boisd.-Lec., ♂.
11. *Pieris protodice* Boisd.-Lec., ♀.
12. *Pieris sisymbrii* Boisduval, ♂.
13. *Pieris occidentalis* Reakirt, ♂.
14. *Pieris virginiensis* Edwards, ♂, *type.*
15. *Pieris napi* Esper, var. *pallida* Scudder, ♀.
16. *Pieris napi* Esper, var. *oleracea-hiemalis* Harris, ♂.
17. *Pieris napi* Esper, var. *pseudo-bryoniæ* Verity, ♀.
18. *Pieris protodice* Boisd.-Lec., var. *vernalis* Edwards, ♂, *type.*
19. *Pieris napi* Esper, var. *acadica* Edwards, ♀.
20. *Kricogonia lyside* (Godart) ♂.
21. *Kricogonia lyside* (Godart) ♀.

EXPLANATION OF PLATE XXXV

1. *Ascia monuste* (Linnæus) ♂.
2. *Ascia monuste* (Linnæus) ♀.
3. *Pieris rapæ* (Linnæus) ♀.
4. *Melete ilaire* (Godart) ♂.
5. *Melete ilaire* (Godart) ♀.
6. *Colias alexandra* Edwards, ♂.
7. *Colias alexandra* Edwards, ♀

8. *Colias scudderi* Reakirt, ♂.
9. *Colias scudderi* Reakirt, ♀.
10. *Colias interior* Scudder, ♂.
11. *Colias interior* Scudder, ♀.
12. *Colias chrysomelas* Henry Edwards, ♂.
13. *Colias chrysomelas* Henry Edwards, ♀.
14. *Colias pelidne* Boisduval, ♂.

15. *Colias eriphyle* Edwards, ♂.

PLATE XXXV

EXPLANATION OF PLATE XXXVI

1. *Zerene eurydice* (Boisduval) ♂.
2. *Zerene evryaice* (Boisduval) ♀.
3. *Zerene cæsonia* (Stoll) ♂.
4. *Zerene cæscnia* (Stoll) ♀.
5. *Colias meadi* Edwards, ♂.
6. *Colias meadi* Edwards, ♀.
7. *Colias ariadne* Edwards, ♂.
8. *Colias ariadne* Edwards, ♀.
9. *Colias keewaydin* Edwards, ♂.
10. *Colias keewaydin* Edwards, ♀.
11. *Colias nastes* Boisduval, ♂.
12. *Colias nastes* Boisduval, ♀.
13. *Colias elis* Strecker, ♂.
14. *Colias elis* Strecker, ♀.
15. *Colias pelidne* Boisd., var. *labradorensis* Scudder, ♂.
16. *Colias pelidne* Boisd., var. *labradorensis* Scudder, ♀.
17. *Colias behri* Edwards, ♂.

Explanation of Plate XXXVII

1. *Eurema longicauda* (Bates) ♂.
2. *Eurema proterpia* (Fabricius) ♂.
3. *Eurema nicippe* (Cramer) ♂.
4. *Eurema nicippe* (Cramer) ♀.
5. *Eurema nicippe* (Cramer) var. *flava* (Strecker) ♂.
6. *Eurema nicippe* (Cramer) ♀, *under side*
7. *Eurema mexicana* (Boisduval) ♂.
8. *Eurema mexicana* (Boisduval) ♂, *under side.*
9. *Eurema damaris* (Felder) ♂.
10. *Eurema damaris* (Felder) ♀, *under side.*
11. *Eurema westwoodi* (Boisduval) ♂.
12. *Eurema elathea* (Cramer) ♂.
13. *Eurema lisa* (Boisd. & Lec.) ♂.
14. *Eurema delia* (Cramer) ♂.
15. *Eurema jucunda* (Boisd. & Lec.) ♂.
16. *Eurema jucunda* (Boisd. & Lec.) ♂, *under side.*
17. *Dismorphia melite* (Linnæus) ♂.
18. *Dismorphia melite* (Linnæus) ♀.

Explanation of Plate XXXIX

1. *Parnassius smintheus* Dbl.-Hew., var. *behri* Edwards, ♂.
2. *Parnassius smintheus* Dbl.-Hew., var. *behri* Edwards, ♀.
3. *Parnassius smintheus* Dbl.-Hew., ♂.
4. *Parnassius smintheus* Dbl.-Hew., ♀.
5. *Parnassius smintheus* Dbl.-Hew., ♂, mate of ♀ *hermodur*.
6. *Parnassius smintheus* Dbl.-Hew., var. *hermodur*, ♀, Henry Edwards.
7. *Parnassius clodius* Ménétries, ♂, (*baldur* Edwards).
8. *Parnassius clodius* Ménétries, ♀, (*baldur* Edwards).
9. *Parnassius clodius* Ménétries, ♂.
10. *Parnassius clodius* Ménétries, ♀.

PLATE XXXIX

Explanation of Plate XLI

1. *Papilio machaon* Linnæus, var. *aliaska* Scudder, ♂.
2. *Papilio nitra* Edwards, ♂, *type*.
3. *Papilio indra* Reakirt, ♀.
4. *Papilio polydamas* Linnæus, ♂.
5. *Papilio troilus* Linnæus, ♂.
6. *Papilio asterius* Cramer, var. *calverleyi* Grote. ♀.

PLATE XLI

Explanation of Plate XLII

1. *Papilio palamedes* Drury, ♀.
2. *Papilio philenor* Linnæus, ♂.
3. *Papilio cresphontes* Cramer, ♂.
4. *Papilio thoas* Linnæus, ♂.

Explanation of Plate XLIV

1. *Papilio ajax* Linnæus, ♂. Spring form *carolinianus* Edwards (1771) = *marcellus* Cramer (1777). This is the spring form common in the eastern states of the U. S. north of Florida.
2. *Papilio ajax* Linnæus. Spring form *floridensis* Holland, ♂, *type*. This is the spring form common in Florida.
3. *Papilio ajax* Linnæus. This is the form figured by George H. Edwards in "The Natural History of Uncommon Birds," Pl. 34, cited by Linnæus. Summer form *telamonides* Felders, ♂ = *lecontei* Rothschild & Jordan, = *marcellus* Leconte, but not Cramer.
4. *Papilio ajax* Linnæus. Spring form *walshi* Edwards, ♂, *type*.
5. *Papilio eurymedon* Boisduval, ♂.

EXPLANATION OF PLATE XLV

1. *Papilio rutulus* Boisduval, ♂.
2. *Pholisora alpheus* Edwards, ♂, *type*.
3. *Calpodes ethlius* (Cramer) ♀.
4. *Pholisora catullus* (Fabricius) ♂.
5. *Thanaos afranius* Lintner, ♂.
6. *Eudamus proteus* (Linnæus) ♀.
7. *Thanaos brizo* Boisd. & Leconte, ♀.

8. *Thanaos clitus* Edwards, ♂, *type*.
9. *Pyrrhopyge araxes*, var. *arizonæ* Godm. & Salvin.
10. *Achalarus lycidas* (Smith & Abbot) ♀, *under side*.
11. *Zestusa dorus* (Edwards) ♂, *type*.
12. *Rhabdoides cellus* (Boisd. & Lec.) ♂.

Explanation of Plate XLVI

1. *Systasea pulverulenta* (Felder) ♂ = *zampa* Edwards.
2. *Erynnis manitoba* (Scudder) ♂.
3. *Erynnis manitoba* (Scudder) ♀.
4. *Atalopedes campestris* (Boisd.) ♂.
5. *Atalopedes campestris* (Boisd.) ♀.
6. *Atrytone arogos* (Boisd. & Lec.) ♂.
7. *Poanes melane* (Edwards) ♂.
8. *Poanes melane* (Edwards) ♀.
9. *Atrytonopsis hianna* (Scudder) ♂.
10. *Atrytonopsis hianna* (Scudder) ♀.
11. *Erynnis ottoë* (Edwards) ♂.
12. *Erynnis ottoë* (Edwards) ♀.
13. *Erynnis sassacus* (Harris) ♂.
14. *Poanes howardi* Skinner, ♂.
15. *Phycanassa viator* Edwards, ♀.
16. *Atrytone pontiac* (Edwards) ♂.
17. *Atrytone pontiac* (Edwards) ♀.
18. *Hylephila phylæus* (Drury) ♂.
19. *Hylephila phylæus* (Drury) ♀.
20. *Problema byssus* (Edwards) ♀.
21. *Atrytone palatka* (Edwards) ♂.
22. *Polites mystic* (Scudder) ♂.
23. *Polites mystic* (Scudder) ♀.
24. *Atrytone logan* (Edwards) ♂.
25. *Atrytone logan* (Edwards) ♀.
26. *Erynnis morrisoni* (Edwards) ♂.
27. *Erynnis morrisoni* (Edwards) ♀.
28. *Catia otho* (Smith & Abbot) ♂.
29. *Catia otho* (Smith & Abbot) ♀.
30. *Polites taumas* (Fabricius) ♀.
31. *Atrytone ruricola* (Boisduval) ♂.
32. *Polites verna* (Edwards) ♂.
33. *Lerodea eufala* (Edwards) ♀.
34. *Prenes ocola* (Edwards) ♂.
35. *Oligoria maculata* (Edwards) ♂.
36. *Amblyscirtes carolina* (Skinner) ♂.
37. *Poanes aaroni* (Skinner) ♂.
38. *Poanes howardi* (Skinner) ♂.
39. *Thorybes æmilia* (Skinner) ♂.
40. *Poanes yehl* (Skinner) ♂.

EXPLANATION OF PLATE XLVII

1. *Pamphila mandan* Edwards, ♂.
2. *Ancyloxypha numitor* (Fabr.) ♂.
3. *Oarisma edwardsi* Barnes, ♂.
4. *Oarisma powesheik* Parker, ♂.
5. *Amblyscirtes vialis* Edwards, ♂.
6. *Amblyscirtes samoset* Scudder, ♂.
7. *Amblyscirtes œnus* Edwards, ♀.
8. *Chærophon simius* (Edwards) ♂.
9. *Copæodes waco* Edwards, ♂.
10. *Pseudocopæodes wrighti* (Edwards) ♂.
11. *Ancyloxypha myrtis* (Edwards) ♂.
12. *Hesperia scriptura* Boisduval, ♀.
13. *Hesperia centaureæ* Rambur, ♂.
14. *Hesperia ruralis* Boisduval, ♀.
15. *Hesperia xantha* Edwards, ♂.
16. *Amblyscirtes textor* Edwards, ♂, *under side.*
17. *Celotes nessus* (Edwards) ♂.
18. *Hesperia communis* Grote, var. *occidentalis* Skinner, ♂.
19. *Hesperia domicella* Erichson, ♂.
20. *Polites taumas* (Fabricius) ♂.
21. *Poanes massasoit* Scudder, ♂.
22. *Poanes massasoit* Scudder, ♀.
23. *Erynnis attalus* (Edwards) ♂.
24. *Polites peckius* (Kirby) ♂.
25. *Polites peckius* (Kirby) ♀.
26. *Polites mardon* (Edwards) ♂.
27. *Erynnis uncas* (Edwards) ♂.
28. *Erynnis uncas* (Edwards) ♀.
29. *Augiades snowi* (Edwards) ♂.
30. *Augiades snowi* (Edwards) ♀.
31. *Poanes taxiles* (Edwards) ♂.
32. *Poanes taxiles* (Edwards) ♀.
33. *Erynnis metea* (Scudder) ♂.
34. *Erynnis metea* (Scudder) ♀.
35. *Erynnis leonardus* (Harris) ♂.
36. *Erynnis leonardus* (Harris) ♀.
37. *Poanes hobomok* (Harris) ♂.
38. *Poanes hobomok* (Harris) ♀.
39. *Poanes zabulon* (Boisd. & Lec.) ♀.
40. *Hylephila phylæus* (Drury) ♂.
41. *Thymelicus brettus* (Boisd. & Lec.) ♀
42. *Polites sabuleti* (Edwards) ♂.
43. *Polites sabuleti* (Edwards) ♀.
44. *Erynnis columbia* (Scudder) ♂.

EXPLANATION OF PLATE XLVIII

1. *Thanaos persius* (Scudder) ♂.
2. *Thanaos somnus* Lintner, ♂.
3. *Thanaos terentius* (Scud. & Burg.) ♀.
4. *Thanaos martialis* (Scudder) ♂.
5. *Thorybes bathyllus* (Sm. & Abbot) ♀.
6. *Thorybes pylades* Scudder, ♀.
7. *Thanaos horatius* (Scud. & Burg.) ♀.
8. *Lerema accius* (Sm. & Abbot) ♂.
9. *Thanaos pacuvius* Lintner, ♀.
10. *Thanaos lucilius* Lintner, ♂.
11. *Thanaos juvenalis* (Fabricius) ♀.
12. *Thanaos funeralis* Lintner, ♂.
13. *Achalarus epigona* (Herr.-Schæff.) ♂.
14. *Pholisora libya* Scudder, ♂.
15. *Thanaos horatius* (Scudder) ♀.
16. *Pholisora hayhursti* Edwards, ♀.
17. *Thanaos icelus* Lintner, ♂.
18. *Colias eurytheme* Boisduval, ♀, albino.

Explanation of Plate XLIX

1. *Phocides batabano* (Lucas) ♂.
2. *Phocides lilea* (Reakirt) ♂.
3. *Phocides urania* (Westw. & Hew.) ♂.
4. *Nascus euribates* (Cramer) ♂.
5. *Polygonus amyntas* (Fabricius) ♂.
6. *Proteides idas* (Cramer) ♂.
7. *Proteides idas* (Cramer) ♀, *under side*.
8. *Epargyreus exadeus* (Cramer) ♂.
9. *Epargyreus exadeus* (Cramer) ♀, *under side*.
10. *Epargyreus zestos* (Geyer) ♀.
11. *Eudamus dorantes* (Stoll) ♂, *under side*.
12. *Eudamus dorantes*, var. *rauterbergi* Skinner, ♂, *under side, paratype*.
13. *Eudamus simplicius* (Stoll) ♂.
14. *Eudamus eurycles* (Latreille) ♂.
15. *Codatractus melon*, var. *arizonensis* (Skinner) ♂, *paratype*.
16. *Eudamus alcæus* (Hewitson) ♀, *under side*.
17. *Eudamus albofasciatus* (Hewitson) ♀, *under side*.
18. *Eudamus zilpa* Butler, ♂, *under side*.
19. *Telegonus hahneli* Staudinger, ♂, *paratype*.

ZEESE-WILKINSON CO., INC., PHOTOGRAV.

EXPLANATION OF PLATE L

1. *Thorybes confusus* Bell, ♂, *paratype.*
2. *Thorybes confusus* Bell, ♀, *paratype.*
3. *Thorybes nevada* Scudder, ♀, *paratype.*
4. *Thorybes drusius* Edwards, ♂, *type.*
5. *Thorybes mexicanus* (Herr.-Schæff.) ♂.
6. *Thorybes mexicanus* (Herr.-Schæff.) ♂, *under side.*
7. *Cogia hippalus* (Edwards) ♀, *type, under side.*
8. *Cogia hippalus* (Edwards) ♂, *type.*
9. *Rhabdoides pseudocellus* (Coolidge & Clemence) ♂.
10. *Cabares potrillo* (Lucas) ♂.
11. *Cogia outis* (Skinner) ♂, *paratype.*
12. *Cogia calchas* (Herr.-Schæff.) ♂.
13. *Phædinus caicus* (Herr.-Schæff.) ♂, *type of moschus* (Edwards).
14. *Phædinus caicus* (H.-S.) ♂, *under side, paratype of moschus* (Edwards).
15. *Hesperia orcas* (Cramer) ♂.
16. *Hesperia syrichtus* (Fabricius) ♀.
17. *Hesperia syrichtus* (Fabricius) ♂, *under side.*
18. *Hesperia montivaga* (Reakirt) ♂, *under side.*
19. *Hesperia communis* Grote, ♂.
20. *Hesperia communis* Grote, ♀.
21. *Hesperia communis* Grote, ♂, *under side.*
22. *Hesperia communis* Grote, ♀, *melanic.*
23. *Hesperia communis* Grote, var. *occidentalis* Skinner, ♂, *under side.*
24. *Hesperia philetas* (Edwards) ♀, *type.*
25. *Heliopetes laviana* (Hewitson) ♂.
26. *Heliopetes laviana* (Hewitson) ♀.
27. *Heliopetes ericetorum* (Boisd.) ♂.
28. *Heliopetes ericetorum* (Boisd.) ♀.
29. *Heliopetes nivella* Mabille, ♂, *under side.*
30. *Heliopetes macaira* (Reakirt) ♂.
31. *Heliopetes macaira* (Reakirt) ♂, *under side.*
32. *Pholisora mejicanus* (Reakirt) ♂.
33. *Pholisora ascalaphus* (Staudinger) ♂, *paratype.*
34. *Pholisora ascalaphus* (Staudinger) ♀, *paratype.*
35. *Pholisora ceos* Edwards, ♂, type.
36. *Pholisora lena* (Edwards) ♂, *type, under side.*
37. *Chiomara asychis* (Cramer) ♂.
38. *Xenophanes tryxus* (Cramer) ♂.
39. *Eantis thraso* (Hübner) ♂.
40. *Melanthes brunnea* (Herr.-Schæff.) ♂.
41. *Melanthes brunnea* (Herr.-Schæff.) ♀.

PLATE L

 ZEESE-WILKINSON CO., INC., PHOTOGRAV.

EXPLANATION OF PLATE LI

1. *Thanaos gesta* Herr.-Schæff., ♂.
2. *Thanaos gesta* Herr.-Schæff., ♀.
3. *Thanaos somnus* Lintner, ♂, *type*.
4. *Thanaos somnus* Lintner, ♀, *type*.
5. *Melanthes zephodes* (Hübner) ♂.
6. *Melanthes zephodes* (Hübner) ♀.
7. *Thanaos burgessi* Skinner, ♂, *paratype*.
8. *Thanaos lacustra* (Wright) ♂.
9. *Thanaos scudderi* Skinner, ♂, *paratype*.
10. *Thanaos tristis* Boisduval, ♂.
11. *Thanaos horatius* (Scud. & Burg.) ♂.
12. *Thanaos propertius* (Scud. & Burg.) ♂.
13. *Grais stigmaticus* (Mabille) ♂.
14. *Timochares ruptifasciatus* (Plœtz) ♂.
15. *Dalla pirus* (Edwards) ♂, *type*.
16. *Oarisma garita* (Reakirt) ♂.
17. *Oarisma garita* (Reakirt) ♂, *under side*.
18. *Pamphila scada* (Edwards) ♂, *type*.
19. *Dalla polingi* (Barnes) ♂, *paratype*.
20. *Dalla polingi* (Barnes) ♂, *under side*.
21. *Copæodes aurantiaca* (Hewitson) ♂.
22. *Copæodes minima* (Edwards) ♂, *type*.
23. *Copæodes minima* (Edwards) ♀, *type*.
24. *Amblyscirtes nysa* Edwards, ♂, *type*.
25. *Amblyscirtes nysa* Edwards, ♀, *type*.
26. *Amblyscirtes eos* (Edw.) ♀, typical *comus* (Edwards).
27. *Amblyscirtes eos* (Edw.) ♂, typical *comus* (Edwards).
28. *Thanaos avinoffi* Holland, ♂, *type*.
29. *Thanaos avinoffi* Holland, ♀, *type*.
30. *Amblyscirtes celia* Skinner, ♂, *paratype*.
31. *Amblyscirtes cassus* (Edw.) ♂, *type*.
32. *Amblyscirtes phylace* (Edw.) ♂, *type*.
33. *Amblyscirtes alternata* (Gr. & Rob.) ♀.
34. *Amblyscirtes alternata* (Gr. & Rob.) ♂.
35. *Amblyscirtes nanno* Edwards, ♂, *type*.
36. *Amblyscirtes nanno* Edwards, ♀, *type*.
37. *Adopæa lineola* (Ochsenheimer) ♂.
38. *Amblyscirtes bellus* (Edw.) ♂, *type*.
39. *Amblyscirtes oslari* (Skinner) ♂, *paratype*.
40. *Copæodes waco* Edwards, var. *candida* Wright, ♀, *under side*.
41. *Choranthus haitensis* Skinner, ♂, *paratype*.
42. *Amblyscirtes nereus* (Edw.) ♂, *type*.
43. *Chærophon carus* (Edwards) ♂, *type*.
44. *Chærophon carus* (Edwards) ♀, *type*.
45. *Chærophon rhesus* (Edwards) ♂, *type*.
46. *Chærophon rhesus* (Edwards) ♀, *type*.
47. *Choranthus radians* (Lucas) ♂, *under side*.
48. *Erynnis laurentina* (Lyman) ♂.
49. *Erynnis laurentina* (Lyman) ♀.

ZEESE-WILKINSON CO., INC., PHOTOGRAV.

EXPLANATION OF PLATE LII

1. *Erynnis colorado* (Scudder) ♂, *type.*
2. *Erynnis colorado* (Scudder) ♀, *under side.*
3. *Erynnis idaho* (Edwards) ♂, *type.*
4. *Erynnis assiniboia* (Lyman) ♂, *under side, paratype,* received from Lyman.
5. *Erynnis oregonia* (Edwards) ♂, *type.*
6. *Erynnis oregonia* (Edwards) ♀, *type.*
7. *Erynnis juba* (Scudder) ♂, Scudder *dei.*
8. *Erynnis juba* (Scudder) ♀, Scudder *det.*
9. *E. juba,* var. *ogdenensis* Holland, ♀, *type.*
10. *Erynnis viridis* (Edwards) ♂, *under side, typical.*
11. *Erynnis woodgatei* (Williams) ♂, *paratype, under side.*
12. *Erynnis nevada* (Scudder) ♂, *type.*
13. *Erynnis nevada* (Scudder) ♀, *type.*
14. *Erynnis nevada* (Scudder) ♀, *type, under side.*
15. *Erynnis morrisoni* (Edwards) ♂, *type, under side.*
16. *Erynnis columbia* (Scudder) ♂, *under side.*
17. *Erynnis cabelus* (Edwards), ♂, *type.*
18. *Erynnis cabelus* (Edwards) ♂, *under side.*
19. *Erynnis harpalus* (Edwards) ♂, *type.*
20. *Erynnis harpalus* (Edwards) ♀, *type.*
21. *Erynnis manitoboides* (Fletcher) ♀, specimen from Fletcher.
22. *Erynnis dakotæ* (Skinner) ♂, *paratype.*

23. *E. sassacus* (Harris) ♂, Scudder *det.*
24. *Erynnis attalus* (Edwards) ♀, *type, under side.*
25. *Erynnis seminole* (Scudder) ♂, *compared with type.*
26. *Erynnis seminole* (Scudder) ♀, *compared with type.*
27. *Erynnis seminole* (Scudder) ♂, *under side.*
28. *Erynnis licinus* (Edwards) ♂, *type.*
29. *Erynnis montana* (Skinner) ♂, *paratype.*
30. *Erynnis pawnee* Dodge, ♂, *paratype.*
31. *Erynnis pawnee* Dodge, ♀, *paratype.*
32. *Erynnis meskei* (Edwards) ♂, *paratype.*
33. *Erynnis meskei* (Edwards) ♀, *type.*
34. *Erynnis meskei* (Edwards) ♀, *type* of *straton* (Edw.) *under side.*
35. *Augiades sylvanoides* (Boisd.) ♂.
36. *Augiades sylvanoides* (Boisd.) ♀.
37. *Polites napa* (Edwards) ♂, *type.*
38. *Polites napa* (Edwards) ♂, *type.*
39. *Augiades nemorum* (Boisd.) ♂.
40. *Augiades nemorum* (Boisd.) ♀.
41. *Augiades pratincola* (Boisd.?) ♂.
42. *Augiades verus* (Edwards) ♂, *type.*
43. *Augiades verus* (Edwards) ♀, *type.*
44. *Augiades milo* (Edwards) ♂, *type.*
45. *Augiades agricola* (Boisd.) ♂.
46. *Augiades agricola* (Boisd.) ♀.

ZEESE-WILKINSON CO., INC., PHOTOGRAV.

Explanation of Plate LIII

1. *Augiades yuma* (Edw.) ♂.
2. *Augiades scudderi* (Skinner) ♂, *paratype.*
3. *Polites manataaqua* (Scud.) ♂.
4. *Polites rhena* (Edw.) ♂, *type.*
5. *Polites alcina* (Skinner) ♂, *paratype.*
6. *Polites taumas* (Fabricius) ♀.
7. *Polites taumas* (Fabr.) ♀, *dimorphic.*
8. *Atrytone ruricola* (Boisd.) ♀, = *vestris auctorum.*
9. *Polites siris* (Edwards) ♂, *type.*
10. *Polites sonora* (Scudder) ♂, Scudder *det.*
11. *Polites sonora* (Scudder) ♀, Scudder *det.*
12. *Polites mardon* (Edwards) ♀, *type.*
13. *Polites utahensis* (Skinner) ♂, *paratype.*
14. *Polites peckius* (Kirby) ♀, *under side.*
15. *Polites draco* (Edwards) ♂, *type.*
16. *Polites draco* (Edwards) ♀, *type, under side.*
17. *Polites tecumseh* (Grinnell) ♂.
18. *Polites chuska* (Edwards) ♂, *type.*
19. *Polites chuska* (Edwards) ♀.
20. *Polites mystic* (Scudder) ♀, *under side.*
21. *Polites baracoa* (Lucas) ♂.
22. *Polites baracoa* (Lucas) ♀.
23. *Polites dakotah* (Edwards) ♂, *type.*
24. *Polites brettus* (Boisd. & Lec.) ♂.
25. *Polites brettus* (Boisd. & Lec.) ♂, *under side.*
26. *Polites brettoides* (Edw.) ♂, *type.*
27. *Polites vibex* (Geyer) ♂.
28. *Polites stigma* (Skinner) ♂, *paratype.*
29. *Catia otho* (Smith & Abbot) ♀, *under side.*
30. *Atrytone lagus* (Edwards) ♂, *type.*
31. *Polites manataaqua* (Scudder) ♂.
32. *Polites manataaqua* (Scudder) ♀.
33. *Atrytone arpa* (Boisd. & Lec.) ♂.
34. *Atrytone arpa* (Boisd. & Lec.) ♀, *under side.*
35. *Atrytone palatka* (Edwards) ♀, *typical, under side.*
36. *Atrytone dion* (Edwards) ♂, *type.*
37. *Atrytone dion* (Edwards) ♀, *under side.*
38. *Problema byssus* (Edwards) ♂, *type.*
39. *Problema kumskaka* (Scudder) ♂, determined by Scudder.
40. *Atrytone osceola* (Lintner) ♂, *paratype.*
41. *Atrytone osceola* (Lintner) ♀, *paratype.*
42. *Poanes hobomok* (Harris) ♂, *under side.*
43. *Poanes hobomok* (Harris) var. *pocohontas* (Scudder) ♀.
44. *Poanes hobomok* (Harris) var. *quadaquina* (Scudder) ♀, *paratype.*
45. *Poanes hobomok* (Harris) var. *alfaratta* Holland, ♀, *type.*
46. *Poanes zabulon* (Boisd. & Lec.) ♂.
47. *Poanes zabulon* (Boisd. & Lec.) ♂, *under side.*

ZEESE-WILKINSON CO., INC., PHOTOGRAV.

Explanation of Plate LIV

1. *Poanes howardi* (Skinner) ♀, *paratype.*
2. *Phycanassa viator* (Edwards) ♂, *type.*
3. *Atrytonopsis vierecki* (Skinner) ♂, *paratype.*
4. *Atrytonopsis python* (Edw.) ♂, *type.*
5. *Atrytonopsis python* (Edw.) ♀, *under side.*
6. *Atrytonopsis loammi* (Whitney) ♂.
7. *Atrytonopsis loammi* (Whitney) ♀, *under side.*
8. *Atrytonopsis loammi* (Whitney) ♀.
9. *Thespieus macareus* (H.-S.) ♂.
10. *Thespieus macareus* (H.-S.) ♂, *under side.*
11. *Atrytonopsis pittacus* (Edw.) ♂, *type.*
12. *Atrytonopsis python*, var. *margarita* (Skinn.) ♂, *paratype.*
13. *Atrytonopsis deva* (Edw.) ♂, *type.*
14. *Atrytonopsis deva* (Edw.) ♀, *type.*
15. *Atrytonopsis lunus* (Edw.) ♂, *type.*
16. *Atrytonopsis lunus* (Edw.) ♀, *type, under side.*
17. *Megistias neamathla* (Skin. & Wms.) ♂, *paratype.*
18. *Megistias lherminieri* (Latr.) ♂.
19. *Megistias lherminieri* (Latr.) ♀.
20. *Prenes panoquin* (Scudder) ♂.
21. *Prenes panoquin* (Scudder) ♀, *under side.*
22. *Prenes ocola* (Edw.) ♀, *type.*
23. *Prenes panoquinoides* (Skin.) ♂, *paratype.*
24. *Prenes errans* (Skin.) ♂, *paratype.*
25. *Prenes nero* (Fabr.) ♂.
26. *Atrytone dukesi* Lindsey, ♂, *paratype.*
27. *Megathymus yuccæ*, var. *coloradensis* Riley, ♂.
28. *Megathymus yuccæ*, var. *coloradensis* Riley, ♂, *under side.*
29. *Megathymus neumægeni* Edwards, ♀.
30. *Megathymus streckeri* Skinner, ♂, *under side.*
31. *Megathymus polingi* Skinner, ♂, *paratype.*
32. *Megateymus polingi* Skinner, ♀, *paratype.*
33. *Megathymus aryxna* Dyar, ♂, *compared with type.*
34. *Megathymus cofaqui* Strecker, ♀.
35. *Megathymus cofaqui* Strecker, ♂.

ZEESE-WILKINSON CO., INC., PHOTOGRAV.

EXPLANATION OF PLATE LV

1. *Lycorea cleobæa*, var. *atergatis* Dbl. & Hew., ♂.
2. *Argynnis cærulescens* Holland, ♀, *type*.
3. *Argynnis cærulescens* Holland, ♂, *type*.
4. *Argynnis cærulescens* Holland, ♀, *under side*.
5. *Argynnis carpenteri* Edwards, ♂, *type*.
6. *Argynnis carpenteri* Edwards, ♀, *type*.
7. *Argynnis purpurascens* Hy. Edwards, ♂, *paratype*.
8. *Brenthis myrina*, var. *neb askensis* Holl., ♂, *type*.
9. *Brenthis gibsoni* Barnes & Benjamin, ♂; *type* of *B. lehmanni* Holland.
10. *Brenthis gibsoni* Barnes & Benjamin, ♀; *allotype* of *B. lehmanni* Holland.
11. *Brenthis triclaris* Hübner, ♂, *typical*.
12. *Brenthis polaris* Boisd., ♂, *under side*.
13. *Brenthis myrina* var. *terræ-novæ* Holl., ♂, *type*.
14. *Brenthis bellona*, var. *toddi* Holl., ♂, *type*.
15. *Brenthis bellona*, var. *toddi* Holl., ♀, *allotype*.
16. *Brenthis butleri* Edwards, ♂, *paratype*.
17. *Brenthis butleri* Edwards, ♀, *paratype*.
18. *Brenthis butleri* Edwards, ♂, *type, under side*.
19. *Brenthis albequina* Holland, ♂, *type*.
20. *Brenthis albequina* Holland, ♀, *type*.
21. *Brenthis albequina* Holland, ♂, *under side*.
22. *Brenthis arctica* Zetterstedt, ♂, from Greenland.
23. *Brenthis arctica* Zetterstedt, ♀, from Greenland.
24. *B. pales* var. *alaskensis* Holl. ♂, *type*.
25. *B. pales* var. *alaskensis* Holl., ♀.
26. *B. bellona*, ab. *pardopsis* Holl., ♀, *type*.
27. *Brenthis improba* (Butler) ♂, *typical*.
28. *Brenthis youngi* Holland, ♂, *type, under side*.

Explanation of Plate LVI

1. *Argynnis leto*, var. *charlottii* Barnes, ♀ , *type.*
2. *Argynnis cybele*, var. *krautwurmi* Holl., ♀ , *type.*
3. *Argynnis utahensis* Skinner, ♂, *paratype, under side.*
4. *Argynnis sakuntala* Skinner, ♀, *paratype, under side.*
5. *Argynnis californica* Skinner, ♂, *paratype, under side.*
6. *Argynnis irene* Boisduval, ♂, *under side.* The figure given is that of a paratype of *A. luski* Barnes.
7. *Argynnis montivaga*, var. *erinna* Edwards ♂, *type, under side.*
8. *Argynnis washingtonia* Barnes & McDunnough, ♂, *under side, typical.*
9. *Brenthis myrina* var. *jenningsæ*, Holl., ♂, *type.*
10. *Melitæa maria* (Skinner) ♂, *paratype, under side.*
11. *Brenthis dawsoni* Barnes & McDunnough, ♂, *paratype.*
12. *Brenthis dæwsoni* Barnes & McDunnough, ♀, *paratype.*
13. *Melitæa damætas* Skinner, ♂, *paratype.*
14. *Melitæa definita* Aaron, ♂, *paratype.*
15. *Melitæa definita* Aaron, ♂, *paratype, under side.*
16. *Melitæa neumægeni* Skinner, ♂, *paratype, under side.*
17. *Brenthis kriemhild* Strecker, ♂. The figure is that of a paratype of *B. laurenti* Skinner.
18. *Melitæa cooperi* Behr, ♂, *type.*
19. *Melitæa cooperi* Behr, ♀, *type, under side.*
20. *Melitæa carmentis* B. & B., ♂, *paratype.*
21. *Melitæa carmentis* B. & B., ♀, *paratype.*
22. *Melitæa gilletti* (Barnes) ♀, *paratype.*
23. *Melitæa magdalena* B. & McD., ♂, *paratype.*
24. *Melitæa magdalena* B. & McD., ♀, *paratype.*
25. *Melitæa flavula* B. & McD., ♂, *paratype.*

Explanation of Plate LVII

(Melitæa)

1. *M. dwinellei* Henry Edwards, ♂.
2. *M. perdiccas* Edwards, ♂, *type.*
3. *M. perdiccas* Edwards, ♀, *type.*
4. *M. olancha* Wright, ♂.
5. *M. olancha* Wright, ♀.
6. *M. sierra* Wright, ♂.
7. *M. sierra* Wright, ♀.
8. *M. quino* Behr, ♂.
9. *M. quino* Behr, ♀.
10. *M. anicia* Doubl. & Hew., ♂.
11. *M. anicia* Doubl. & Hew., ♀.
12. *M. helvia* Scudder, ♂.
13. *M. helvia* Scudder, ♀.
14. *M. bernadetta* (Leussler) ♂, *paratype.*
15. *M. eurytion* Mead, ♂, *type.*
16. *M. eurytion* Mead, ♀, *type.*
17. *M. truckeënsis* (Gunder) ♀.
18. *M. capella* Barnes, ♂, *paratype.*
19. *M. capella* Barnes, ♀, *paratype.*
20. *M. alena* Barnes & Benj., ♂, *paratype.*
21. *M. alena* Barnes & Benj., ♀, *paratype.*
22. *M. morandi* (Gunder) ♂, *holotype.*
23. *M. morandi* (Gunder) ♀, *allotype.*
24. *M. irelandi* (Gunder) ♂, *holotype.*
25. *M. irelandi* (Gunder) ♀, *allotype.*
26. *M. monoënsis* (Gunder) ♂, *paratype.*
27. *M. monoënsis* (Gunder) ♀, *paratype.*
28. *M. aurilacus* (Gunder) ♂, *paratype.*
29. *M. aurilacus* (Gunder) ♀, *paratype.*

ZEESE-WILKINSON CO., PHOTOGRAV

EXPLANATION OF PLATE LVIII

(Melitæa)

1. *M. wheeleri* Hy. Edwards, ♂, *paratype*.
2. *M. colonia* Wright, ♂.
3. *M. colonia* Wright, ♀.
4. *M. rubicunda* Hy. Edwards, ♀.
5. *M. editha* Boisduval, ♂, *under side*.
6. *M. editha* Boisduval, ♀.
7. *M. augusta* Edwards, ♀, *type*.
8. *M. baroni* Edwards, ♀, *type, under side*.
9. *M. arachne* Edwards, ♀.
10. *M. arachne*, ab. *gunderiæ* Holland, *type*.
11. *M. pola* Boisduval = *monache* Comstock, ♂.
12. *M. minuta* Edwards, ♂, *under side*.
13. *M. minuta* Edwards, ♀, *type*.
14. *M. nympha* Edwards, ♀, *type*.
15. *M. nympha* Edwards, ♂, *under side*.
16. *M. gabbi* Behr, ♂, *under side*.
17. *M. gabbi* Behr, ♀.
18. *M. gilensis* Holland, ♂, *type*.
19. *M. calydon* Mead, ♂, *type*.
20. *M. calydon* Mead, ♀, *type*.
21. *M. palla* Boisduval, ♂.
22. *M. palla* Boisduval, ♀.
23. *M. palla* Boisd., var. *sterope*, Edw. ♀, *type, albinic* ♀.
24. *M. palla* Boisd., var. *eremita* Wright, *melanic* ♀.
25. *M. malcolmi* Comstock, ♂.
26. *M. malcolmi* Comstock, ♀.
27. *M. acastus* Edwards, ♂.
28. *M. hoffmanni* Behr, var. *segregata* Barnes & McDunnough, ♂, *paratype*.
29. *M. hoffmanni* Behr, var. *segregata* Barnes & McDunnough, ♀, *paratype*.
30. *M. cyneas* Godman & Salvin, ♂.
31. *M. cyneas* Godman & Salvin, ♂, *under side*.

ZEESE-WILKINSON CO. PHOTOGRAV.

EXPLANATION OF PLATE LIX

1. *Melitæa chalcedona* Doubl. & Hew., ♀.
2. *Melitæa nubigena* Behr, *type, fide* Hy. Edw.
3. *Melitæa brucei* Edwards, ♂, *type*.
4. *Melitæa brucei* Edwards, ♀, *type*.
5. *Melitæa theona* Ménétries, ♂.
6. *M. fulvia* Edwards, ♂, *type, under side*.
7. *Melitæa bolli* Edwards, ♂, *type*.
8. *Melitæa bolli* Edwards, ♀, *type*.
9. *Melitæa leanira* Felder, ♂, *under side*.
10. *M. leanira* Felder, ♀.
11. *M. harrisi,* var. *albimontana* Avinoff, ♂, *type*.
12. *M. harrisi,* var. *liggetti* Avinoff, ♂, *type*.
13. *M. harrisi,* var. *liggetti* Avinoff, ♀, *type*.
14. *Anthanassa texana* (Edw.) var. *seminole* (Skinner), ♂.
15. *Microtia elva* Bates, ♂.
16. *Microtia elva* Bates, ♀.
17. *Chlosyne erodyle,* (Bates) ♂.
18. *Chlosyne crocale* (Edw.), var. *rufescens* (Edw.) ♂.
19. *Chlosyne californica* (Wright) ♂.
20. *Chlosyne c lifornica* (Wright) ♀.
21. *Melitæa callina* Boisd., ♀, *type*.
22. *Phyciodes thebais* Godm. & Salv., ♂, type of *arida* Skinner.
23. *Brenthis improba* (Butler) ♀, (Baffin-Land).
24. *Polygonia oreas* (Edw.) ♂, *type*.
25. *Argynnis gunderi* Comstock ♂, *under side*.
26. *Polygonia rusticus* (Edw.) ♂, *type*.
27. *Polygonia oreas* (Edw.) ♂, *under side*.
28. *Anartia fatima* (Fabr.) ♂.
29. *Eunica tatila* H.-S., ♂.
30. *Basilarchia archippus* (Cram.) ab. *pseudodorippus* (Strecker) ♂, *type*.

ZEESE-WILKINSON CO., PHOTOGRAV

Explanation of Plate LX

Nymphalidæ and Satyrinæ

(All figures very slightly reduced)

1. *Historis odia* (Fabricius) ♂.
2. *Coëa acheronta* (Fabricius) ♂.
3. *Myscelia ethusa* (Boisduval) ♂.
4. *Myscelia ethusa* (Boisduval) ♀.
5. *Dynamine dyonis* Geyer, ♂, *under side.*
6. *Asterocampa texana* (Skinner) ♂, *paratype.*
7. *Brenthis chariclea* (Schneider) var. *grandis* B. & McD., ♀, *paratype.*
8. *B. chariclea* (Schneid.) var. *grandis* B. & McD., ♀, *paratype, under side.*
9. *B. chariclea* (Schneid.) var. *rainieri* B. & McD., ♂, *paratype.*
10. *B. chariclea* (Schneid.) var. *rainieri* B. & McD., ♀, *paratype, under side.*
11. *Paramecera xicaque* Reakirt, ♂.
12. *Brenthis improba* Butler, ♂, *under side.*
13. *B. tarquinius* Curtis, ♂, *under side.*
14. *B. nichollæ* Barnes & Benjamin ♂, *holotype.*
15. *B. nichollæ* Barnes & Benjamin, ♀, *allotype.*
16. *Cænonympha ampelos* Edwards, ♀, topotypical, from Salem, Oregon.
17. *C. columbiana* McDunnough, ♀, *paratype.*
18. *C. columbiana* McDunnough, ♂, *paratype, under side.*
19. *C. benjamini* McDunnough, ♂, *paratype, under side.*
20. *C. benjamini* McDunnough, ♀, *paratype.*
21. *C. yukonensis* Holland, ♂, *type.*
22. *C. yukonensis* Holland, ♀, *paratype, under side.*
23. *C. insulana* McDunnough, ♀, *paratype.*
24. *C. insulana* McDunnough, ♂, *paratype, under side.*
25. *C. furcæ* Barnes & Benjamin, ♂, Grand Canyon, Ariz., Holland *coll.*
26. *C. furcæ* Barnes & Benjamin, ♀. Grand Canyon, Ariz., Holland *coll.*

ZEESE-WILKINSON CO., PHOTOGRAV.

Explanation of Plate LXI

1. *Erebia steckeri* Holland, ♂, *type*.
2. *Erebia steckeri*, ♂, *type, under side*.
3. *Erebia steckeri*, ♀, *type*.
4. *Erebia steckeri*, ♀, *type, under side*.
5. *Erebia fasciata* Butler, ♂, *paratype*.
6. *Erebia fasciata*, ♀, *paratype, under side*.
7. *Erebia avinoffi* Holland, ♀, *holotype, under side*.
8. *Erebia avinoffi*, ♂, *allotype*.
9. *Erebia avinoffi*, ♀, *paratype, under side* (from Cape Tsukotski, Siberia).
10. *Erebia ethela* Edwards, ♂, *type, under side*.
11. *Erebia ethela*, ♀, *type, under side*.
12. *Erebia sofia* Strecker, ♀, *under side* (from Eagle City, Alaska.)
13. *Erebia sofia* var. *alaskensis* Holland, ♂, *type*.
14. *Erebia sofia* var. *alaskensis* Holland, ♂, *paratype, under side*.
15. *Erebia sofia* var. *alaskensis* Holland, ♂, *paratype*.
16. *Erebia discoidalis* (Kirby), ♂, *under side*.
17. *Erebia disa* var. *mancinus* Dbly. & Hew., ♂, *under side*.
18. *Erebia vidleri* Elwes, ♂.
19. *Erebia vidleri*, ♀, *under side*.
20. *Erebia brucei* Elwes, ♀.
21. *Erebia rossi*, var. *kuskoquima* Holl., ♂, *type*.
22. *Erebia rossi*, var. *kuskoquima* Holl., ♀, *type*.
23. *Erebia rossi*, var. *kuskoquima* Holl., ♂, *under side*.
24. *Erebia epipsodea* Butler, ♀, from Yukon Valley.
25. *Erebia epipsodea*, ♂, from Montana, under side.
26. *Erebia epipsodea* Butler, ♀, from Montana.
27. *Erebia epipsodea*, ♂, from Yukon Valley.
28. *Erebia youngi* Holland, ♂, *type*.
29. *Erebia youngi*, ♀, *allotype*.
30. *Erebia youngi*, ♀, *paratype, under side*.

ZEESE-WILKINSON CO., PHOTOGRAV

Explanation of Plate LXII

1. *Œneis nevadensis* (Felders) ♂.
2. *Œneis nevadensis* (Felders) ♂, *under side.*
3. *Œneis gigas* Butler, ♂, *under side.*
4. *Œneis ivallda* (Mead) ♀, *type.*
5. *Œneis macouni* (Edw.) ♂, *type, under side.*
6. *Œneis iduna* (Edw.) ♂, *type, under side.*
7. *Œneis calais* (Scudder) ♀, *type.*
8. *Œneis chryxus* (Dbly. & Hew.) ♀, *under side.*
9. *Œneis chryxus* (Dbly. & Hew.) ♂, *under side.*
10. *Œneis alaskensis* Holland, ♂, *type.*
11. *Œneis alaskensis* Holland, ♀, *type.*
12. *Œneis uhleri* (Reakirt) ♀, *under side.*
13. *Œneis varuna* (Edw.) ♂, *type.*
14. *Œneis varuna* (Edw.) ♀, *type.*
15. *Œneis alberta* Elwes, ♂.
16. *Œneis alberta* Elwes, ♀.

17. *Œneis norna* (Thunberg) ♂, *under side,* typical male from Finland.
18. *Œneis norna* (Thunberg) ♀, from Nushagak, Alaska.
19. *Œneis katahdin* (Newcomb) ♂, *paratype.*
20. *Œneis katahdin* (Newcomb) ♀, *paratype, under side.*
21. *Œneis peartiæ* (Edw.) ♂, *type.*
22. *Œneis norna* (Thunberg) ♂, var. from Finland, occurs in Alaska also.
23. *Œneis assimilis* Butler, ♂, Butler *det.*
24. *Œneis assimilis* Butler, ♂, Butler *det., under side.*
25. *Œneis æno* (Boisd.?) (Edwards) ♀.
26. *Œneis æno* (Boisd.?) (Edwards) ♂, *under side*

EXPLANATION OF PLATE LXIII

1. *Œneis semplei* Holland, ♂, *type*.
2. *Œneis semplei* Holland, ♀, *allotype*.
3. *Œneis semplei* Holland, ♂, *paratype, under side*.
4. *Œneis beani* Elwes, ♂.
5. *Œneis beani* Elwes, ♀, *under side*.
6. *Œneis polixenes* (Fabr.) ♂, *under side*.
7. *Œneis polixenes* (Fabr.) ♀.
8. *Œneis semidea* (Say) ♂, *under side*.
9. *Œneis gibsoni* Holland, ♀, *type, under side*.
10. *Œneis gibsoni* Holland, ♂, *type, under side*.
11. *Satyrodes eurydice* var. *fumosus* Leussler, ♂, *paratype*.
12. *Cercyonis silvestris* (Edw.) ♀, *type*.
13. *Cercyonis silvestris* (Edw.) ♀, *paratype, under side*.
14. *Cercyonis silvestris* (Edw.) ♂, *type*.
15. *Cercyonis alope*, var. *maritima* (Edw.) ♂.
16. *Cercyonis wheeleri* (Edw.) ♀, *type*.
17. *Cercyonis boöpis* (Edw.) ♀.
18. *Cercyonis boöpis* (Edw.) ♂, *type*.
19. *Cercyonis paula* (Edw.) ♀, *type*.
20. *Cercyonis ariane* (Boisd.) ♀, *under side, from Oregon*.
21. *Cercyonis alope*, var. *texana* (Edw.) ♂, *type, under side*.
22. *Cercyonis æta* (Boisd.) ♂, *under side*.
23. *Cercyonis paula* (Edw.) ♀, *under side*.
24. *Cercyonis charon* (Edw.) ♂, *type, under side*.
25. *Cercyonis charon* (Edw.) ♀, *type, under side*.
26. *Œneis subhyalina* (Curtis) ♀, *under side*.
27. *Œneis subhyalina* (Curtis) ♂. (Nos. 26 and 27 are from northern Labrador).

ZEESE-WILKINSON CO., PHOTOGRAV

EXPLANATION OF PLATE LXIV

1. *Apodemai marginalis* Skinner, ♂, *paratype*.
2. *Lasaia narses* Staudinger, ♂, *paratype*.
3. *Lasaia narses* Staudinger, ♀, *paratype*.
4. *Eumæus minyas* (Hübner) ♀.
5. *Eumæus minyas* (Hübner) ♂, *under side*.
6. *Thecla iroides* Boisd., ♂.
7. *Thecla iroides* Boisd., ♀, *under side*.
8. *Thecla irus* (Godart) ♀.
9. *Thecla polios* (Cook & Watson) ♂, *type*.
10. *Thecla mossi* Hy. Edwards, ♂, *type*.
11. *Thecla fotis* Strecker, ♀, *under side*.
12. *Thecla jada* Hewitson, ♂.
13. *Thecla jada* Hewitson, ♂, *under side*
14. *Thecla pastor* Butler & Druce, ♂.
15. *Thecla pastor* Butler & Druce, ♀, *under side*.
16. *Thecla sheridani* Edwards, ♂, *type, under side*.
17. *Thecla apama* Edwards, ♀, *type, under side*.
18. *Thecla loki* Skinner, ♀, *paratype, under side*.
19. *Thecla tacita* Hy. Edwards, ♂, *type*.
20. *Thecla xami* Reakirt, ♂, *under side*.
21. *Thecla calanus* Hübner, ♂, *under side*.
22. *Thecla telea* Hewitson, ♂.
23. *Thecla telea* Hewitson, ♂, *under side*.
24. *Thecla californica* Edwards, ♂, *type*.
25. *Thecla californica* Edwards, ♀, *type, under side*.
26. *Thecla melinus* var. *pudica* Hy. Edwards, ♂, *under side*.
27. *Thecla dryope* Edwards, ♂, *type*.
28. *Thecla dryope* Edwards, ♂, *under side*.
29. *Thecla azia* Hewitson, ♂.
30. *Thecla azia* Hewitson, ♂, *under side*.
31. *Thecla itys* Edwards, ♂.
32. *Thecla endymion* (Cramer), ♂.
33. *Thecla putnami* Hy. Edwards, ♂.
34. *Thecla putnami* Hy. Edwards, ♀, *under side*.
35. *Thecla columella* (Fabricius) ♂.
36. *Thecla columella* (Fabricius) ♀, *under side*.
37. *Thecla leda* Edwards, ♂, *type*.
38. *Thecla leda* Edwards, ♀.
39. *Chrysophanus cupreus* Edwards, ♂, *type*.
40. *Chrysophanus cupreus* Edwards, ♀, *type*.
41. *Chrysophanus amicetus* Scudder, ♂.
42. *Chrysophanus amicetus* Scudder, ♀, *under side*.
43. *Chrysophanus dorcas* Kirby, ♂.
44. *Chrysophanus florus* Edwards, ♂, *typical*.
45. *Chrysophanus hypophlœas,* ab. *fasciata* Strecker, *paratype*.
46. *Thecla hadros* Cook & Watson, ♂, *paratype*.
47. *Chrysophanus charlottensis* Holland, ♂, *type*.
48. *Chrysophanus charlottensis* Holland, ♂, *paratype, under side*.
49. *Chrysophanus charlottensis* Holland, ♀, *allotype*.
50. *Chrysophanus hermes* Edwards, ♂, *type*.

PLATE LXIV

Explanation of Plate LXV

(Lycænidæ)

1. *Chrysophanus nivalis* Boisd., ♂.
2. *Chrysophanus nivalis* Boisd., ♀.
3. *Chrysophanus nivalis* Boisd., ♀, *under side.*
4. *Chrysophanus dione* Scudder, ♂.
5. *Chrysophanus dione* Scudder, ♀.
6. *Thecla spadix* Hy. Edwards, ♂.
7. *Thecla spadix* Hy. Edwards, ♀.
8. *Thecla spadix* Hy. Edwards, ♂, *under side.*
9. *Thecla avalona* Wright, ♂.
10. *Thecla atrofasciata* McD., ♂, *under side.*
11. *Thecla autolycus* Edw., ♂, *under side.*
12. *Thecla alcestis* Edw., ♂, *under side.*
13. *Thecla oslari* Dyar, ♂, *type, under side.*
14. *Thecla tetra* Edw., ♂, *type, under side.*
15. *Thecla ilavia* Beutenmüller, ♂, *paratype, under side.*
16. *Thecla provo* Wats. & Comst., ♂, *paratype.*
17. *Thecla chlorophora* Wats. & Comst., ♂, *paratype, under side.*
18. *Lycæna icarioides* Boisd., ♂.
19. *Lycæna mintha* Edw., ♂, *type.*
20. *Lycæna lycea* Edw., ♂, *type.*
21. *Lycæna lycea* Edw., ♀, *typical.*
22. *Lycæna fulla* Edw., ♂, *type, under side.*
23. *Lycæna ardea* Edw., ♂, comp. with type.
24. *Lycæna ardea* Edw., ♀, *under side.*
25. *Lycæna blackmorei* B. & McD., ♂, *paratype.*
26. *Lycæna blackmorei* B. & McD., ♀, *paratype.*
27. *Lycæna blackmorei* B. & McD., ♂, *paratype, under side.*
28. *Lycæna amica* Edw., ♂.
29. *Lycæna amica* Edw., ♂, *under side.*
30. *Lycæna insulana* Blackmore, ♂.
31. *Lycæna insulana* Blackmore, ♂, *under side.*
32. *Lycæna hilda* Grinnell, ♂, *paratype.*
33. *Lycæna hilda* Grinnell, ♀, *paratype.*
34. *Lycæna hilda* Grinnell, ♂, *under side.*
35. *Lycæna pheres* Boisd., ♂.
36. *Lycæna pembina* Edw., ♂.
37. *Lycæna pembina* Edw., ♀.
38. *Lycæna pembina* Edw., ♂, *under side.*
39. *Lycæna sæpiolus* Boisd., ♀, *blue form.*
40. *Lycæna helios* Edw., ♂, *under side.*
41. *Lycæna xerces* Boisd., ♂, *under side.*
42. *Lycæna polyphemus* Boisd., ♂, *under side.*
43. *Lycæna mertila* Edw., ♀, type.

ZEESE-WILKINSON CO., PHOTOGRAV

Explanation of Plate LXVI

(Lycænidæ)

1. *Lycæna maricopa* Reakirt, ♂, *under side.*
2. *L. columbia* Skinner, ♂, *paratype.*
3. *L. columbia* Skinner, ♂, *under side.*
4. *L. oro* Scudder, ♂, *typical.*
5. *L. oro* Scudder, ♀, *typical.*
6. *L. oro* Scudder, ♂, *under side.*
7. *L. couperi* Grote, ♂, from Anticosti.
8. *L. couperi* Grote, ♀, from Anticosti.
9. *L. antiacis* Boisduval, ♂, *under side.*
10. *L. xerces* Boisduval, ♂.
11. *L. xerces* Boisduval, ♀.
12. *L. scudderi* Edwards, ♂, *type, under side.*
13. *L. kodiak* Edwards, ♂.
14. *L. kodiak* Edwards, ♀.
15. *L. kodiak* Edwards, ♂, *under side.*
16. *L. anetta* Edwards, ♂, *under side.*
17. *L. melissa* Edwards, ♀, *type, under side.*
18. *L. lotis* Lintner, ♂, *typical.*
19. *L. lotis* Lintner, ♀, *typical.*
20. *L. lotis* Lintner, ♂, *under side.*
21. *L. anna* Edwards, ♂, *type.*
22. *L. anna* Edwards, ♀, *type.*
23. *L. anna* Edwards, ♂, *under side.*
24. *L. acmon* West. & Hew., ♀, *under side.*
25. *L. acmon* West. & Hew., ♂, *var., under side.*
26. *L. lupini* Boisduval, ♂, *typical.*
27. *L. lupini* Boisduval, ♀, *typical.*
28. *L. lupini* Boisduval, ♂, *under side.*
29. *L. chlorina* Skinner, ♂.
30. *L. chlorina* Skinner, ♀.
31. *L. emigdionis* Grinnell, ♂.
32. *L. emigdionis* Grinnell, ♀.
33. *L. emigdionis* Grinnell, ♂, *under side.*
34. *L. neurona* Skinner, ♂, *paratype.*
35. *L. battoides* Behr, ♀, *under side.*
36. *L. battoides*, var. *oregonensis* B. & McD., ♂, *paratype.*
37. *L. battoides*, var. *bernardino* B. & McD., ♂, *paratype.*
38. *L. glaucon*, var. *intermedia* B. & McD., ♂, *paratype.*
39. *L. rita* B. & McD., ♂, *paratype.*
40. *L. rita* B. & McD., ♂, *paratype, under side.*
41. *L. enoptes* Boisduval, var. *ancilla* B. & McD., ♂, *paratype.*
42. *L. enoptes* Boisd., var. *ancilla* B. & McD., ♀, *paratype.*
43. *L. enoptes* Boisd., var. *ancilla* B. & McD., ♀, *under side.*
44. *L. mohave* Watson & Comstock, ♂, *type, under side.*
45. *L. sonorensis* Felders, ♂, *under side.*
46. *L. spaldingi* B. & McD., ♂, *paratype, under side.*
47. *L. catalina* Reakirt, ♂, *under side.*
48. *L. daunia* Edwards, ♂, *under side.*
49. *L. podarce* Felders, ♀.
50. *L. podarce* Felders, ♂, *under side.*
51. *L. cyna* Edwards, ♂, *typical.*

EXPLANATION OF PLATE LXVII

1. *Lycæna gyas* Edwards, ♂, *typical.*
2. *L. gyas* Edwards, ♀.
3. *L. gyas* Edwards, ♂, *under side.*
4. *L. zachæina* Butler & Druce, ♂.
5. *L. zachæina* Butler & Druce, ♀.
6. *L. shasta* Edwards, ♂, *under side.*
7. *L. yukona* Holland, ♂, *typical.*
8. *L. yukona* Holland, ♀, *typical.*
9. *L. yukona* Holland, ♂, *under side.*
10. *L. gazora* Boisduval, ♂.
11. *L. herri* Grinnell, ♂, *typical.*
12. *L. herri* Grinnell, ♀, *typical.*
13. *L. echo* Edwards, ♀, *under side.*
14. *Ascia amaryllis*, var. *josepha* (G. &. S.) ♂.
15. *Ascia monuste* (Linnæus) ♂.

16. *Ascia monuste*, dimorphic ♀, *phileta* (Fabr.)
    (Fig. 15 was taken *in copula* with fig. 16.)
17. *Ascia monuste*, var. *crameri* Holland, ♂, *type.*
18. *Ascia monuste*, var. *raza* Klots, *paratype, under side.*
19. *Callidryas agarithe* Boisd., ♀.
20. *Colias skinneri* Barnes, ♂, *type.*
21. *Colias skinneri* Barnes, ♀, *type.*
22. *Callidryas statira* (Cramer), ♂.
23. *Callidryas statira* (Cramer), ♀.
24. *Pieris hulda* Edwards, ♂, *type.*
25. *Pieris hulda* Edwards, ♀, *type.*
26. *Pieris calyce* Edwards, ♂, *type.*
27. *Euchloë hyantis* (Edwards) ♂, *type.*
28. *Euchloë olympia* (Edwards) ♂, *type.*
29. *Pieris nelsoni* Edwards, ♂, *type.*
30. *Colias boothi* Curtis, ♂, *type.*

ZEESE-WILKINSON CO., PHOTOGRAV

EXPLANATION OF PLATE LXVIII

1. *Lycæna cyna* Edwards, ♀, *type.*
2. *Lycæna filenus* Poey, ♂.
3. *Lycæna filenus* Poey, ♀.
4. *Lycæna filenus* Poey, ♂, *under side.*
5. *Chrysophanus fieldeni* McLachlan, ♂.
6. *Chrysophanus fieldeni* McLachlan, ♀, *under side.*
7. *Lycæna aquilo*, var. *suttoni* Holland, ♂, *type.*
8. *Lycæna aquilo*, var. *suttoni* Holland, ♀, *type.*
9. *L. aquilo*, var. *suttoni*, ♂, *paratype, under side.*
10. *Chrysophanus epixanthe* Boisd., ♂.
11. *Chrysophanus epixanthe* Boisd., ♀.
12. *Chrysophanus epixanthe* Boisd., ♀, *under side.*
13. *Colias philodice* Godart, ♂, *melanic.*
14. *Colias christina* Edwards, ♂, *type.*
15. *Colias christina* Edwards, ♀, *type.*
16. *Colias occidentalis* Scudder, ♂, *type.*
17. *Colias occidentalis* Scudder, ♀, *type.*
18. *Colias barbara* Hy. Edwards, ♂, *type.*
19. *Colias barbara* Hy. Edwards, ♀, *type.*
20. *Colias harfordi* Hy. Edwards, ♂, *type.*
21. *Colias harfordi* Hy. Edwards, ♀, *type.*
22. *Colias emilia* Edwards, ♂, *type.*
23. *Colias emilia* Edwards, ♀, *type.*
24. *Colias edwardsi* Edwards, ♂, *type.*
25. *Colias edwardsi* Edwards, ♀, *type.*
26. *Colias astræa* Edwards, ♂, *type.*
27. *Colias astræa* Edwards, ♀, *type.*
28. *Colias palæno* (Linnæus) ♂, from Lapland.
29. *Colias palæno* (Linnæus) ♀, from Lapland.
30. *Colias chippewa* Kirby, ♂.
31. *Colias chippewa* Kirby, ♀.
32. *Colias rossi* Guenée, ♂, from Southhampton Isd.
33. *Colias chione* Curtis, ♂, from Southhampton Isd.

Explanation of Plate LXIX

(Parnassius)

1. *Parnassius eversmanni* Ménétries, ♂.
2. *P. eversmanni* Mén., ♀, = *P. thor* Hy. Edwards.
3. *P. delius* var. *golovinus* Holland, ♂, *type*.
4. *P. delius* var. *golovinus* Holl., ♂, *under side*.
5. *P. delius* var. *golovinus* Holl., ♀, *allotype*.
6. *P. delius* var. *golovinus* Holl., ♀, *under side*.
7. *P. claudianus* Stichel, ♂.
8. *P. claudianus* Stichel, ♀.
9. *P. menetriesi* Henry Edwards, ♂.
10. *P. menetriesi* Henry Edwards, ♀.
11. *P. altaurus* Dyar, ♂.
12. *P. smintheus* var. *sayi* Edw., ♂, *type*.
13. *P. smintheus* var. *sayi* Edw., ♀, *type*.
14. *P. smintheus* var. *sayi* Edw., ♂, small altico line form,-*minusculus* Bryk.
15. *P. smintheus* var. *sayi* Edw., ♂, small altico line form,-*nanus* Neumœgen.

Explanation of Plate LXX

(*Papilio*. All figures two thirds natural size)

1. *Papilio devilliersi* Godart, ♂, *under side*.
2. *P. rutulus* var. *arizonensis* Edw., ♂, *type*.
3. *P. rutulus* var. *arcticus* Skinner, ♀, *paratype*.
4. *P. turnus* var. *australis* Maynard, ♂.
5. *P. oregonius* Edwards, ♂, *type*.
6. *P. turnus* var. *canadensis* Rothschild & Jordan, ♂.
7. *P. turnus* var. *canadensis* Rothschild & Jordan, ♀.
8. *P. americus* Kollar, ♂, Arizona (Wheeler Expedition).
9. *P. pergamus* Henry Edwards, ♂, *typical*.
10. *P. ponceanus* Schaus, ♀, *typical*, from Miami, Fla.
11. *P. celadon* Lucas, ♂.
12. *P. asterius*, var. *curvifascia* Skinner, ♂, *paratype*.

ZEESE-WILKINSON CO., INC., PHOTOGRAV.

EXPLANATION OF PLATE LXXI

1. *Colænis cillene* (Cramer) ♂.
2. *Colænis cillene* (Cramer) ♀.
3. *Smyrna karwinskii* Hübner, ♂.
4. *Argynnis hydaspe* Boisduval, ♂, *type.*
5. *Argynnis mormonia* Boisduval, ♂, *paratype, under side.*
6. *Argynnis mormonia* Boisduval, ♀, *type.*
7. *Polygonia silvius* (Edwards) ♀, *type.*
8. *Papilio ornythion* Boisduval, ♂.
9. *Cercyonis behri* Grinnell, ♂.
10. *Cercyonis behri* Grinnell, ♀, *under side.*
11. *Gonepteryx clorinde* (Godart) ♂.
12. *Neophasia terlooti* Behr, ♂.
13. *Neophasia terlooti* Behr, *dimorphic* ♀, = *princetonia* Poling.
14. *Euchloë browningi* (Skinner) ♂, *paratype.*
15. *Euchloë flavida* (Skinner) ♂, *paratype.*
16. *Atrytonopsis edwardsi* Barnes & McDunnough, ♂.
17. *Megathymus albocincta* Holland, ♂, *type.*
18. *Megathymus albocincta* Holland, ♂, *under side.*

EXPLANATION OF PLATE LXXII

1. *Megathymus ursus* Poling, ♂, *type*.
2. *Ithomia* (?) *lycaste* (Fabricius) (from Jones' "Icones").
3. *Œneis yukonensis* Gibson, ♂, *type*, (after Gibson).
4. *Œneis peartiæ* Edwards, ♀, (after Gibson).
5. *Œneis semidea arctica*, ♂, *type* (after Gibson).
6. *Œneis cairnesi* Gibson, ♂, *type* (after Gibson).
7. *Brenthis natazhati* Gibson, ♂, *type* (after Gibson).
8. *Brenthis natazhati* Gibson, ♀, (after Gibson).
9. *Brenthis distincta* Gibson, ♀, *type* (after Gibson).
10. *Megathymus leussleri* Holland, ♂, *type*.
11. *Megathymus leussleri* Holland, ♂, *under side*.
12. *Megathymus leussleri* Holland, ♀, *allotype*.
13. *Megathymus stephensi* Skinner, ♂, *paratype*.
14. *Megathymus stephensi* Skinner, ♀, *under side*.
15. *Erynnis lasus* (Edwards) ♂, *compared with type*.
16. *Erynnis lasus* (Edwards) ♀.
17. *Erynnis lasus* (Edwards) ♀, *under side*.

ZEESE-WILKINSON CO., PHOTOGRAV

Explanation of Plate LXXIII

1. *Basilarchia floridensis* (Strecker) ♂, *type* of
   B. *eros* Edwards, ♂.
2. *Basilarchia floridensis* (Strecker) ♂, *under side.*
3. *Erebia rossi* (Curtis) ♂, *typical.*
4. *Erebia rossi* (Curtis) ♀, *typical, under side.*
5. *Euchloë lotta* Beutenmueller, ♂, *typical.*
6. *Pseudocopaeodes eunus* (Edwards) ♂, *type.*
7. *Anthanassa* (?) *leucodesma* (Felder) ♀.
8. *Melitæa hutchinsi* (McDunnough) ♂.
9. *Melitæa hutchinsi* (McDunnough) ♀.
10. *Erynnis lindseyi* Holland, ♂, *type.*
11. *Erynnis lindseyi* Holland, ♀, *type.*
12. *Erynnis ruricola* (Boisd.) ♂, *type, under side.*
13. *Lycæna afra* Edwards, ♂, *type.*
14. *Lycæna afra* Edwards, ♀, *type, under side.*
15. *Ancyloxpha arene* (Edwards) ♂.
16. *Ancyloxypha arene* (Edwards) ♀, *under side.*
17. *Satyrium fuliginosum* (Edwards) ♂, *type.*
18. *Satyrium fuliginosum* (Edwards) ♀, *type.*
19. *Satyrium fuliginosum* (Edwards) ♀, *under side.*
20. *Erynnis ogallala* (Leussler) ♂, *paratype.*
21. *Erynnis ogallala* (Leussler) ♂, *paratype, under side.*
22. *Colias hecla* Lefevre, ♂.
23. *Colias hecla* Lefevre, ♀.
24. *Colias hecla* Lefevre, ♀, *under side.*
25. *Eurema gundlachia* (Poey) ♂.
26. *Colias boothi* Curtis, ♂.
27. *Colias boothi* Curtis, ♂, *under side.*
28. *Colias moina* Strecker, ♀, *under side.*
29. *Colias philodice* Godart, ♀, *albino.*
30. *Callidryas cipris* (Fabricius) ♂.

ZEESE-WILKINSON CO., PHOTOGRAV

Explanation of Plate LXXIV

1. *Brenthis kriemhild* Strecker, ♂, *type* (Utah).
2. *Brenthis kriemhild* Strecker, ♂, *type, under side.*
3. *Brenthis kriemhild* Strecker, ♀, *type* (Arizona).
4. *Brenthis kriemhild* Strecker, ♀, *type, under side* (Arizona).
5. *Brenthis kriemhild* Strecker, ♀, *type* (Colo.).
6. *Brenthis kriemhild* Strecker, ♀, *type, under side* (Colo.).
7. *Brenthis andersoni* Dyar, ♂, *type.*

8. *Brenthis andersoni* Dyar, *type, under side.*
9. *Melitæa hanhami* Fletcher, ♂, *type.*
10. *Melitæa hanhami* Fletcher, ♂, *type, under side.*
11. *Coenonympha brenda* Edwards, ♂, *type.*
12. *Coenonympha brenda* Edwards, ♂, *type, under side.*
13–14. *Myscelia skinneri* Mengel, ♂, *type.*
15–16. *Myscelia skinneri* Mengel, ♀, *type.*

John C. Bragdon, Inc., Engraver

EXPLANATION OF PLATE LXXV

1. *Mitoura johnsoni* (Skinner) ♂, *type.*
2. *Mitoura johnsoni* (Skinner) ♂, *type. under side.*
3. *Parnassius menetriesi* ab. *immaculatus* Skinner, ♂, *type.*
4. *Colias pallida* Skinner, ♀, *type.*
5. *Papilio philenor* var. *hirsutus* Skinner, ♀, *type.*
6. *Papilio rutulus* var. *arcticus* Skinner, ♂, *type, under side.*
7. *Murgaria coyote* (Skinner) ♂, *type.*
7a. *Murgaria coyote* (Skinner) ♂, *type, under side.*
8. *Phœdinus mysie* (Dyar) ♂, *type.*
8a. *Phœdinus mysie* (Dyar) ♂, *type, under side.*
9. *Phemiades jamaicensis* Schaus, ♂, *type.*
9a. *Phemiades jamaicensis* Schaus, ♂, *type, under side.*
10. *Œneis caryi* Dyar, ♂, *type.*
10a. *Œneis caryi* Dyar, ♂ *type, under side.*
11. *Œneis nahanni* Dyar, ♂, *type.*
11a. *Œneis nahanni* Dyar, ♂, *type, under side.*
12. *Atrytonopsis cestus* (Edwards) ♂, *type.*
12a. *Atrytonopsis cestus* (Edwards) ♂, *type, under side, enlarged.*
13. *Erynnis horus* (Edwards) ♀, *type.*
14. *Erynnis horus* (Edwards) ♀, *type, under side.*
15. *Thanaos tatius* Edwards, ♂, *type.*
16. *Thanaos tatius* Edwards, ♂, *type, under side, enlarged.*
17. *Problema bulenta* (Boisd. & Lec.) ♂.
17a. *Problema bulenta* (Boisd. & Lec.) ♂, *under side.*
18. *Problema bulenta* (Boisd. & Lec.) ♀.
18a. *Problema bulenta* (Boisd. & Lec.) ♀, *under side.*
19. *Œneis simulans* Gibson, ♂, *type, under side.*
20. *Œneis cairnesi* Gibson, ♂, *type, under side.*

John C. Bragdon, Inc., Engraver

Explanation of Plate LXXVI

1. *Caria domitianus* (Fabr.) ♂; 1a, Do., *under side.*

2. *Caria melicerta* Schaus, ♂, *type*; 2a, Do., *under side.*

3. *Caria ino* Godman & Salvin, ♂; 3a, Do., *under side.*

4. *Apodemia multiplaga* Schaus, ♂, *paratype;* 4a, Do., *under side.*

5. *Apodemia phyciodoides* B. & McD., ♂, *type;* 5a, Do., *under side.*

6. *Apodemia phyciodoides* B. & McD., ♀, *allotype;* 6a, Do., *under side.*

7. *Calephelis perditalis* B. & McD., ♂, *paratype;* 7a, Do., *under side.*

8. *Calephelis perditalis* B. & McD., ♀, *paratype;* 8a, Do., *under side.*

9. *Calephelis louisiana* Holland, ♂, *type; 9a,* Do., *under side.*

10. *Apodemia hepburni* Godm. & Salv., 10a, Do., *under side* (after G. & S.).

11. *Calephelis wrighti* Holland, ♂; 11a, Do., *under side* (after Wright).

12. *Thecla ontario* Edwards, ♀; 12a, Do., *under side* (after Edwards).

13. *Thecla critola* Hewitson, ♂; 13a, Do., *under side* (after Hewitson).

14. *Thecla auretorum* Boisduval, ♂, *type* (after Oberthür).

15. *Thecla sylvinus* Boisduval, ♂, *type* (after Oberthür).

16. *Thecla heathi* Fletcher, ♀, *type* (after Fletcher).

17. *Chlosyne endeis* (G. & S.) ♂; 17a, Do., *under side* (after G. & S.).

18. *Papilio acauda* Oberthür, ♂. (*corbis* G. & S.) (after G. & S.).

19. *Parnassius apricatus* Stichel, ♂, *type* (after Stichel, in Seitz, Gr. Schm., V, Pl. 17d).

20. *Œneis daura* Strecker, ♂, *type;* 20a, Do., *under side.*

21. Chrysalis of *Spalgis lemolea* Druce (*S-signata* Holl.) (after Holland).

22. Chrysalis of *Spalgis epius* Westwood (after Moore).

23. Chrysalis of *Feniseca tarquinius* Boisduval. (Holland *del*. July 26, 1930.).

John C. Bragdon, Inc.

THE FIRST PICTURE OF AN AMERICAN BUTTERFLY